BIOTECHNOLOGY IN LIVESTOCK IN DEVELOPING COUNTRIES

Biotechnology in Livestock in Developing Countries

Proceedings of *Biotechnology 1989*
An International Conference on the Application of Biotechnology to Livestock in Developing Countries held in the University of Edinburgh from the 4th to 8th September 1989, organized by the staff of the Centre for Tropical Veterinary Medicine.

Edited by

A.G. HUNTER, BVM&S, MRCVS, DTVM
Senior Lecturer in Tropical Animal Health
Centre for Tropical Veterinary Medicine
University of Edinburgh

1991
Centre for Tropical Veterinary Medicine
The University of Edinburgh

Printed in Great Britain by
Ritchie of Edinburgh Ltd.

ISBN 0 907146 07 4

Preface

Throughout the eighties and into the nineties, the scientific world has made significant and exciting advances in biotechnology; advances which could provide improved strains of domestic livestock, better quality foodstuff, highly sensitive and specific diagnostic techniques and superior vaccines. Opinions differ, however, on the benefits to be gained from these developments and many people question the desirability of applying some of the advances in biotechnology, especially in developing countries. Technicians and veterinarians responsible for the day-to-day management of livestock are aware that the health, performance and general welfare of livestock depends on good husbandry. These people may be concerned that the development of livestock and veterinary science will be increasingly placed in the hands of molecular biologists, geneticists, immunologists and other scientists with little practical experience of livestock.

Nowhere is this concern greater than in developing countries; innovations in biotechnology can appear light years away from day-to-day problems associated with livestock production and health in many developing countries with limited resources and insufficient trained personnel. Some of this concern may be well-placed, but aspects of biotechnology if properly channelled will be beneficial even in the poorest of countries. To achieve maximum benefit from recent developments, veterinarians and livestock technicians must overcome some of their apprehension and discuss ideas openly with biotechnologists to ensure the correct direction of future research and development in livestock and veterinary science.

As a contribution to the type of dialogue required, in choosing speakers for the Conference we invited scientists knowledgeable in biotechnology and specialists concerned with livestock in developing countries to present papers on aspects of animal production (breeding, nutrition and physiology) and animal health (diagnosis and vaccines). The final session consisted of overviews of biotechnology in different regions of the developing world.

Delegates and speakers from more than 30 countries attended and for many, the most illuminating parts of the Conference were the lively and sometimes almost heated debates at the end of each session. Edited accounts of these discussions are included in the proceedings. The end result is this book in which recent advances in biotechnology are highlighted and their application to animal production and health in developing countries critically evaluated. I sincerely hope that anyone interested in the development of animal production and health in the third world will find this book interesting and of value.

ARCHIE HUNTER
Edinburgh, May 1991

Foreword

I am very pleased to welcome you to this Conference. The CTVM staff have been organizing international conferences since 1974 as a contribution to the periodic review of a variety of important aspects of veterinary science and animal production in the developing countries of the tropics. The first of these conferences was concerned with Beef Cattle Production in Developing Countries; unfortunately the proceedings of this Conference, which emerged as a valuable textbook, are now out of print. In 1976 we held a conference on Tick-borne Diseases and their Vectors and the book of the proceedings, edited by Dr. J.K.H. Wilde is still available. The third, in 1979, was organized under the auspices of the British Society of Animal Production and was on Intensive Animal Production in Developing Countries and the fourth, on Milk Production in Developing Countries, was held in 1984.

Biotechnology is one of today's *buzz* words that has not yet reached the stage of being clearly defined in dictionaries. It encompasses a variety of different biological techniques and most of these will be discussed at this Conference. At the end of the week we should all have a good idea of what the term means and whether the new technologies have yet reached the stage of being useful to those of us who are concerned with food production in the third world.

The Conference Committee, under the chairmanship of Mr. A.G. Hunter, have worked very hard to prepare an interesting and informative programme. We are grateful for your attendance and trust that you will play a full part in the discussions, both formal and informal. Those of you who have not visited Edinburgh before will find that it is a beautiful and historic city; I hope that you will have time to enjoy the many attractions of the city and surrounding area.

D.W. BROCKLESBY
Director, CTVM
4th September, 1989

Acknowledgements

The successful organization of the Conference and the publication of the proceedings is due to the support and assistance of my colleagues at the CTVM. In particular I would like to thank the other members of the Organizing Committee, Gordon Brown for general assistance in administration, Jeanette MacDonald and Pauline McManus who attended to most of the administration and spent many long hours meticulously preparing the camera-ready typescript for the printers, Denis Fielding for organizing the poster sessions and Tony Smith for general assistance and advice. Grateful thanks are also due to Bob Archibald for redrawing many diagrams, Bob Munro for photographic assistance, and Joan Dick, Jennifer Johnson and Susan Smyth for checking references. I would also like to thank Professor D.W. Brocklesby for opening the Conference and welcoming delegates, and to Dr. A.D. Irvin of the Overseas Development Administration for his closing address which so concisely put many of the points raised in the Conference into perspective. I am also grateful to the chairmen of the different sessions who kept things moving and to the students who paged delegates during the discussions. Finally I am indebted to all the speakers and to the delegates for their attendance, their presentation of posters and their lively participation in the discussions.

The Organizing Committee is extremely grateful for the generous support of the Scottish Development Agency. We would also like to express our gratitude to the Commonwealth Foundation and the C.T.A. of the ACP-EEC Lomé Convention for sponsoring the attendance of certain participants. Coopers Animal Health Ltd. kindly funded the cost of the Conference wallets and we are also grateful for the donations to the running of the Conference from Norden Laboratories and Cairns Veterinary Bookshops.

Contents

5. ANIMAL HEALTH, VACCINES

Chairmen: H.W. Reid, Moredun Research Institute, Edinburgh and A.G. Hunter, CTVM, Edinburgh.

6. BIOTECHNOLOGY IN DEVELOPING COUNTRIES

Chairman: S. Anderson, University of Yucatan, Mexico

CLOSING ADDRESS

Contributors

MR. C.G.D. BROWN, BVM&S, MRCVS. Senior Research Fellow and Head of Protozoology Section, Centre for Tropical Veterinary Medicine, University of Edinburgh. Formerly FAO Staff Member, UNDP/FAO Tick-borne Diseases Project, East African Veterinary Research Organisation, Muguga, Kenya. Interests include theileriosis and other tick-borne diseases of livestock.

DR. R. BARZILAI, PhD, MSc. Head, Division of Biology, Israel Institute for Biological Sciences, Ness Ziona, Israel. Interests include Rift Valley fever and viral haemorrhagic fevers.

DR. J. CHESHAM, BSc, PhD, MIBiol. Research and Development Manager, Cambridge Veterinary Sciences (A Division of Cambridge Life Sciences plc), Cambridge. Formerly Research Scientist at ICI. Interests include novel immunoassay systems, and their application to veterinary immunodiagnosis, in particular residue testing and disease diagnosis.

MR. C.J. DABORN, BVM, MSc, MRCVS. Lecturer, Tropical Animal Health and Course Supervisor of Tropical Veterinary Medicine Course, Centre for Tropical Veterinary Medicine, University of Edinburgh. Formerly Group Livestock Manager, Intabex, Zambia. Interests include epidemiology of bacterial zoonoses and control of diseases transmissible from wildlife to domestic stock.

DR. T.R. DOEL, BTech(hons), PhD. Head, Vaccine Research Department, AFRC Institute of Animal Health, Pirbright. Interests include synthetic and conventional FMD vaccines and synthetic vaccines in general.

DR. D. FIELDING, BSc, MSc, PhD. Senior Lecturer, Tropical Animal Health and Production, Edinburgh School of Agriculture. Formerly Animal Production Officer, FAO. Interests include tropical equines.

DR. C.S. GALINA, MVZ, PhD. Associate Professor, Department of Reproduction, Faculty of Veterinary Medicine, University of Mexico. Interests include reproduction in Zebu cattle.

DR. L.J.S. HARRISON, BSc, PhD. Research Fellow, Helminthology Section, Centre for Tropical Veterinary Medicine, University of Edinburgh. Formerly Research Associate, CTVM. Research interests include immunochemistry and molecular biology of helminth parasites of domestic ruminants.

DR. J. HODGES, BSc(hons), MA, PhD, AMP. Senior Officer (Animal Breeding and Genetics Resources), FAO, Rome. Formerly Professor of Animal Genetics, University of British Columbia, Canada. Research interests include animal breeding and genetic resources.

MR. A.G. HUNTER, BVM&S, DTVM, MRCVS. Senior Lecturer, Course Supervisor Tropical Veterinary Science course, Centre for Tropical Veterinary Medicine, University of Edinburgh. Formerly Veterinary Investigation Officer, Edinburgh Veterinary Investigation Centre. Research interests include veterinary diagnoses and trypanosomiasis.

DR. M.H. JEGGO, MRCVS, BVM, MSc, PhD. Regional Expert for Africa, in the Joint FAO/IAEA Division, IAEA, Vienna. Formerly Principal Veterinary Research Officer, Pirbright. Research interests include immunoassays.

DR. J.-P. LECOCQ, PhD. Director of Research, Transgene, Strasbourg, France. Formerly Project Leader, SK-RIT, Belgium. Research interests include applications of DNA recombinant technology.

MR. K.T. LIM, BSc(hons). Research Officer in the ASEAN Poultry Disease Research and Training Centre (Virology Section), Veterinary Research Institute, Ipoh, Malaysia. Formerly Research Officer at the Regional Diagnostic Laboratory, Petaling Jaya. Research interests include viral diseases of livestock production of diagnostic biologicals and inactivated vaccines for Newcastle disease.

MR. J.S. MACFARLANE, MSc, CBiol, MIBiol, NDA, NDDH, DipTAPH Scientific FZS. Private Consultant, Honorary Fellow in Reproductive Physiology, Centre for Tropical Veterinary Medicine, University of Edinburgh. Formerly World Bank Livestock Development Project, Nigeria. Research interests include animal health and production with particular interest in reproduction technology, artificial insemination and embryo transfer.

DR. T.B. MEPHAM, BSc, PhD. Reader in Lactational Physiology, Faculty of Agricultural and Food Sciences, University of Nottingham. Formerly Senior Scientific Officer, ARC Institute of Animal Physiology, Cambridge. Research interests include physiology of lactation and history philosophy and social relations of biology.

DR. C.A. MORGAN, BSc, PhD. Nutrition Specialist, The East of Scotland College of Agriculture, Edinburgh. Formerly Postdoctoral Researcher, ESCA. Research interests include digestion and nutrient use in pigsty experimentation and simulation modelling.

DR. R.A. PEARSON, BSc, PhD. Research Fellow, Centre for Tropical Veterinary Medicine, University of Edinburgh. Formerly Research Scientist, Poultry Research Centre, Roslin, Edinburgh. Research interests include nutrition and physiology of draught animals, ruminants and poultry.

DR. A.R. PETERS, BA, DVetMed, PhD, FRCVS, F.I.Biol. Regulatory Manager, Hoechst Animal Health, Milton Keynes. Formerly Senior Veterinary Advisor, Meat and Livestock Commission. Research interests include endocrine manipulation of animal growth, reproduction and lactation and consumer attitudes to biotechnology.

DR. G.R. SCOTT, OBE, BSc, MS, PhD, MRCVS. Reader, Centre for Tropical Veterinary Medicine, University of Edinburgh. Formerly Acting Director, East African Veterinary Research Organisation, Kenya. Research interests include viral plagues and animal rickettsias.

DR. D.K. SINGH, MVSc&AH, PhD. Senior Scientist, National Dairy Development Board, India. Formerly Assistant Professor, J.M. Agricultural University, India. Research interests include bovine tropical theileriosis and blood protozoa.

DR. A.J. SMITH, BSc, MSc, PhD, NDA. Senior Lecturer, Centre for Tropical Veterinary Medicine, University of Edinburgh. Formerly Lecturer, University of Rhodesia (Zimbabwe). Research interests include draught animals, village poultry production, and use of animals in tropical agricultural systems.

DR. A. TAIT, BSc, PhD. Director, The Wellcome Unit of Molecular Parasitology, Glasgow. Formerly Wellcome Senior Lecturer, University of Edinburgh. Research interests include parasite molecular genetics (trypanosomes, theileria).

DR. A. TEALE, MA, VetMB, MSc, PhD, MRCVS. Scientist, International Laboratory for Research on Animal Diseases, Kenya. Formerly Technical Cooperation Officer, Overseas Development Administration. Research interests include bovine genetics and in particular the control of disease resistance in livestock.

DR. J.H. TOPPS, BSc, PhD, DSc, FRCS. Head, Department of Agricultural Biochemistry, University of Aberdeen. Formerly Senior Lecturer, University of Aberdeen. Research interests include ruminant nutrition and tropical animal production.

MR. J.D. TURTON, BSc, MRCVS, DTVM. Chief Managing Editor (Animal Sciences), CAB International. Formerly Director, Commonwealth Bureau of Animal Breeding and Genetics, Edinburgh. Research interests include genetic improvement of livestock and genetic engineering.

MR. J.A. WOOLLIAMS, MA, DipMathStats. Senior Scientific Officer, AFRC Institute of Animal Physiology and Genetics Research, Edinburgh Research Station. Research interests include application of embryo technology to animal breeding and prediction of dairy merit in juvenile cattle.

Organizing Committee

MR. A.G. HUNTER (Chairman), CTVM, University of Edinburgh.

MR. G.F. BROWN, CTVM, University of Edinburgh.

DR. D. FIELDING, CTVM, University of Edinburgh.

MRS. J.B. MacDONALD, CTVM, University of Edinburgh.

MISS P. McMANUS, CTVM, University of Edinburgh.

DR. A.J. SMITH, CTVM, University of Edinburgh.

Glossary of Abbreviations

ABTS	Azino-ethyl-benz-thiazoline-6 sulfonic acid
AGDP	Agar gel double immunodiffusion precipitation
AGID	Agar gel immunodiffusion
AI	Artificial insemination
APPL	Acid precipitable polymeric lignin
ASO	Allele-specific oligonucleotide
BCIP	Bromo chloro indolyl phosphate
BLUP	Best linear unbiased predictor
BNF	Biological nitrogen fixation
bp	Base pair
bST	Bovine somatotropin
bTP	Bovine trophoblast protein
BTV	Bluetongue virus
CAMP	Cyclic adenosine monophosphate
CAP	Chlormadinone acetate
CB	Crossbred
CBHI	Exo-cellobiohydrolase I
CCPP	Contagious caprine pleuropneumonia
cDNA	Complementary deoxyribonucleic acid
CFT	Complement fixation test
CG	Chorionic gonadotropin
CLA	Common leucocyte antigen
CP	Crude protein
CS	Circumsporozoite
CSC	Cotton seed cake
CTL	Cytotoxic T-cell
DCP	Digestible crude protein
DDV	Dehydrodivanillin
DE	Digestible energy
DGR	Dominant genetic repeat

ECF	East Coast fever
EGF	Epidermal growth factor
EIA	Enzyme immunoassay
ELISA	Enzyme-linked immunosorbent assay
ET	Embryo transfer
E/S compartment	Extra-secretory compartment
FMDV	Foot-and mouth disease virus
FSH	Follicle stimulating hormone
GH	Growth hormone
GNC	Groundnut cake
GnRH	Gonadotropin releasing hormone
GPI	Glycophosphatidyl inositol
GRF	Growth hormone releasing factor
GUTS	Ground up tick supernate
h^2	Heritability
HAT medium	Medium containing hypoxanthine, aminopterin and thymidine
hCG	Human chorionic gonadotropin
HI	Haemagglutinin inhibition
HLA	Human leucocyte antigen
HPLC	High performance liquid chromatography
HRP	Horseradish peroxidase
hST	Human somatotropin
ID	Immunodiffusion
IF	Immunofluorescence
IFAT	Indirect fluorescence antibody test
IIF	Indirect immunofluorescence
IGF I	Insulin-like growth factor
KAG vaccine	Kabete attenuated goat vaccine
Kd	K dalton
KLH	Keyhole limpet haemocyanin
LCFA	Long chain fatty acid
LDC	Lesser developed country
LH	Luteinizing hormone
LN_2	Liquid nitrogen
MAb/McAb/McA	Monoclonal antibody
MAP	Medroxyprogesterone acetate
MAS	Marker assisted selection
MBF	Mammary blood flow
ME	Metabolizable energy
MGA	Melengestrol acetate
MHC	Major histocompatibility complex
MOET	Multiple ovulation embryo transfer
mRNA	Messenger ribonucleic acid
MSA	Major surface antigen
NDF	Neutral detergent fibre

NEFA	Non-esterified fatty acid
NMR	Nuclear magnetic resonance
OD	Optical density
ONBS	Open nucleus breeding system
OPD	Ortho-phenylene-diamine
oTP	Ovine trophoblast protein
PAGE	Polyacrilamide gel electrophoresis
PARC	Pan African Rinderpest Campaign
PCR	Polymerase chain reaction
PG	Prostaglandin
pGH	Pituitary growth hormone
PL	Placental lactogen
PMSG	Pregnant mare serum gonadotropin
Pr	Potential protein deposition rate
PRL	Prolactin
pST	Porcine somatotropin
Pt	Current protein mass
Ptm	Mature protein masss
QTL	Quantitative trait loci
RAP	Rhoptry-associated protein
rbGH	Recombinant bovine growth hormone
REML	Restricted maximum likelihood
RESA	Ring-infected erythrocyte surface antigen
RFLP	Restriction fragment length polymorphism
RIA	Radio-immunoassay
RPV	Rinderpest virus
SDS-PAGE	Sodium dodecyl sulphate-polyacrilamide gel electrophoresis
SRIF	Somatotropin release inhibiting factor (Somatostatin)
ST	Somatotropin
TGF	Transforming growth factor
TMB	Tetramethyl benzidine
UMB	Urea molasses block
Va	Additive genetic variation
VAM	Vesicular-arbuscular mycorrhiza
VIA	Virus infection associated
VN	Virus neutralization
Vp	Total variation
VRGP	Vaccinia-rabies glycoprotein vaccine

1.

INTRODUCTION

Chairman: A.G. Hunter
Centre for Tropical Veterinary Medicine
Edinburgh

1.1

Constraints to Animal Production and Health in the Tropics

A.J. SMITH and C.J. DABORN
Centre for Tropical Veterinary Medicine,
University of Edinburgh, Scotland

INTRODUCTION

The domestic farm animal population of the world is extremely large but the grand total of cattle, pigs, sheep, goats, buffalo and camels is somewhat less than the total human population. The relation has moved unrelentingly in favour of the humans. Thus although the population of all farm livestock has grown over the last 20 years the human population has grown much faster (Fig. 1). Of this animal population two-thirds of the cattle, most of the buffalo, camels, goats and pigs and over one-half of the sheep are found in developing countries (Table 1).

Animals kept in developing countries are in general far less productive than those kept in developed ones (Tables 2 and 3). For example, in Latin America cattle take three to four years or longer to reach slaughter weight and only 40 calves are reared per 100 breeding cows each year. In India lactation yields of

TABLE 1 *Population of domestic livestock and man in developing and developed countries in 1987 (millions).*

	Cattle	Buffalo	Camels	Sheep	Goats	Pigs	Man
Developed	412.4	0.7	0.3	546.9	28.9	347.1	1,228
Developing	865.3	137.7	18.2	610.8	427.9	492.9	3,069
World	1,277.7	138.4	18.5	1,157.7	501.8	839.8	4,997

Source: FAO (1987)

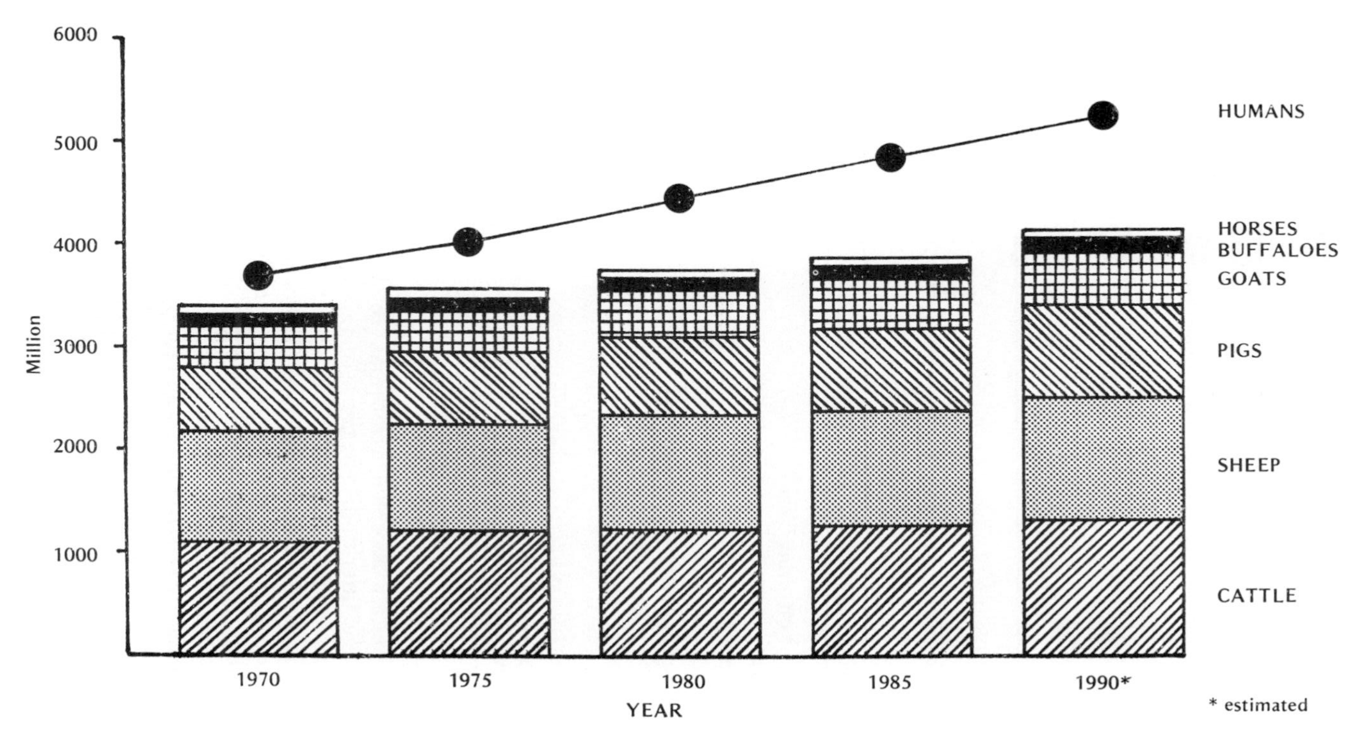

Fig. 1 *Changes in human and animal population over the past 20 years.*

TABLE 2 *Regional production of some livestock products per head of animal population.*

	Kg/Product/Head/Livestock Population		
	Beef/Veal	Mutton/Lamb	Pork
U.S.A./Canada	93	11	98
Latin America	36	3	16
Africa	15	3	29
Near East	17	4	12
Far East	4	4	24

Source: Nestel (1974)

TABLE 3 *Estimates of the productivity of domestic farm animals in developed and developing countries.*

	Sheep	Cow/Steer	Pig
No. of offspring/year			
Developed countries	1.5	0.9	18
Developing countries	0.8	0.4	5
Growth rate (g liveweight/day)			
Developed countries	100	1,000	500
Developing countries	40	500	40
Milk yield (litres/lactation)			
Developed countries	–	3,500	–
Developing countries	–	500	–

Source: Payne and Smith (1974)

500 kg per cow are accepted as normal. In Africa indigenous pigs may produce only one litter each year consisting of three to five piglets.

These figures compare very unfavourably with those achieved by domestic animals kept in the developed regions of the world. Why are animals kept in the tropics so unproductive? If the reasons are dispassionately examined it will be seen that they are many and various with the relative importance of each varying from region to region in the developing world. The limiting factors will be discussed sequentially and the possible areas where biotechnology could make an impact will be highlighted. The factors that limit animal production can be listed under seven broad headings:

- The direct and indirect effects of climate.
- The genetic merit of the available livestock.

- The quality and seasonal availability of food supplies.
- The effects of endemic, pandemic and epidemic diseases.
- The level and type of management with particular reference to the effect of social and religious attitudes.
- The demand for the animal products and the effects of price, transport, processing and marketing facilities.
- The availability of credit particularly to poorer farmers.

THE DIRECT AND INDIRECT EFFECTS OF CLIMATE ON FARM ANIMALS

The main climatic elements that exert a direct influence on the productivity of farm animals are the following:

- Ambient temperature
- Rainfall
- Radiation
- Humidity
- Wind
- Day length

The influence of these factors can be represented diagrammatically (Fig. 2).

The free-ranging animal is the one that is most affected by climate, for example it has been shown that a cow grazing in the sun in the tropics can

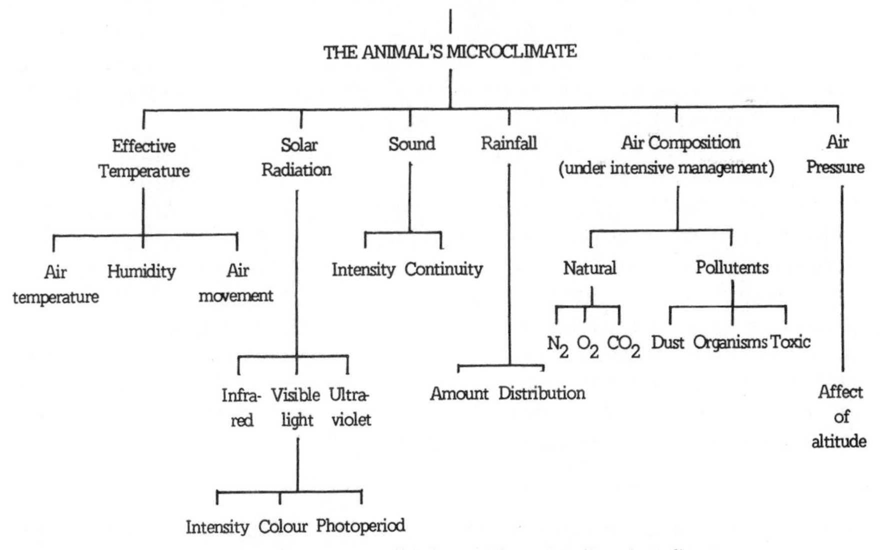

Fig. 2 *The factors contributing to the animal's microclimate.*

TABLE 4 *The heat balance of* Bos indicus *measured in a radiant environment at noon (KJ m²hr).*

Metabolic heat production	Radiant heat absorbed	Re-radiated heat	Con-vective heat loss	Cut-aneous heat loss	Res-piratory heat loss	Gain	Loss
248	3,116	1,940	311	714	176	3,364	3,141

After: Robertshaw and Finch (1976)

TABLE 5 *Approximate comparative maximum sweat production rates by man and some of his domestic animals.*

Cattle	14
Sheep	1
Man	70
Pig	0.5

Data from several sources

receive ten times as much heat load from solar radiation as it does from the metabolism of its food (Table 4).

To a greater or lesser extent pigs, poultry and dairy cows that are kept intensively can be protected from the deleterious effects of climatic extremes. However the cost of providing this protection can prove to be very expensive and may be justifiable only in countries where animals and animal products command high prices relative to farm building costs.

The overall impact of direct climatic stress is to dramatically reduce the rate of reproduction (egg production in poultry, fertility in mammals), milk production, growth rate and the time taken to reach maturity. Animals with a limited ability to sweat such as pigs and buffaloes are particularly vulnerable to heat stress. Those that are high producing generally produce more heat and are therefore more vulnerable to heat stress than those that are low producing. It should always be remembered that farm animals are less heat tolerant than humans and that their productivity normally declines when the ambient temperature exceeds 25°C for an extended period of time. Most farm animals are less able to produce sweat than man (Table 5) or to maintain sweating for an extended period of time (Fig. 3).

THE GENETIC MERIT OF THE AVAILABLE LIVESTOCK

A primary problem for indigenous livestock may be that one of the penalties of being well-adapted to a harsh environment is low productivity. Natural

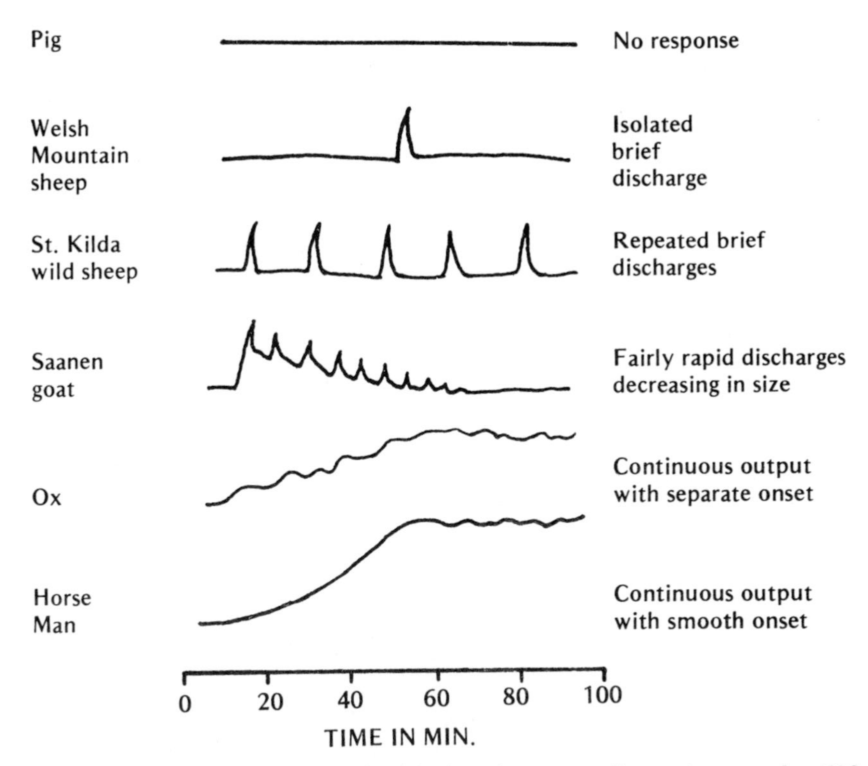

Fig. 3 *Diagram of typical sweat gland activity in various mammalian species exposed to 40°C environmental temperature.*

(Based on work by Bligh, Environl Res., 1967 and Comp. Biochem. Physiol., 1969 but taken from Richards, 1973).

selection has been for survival and not for production. Both high rates of milk production and rapid growth rates exacerbate the effects of climatic stress by increasing the animal's metabolic rate. Selection for rapid growth rate produces animals with large mature body sizes. These animals may be less able to survive under adverse conditions, especially marginal conditions of grazing and water supply.

The most important of the large livestock in developing countries are cattle and the problems of their genetic improvement will be discussed first. Zebu cattle (*Bos indicus*) are far more common in developing countries than taurine cattle (*Bos taurus*) the latter being the most common type in developed countries. Because of this association it is not surprising that the taurine (European) cattle are more productive than the indicus types. The lower productivity of zebu cattle is particularly noticeable in the case of milk production. The potential production of some types of zebu cattle could be as low as 1,000 kg per lactation although others could be capable of producing

5,000 kg or more. The low output of these cattle together with the fact that they let-down their milk only in the presence of the calf limits their value as milk producing animals. Similarly, the growth rate of zebu cattle is generally slower than that of taurines and under high planes of nutrition they are prone to suffer from laminitis (excessive growth of hoof).

However there is an 'up' side to these animals. Those that are kept in dry climates have considerable advantages over taurines; they can cope with poor quality grasses and can graze further from water than European cattle, they are often well-adapted to the disease challenge in their area and have more durable teeth. One research worker in Zimbabwe found that the teeth of Hereford cattle were particularly vulnerable to erosion when they were grazed on fibrous savannah grasses.

Therefore we should ask ourselves the question, is it possible to improve the productivity of farm livestock and particularly those exposed to range conditions without impairing their inherent ability to survive rigorous conditions? If it is possible to identify ways that this can be achieved then biotechnology may have a part to play in speeding up the changes required. This could be particularly true in the case of herds and flocks where fertility is low and death rates are high. In herds, for example, where calf weaning rates do not exceed 50%, the improvement of the female line by selection is virtually impossible because all the females need to be kept for breeding. The use of embryo transplants and other new techniques might help to overcome this problem.

The above problem is not so apparent in species with a high rate of reproduction such as pigs and poultry. It is very easy to replace whole populations in one or two generations. It is also comparatively easy to adapt intensive systems of management of these animals to the tropics. Therefore there is little or no difficulty in setting up highly productive pig and poultry enterprises in developing countries. Consequently the possibility of using biotechnology for genetic improvement under these circumstances may not be rewarding. As has been said before, it is pointless to import highly productive stock into areas where management is inadequate or where food supplies are limiting.

Under these latter conditions some form of scavenging pig or poultry production is probably preferable. The productivity of this form of livestock can be improved by genetic means but not by using hybrid stock with poor scavenging instincts. Scavenger poultry can be best improved using a cockerel exchange scheme employing dual-purpose traditional breeds such as Black Australorps and Rhode Island Reds. Similary there is no point in 'improving' traditional pigs by crossing them with modern lean hybrids if the market demand is for fat pigs rather than lean ones.

THE AVAILABILITY OF FOOD SUPPLIES

The nutrition and management of pigs and poultry in the tropics is similar to that practised in temperate zones when they are kept intensively. However the lack of availability of food for animals is one of the principal constraints to nonruminant production in the tropics. If food is in short supply, pigs and poultry kept intensively may compete with humans for the limited supplies available. Little is known about the food intake of pigs and poultry kept under scavenging conditions.

The effect of nutrition on the productivity of ruminants in the tropics is very marked indeed. In the dry tropics and subhumid tropics the quality of the herbage is very variable. The grazing season is short and the deterioration in the quality of grass rapid (Table 6).

TABLE 6 *Seasonal changes in grass quality in Mashonaland, Zimbabwe.*

Time of year	Crude protein %	TDN %	Digestive protein %
Mid-November	9.0	57.0	4.7
Mid-January to end February	7.6	48.0	3.1
March	5.3	45.0	0.75
April	3.5	45.0	very little

N.B. Rainy season lasts from November until February in these parts of Zimbabwe.

Source: Oliver (1971)

Consequently if this grass is used to feed dairy cattle, it contains sufficient protein for ten litres of milk in addition to maintenance for only two months of the year. For the rest of the year the grass will be sufficient for maintenance or even less than maintenance. Thus grass can be used for milk producing cows for only a short season in semi-arid subhumid tropical countries like Zimbabwe and much more reliance has to be placed on concentrate food and/or irrigated pastures than in temperate zones. If the farmer is poor and cannot afford to irrigate or has to use all his maize for his own use, his dairy cattle will be underfed and milk yield will be very low.

The production of beef is also fraught with problems. Beef production will normally be carried out in the low rainfall areas of tropical countries because the higher rainfall areas will be used for the production of crops. The lower the annual rainfall the less reliable it is within years and between years. Thus there is no guarantee when the rainfall season will start and when it does come it will tend to be very local in its distribution. Rain comes in the form of thunder showers and it is possible for one part of a farm to have several centimetres of rain while another part has none at all. For all the above reasons the grass cover in these regions can vary from good to nil.

The low protein content of the grass in the subhumid tropics affects the productivity of beef animals in a similar way to dairy cows. When the protein level of the grass falls below 7% the consumption of it by cattle decreases. To encourage consumption of grass with a low protein content it is necessary to provide a protein supplement in the form of either a urea or biuret lick or else feed the animals on a protein meal supplement. If a supplement is not provided beef cattle will lose weight in the dry months and then regain weight during the next rainy season. Consequently the growth of cattle takes place in a switchback fashion (Fig. 4). Therefore overall growth is rather slow and it takes cattle three to four years to reach maturity. Underfed animals may exhibit compensatory growth with high rates of gain if they are fed on high energy diets. Compensatory growth has been taken advantage of in the various feedlot systems developed in tropical countries. Two of the best known of these were the ones at Nakuru in Kenya and at Mokwa in the middle belt of Nigeria. However such schemes are normally unprofitable because of the high cost of grain relative to the price of beef (Table 7).

Breeding cattle kept on savannah grasslands also tends to be unproductive. They lose weight when suckling their calves and do not ovulate during the

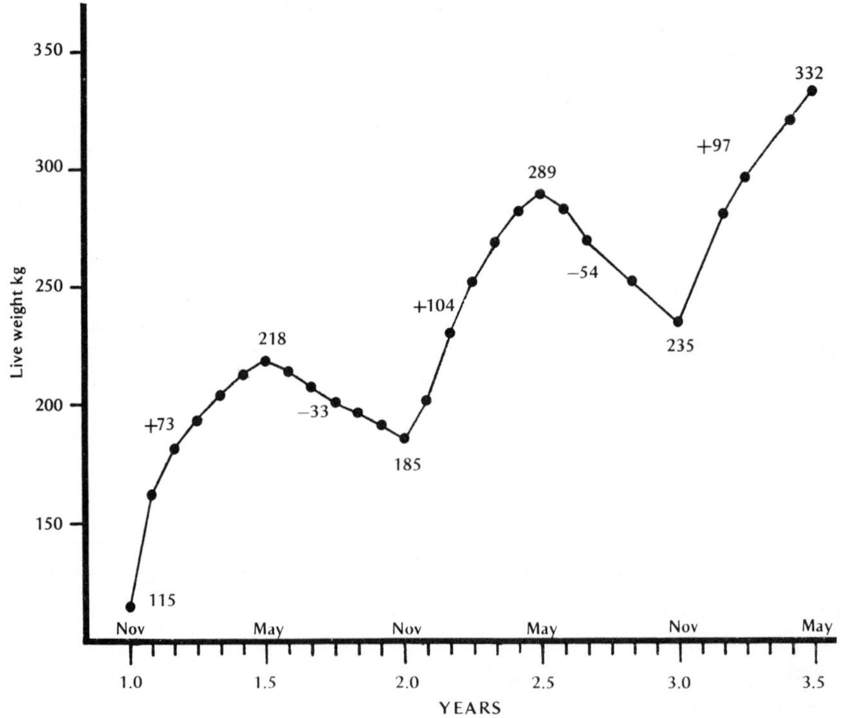

Fig. 4 *Seasonal livestock changes in cattle 1-4 years old grazing native pastures at Katherine, Northern Australia.*

* adapted: Norman (1966)

TABLE 7 *Profit margins in beef fattening expressed as a percentage of gross output.*

Price ratios Maize/Beef	Feeder steer price as % of fat steer price 60	70	80	90	100
	Profit as % of gross output				
1:10	23	17	8	0	-7
1:9	21	15	6	-2	-9
1:8	18	12	3	-4	-12
1:7	15	9	0	-7	-15
1:6	11	5	-14	-11	-19
1:5	5	1	-10	-17	-25
1:4	-4	-10	-19	-26	-34

Source: Schaefer-Kehnert (1981)

TABLE 8 *The response of breeding cows on range in terms of calving percentage to hand-feeding in winter.*

Author	Supplement	Fertility %
Bauer	Nil	77
	420 cubes[1]	88
Bembridge	Nil	63
	454–980 g CSC[2]	76
Elliot	Nil	58
	908 g CSC[2]	82
Ward	Nil	60
	908 g GNC[3]	75

[1] 50% Crude protein
[2] CSC Cotton seed cake
[3] GNC Groundnut cake

Source: Oliver and Richardson (1976)

long sucking period. As a consequence they produce a calf on average only once every two years. Thus the calving percentage of range cows varies from 40% to 60%. This level can be increased to 80% by supplementary feeding breeding cows kept on poor quality pastures (Table 8).

Early weaning (at 2½ to 3 months) can achieve the same objective but it is very difficult to rear the calves when they are weaned at this early age.

Biotechnology might have a part to play in enabling animals on poor range conditions to be better fed. This could be achieved either by breeding more productive plants (grass and legumes) for arid lands that contain a greater percentage of protein or by changing the rumen microflora of ruminants to enable them to be better able to digest low quality foodstuffs. The main ways in which the activity of rumen microbes can be enhanced have been discussed by Armstrong and Gilbert (1985).

Sheep and goats tend to be kept in the driest regions of the tropics and subtropics and are unproductive and are often used as scavenger flocks. Hair sheep are commonly kept in these regions because they are more heat tolerant than wool sheep and because the seeds of various grasses and weeds lodge in wool and make the life of wool sheep very uncomfortable. Some breeds of tropical sheep such as the Awassi are used for milk production, others such as the Barbados Black Belly can be extremely prolific when well-managed. Generally speaking however, sheep, are kept on the poor land in the tropics where high fertility and high lactation yield would be a disadvantage.

In the dry tropics, stocking rates of all ruminant animals must be limited to the carrying capacity of the land in the dry season, which can vary considerably from year to year because of yearly variations in rainfall (Table 9).

TABLE 9 *Variability of annual rainfall in East African rangelands.*

	Annual Rainfall (mm)		
Site	**Mean**	**Least**	**Most**
Garissa	267	69	610
Dodoma	580	307	1,082
Mbarara	922	696	1,519

Source: Osbourn (1976)

It is usually uneconomic to conserve forage on any scale in the dry tropics or to feed the crop and by-product concentrate feeds that are high in energy to grazing stock. Output can best be increased by supplementary feeding with nitrogenous foods to enable the stock to consume low value roughage which would otherwise go up in smoke at the end of the dry season.

In the humid tropics where the dry season is comparatively short, crop and by-product foods are more freely available and some conservation of food may be economical. In these regions climatic conditions are very favourable for growth of all forms of forage and a far higher yield of dry matter per unit area of land can be achieved than is possible in mid latitude regions of the world (Table 10).

In addition in these regions livestock can utilize forage grown under tree crops such as coconuts and very large quantities of by-product foods are potentially available.

The major nutritional problem in the equatorial tropics is that of

TABLE 10 *Dry matter yield per hectare of intensely managed forage in different climatic zones.*

Forage	Location	Climate	Dry matter (kg/ha)
Napier	Puerto Rico	Humid tropical	42,600
Guinea	Puerto Rico	Humid tropical	34,750
Pangola	Puerto Rico	Humid tropical	33,620
Para	Puerto Rico	Humid tropical	30,270
Mixed	New Zealand	Warm temperate	25,220

Source: Payne and Smith (1976)

ascertaining the most economic method of feeding to livestock the very large quantities of forage and by-product feeds that can be grown. Biotechnology might be used to improve the quality of food that is available in these regions.

THE EFFECTS OF EPIDEMIC, PANDEMIC AND EPIDEMIC DISEASES

Animal disease can be classified under three broad categories:

- Highly infectious (Epidemics and Pandemics)
- Less infectious but widespread (Endemic)
- Non infectious

Epidemics and Pandemics

Animals in the tropics are particularly prone to large-scale disease epidemics that can occasionally reach pandemic proportions. The most notable example was the rinderpest outbreak of 1899 that swept from West Asia through the Horn of Africa and on down through the entire continent killing large numbers of domestic and wild cloven-hoofed animals.

Most epidemics are due to viral diseases and are a consequence of the infectious agent sweeping through large groups of susceptible animal populations. Mass vaccination campaigns to immunize at least 80% of the population, combined with movement control, are the most effective methods of containing disease epidemics (Fig. 5).

Many veterinary services were established primarily for the organization and implementation of mass vaccination campaigns to control disease epidemics. They have been largely successful in preventing disease outbreaks of 1899 proportions but many countries face problems in maintaining their control programmes.

The wider functions of today's veterinary services with their greatly enlarged staff structure has placed a serious financial constraint on their ability to service field vaccination campaigns. This has led to the re-emergence of large populations of inadequately immunized livestock. The

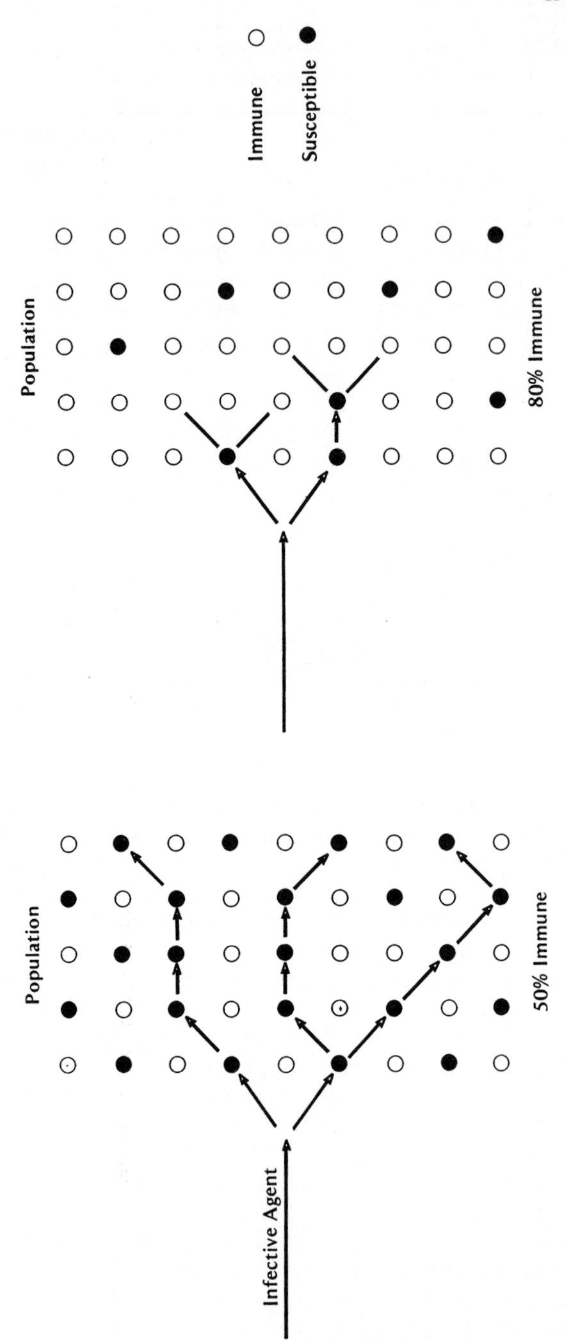

Fig. 5 *Diagrammatic representation of the transmission of an infective agent through an animal population.*

adapted: Thrusfield (1986)

transmission of infection amongst such groups is aided by animal movement within and between groups. Such movement occurs extensively in the tropics as a consequence of nomadism, transhumance, marketing and cattle theft. There has recently been a marked increase in large-scale livestock movement necessitated by wars and natural disasters. Initiatives such as the Pan African Rinderpest Campaign (PARC) are urgently required to prevent widespread disease outbreaks and consequent large-scale deprivation amongst the tropical livestock population. Biotechnology may hold the key for future epidemic disease control programmes by providing vaccines with better immunogenicity, heat tolerance, longer shelf life and, most importantly, that are cheap and which can be produced locally.

Endemic diseases

Endemic diseases are widespread throughout the tropics and have a significant impact on livestock productivity. The distribution of endemic disease in the tropics is due to a number of interrelated factors that include climate, vegetation, nutrition and husbandry in addition to the level of preventive medicine practised. The mix of endemic disease challenge faced by animals varies from region to region. Helminths and bacterial diseases such as tuberculosis and brucellosis are generally found in all areas whilst other conditions occur in geographically defined areas, e.g. tick-borne diseases, trypanosomiasis and contagious bovine and caprine pleuropneumonia.

Endemic disease has posed a particular problem to the programme to improve tropical livestock production through the introduction of exotic breeds. The various stresses imposed on exotic animals in their new environment is generally ultimately expressed as a diseased animal afflicted with one or more of the area's endemic diseases.

Whilst improved husbandry and preventive medicine strategies can overcome many of the problems posed by endemic disease, costs – particularly the marked price increase of acaricides and anthelmintics – have necessitated a shift towards programmes that exploit the environmental adaption and disease resistant qualities of the indigenous breeds. Biotechnology has an important role to play in providing simpler and more sensitive diagnostic tests to detect subclinically diseased and carrier animals. This would be a major asset for disease eradication programmes in the case of zoonosis such as tuberculosis and brucellosis and make a significant contribution to public health.

Noninfectious diseases

Noninfectious diseases such as mineral deficiencies appear to be a more significant problem in the tropics compared with the temperate zones. This is undoubtedly due to the quality of the tropical soils which are often deficient in both macro and micro nutritional mineral elements, and the general under-use of mineral dietary supplements. Phosphorous deficiency is a widespread problem whilst other elements such as copper, cobalt and iodine may also be deficient in geographically defined localities.

The tropical environment is rich in natural toxins such as plant poisons and mycotoxins. There is also an accelerating move to emulate the temperate zone countries in the production of man-made pollutants to add to the threat posed by natural toxins. Again biotechnology can assist by providing suitable diagnostic tests to identify noninfectious disease problems. The development of the metabolic profile has proved a valuable tool for monitoring herd nutritional status.

A well-organized veterinary service can be extremely successful in controlling animal disease problems through the appropriate use of conventional and new techniques of preventive medicine. This success, if not matched by an equivalent improvement in offtake, may ultimately be self-defeating. Livestock owners must be brought into the cash economy with stable productive herds making a significant contribution to the local and national revenue. An efficient marketing system offering attractive prices is the key to this objective and provides the means by which investment by all sectors in the livestock industry be repaid.

In conclusion, the impact of biotechnology on this sector is likely to be by providing better diagnostic techniques and 'improved' vaccines that are not dependent on a fragile 'cold chain' between source and recipient.

THE LEVEL OF MANAGEMENT AS AFFECTED BY SOCIAL ATTITUDES

The absence of land tenure for many of the livestock keeping communities in the tropics actively discourages investment by individuals in land improvements. This is particularly true for investment in rangeland where measures to improve productivity such as pasture establishment and rotational grazing require seed, fertilizer and fencing. Without land ownership by individuals these improvements can only be financed through communal grazing schemes. Such schemes have shown promising results when initiated with government development funds but all too often collapse once handed over to the local community. Opposition to community charges appears to be a global trait!

Management is influenced by the cultural attitudes of the community in which the farmer lives, his educational level, his degree of skill and the advice and support he receives from his country's extension service. The ability of the latter depends to a considerable extent on what factual information can be made available from research carried out locally.

Cultural attitudes are possibly of more importance in livestock production than in any other sector of agriculture. It is, for example, extremely difficult to improve the genetic merit of cattle in countries such as India, where the slaughter of culled animals is taboo. Similarly it is difficult to improve the productivity of livestock in countries where the human populations place more importance on the quantity rather than quality of their livestock. Almost everywhere in the tropical world large livestock, such as cattle and water buffaloes, are raised not just for direct economic motives, but also on account of the prestige that ownership confers.

However the social function of cattle can be overstated. More important may be the need to keep a certain number of cattle to meet the family's need for milk and draught power. Also in cultures where land is not owned and the local currency unreliable, increased cattle numbers give the individual more prestige and more security.

In other parts of the world other traditions have to be taken into consideration. For example in parts of Africa and elsewhere nomadism is practised. This is a highly developed system of animal husbandry which has been practised successfully for thousands of years in the semi-arid regions of the world. It is essentially a rational system of conservation of pastures during the rains in areas which are uninhabitable for most of the year. The provision of ill-considered water supplies by governments has, almost inevitably, led to a settlement by people outside tribal control and the inevitable destruction of the environment by cultivation and overgrazing.

THE AVAILABILITY OF TRANSPORT AND PROCESSING AND MARKETING FACILITIES

All too often strenous efforts are made to increase productivity on the farm whilst little attention is paid to the availability of processing facilities, the price structure and the marketing system. Even if many livestock producers are motivated by some noneconomic factors they are usually still responsive to price changes, and require an efficient marketing service. They also need to have confidence in the currency and goods or service which can be purchased with the currency when earned. Often the best way to increase the efficiency of livestock production is to offer the farmers a realistic price for the products they are producing.

In almost all countries the processing facilities, if intelligently manipulated, can be used to create new opportunities for traditional livestock industries. For example, in arid regions the organization of feedlots to finish cattle purchased by a marketing organization could assist in the reduction of excessive stocking rates on grazing lands. In the humid tropics a breeding-marketing organization could allocate growing cattle to smallholders to utilize forage and by-product feeds that would otherwise be wasted. Means must also be provided to keep the meat in good condition and fit for human consumption and export.

AVAILABILITY OF CREDIT

All livestock farmers, large or small, nomads or specialized producers are likely to require some form of credit if they are going to expand or to radically change their operations. Only too often credit is available only to the large specialized, land-owning producers and the credit needs of small producers and large producers who own livestock but not land, are totally neglected by formal leading agencies. The small-scale farmers have to rely on the informal sectors and borrow money at very high interest rates from money lenders. Traditional attitudes to the granting of credit, essentially based on using freehold title to land as security for loans, must be changed if the credit requirements of an expanding and changing livestock industry are to be satisfied.

CONCLUSIONS

From the above discussion it can be seen that there are many factors that limited animal production in the tropics. Many of these factors are social and economic and not necessarily amenable to impacts of technical nature. Biotechnology could be applied to some technical inputs but it will not be a panacea and may even have negative results if misapplied. It is unlikely that biotechnology will succeed where conventional inputs have failed particularly in countries lacking basic infrastructures.

REFERENCES

Armstrong, D.G. and Gilbert, H.J. (1985). Biotechnology and the Rumen – A Mini Review. *Journal of the Science of Food and Agriculture*, **36**, 1039–1046.

F.A.O (1987). FAO Yearbook, *Production*. Volume 41.

Nestel, B.L. (1974). World animal production and feed supplies. In: *Animal Feeds of Tropical and Sub-tropical Origin* (ed. D. Halliday). Tropical Products Institute, London.

Norman, M.J.T. (1966). *Katherine Research Station 1956–64*. A review of published works, CSIRO, Australia. Division of Land Research Technical Paper No. 28.

Oliver, J. (1971). *An Introduction to Dairying in Rhodesia*. University of Rhodesia, Salisbury.

Oliver, J. and Richardson, F.D. (1976). Relationship between reconception rate in beef cattle and bodyweight change. In: *Beef Cattle Production in Developing Countries* (ed. A.J. Smith). Centre for Tropical Veterinary Medicine, University of Edinburgh.

Osbourn, D.F. (1976). The utilization of natural grasslands in the tropics. In: *Beef Cattle Production in Developing Countries* (ed. A.J. Smith). Centre for Tropical Veterinary Medicine, University of Edinburgh.

Payne, W.J.A. and Smith, A.J. (1974). Factors limiting the production of animal products in the tropics with particular reference to animal feeds. In: *Animal Feeds of Tropical and Sub-tropical Origin* (ed. D. Halliday). Tropical Products Institute, London.

Richards, S.A. (1973). *Temperature Regulation*. Wykeham Publications, London.

Robertshaw, D. and Finch, V. (1976). Effect of climate on the productivity of beef cattle. In: *Beef Cattle Production in Developing Countries* (ed. A.J. Smith). Centre for Tropical Veterinary Medicine, University of Edinburgh.

Schaefer-Kehnert, W. (1981). Appraisal and finance of intensive animal production schemes. In: *Intensive Animal Production in Developing Countries* (ed. A.J. Smith). BSAP, Thames Ditton.

Thrusfield, M.V. (1986). *Veterinary Epidemiology*. Butterworths, London.

1.2

What Do We Understand By Biotechnology?

J.D. TURTON
C.A.B. International, Oxon, England

> "When *I* use a word", Humpty Dumpty said in a rather scornful tone, "it means just what I chose it to mean – neither more nor less."
> Lewis Carroll: *Through the Looking Glass*

There have been a number of short definitions of biotechnology. Here are two of them: (1) The application of organisms, biological systems or biological processes to manufacturing and service industries (Coombs, 1986); (2) The commercial exploitation of living organisms or their components (Primrose, 1987).

Obviously, to be of practical assistance to an enquirer as to the nature of biotechnology, a definition needs to specify much more detail than is given in the above. But that is not the end of the matter. Within a specific subject area, some scientific investigations, techniques or developments may be classed validly as biotechnology, others may not. Opinions may differ between individuals as to whether an item is biotechnological or not.

There is also something of a 'political' dimension to biotechnology, in the sense that biotechnology research is regarded in a favourable light when the time comes to allocate research grants. Human nature being what it is, this has tended to lead to a liberal interpretation of where the margins of biotechnology lie.

In considering the scope of biotechnology, it is necessary to take a brief, historical look at the matter. A major area of biotechnology is the use of microorganisms to bring about chemical changes, and a prime example of this is fermentation to produce alcoholic beverages. This goes back to biblical times, if not earlier, although those carrying out brewing would be blissfully unaware that they were dabbling in biotechnology.

Primrose (1987) has outlined the beginnings of what is known as industrial biotechnology. Apart from the discovery of distillation of wines and beer to produce spirits, and this was being done in the 14th century AD, there was little or no 'biotechnological' advance until the First World War. Then, Germany was obliged to develop microbial production of glycerol by yeast, as the British naval blockade prevented the importation of the vegetable oils which had hitherto been used in glycerol production. Britain had to develop acetone and butanol fermentation, using a *Clostridium*, as these chemicals had largely been imported from Germany. Glycerol and acetone were needed for the munitions industry, and butanol was used in the manufacture of artificial rubber. Thus, the modern fermentation industry was born, and was the founding technology of what became known as industrial biotechnology.

The next major step was the large-scale production of antibiotics, initially penicillin and streptomycin, followed in the 1960s by large-scale animal cell culture for vaccine production. But the main thrust of biotechnology was to change as a result of the recombinant DNA technology developed in the 1970s, and its application as practical genetic engineering in the 1970s with prokaryotes and yeast, and the early 1980s with higher eukaryotes. It is interesting to note, however, that the historical predominance of the industrial side was still evident in the early 1980s. In U.K., The Science and Engineering Research Council established a Biotechnology Directorate in 1981, and its first Director was an engineer, the emphasis being clearly on engineering rather than biology (Connor, 1988).

As a starting point for more detailed discussion of biotechnology as it applies to animals, it is convenient to think of it as embracing

1) industrial biotechnology (the commercial exploitation of micro-organisms)
2) cell culture for the production of vaccines, pharmaceutical proteins and monoclonal antibodies
3) the manipulation of reproductive or other biological processes
4) genetic biotechnology, based on recombinant DNA technology.

It is now becoming common to refer to items 2–4 as agricultural/biomedical biotechnology.

But this classification does not dispose of all problems as to what is legitimately biotechnology, particularly in agricultural biotechnology. There are two dimensions to biotechnology. In both of the general definitions given at the beginning of this paper, stress is laid on the strong commercial or manufacturing connotation of biotechnology. Thus, for a technique, process or piece of research work to be biotechnological it must be in use commercially, have the potential for this, or have relevance to a biotechnological process. The second dimension is closeness to the frontiers of science.

When one considers the 'new' biotechnology, rather than the older industrial biotechnology, the above definitions require some extension and rephrasing. The qualifications for techniques or research to be biotechnological are (1) that they involve sophisticated methods of relatively recent origin and (2) that they are being applied on a large-scale to improve output and/or efficiency in agriculture or human and animal health, or the quality of human life, or have the potential for such applications.

The necessity to accommodate within the confines of biotechnology work which has relevance to biotechnological processes or techniques also has to be addressed. Such work is the platform on which practical biotechnology rests. It can be regarded as being basic to, or at one remove from, practical processes or techniques. An example of this would be work elucidating how a gene of potential economic importance functions at the molecular level. Such knowledge is fundamental to devising ways in which the product of this gene, either *in vitro* or in the live animal or plant, can be exploited commercially, to the benefit of man or agriculture.

It is now necessary to pass from the general to the particular, and indicate the different subject areas of biotechnology. Some have only marginal relevance to livestock production and health, and will be given only passing mention. In the case of others, fuller consideration will be given to the subject scope. As certain terms may be unfamiliar to some readers, definitions of these are given in a glossary at the end of the paper.

INDUSTRIAL BIOTECHNOLOGY

The following list defines the main scope of this branch of biotechnology. It has been derived mainly from the subject coverage definitions of the principal primary journals on biotechnology and those of secondary (abstract) journals.

- Fermentation in relation to the production of beverages, foodstuffs, antibiotics and organic chemicals
- Cell and enzyme immobilization
- Production of single-cell proteins
- Energy and fuel production from biomass
- Large-scale production of microorganisms
- Biodegradation of waste materials
- Water purification by biological means
- Downstream processing
- Design and use of bioreactors
- Analytical and control equipment for biological purposes

AGRICULTURAL BIOTECHNOLOGY

This can be broadly divided into the following categories, some items of which are discussed below.

- Genetic engineering and associated molecular biotechnology

- Cell, tissue and organ culture
- Immunological techniques
- Reproductive and performance enhancing techniques
- Bioengineering
- Applications of microorganisms in the feed industry

One other item that has application in agricultural biotechnology is biodegradation of wastes, and this has already been listed under industrial biotechnology, as this is where it has its roots, and techniques are similar whether applied to factory or farm wastes.

The techniques used in the above fields often extend across the traditional disciplines which go to make up agricultural and allied sciences in the broadest sense. The developments in molecular biology and genetic engineering have blurred the hitherto discrete nature of fields such as cell biology, veterinary medicine and genetics. We now find, for example, research groups working to engineer viruses genetically with a view to their use in vaccines. Other groups are using the same techniques to engineer viruses as vectors for transferring genes to cells in culture or to the germ line of animals.

DNA probes are used to detect pathogenic agents and genes, to check putative parentage, and in forensic science. Thus, it is necessary in the main to approach consideration of the subdivisions of agricultural biotechnology in the light of the techniques and their application, rather than by taking the traditional areas, such as veterinary medicine and animal breeding, as a starting point.

Genetic engineering and associated molecular biology

The ability to produce recombinant DNA stemmed from the discovery of restriction endonucleases in 1970. This was followed in 1972 by the discovery of how to join DNA fragments, and in 1973 the first plasmid vector was constructed. Gene transfer requires four steps: (1) a method of cutting and joining DNA; (2) a vector (gene carrier) that can replicate itself and a foreign DNA segment that has been inserted in it; (3) a method of producing enough DNA for insertion into the germ line of animals or plants, or into their cells (e.g. cloning in bacteria); (4) a method of introducing DNA into the target cells.

Although the first three of these steps became possible in the early 1970s, it was not until eight years later that the fourth step was achieved for the germ cells of animals. In 1977, rapid methods of determining the nucleotide sequences of genes were developed, which opened the way for molecular dissection of genes and elucidation of the way they function at the molecular level.

Sequencing and molecular dissection of genes

Many genes have been sequenced, and their mode of functioning investigated. It is necessary to identify those parts of genes which code for amino acids (exons) and the intervening, non-coding sequences known as introns (found in eukaryotes but not in prokaryotes), the site of attachment of the enzyme responsible for replication of the gene (known as the promoter), and sequences which increase rate of production of the gene product (enhancers). It is also necessary to know if the protein product of a gene is modified in any way after assembly in the ribosomes (translation), as is often the case in eukaryotes. For example, glycosylation may occur. For a transferred gene to function adequately, the conditions for expression in the right tissue, at the right time, and the correct developmental stage of the animal must be fulfilled. Incidentally, promoter and gene do not have to come from the same species in order to provide a functional unit. Molecular dissection is thus an essential part of genetic engineering, and hence of biotechnology.

Research and development covering the four steps in gene transfer form a major part of the 'new' biotechnology. Much attention is being paid to the development of more efficient vectors. Retroviruses, which are RNA viruses, have been used as vectors for some time. As part of their life cycle, provirus becomes incorporated into host DNA, so that foreign genes which have been inserted into retrovirus also become integrated into the host DNA. Retroviruses are currently being used to transfer genes to embryo stem cells, which are developmentally totipotent, and some of these transferred genes find their way into germ cells. They are also being explored as a means of transferring genes into fowl embryos.

However, retroviruses are potentially oncogenic because of the effect of the provirus inserts. Poxviruses, which are DNA viruses, do not have this provirus stage, and hence are nontumorigenic. They also tolerate larger foreign DNA inserts than retroviruses. Poxviruses are being genetically engineered to produce vaccines, by having inserted into them genes coding for antigens found on pathogenic agents. Recombinant technology is being used in attempts to produce vaccines against rinderpest, foot and mouth disease, and bluetongue, for example (Agriculture and Food Research Council, 1989). In theory, it should be possible to insert genes controlling antigens from several disease organisms, thus providing 'single-shot' protection against several diseases. A recombinant rabies vaccine has been developed for oral administration to wildlife.

These viruses are a subject of much research. Work is also being done on the more traditional vectors – bacteriophages, plasmids and cosmids.

The oldest method of DNA transfer into cells is that in which a coprecipitate of DNA and calcium phosphate is phagocytosed by cells, some of which integrate the foreign DNA into their genome. Techniques not involving biological vectors are under study, such as electroporation (DNA uptake assisted by an electric current), fusion of cells with DNA-loaded liposomes, and bombarding cells with DNA-coated microprojectiles.

The production of sufficient DNA for transfer or other purposes has traditionally required cloning in bacteria. Within the past two years, a technique has been developed, known as the polymerase chain reaction, which permits single-copy DNA to be amplified exponentially until an amount sufficient for transfer or other purposes is produced (Saiki, Gelfand, Stoffel, Scharf, Higuchi, Horn, Mullis and Erlich, 1988).

It has recently become possible to 'target' mutations in specific genes in mouse embryo stem cells, provided one has a cloned, genomic fragment of the chosen locus (Capecchi, 1989). This promises to be a powerful technique for generating mice of any desired genotype at a locus, e.g. to produce mouse models of a genetic disease or to study gene function.

There are several other techniques which come under the umbrella of genetic engineering. Restriction fragment length polymorphism is used for gene mapping, and also has possible application in the estimation of breeding value (Soller and Beckmann, 1982). DNA fingerprinting is used to provide unique markers of individual animals and humans (hence its forensic use). Anti-sense RNA or DNA can be used to 'switch off' genes, and this has possible application for counteracting genetic defects, modifying physiological pathways, or elucidating the effects of genes. Fuller discussion of these techniques is given in the review by Turton (1989).

DNA probes are short sequences of known genetic origin, labelled in such a way that they can be readily recognized. The earliest labels were radioactive, but non-radioactive labelling (such as with biotin) is now available. Such probes are used to identify genes and pathogenic organisms. Tests based on such probes are of obvious biotechnological significance.

Immunological techniques

Monoclonal antibodies and their use are part of biotechnology. Their impact in immunoassays, diagnostics, vaccines, tissue typing and therapy is of major significance. Techniques and equipment used in the production of monoclonals also form part of biotechnology. Another technique involves anti-idiotypes as hormone mimics. Protein hormones, such as growth hormone, are antigenic, and antibodies against specific epitopes are known as idiotypes. As idiotype proteins are themselves antigenic, antibodies can be produced against idiotypes themselves. These anti-idiotypes resemble parts of the original hormone, and can function as a substitute for the hormone. This has been shown to occur with growth hormone anti-idiotype (Agriculture and Food Research Council, 1989). Animals can produce their own anti-idiotypes by being immunized with idiotype, so, for example, vaccination with growth hormone idiotype should have a long-term growth promoting effect.

Cell culture

Large-scale cell culture is a traditional biotechnological activity, particularly for vaccine production (e.g. for rabies, foot and mouth disease, distemper, etc.) and the production of therapeutic proteins (e.g. interferon and interleukin). Some cell lines have been derived by recombinant DNA technology in order to produce greater amounts of therapeutic proteins (e.g.

tissue plasminogen activator and blood clotting faction IX). The bioengineering of large-scale cell culture is an important branch of biotechnology.

Reproductive techniques

There is a whole battery of reproductive techniques and procedures which qualify as part of biotechnology. The inclusion of some may be arguable on the grounds that they are not of particularly recent provenance, but nevertheless they are often included within biotechnology.

There can be little argument that embryo manipulation techniques are truly biotechnological. These include the splitting and freezing of embryos, *in vitro* fertilization, blastomere fusion to produce chimaeras, and embryo sexing. The large-scale use of *in vitro* fertilization of cattle oocytes is now a reality, and as a technique to assist genetic improvement may become as common as artificial insemination (Gordon, 1989). Nucleus transfer in sheep embryos can now be carried out (Willadsen, 1986).

In aquaculture, gynogenesis is used to produce triploid fish and hormonal sex reversal to produce monosex broods, both being techniques that improve the productivity of aquaculture systems.

In sheep, melatonin is being used to advance the breeding season and induce oestrus. Other techniques for manipulating the reproductive cycle, such as oestrus synchronization by hormone treatment, the induction and synchronization of parturition, and pregnancy diagnosis from estimation of sex hormone concentrations in milk by immunoassays are often considered as biotechnology. The dividing line between what is obviously biotechnology and what is not – based on the criteria of large-scale applicability and sophistication/newness of techniques – is often blurred. The processing of frozen semen is sometimes regarded as biotechnology, although it is far from being a new technique. Perhaps the answer for the more marginal techniques is to restrict classification as biotechnology to significant new developments.

Feed biotechnology

There are some topics which have their origins in industrial biotechnology, yet do not fit comfortably in the latter. These relate to the feed industry and nutrition. The following potential areas of biotechnological development for the feed industry, excluding techniques involving recombinant DNA, were listed by Lyons (1988a).

- amino acid production by bacteria and yeasts
- isolation of peptides from bacteria
- vitamin production from yeast cultures
- microorganisms to increase the content of biologically available minerals in feeds
- silage inoculants

- modifying rumen fermentation using cultured yeasts and bacteria
- microencapsulation of bacteria in fats to bypass the rumen for delivery to the site of action in the intestine (anti-coliform and anti-salmonella activity)
- immobilized enzymes for insertion into the rumen or hindgut to ensure digestion of a particular dietary component.

Biotechnology is also providing a novel approach to some of the environmental pollution problems of intensive agriculture and even of pet animals. The feeding of diets containing sarsaponin, an extract of the *Yucca schidigera* plant, to reduce ammonia production in faecal decomposition and reduce the odour of dog faeces, is an example of this (Lyons, 1989b).

The inclusion of yeast or bacterial cultures in feed (probiotics) for improving overall performance of farm livestock is also considered as part of biotechnology, and may receive something of a boost in view of current EEC attitudes to hormonal and other growth promoters, and consumer concern about the use of antibiotics in feed (Harker, 1989).

GLOSSARY

Bacteriophages: Viruses that infect bacteria.

Biodegradation: The breakdown of organic matter (often wastes) by microorganisms.

Biomass: There are two biotechnological meanings (1) The cell mass in fermentation. (2) Organic matter to be used as a source of energy, or from which chemicals are produced.

Bioreactors: Containers in which biotechnological reactions are carried out, e.g. large-scale cell culture vessels.

Cosmids: Self-replicating particles of DNA artificially constructed from a plasmid into which DNA from a lambda phage – the so-called cohesive sites – has been inserted.

Downstream processing: Techniques used in the recovery of the end products of fermentation or other biotechnological processes.

Eukaryotes: Organisms with a distinct nucleus bounded by a nuclear membrane.

Gynogenesis: Parthenogenetic development of ova, for example in fish, by activation of the ova by spermatozoa rendered infertile by irradiation. By combining this with appropriate procedures, such as heat shock, diploid and triploid fish develop from the ova.

Immobilization: The entrapment of enzymes, bacteria, animal or plant cells, or organelles in an inert, solid support or matrix.

Liposomes: Artificially constructed lipid vesicles.

Plasmids: Autonomously replicating circles of DNA found in bacteria. They carry genes essential to bacteria, including antibiotic resistance genes.

Prokaryotes: Lower organisms, such as bacteria, which lack a nucleus bounded by a nuclear membrane.

Recombinant DNA: DNA resulting from the splicing together, *in vitro*, of DNA from different sources e.g. vector DNA and DNA from another species of organism.

Restriction endonucleases: Enzymes that cut DNA at specific, short sequences of nucleotides.

Single-cell proteins: Proteins produced by yeasts, bacteria, fungi or algae from a variety of substrates, for use in animal feeds.

REFERENCES

Agricultural and Food Research Council (1989). Annual Report.

Capecchi, M.R. (1989). The new mouse genetics: altering the genome by gene targeting. *Trends in Genetics*, **5**, 70–76.

Connor, S. (1988). The battle for Britain's biotechnology. *New Scientist*, **19** (1625), 45–50.

Coombs, J. (1986). *Macmillan Dictionary of Biotechnology*. The Macmillan Press Ltd., London, 326 pp.

Gordon, I. (1989). Large-scale production of cattle embryos by *in vitro* culture methods. *AgBiotech News and Information*, **1** (3), 345–348.

Harker, A.J. (1989). Probiotics and acidification as part of a 'natural' pig production programme. In: *Biotechnology in the Feed Industry. Proceedings of Alltech's Fourth Annual Symposium* (ed. T.P. Lyons) pp. 8. Alltech Technical Publications, Nicholasville, Kentucky.

Lyons, T.P. (1988a). Applications for biotechnology in the feed industry: the way forward. In: *Biotechnology in the Feed Industry. Proceedings of Alltech's Fourth Annual Symposium* (ed. T.P. Lyons) pp. 2–5. Alltech Technical Publications, Nicholasville, Kentucky.

Lyons, T.P. (1988b). Novel biotechnology approaches to the environmental problems of intensive livestock production. In: *Biotechnology in the Feed Industry. Proceedings of Alltech's Fourth Annual Symposium* (ed. T.P. Lyons). Alltech Technical Publications, Nicholasville, Kentucky.

Primrose, S.B. (1987). *Modern Biotechnology*. Blackwell Scientific Publications, Oxford. 176 pp.

Saiki, R.K., Gelfand, D.H., Stoffel, S., Scharf, S.J., Higuchi, R., Horn, G.T., Mullis, K.B. and Erlich, H.A. (1988). Primer-directed enzymatic amplification of DNA with a thermostable DNA polymerase. *Science*, **239**, 487–494.

Soller, M. and Beckmann, J.S. (1982). Restriction fragment length polymorphisms and genetic improvement. In: *2nd World Congress on Genetics Applied to Livestock Production*, **6**, 395–404.

Turton, J.D. (1989). The application of genetic biotechnology in animal breeding. *AgBiotech News and Information*, **1** (2), 183–187.

Willadsen, S.M. (1986). Nuclear transplantation in sheep embryos. *Nature, U.K.*, **320** (6057), 63–65.

2.

ANIMAL PRODUCTION, BREEDING

Chairman: J.D. Turton
CAB International
U.K.

2.1

Basic Approach to Breeding as a Means of Improving Livestock Production

G. WIENER[1] and J.A. WOOLLIAMS[2]
[1]*Centre for Tropical Veterinary Medicine, Edinburgh University, Scotland*

[2]*AFRC Institute of Animal Physiology and Genetics Research, Edinburgh Research Station, Midlothian, U.K.*

INTRODUCTION

The first step in livestock improvement requires an assessment of the opportunities for change. It will be rare that an improvement in management, feeding, health care – the environment in general – does not bring about an increase in the productivity of animals; nevertheless, it also requires consideration whether such changes are cost effective. Similarly, and almost by definition, an improvement in the genetic merit of animals will produce an increase in output under any conditions, but this may not be substantial or cost effective until the 'environment' is improved too. While all this may seem fairly obvious, it is important to stress that genetic and nongenetic improvements ought to go hand in hand, and that, in practice, they reinforce each other's effects. Thus, improvement in management and feeding may be rewarded by a better response in animal production from an 'improved' breed than from the original stock.

This paper will review the methodology available for genetic change which, for the most part, involves the principles underlying crossbreeding – the most common way of introducing genes from an external population – and those underlying selection – the way of building up genetic superiority from within the local population. In this context, the new technologies can be seen as aids for accelerating progress and for creating new opportunities within the framework of traditional animal breeding. (The theories and applications of selection and of crossbreeding are dealt with in some detail by Falconer (1989) and by Nicholas (1987).)

ACTUAL RATES OF IMPROVEMENT

Crossbreeding

The rate of change depends on the genetic differences between the two breeds or strains being crossed, on the amount of hybrid vigour resulting from the cross, on the level at which crossbreeding is 'stabilized' and on the proportion of the total population which can be maintained as crosses. Improvements in animal output can be very substantial and initially very rapid.

In relation to milk production in developing countries, for which crossbreeding has been particularly widely practised, a number of examples are reviewed by Cunningham and Syrstad (1987).

Selection

The process of genetic improvement based on choosing, as parents, the 'best' within a population (breed, strain, herd, etc.) is sometimes regarded as too slow for use in developing countries, when starting with stock at often low levels of performance. It has to be said, however, that such improvements though individually small per year are cumulative and hence build up to substantial levels over time. The actual factors affecting rates of change will be considered later.

Smith (1984) estimated that the rates of genetic response in, for example, gain in weight, which are possible per year using natural service, ranged from 1.4% of the mean for beef cattle and sheep, to 2.7% in pigs and 3.2% in poultry. For sex-limited traits, which are technically more difficult to improve by selection, the corresponding percentages show convincing progress, notwithstanding. Thus, egg production 2.1%, litter size in pigs 3.0% and in sheep 2.1%, and milk yield in cattle 1.5%. Smith further provides examples of rates actually achieved in selection experiments and in practical breeding programmes. In general the rates achieved, particularly in the breeding programmes, were below those theoretically possible. In practice there is often a temptation to select on more criteria than those from which most of the economic advantage is derived, and this clearly reduces the rate of progress made in the main trait. None-the-less, the cumulative benefits over, say, a ten year period can be very significant. Also, in practical terms there is an advantage to be gained from relatively slow but steady genetic improvements rather than large single steps. In the 'slow but steady' case it is more realistic to expect concomitant improvements in feeding and management to keep pace with the improvements in genetic merit.

GENETIC MERIT – a caution on genotype-environment interaction

The level of production attained by a breed, say, under one set of conditions is not necessarily a guide to its performance under another set of conditions. This is especially true when considering the performance of temperate breeds for use in the tropics. The concept of genotype-environment interaction is of great practical consequence when the differences in the 'native' environments of two breeds is very different. The important criterion is the genetic potential under the circumstances under which the breed or the crossbred is expected to perform.

Similarly, the amount of hybrid vigour expressed by a cross – as in crosses between temperate and tropical breeds – is dependent on the environment. As a pure breed, a temperate breed might not even survive the climatic, health, and feed challenges of a developing country, and the local breed, whilst a survivor, may not be a good producer. If under such circumstances a cross between the two types were to do well the outcome is correctly described as hybrid vigour – measured in relation to the average of the two parental breeds. But given much more favourable circumstances, such hybrid vigour may disappear or be much diminished. In principle, similar considerations apply to comparisons of selected and unselected strains within a breed – if the two have been developed under different conditions of feeding and management. 'Genetic merit' is, therefore, a relative rather than an absolute concept.

THE GENETIC BASIS OF CROSSBREEDING STRATEGIES

Provided different breeds are represented by large numbers of animals, which are, in turn, representative of the whole population, and the comparison of different breeds is made under identical conditions (preferably running together as a single group) then any differences in performance between the breeds are *genetic* in origin. This, condition is rarely met in developing countries, especially in the tropics and subtropics, particularly when one of the breeds under consideration is an exotic. However, for present purposes it will be assumed that 'breed values' are 'known'.

Under these idealised circumstances, the first expectation from the crossing of two breeds is that the performance of the progeny will be half way between that of the two parent breeds (the 'additive' genetic effect).

For example, if postweaning growth of Breed A is 100 g/day and of Breed B is 140 g/day, then the expected postweaning growth of the crossbred is 120 g/day.

Heterosis

However, in the case of crossbreeding there is sometimes a bonus of heterosis (when positive, also called 'hybrid vigour') which is measured as the *deviation* of the progeny performance from the *average* of the two parent breeds. This hybrid vigour, when it occurs, arises from the condition of heterozygocity (which is expected to be greater in crosses than in pure breeds – especially if the two pure breeds differ considerably from each other) combined with the gene action known as 'dominance' (and also 'epistasis').

The expression of hybrid vigour is always at its maximum (100%) in the first cross (F1) between two breeds P(i) and P(ii) and varying amounts of the hybrid vigour are lost in later generations of crossing.

Thus:

P(i)	*	P(ii)	=	F1	100%	of any hybrid vigour
F1	*	F1	=	F2	50%	"
F1	*	P	=	B	50%	"
B	*	B			37.5%	"
F2	*	F2	=	F3	50%	"

Individual and maternal heterosis

Heterosis can be manifested both by the individual animal and by its dam in providing a better maternal environment for the offspring. Depending on the relative importance of these two aspects, different crossing systems are available to exploit these two appropriately. The theory and application of different systems of crossing are given in some detail by Cunningham and Syrstad (1987).

Finding the magnitude of heterosis

Unfortunately, it is rarely possible, in the kind of situation met in most developing countries, to measure the acutal extent of heterosis (hybrid vigour) with accuracy – or quickly – because ideally this requires that both the pure breeds involved and the reciprocal crosses between them be kept in quite large numbers together and managed alike. (Especially in the tropics, the 'exotic' breed is rarely represented by large numbers of breeding females, available to be bred pure and also crossed with the local. Even if this condition were met, the exotic breed is usually regarded as too precious to be treated in the same way as local animals.) Since, however, it is important to get some idea of the magnitude of heterosis as a contribution to the F1 performance, an alternative but less efficient method is to compare F1 animal performance with that of *contemporary* F2 which has only 50% of the heterosis but the same average additive genetic expectations (contemporary backcrosses can also be put into the comparison after making allowance for their different additive genetic make-up.)

Proportion of herd or flock crossbred

The reason for the importance of 'finding out' about the magnitude of heterosis is that the answers matter for the economics of choosing the breeding strategy. If heterosis is absent or negligible, a crossbred type which meets the requirements of farmers can quite readily be 'fixed' by interbreeding without loss of productivity. (This is likely for traits like mature body weight or fleece quality or the percentage of fat in milk.) If, however, heterosis is a major component of the 'merit' of a first cross (as could well be the case for reproductive and survival traits), the interbreeding of the crosses – the 'fixing' of the crossbred type – will lead to loss of heterosis. If that is a large amount in terms of performance, it might be better to continually recreate first crosses. That, in turn, carries the 'penalty' that only a proportion of the local population can be crossbred; the rest has to be the original purebred (local) population which has to be maintained in order to produce the crosses. Moreover, if the crossbred type is not to be 'fixed' provision must also be made for maintaining sufficient of the exotics as purebreds to provide breeding males, or to use imported semen with AI.

If heterosis is indeed a very major component in the performance level of the first cross, it is also likely that further infusions of 'exotic' blood (grading-up) will not lead to further improvements in productivity. Preferably this is best discovered for each situation by actual trial, but it is quite common experience that the optimum level of 'exotic' blood is around 50% with the other half derived from an indigenous breed.

The economics and practicalities of the situation therefore require a compromise between, on the one hand, a totally crossbred population (e.g. a new synthetic breed) with each animal at a somewhat lower performance than the maximum, and, on the other hand, a population where a proportion are first crosses (expressing maximum heterosis) but where the remainder – probably the majority – remain the indigenous breed with a lower level of production. However, if the indigenous pure breed and the crossbred type can occupy different environmental niches, the problem is simplified. It then becomes a question of deciding whether enough of the indigenous purebreds can be set aside for crossbreeding purposes without endangering the replacement capacity of the indigenous pure breed. (A system of breed stratification is 'traditional' for sheep in the U.K. where hill breeds are bred pure on the hills, but are taken to better land for crossbreeding when they get older.)

Other crossing systems such as criss-crossing or three-breed crossing (Cunningham and Syrstad, 1987) exploit heterosis especially by using crossbred females as dams (see above for maternal heterosis). But each of these systems presents additional operational difficulties which are likely to be drawbacks in developing countries, and the performance level in these more complicated systems can be rather variable from one generation to the next.

SELECTION WITHIN BREEDS

Selection is the basic procedure used both by nature and by man to change the attributes of animals. In any programme of livestock improvement the first difficulty, and sometimes the greatest, is to decide on the objectives for the improvement and hence for the process of selection – and to make the objectives realistic (attainable) and to hold to them for a reasonable period of years.

Because in the process of selection some animals are chosen in preference to others, it follows that the frequencies of particular genes change between parent and offspring generations and in this way change performance. Selection as normally practiced works only on the additive part of the genetic variation V_A which is the chief component of resemblance between relatives. The ratio of the additive genetic variation to the total variation (V_A/V_P) is often referred to as the heritability (h^2). When this value is high it means that a large part of the variation available for selection is genetic in origin, and vice versa when the heritability estimate is low. In consequence, a high heritability will give a more rapid response than a low heritability.

The response to selection per generation depends not only on the heritability but on the selection pressure applied which is reflected by the average superiority of the selected parents over the mean of their group (*selection differential*). The smaller the proportion selected the higher the selection differential (S).

In practice, a lot of attention is paid by many breeders to making the *accuracy* of selection as great as possible by getting many records on an individual, and by gathering information about the performance of relatives, which could, of course, include information on progeny (progeny testing). These procedures increase the interval between generations. However, the practical benefit of genetic improvement should really be measured as the *progress per year*. Thus, to arrive at the correct compromise, a balance has to be struck between accuracy of selection and the speed with which generations can be turned over. For traits which are limited in their expression to one sex (e.g. maternal traits) it may be necessary to evaluate males on the performance of their female relatives, often including progeny testing.

For any traits of very low heritability it may indeed be essential to obtain many records on an individual and to obtain records from relatives. However, even then, alternatives might be explored to shorten the generation interval.

Avoidance of inbreeding

When selecting for superior performance there is a danger that the individuals in the selected breeding population – particularly the sires – can become quite few in number and that, in consequence, inbreeding will arise through the mating of relatives to each other, e.g. animals with a common grandparent or even half-sibs.

Inbreeding should be avoided whenever possible since it nearly always leads to reduced productivity, and in the long-term to a reduction in the genetic variation which is the necessary basis for further selection. A first precaution is to ensure adequate numbers of animals (sires) in the top (nucleus) group. Clearly, this reduces the genetic superiority of the selected group relative to the average, but this is a price which has to be paid in order to reduce the inbreeding risks and in turn protect the long-term effectiveness of the programme.

How many traits to select?

Many breeders want to improve 'everything' – or at least several traits at the same time. However, the more traits are included in the selection process, the smaller is the progress for any one trait – and zero progress is not at all unlikely. This puts emphasis on the importance of getting the objectives right.

If more than one trait must be improved in a particular population of animals, there are basically three ways of setting about it: 1) tandem selection where one trait is improved to the desired level first, followed by the next, etc. 2) independent culling levels whereby a particular performance level is set for each of the traits, and no animal selected for breeding is allowed to fall below these levels; 3) index selection whereby the traits are combined so as to maximise the overall progress in terms of economic merit.

At least in theory, index selection is always the most efficient and that advantage over other methods increases with the number of traits included in the selection. (Tandem selection is always the poorest method.) For an index, the importance given to different traits takes account of their heritabilities and the genetic correlations among the traits, and a weighting is introduced to reflect the economic importance of each component trait.

Selection environment

Selection is often carried out in an environment more favourable than that in which the animals produced by the scheme are expected to perform. This is done in the belief that for successful selection the animals must be able to express their full potential. If not mistaken, this concept carries the danger that, if large genotype-environment interaction occurs, the superiority achieved by selection may not be expressed where it is needed. Whether or not this occurs is a matter for trial and may then lead to modifications in the management of a selection scheme. The safest procedure, although not necessarily the fastest rate of progress, is achieved by selecting in the environment in which the animals will subsequently have to produce.

Selection schemes

These benefit from being on a large-scale to avoid inbreeding and to increase the selection differential and the potential accuracy of selection. This is not, however, always possible or even desirable at a single location. Grouping of herds or flocks into various forms of cooperative schemes provides a practical alternative. The newer 'technologies', and in particular multiple ovulation and embryo transfer, offer new opportunities which will be referred to below. In order to provide adequate numbers it will often be necessary to introduce a system of multiplication of the animals first selected in the nucleus group. In any improvement programme involving selection, it is also important to determine whether the 'improved' stock will, in turn, respond to improved feeding and management to give a better economic return.

RECENT TECHNICAL DEVELOPMENTS AS AIDS TO BREEDING SCHEMES

It is not the intention here to describe such developments or their implications in detail since much of this is the role of other contributors to this Proceedings. However, it is important in the context of this paper to highlight the aspects of basic animal breeding practice to which the new developments most clearly relate.

Advances in statistical and computing procedures

Over the last two decades these advances have almost revolutionized the opportunities for dealing with complex and often 'messy' data, particularly those collected from animals on farms. This has been particularly helpful in making it easier to recognize the genetic component of total variation – by allowing for the effects of some environmental variables – and hence, for example, increasing the accuracy of selection. 'Best Linear Unbiased Predictor' (BLUP) and 'Restricted Maximum Likelihood' (REML) are two of these, with BLUP at present one of the most widely used.

Technical advances

These mostly revolve around manipulation of embryos – and the production of many more embryos from an individual than would normally be produced. In terms of breeding programmes (for example, national programmes for genetic improvement of milk production) this has led to the development of multiple ovulation and embryo (MOET) schemes which can potentially provide as much genetic progress as large progeny testing schemes but with a fraction of the resources (Nicholas and Smith, 1983; Woolliams, 1989). At the same time, the technical inputs and infrastructure can be limited to one location. Other developments of note include the techniques of embryo splitting, nuclear transfer and embryo sexing. Woolliams and Wilmut (1989) have reviewed and assessed the likely impact of most of these possibilities for breeding schemes. It is not surprising that some potential benefits – reduction in generation interval, increase in selection differential, improvements in accuracy of selection – are offset by some potential disadvantages – increased inbreeding, reduced genetic variability. (Not each technique shares each potential benefit or disadvantage.) Perhaps it should be added that these techniques are helpful only if they are reliable in the hands of those who actually have to use them, for example in a developing country, and not just in the hands of the experts who have developed them.

Physiological genetics

A number of economically important traits, for example, the production of offspring or of milk, are expressed only in the female and relatively late in life. The search for physiological or biochemical criteria, which are thought to underlie the production traits, is aimed at finding those which are expressed in both sexes and early in life. The impact therefore arises from reductions in generation interval, from improvements in the selection differential, and, when used in conjunction with 'conventional' traits, improving accuracy of recognizing genetic merit. Such 'indirect' criteria may also help in improving traits which cannot readily be measured in the live animal, or traits the expression of which is intrinsically undesirable (like disease or death). A very general survey of possibilities was given by Wiener (1986) and the impact of including physiological criteria into selection for milk production in cattle was calculated by Woolliams and Smith (1988) and shown to be substantial – up to double the rate of progress in the best scenario without such a criterion. (The calculations were of more than theoretical interest because they rested on the foundation of at least one criterion – blood urea nitrogen – which has been researched both in Edinburgh and elsewhere and found to give reasonably consistent 'predictive' results. Other potential criteria are also being investigated.)

Molecular genetics

As yet, the opportunities from the spectacular advances in this area are speculative rather than demonstrable. However, it is clear that one impact will be in the introduction of new genetic variation to populations lacking it, for example in the realm of introducing disease resistance, novel or transformed animal products, or, for example, the capacity for cattle to produce twins regularly.

Conventional animal breeding works on entire phenotypes – even though particular traits, usually controlled by many genes, may be emphasised in a selection or a crossbreeding programme. The introduction of novel genes with major effects into the genome of animals, or the deletion of genes with unwanted but major effects, may have consequences for fitness and for traits other than those directly manipulated. It thus becomes important to consider that the new advances must entail extensive testing of the animals concerned. The aim must be to ensure that benefits in terms of new or radically altered traits are not counteracted by poorer performance in the wide range of other economically important respects. Thereafter, it will still be the task of the older established animal breeding techniques – aided by new technology – to multiply the new, genetically engineered type and to further improve its general, economic usefulness.

REFERENCES

Cunningham, E.P. and Syrstad, O. (1987). *Crossbreeding* Bos indicus *and* Bos taurus *for Milk Production in the Tropics*. FAO Animal Production and Health Paper 68. Food and Agriculture Organisation of the United Nations, Rome 1987.

Falconer, D.S. (1989). *An Introduction to Quantitative Genetics* (3rd ed.), Longman Scientific and Technical, London.

Nicholas, F.W. (1987). *Veterinary Genetics*. Clarendon Press, Oxford.

Nicholas, F.W. and Smith, C. (1983). Increased rates of genetic change in dairy cattle by embryo transfer and splitting. *Animal Production*, **36**, 341–353.

Smith, C. (1984). Rates of genetic change in farm livestock. *Research and Development in Agriculture*, **1**, 79–85.

Wiener, G. (1986). *Genetic Variation in Physiological Factors Relating to Livestock Improvement*. Report - 1986, pp. 14-16. AFRC Animal Breeding Research Organisation, Edinburgh.

Woolliams, J.A. (1989). Modifications to MOET nucleus breeding schemes to improve rates of genetic progress and decrease rates of inbreeding in dairy cattle. *Animal Production,* **49**, 1-14.

Woolliams, J.A. and Smith, C. (1988). The value of indicator traits in the genetic improvement of dairy cattle. *Animal Production,* **46**, 333-345.

Woolliams, J.A. and Wilmut, I. (1989). Embryo manipulation in cattle breeding and production. *Animal Production,* **48**, 3-30.

2.2

The Role of Embryo Transfer Technology

E.J.C. POLGE
Animal Biotechnology Cambridge Ltd, Cambridge, U.K.

ABSTRACT

Practical techniques for embryo transfer in farm animals were developed about 20 years ago and since then they have been applied increasingly in animal breeding especially in cattle. The methods so far have been based on superovulation of selected donor animals by administration of gonadotrophic hormones, fertilization *in vivo* by artificial insemination, collection of embryos by flushing the reproductive tract, and transfer to recipients at an appropriate stage of the reproductive cycle. Both collection and transfer of embryos in cattle can be carried out repeatedly by non-surgical procedures and the average number of embryos collected at one time is about six. In pigs surgical procedures are required, but in sheep embryo transfer can be carried out by laparoscopy.

Embryo transfer enables more rapid multiplication of breeds or genetically elite animals. Preservation of embryos by deep freezing and storage in liquid nitrogen has also enabled import or export of embryos between countries and the banking of valuable genetic material. Since the zona pellucida excludes a number of viruses and other organisms, embryo transfer can be one of the safest ways of transporting genetic material between countries.

Recently multiple ovulation and embryo transfer (MOET) is being applied to increase the rate of genetic progress in cattle improvement schemes. The emphasis of selection is based on the performance of several sisters from individual elite cows instead of the traditional progeny testing methods and advantage is taken of a reduction in the interval between generations. Such schemes may be particularly applicable to cattle improvement in developing countries using a small selected nucleus herd.

New technologies have been established for large-scale production of embryos by *in vitro* methods. These involve the recovery of immature oocytes from ovaries, their maturation and fertilization *in vitro* and culture to the blastocyst stage before freezing and storage in liquid nitrogen. These are now being used for more widespread applications of embryo transfer.

Embryo transplantation also enables additional techniques of embryo manipulation to be applied effectively. The sex of embryos to be transplanted can be determined by the use of molecular probes and methods are being developed for the multiplication of embryos of high genetic merit by means of nuclear transplantation. Transgenic animals have already been produced by methods in which foreign cloned genes have been introduced into embryos at an early stage of development and all these technologies offer many new opportunities for improving animal performance or products.

2.3

Biotechnology Applied to Animal Breeding and Genetics

J. HODGES
Food & Agriculture Organization, Rome, Italy

INTRODUCTION

The application of molecular biology to animal breeding and genetics is expected to take domestic animal production into a new era. Although this will not happen immediately, clearly the potential is so great that it will surely continue to be the subject of intensive research and development. In evaluating the likely impact, the field of animal breeding must be linked with the field of reproduction. It is the combination of the two which offers the promise. This paper does not consider the technical methodology of reproductive manipulation *per se*. It recognizes the combined results which molecular biology applied both to animal genetics and mammalian reproduction, are having upon animal breeding methods and progress.

Animal breeding has passed through several eras. The rate of change is accelerating. The first stage of domestication lasted for thousands of years and resulted in the relatively few species of domestic animals which today meet the human need for meat, milk, animal fibre and draught animal power. The second stage was also slow. It involved the movement of human populations accompanied by their domestic animals across the earth into new environments. In these different environments, animals became adapted to the challenges of more hostile climates, endemic pests and diseases and varying qualities and quantities of feed and water. In this way through genetic drift and natural selection, isolated populations of animals became specifically adapted to their environments, though still able to interbreed with other populations within the species. Thus, the first era in centres of domestication followed by the dispersion of groups into many environments has given mankind an enormous number of adapted breeds which are still part of the same gene pool of the species.

The third stage was the development of controlled mating and the human selection of preferred phenotypes and eventually of genotypes. In its most organized form this stage resulted in the creation of registers of matings and the identification of elite animals which, compared with their ancestors, were to some extent homozygous. These animals once registered in a Herd Book, have been used selectively and have marked ensuing generations with their genetic characteristics. Originally these traits may have been closely related to survival and economic performance, but in temperate regions where the environment is not so hostile, breeds were also selected sometimes for phenotypic traits of little or no economic value apart from their appearance. Herd Books which had their origin in the U.K. in the 18th century thus formalized and intensified human selection activity which had been in progress among livestock breeders everywhere for centuries.

The fourth stage began in the middle of the 20th century with the discovery of a practical field method of using artificial insemination. Concurrently the development of quantitative genetics broke open new methods for the selection of economically important, polygenic traits. The progress achieved in increased production during the last 30 years is well-known. It is built upon the twin approaches of intensifying selection of the existing inbred pure populations and also upon the planned use of crossbreeding. These twin approaches are used separately or in combination in nearly all current livestock improvement programmes. The ability to freeze semen and more recently embryos and to ship them worldwide in association with AI, has also stimulated the genetic improvement of livestock in both developed and developing countries, provided genetic programmes are carefully designed.

The fifth and new era of biotechnology has started. It may be decades before it changes practical animal breeding, but judging by the increased pace from the first era until now, it will come more quickly than expected. A more detailed review of other aspects of animal production and health is given by Hodges (1986). Biotechnology offers change for animal breeding and genetics in several different ways.

- First there is the possibility of 'inbreeding' or 'crossbreeding' by the transfer of genes and designer genomes to suit the animal breeder.
- Second is the possibility of more rapid multiplication of preferred genotypes by splitting, cloning and other manipulations of embryos.
- Third is the possibility of enriching the conventional quantitative genetic approaches of selective breeding.

Each of these three areas is reviewed in turn, with examples, to illustrate the contemporary options being developed.

THE PRODUCTION OF TRANSGENIC ANIMALS

Animal breeding and gentics have always aimed at the production of an offspring generation which is an improvement on the parental generation. The methodology has been indirect by the use of phenotypically observed traits. It is uncertain in individual animals. That is why animal breeders work with populations in which the mean can be moved, resulting in an overall improvement in the population. Although the aim is to change the phenotypic performance, the genetic mechanism controlling performance is the gene which has previously been inaccessible directly. Genes are segments of DNA which are subject to crossing over, random segregation and recombination in the production of every mammalian sperm and oocyte. Animal breeders have therefore found it very difficult to predict the outcome of any individual mating. This has led some animal breeders to value the homozygous state which is increased by inbreeding. However, as is well-known, there are severe disadvantages to inbreeding, since the homozygous condition for many genes results in reduced performance or even abnormalities. Thus the search for the animal which is pure breeding for the desired traits is often marred by the discovery that the animal also carries unattractive genes which appear in inbred offspring.

The problem has been that no mechanism has existed hitherto, for directly selecting some genes and rejecting other genes in parents. It has all depended upon the uncontrolled consequences of crossing over, random segregation and recombination. In practice, as mentioned, the remedy has been to deal in large numbers of animals and improve the population on average.

Biotechnology now offers, for the first time, a mechanism for deliberately selecting or rejecting a segment of DNA. The ability to 'cut and join' has opened up the possibility of creating transgenic domestic animals, as was anticipated when the first viable transgenic mice were reported by Palmiter, Brinster, Hammer, Trumbauer, Rosenfeld, Birnberg and Evans (1982). Substantial problems remain at present in the technique. The first of these is that the insertion of genes into animal germlines is still uncertain and is solved only by producing many individuals and waiting to see which of them have successfully incorporated the transgene into their own genome. The most effective method of inserting DNA into mammals has been into the embryo using pronuclear injection. It has so far proved very inefficient in cattle. The possibility of embryonic stem cell introduction into embryos is being actively explored to improve this success rate. The second major problem is the need to insert the DNA at defined locations in the genome of the embryo. At present DNA is inserted randomly and may enter an inert area of the genome where it is nonoperative or may have a negative effect upon the expression of other genes. Thus, the need for site-specific recombinant DNA in host animal cells is a high priority to permit the application in practice. Assuming that these problems will be overcome in time, it is expected that the future uses of recombinant DNA technology in farm animals will fall into four areas as follows:-

- The introduction of new functions. As an example, one may propose the introduction of genes conveying adaptive traits or deletion of adverse genes.

- Enhancement of productivity by the substitution of alleles. An example would be the replacement of alleles in a polygenic trait that are responsible for lower productivity by inserting alleles from the same species or different species causing higher productivity. The Booroola gene for fecundity in sheep would be an attractive example (Bindon, 1984).
- Elevating production by the duplication of sets of alleles. It is not yet clear whether multiplying certain segments of DNA is an effective way of increasing the genetic effect of a trait. There is some evidence to support the idea. As Robertson (1985), has pointed out, this approach produces genetic variation of an entirely different kind that was not previously available for selection.
- Controlling genome activity. Although poorly developed currently, this area could potentially become of the greatest importance in the future. The idea is to insert recombinant DNA so that the timing of certain developmental functions can be controlled. Examples are the onset of puberty or controlling the amount of endogenous growth hormone produced.

Little progress will be made in most of this type of work without genome maps, since it is essential to be able to identify the appropriate segments of DNA. Genome mapping is greatly assisted by genetic markers which are points of the DNA that can be easily identified. Between two markers the length of DNA can be located and experimentally the presence of specific genes in this length of DNA can be detected. Genome maps are expensive to produce and it is unlikely that funds will ever be available for mapping the genome of, say cattle, solely from scratch. However, the good news on this topic for animal breeders is the recent decision of the U.S. Congress to vote several billion dollars to map the human genome. Since there are strong parallels in the order and composition of blocks of DNA between related species, the human genome map will throw great light upon the genome maps of domestic mammalian species. The creation of genome library centres for maps of different domestic species is now in progress and data from researchers throughout the world will gradually build up the genome maps in the same way the earth was mapped by many voyages of discovery.

A novel technique for locating the DNA responsible for an important adaptive trait in cattle has been proposed by Soller and Beckmann (1982, 1985). The technique known as restriction fragment length polymorphism (RFLP) is an ingenious combination of the classical and molecular approaches to the genetics to segregation and recombination in a sample of crossbred individuals.

Two groups of parents are chosen to produce crossbred offspring. One set of parents carry the trait of interest and the other set do not. Structured crossbreeding of the filial generations provides the chance for quantitative measurement of the trait phenotypically. The DNA of the individual crossbred and parental animals is also studied using genetic markers. The two sets of data are correlated and the presence or absence of the trait can be associated with the presence or absence of specific segments of DNA. It has been proposed by Soller and Beckmann (1982, 1985) for example, that the genes for trypanotolerance in West African cattle can be identified. The possibilities then would exist for transferring such genes to a breed of higher economic merit which would otherwise suffer from trypanosomiasis.

The possibilities for such direct use of recombinant DNA in transgenic domestic animals still lie ahead. The potential however is extremely great. One of the greatest applications of transgenic animals in years to come may be the creation of higher producing animals adapted for the tropics. The existing situation is extremely difficult. Crossbreeding of temperate and tropical breeds is the only solution and it is expensive, slow and difficult to organize. Many developing countries have devoted the resources of whole animal research stations to crossbreeding research. Many researchers have given ten to 20 years to a single crossbreeding experiment with ruminants. Although it has been the only way, the results are often difficult to interpret and apply (FAO, 1987). Trade-offs have to be made between desired traits. There are difficulties in maintaining the crossbred animals with the right gene mix on a field scale. This is essential for the benefit of the small livestock producer, who otherwise will suffer from reduced production if his animals have too many indigenous genes, or lost viability and survival if his animals have too many temperate genes. Transgenic animals, produced according to a genetic design appear in the long-term to offer a solution. They will then have to be replicated in abundance. This leads to the next aspect of biotechnology applied to animal breeding and genetics.

BIOTECHNOLOGY AND EMBRYO MANIPULATION

Embryo manipulation includes multiple ovulation embryo transfer (MOET), freezing and long-term storage of embryos, sexing, splitting, cloning and *in vitro* fertilization. It also includes collection of oocytes and their freezing, storing and subsequent *in vitro* fertilization. It may be asked why these techniques of manipulative reproduction are grouped with biotechnology. The answer is that molecular engineering of mammals is dependent upon the embryo for two reasons. First, the embryo contains the target germ-line cells for transfer DNA. Second, the production of transgenic animals will require multiplication in the diploid form. The embryo is suited to this.

Since embryo manipulation is the subject of another presentation here (Polge, this volume) it will not be covered in this paper. However, it is so essential and intertwined with the use of biotechnology for animal breeding and genetics, that a few comments are essential. Embryo transfer and manipulation are not ends in themselves. AI similarly was not an end in itself. They are techniques expected to contribute to the genetic improvement of livestock. While AI had the advantage of limiting the spread of venereal disease, the embryo has the advantage of being relatively free of most diseases if strict handling and washing routines are followed. However, it is unlikely that the use of embryos could be justified on the grounds of disease control alone in normal field conditions. By contrast, there is a general hope that embryo technology will increase the rate of genetic improvement. This expectation leads to the third area in which biotechnology may be expected to affect animal breeding and genetics. It is in the enhancement of conventional quantitative selection programmes.

ENRICHMENT OF SELECTION PROCEDURES

First a brief word about the prospects for marker assisted selection (MAS) to enhance normal selection methods, particularly those concerned with quantitative trait loci (QTL). Whereas the selection and identification of traits controlled by single or few genes may be advanced by MAS, the use with QTL is not so promising at present. Smith and Simpson (1985) pointed out the problems which can occur with, for example, sampling errors in evaluation of QTL, losses due to crossingover, undetected crossovers, and incomplete evaluation of offspring.

The area of conventional genetic improvement most likely to be affected by biotechnology in the near future is the selection and improvement of a group of economically important traits such as milk yield. Biotechnology offers the new method of Open Nucleus Breeding System (ONBS). This will now be described in some detail since it is the most valuable application on a field scale which biotechnology currently offers animal breeding and genetics. Also it has particular attractions and merit worth exploring for developing conditions.

The concept of ONBS

In many developed countries genetic improvement is achieved by the use of field performance recording on a large-scale. For example, the progeny testing of dairy bulls using daughters' records has been highly successful when combined with AI. However, in many developing country conditions, where field recording and AI are not possible, genetic improvement has been limited. The advent of MOET may offer a new means of achieving genetic progress by the use of ONBS, using the sibling test instead of the daughter test (Hodges, 1988). The genetic theory has been established (Nicholas and Smith, 1983; Christensen and Liboriussen, 1986; Smith, 1988a) and in a few developed countries trials are being established to test the feasibility in practice. Meanwhile, it is suggested that ONBS may be especially valuable for developing countries (Smith, 1988a and 1988b) where AI and field progeny testing have largely failed.

The genetic relationships of brother and sister are the same as those of father and daughter. The system makes use of full and half-sibs to estimate the breeding value of males under test. First, the unrecorded base population is screened to find apparently superior females. This can be done either with a very simple recording system introduced temporarily in the field or by relying upon the owner's knowledge of the animals. These exceptional animals are brought together in the nucleus flock or herd to form a test group under controlled management where recording of their performance traits can be carried out routinely and where embryo transfer facilities can be located. The elite females from this test group are brought into multiple ovulation and their embryos are transferred to the other females in the test group and unrecorded females in the base population. The offspring, both males and females, are kept in the test group where their traits of interest are recorded. Then the male offspring are evaluated on the basis of their siblings' performances and their own records where these are available for a trait recordable in both sexes. The best of the males are then used extensively in the base population either by AI or natural service.

The female offspring are next considered as potential elite females to donate embryos by MOET for the following cycle. This selection involves appraising them against the elite cows already in the nucleus flock or herd which have already been used for MOET. The critical decision about which females to retain for MOET is a balance between those with the highest individual genetic merit combined with their suitability for multiple ovulation, while seeking to minimize the generation interval between each cycle of MOET.

The comparison between progeny and sibling tests is illustrated in Figs. 1 and 2 for dairy cattle. Sibling test results are obtained in four years compared with seven for progeny testing. This difference may be larger when, as often happens, the age of the first calving of daughters in the field progeny testing scheme is delayed. On the other hand the female siblings in the nucleus herd under controlled conditions can be calved at younger ages. Although the sibling test is less accurate due to there being fewer siblings for each male on test in an ONBS than there are offspring in a field progeny testing plan, the shorter generation interval of the sibling test provides higher genetic gains per year.

Open nucleus breeding system for dairy cattle

The ONBS is illustrated now for a dairy cattle ONBS in a developed country (Fig. 3). It is assumed in this example that when the ONBS is in full operation, the nucleus herd will comprise 250 females. These will include the elite females subject to MOET, and their female offspring in first lactation and other cows screened from the base population and on test. The younger animals must also be kept in addition. From this herd of lactating cows on test, it is assumed for the example that each year the 32 top performance animals are chosen for MOET using semen from eight elite sires. This semen may be locally produced from previously tested males in the scheme, or it may be introduced from other improvement programmes elsewhere. In this way the Nucleus Breeding System is Open.

It should be noted that the figures here chosen for illustration are arbitrary. The genetic progress per year will depend upon the selection intensity which is determined by the actual figures used in practice. Thus numbers used here

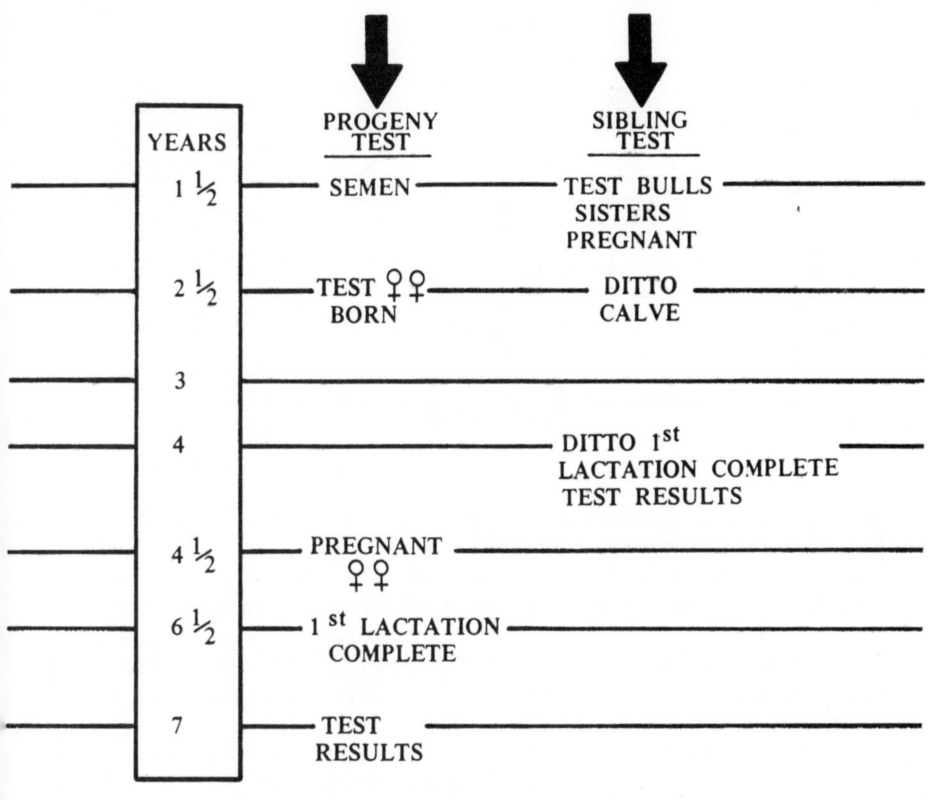

Fig. 1 *Time frame for progeny and sibling tests.*

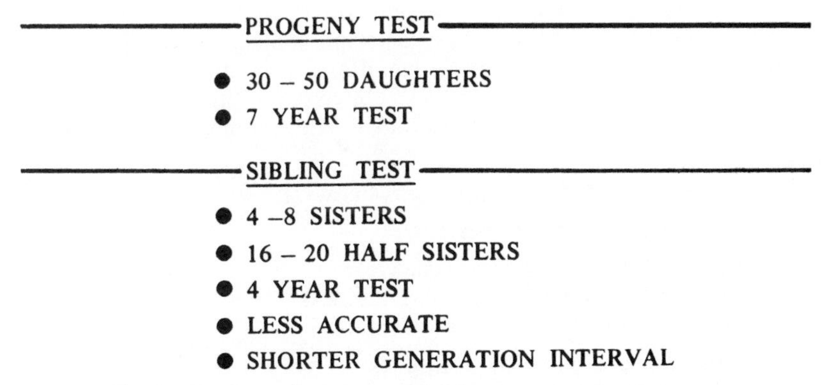

Fig. 2 *Numbers of relatives needed for progeny and sibling tests.*

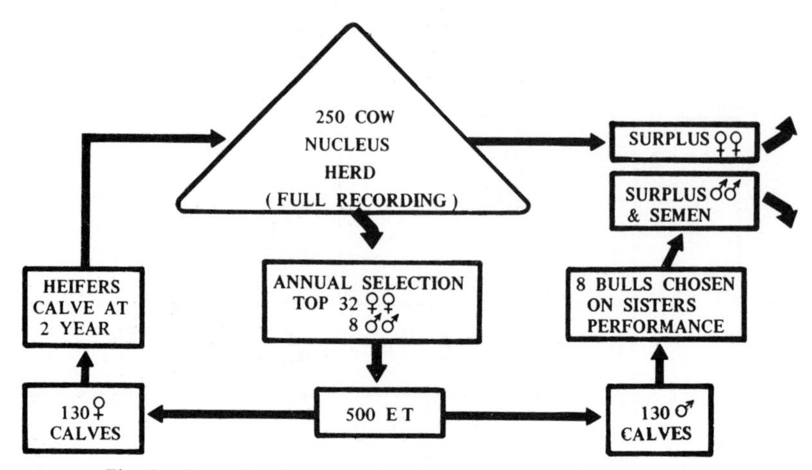

Fig. 3 *Example of open nucleus breeding system for dairy cattle.*

must be regarded solely as an example. The actual size of any ONBS will depend upon a variety of factors which will be discussed later in the paper.

Fig. 3 shows that in this example, it may be possible under developed country conditions to produce 500 embryos annually from the 32 elite cows, from which an estimated 260 calves are born. In developing country conditions, where local conditions for MOET are less favourable, it is sure to be considerably less. For ease of illustration, it is now assumed that all 260 animals remain alive, fertile and available for selection. In practice an inevitable but variable loss will occur from different causes such as failure of heifers to conceive or to complete a pregnancy or lactation. There will also be some loss and infertility among males. These losses, though of importance in practice, are ignored here to simplify the logistics which show animals moving through an ONBS for dairy cattle. The 130 females calve at two years of age and are milked in the test group with full recording. (In the case of a scheme combining milk and growth selection then both the males and females would be growth recorded.) When the first lactation records are available, either complete or estimated from partial lactations, they are used to calculate breeding values for the sibling males. On average this will involve four full-sibs and 12 half-sibs per bull evaluated. The summary average logistics are given:

- 32 elite cows for MOET with 8 sires (4 cows per sire)
- 512 embryos recovered (16 per cow)
- 256 successful pregnancies (50% success)
  (8 calves per cow – 4 females and 4 males)
  (130 heifer and 130 bull calves in total)
- 130 bulls to be evaluated by sibling test
  (4 full sisters, 12 half-sisters per bull)

An elite group from these 130 test bulls with breeding values is now chosen for extensive use when AI is available. Where there is need or demand for natural service, then a higher proportion of the above-average bulls is made available for use in the base population. Annually the test females whose records have been used for their brother's genetic evaluation, are then evaluated on individual performance records and the elite cows among them are retained for MOET as long as they remain responsive to the technique. This means that annually about 130 lactating cows will return to the base population leaving the best 120 cows in the test herd drawn from those who have just completed a first lactation and from older cows previously subjected to MOET. This permits the new crop of 130 replacement heifers to enter for their first lactation and thus maintain the size at 250.

Genetic progress in ONBS

First, it is appropriate to define 'Adult' and 'Juvenile' MOET. These alternatives are applicable in principle to several species, but illustrated for dairy cattle (Fig. 4). Adult MOET means that embryo transfer takes place only after the first lactation when the individual cow records of performance are available. Juvenile MOET means embryo transfer at about one year of age when the heifer is sexually mature, but has no lactation records on which to evaluate her genetically. Adult MOET with dairy cattle gives a generation interval of about 3.7 years, whereas Juvenile MOET reduces this to 1.8 years. Fig. 5 shows the theoretical rates of genetic change per year for milk yield in dairy cattle using different selection systems. These are potential changes. The actual gains will always depend upon the numbers of animals and the selection pressure. The theoretical gains show that ONBS using MOET may

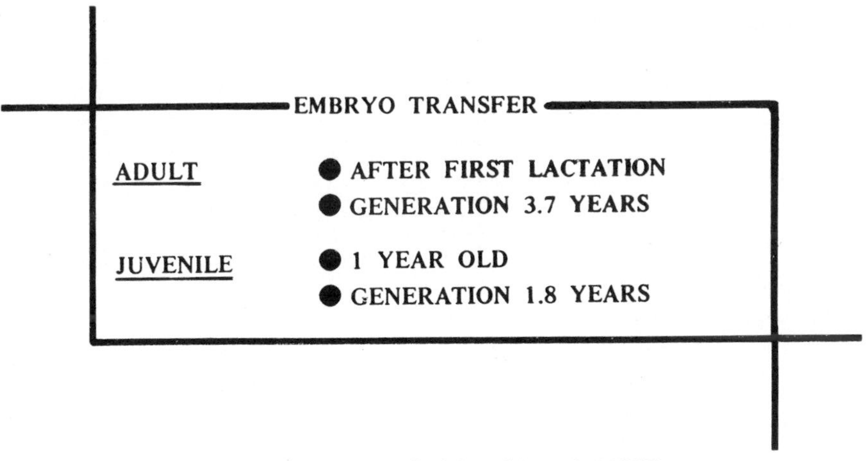

Fig. 4 *Definition of adult and juvenile MOET.*
From: Smith. C. (1988)

	GENETIC RESPONSE (% PER YEAR)
PROGENY TESTING SCHEMES	
• RATES CURRENTLY ACHIEVED	0.2 – 1.1
RATES POSSIBLE	
• CURRENT SYSTEM	1.5
• EFFICIENT SYSTEM	2.0
• EFFICIENT SYST. WITH FEMALES SELECTED & BRED WITH ADULT MOET	2.0 – 2.3
• EFFICIENT SYST. WITH FEMALES SELECTED & BRED WITH JUVENILE MOET	2.1 – 2.3
MOET NUCLEUS HERD SCHEMES	
RATES POSSIBLE:	
• ADULT MOET NUCLEUS SCHEME	1.8 – 2.4
• JUVENILE MOET NUCLEUS SCHEME	2.6 – 3.5
(WITH EMBRYO SPLITTING × 2)	2.7 – 3.8
(WITH EMBRYO SPLITTING × 16)	2.9 – 3.9
• JUVENILE MOET NUCLEUS SCHEME WITH INDICATOR TRAIT (Co-heritability = 0.25)	2.7 – 4.8

THE RANGE IN RESPONSE WITHIN A SYSTEM REFERS TO MODERATE AND HIGH MOET RATES. MODERATE 4 MALES, 4 FEMALES PER FULL SIBSHIP AT SELECTION; 8 DONORS PER SIRE. HIGH 8 MALES, 8 FEMALES PER FULL SIBSHIP AT SELECTION; 16 DONORS PER SIRE. COEFFICIENT OF VARIATION = 0.15.

Fig. 5 *Possible rates of genetic change per year for milk yield in dairy cattle with different breeding selection systems.*

From: Woolliams and Smith (1988)

RATE OF ANNUAL GENETIC CHANGE (% MEAN)	CATTLE	SHEEP	PIGS
GROWTH	1.4	1.4	2.7
	2.6	2.4*	3.2
LEAN	0.5	0.9	1.6
	1.0	1.8*	1.9
SEX LIMITED TRAITS	MILK YIELD	LITTER SIZE	LITTER SIZE
	1.5	2.1	4.7
	2.0	3.4*	5.5

* JUVENILE EMBRYO TRANSFER

NORMAL REPRODUCTION
— EMBRYO TRANSFER (underlined values)

Fig. 6 *Annual rates of genetic change from use of ONBS in cattle, sheep and pigs.*

From: Smith (1984; 1988a)

be a worthwhile alternative to progeny testing. In developing countries the ONBS merits further research to test its practical feasibility since field progeny testing is rarely possible, whereas governments often have livestock station facilities already in their control which may be used for ONBS.

Fig. 6 shows the annual rates of genetic change which may be expected on theoretical grounds from use of ONBS for traits other than milk in cattle and also traits in sheep and pigs.

The scale of each ONBS needs to be designed individually for actual conditions and species. It is not possible to give these in the abstract and expect that they will automatically fit any or all circumstances. Some of the critical issues are the size and distribution of the base population, the management system under which the base population is kept, the numbers of animals which can be accommodated in the nucleus herd facilities and the level of success with MOET. Calculations to take account of animals being held while awaiting test must be made and cost-benefit evaluations are needed on the advantages and disadvantages of alternative strategies for age at first parturition and use of Juvenile or Adult MOET. Another important point is whether semen is to be used by AI from the elite proven sires or whether genes from the elite proven animals are to be spread through the base population also or only by natural service.

A most important issue in developing countries relates to the genetic improvement strategy (Fig. 7). Is it designed to improve the purebred indigenous breed, as for example in an environment with highly specific adaptability needs - or can exotics be introduced as purebreds where the environment and management can be adapted to their needs? Very often in developing countries the first option is not desirable and the second is not possible. Therefore crossbreeding is often the preferred route. ONBS could be adapted for controlling the gene mix in a base population. The type of semen used for MOET on the elite indigenous females must be adjusted

OPEN NUCLEUS BREEDING SYSTEM

- PUREBRED IMPORTED BREEDS
- INDIGENOUS PUREBRED BREED
- INDIGENOUS FEMALES (ADAPTED) & IMPORTED MALES / SEMEN (HIGHER PERFORMANCE) CONTROL % GENE MIX

Fig. 7 *Options for use of ONBS system.*

subsequently as the base population becomes crossbred. When the exceptional females resulting from the sib test are crossbreds and are themselves treated by MOET with semen from crossbred males, they maintain the desired gene mix.

CONCLUSIONS FOR DEVELOPING COUNTRIES

The benefits of ONBS combined with MOET, compared with field breeding schemes are summarized in Fig. 8. The specific advantages and expected rates of annual genetic gain should be assessed in each case and must include not only the genetic aspects, but also the logistic and economic factors.

Another important concern should always be the training of the staff at all levels so that they fully understand the theoretical basis of ONBS and MOET. The staff to be trained naturally must include the station personnel who are responsible for the livestock in the nucleus herd of flock. The training of extension staff is vital as they will be involved in sharing the details with the livestock owners in the area whose animals form part of the base population. The success of such a system is dependent upon the willing cooperation of the owners of the livestock. They, as always, need to be convinced of the value of this new scheme being proposed by the government. Patience and skill in describing its operation, benefits and possible risks must be employed. Ideally the ONBS/MOET system should have a cooperative aspect which brings the leaders of the local livestock owners into the discussions and decisions,

ADVANTAGES

- GENETIC LIFT IN ESTABLISHING THE UNIT
- FASTER RATES OF GENETIC CHANGE
- CONTROL OVER HUSBANDRY & TESTING
- MORE SELECTION POSSIBLE FOR ECONOMIC MERIT
- USE OF TRAITS DIFFICULT TO RECORD IN FIELD
- CONCENTRATION OF BREEDING RESOURCES
- POSSIBLE USE OF EXPENSIVE TECHNOLOGIES
- ECONOMIC BENEFITS OBTAINED SOONER
- LOW COSTS ON A NATIONAL SCALE
- SEPARATE NUCLEUS UNITS FOR DIFFERENT SETS OF BREEDING OBJECTIVES / ENVIRONMENTS

DISADVANTAGES

- RISK OF DISEASE AND LOSS
  (avoid by dispersing age classes)
- RISK FROM CONCENTRATING STOCK & RESOURCES IN ONE UNIT
- POSSIBLE GENOTYPE x ENVIRONMENT INTERACTIONS IN COMMERCIAL PRODUCTION
- NEW FUNDS NEEDED TO SET UP AND OPERATE
- RE-EDUCATION OF PRODUCERS TO ACCEPT MOET BRED STOCKS

Fig. 8 *Advantages and disadvantages of nucleus breeding units compared with field breeding schemes.*
From: Smith (1988a)

especially concerning the evaluation of the animals and choice of which males are to be used in the base population.

An old problem with trying to buy outstanding animals from local owners for a government programme, has been their natural reluctance to part with their best animals. It is understandable. Cooperation between the government who operate the nucleus flock or herd and the owners may be made more productive and successful if the females screened from the base population are loaned rather than bought. As borrowed females they then enter the test flock or herd for a period of recording. When they return to the owner it should be possible to provide a genetically superior offspring to accompany them as a return to the owner.

The theory of ONBS appears to be very attractive. The system is already being tested in some developed countries in Europe for dairy cattle. It now needs to be tested and practical protocols designed for application in developing countries. Only then will it be possible to calculate how much of the theoretical genetic gain can be achieved in practice with defined species and traits and whether the needed levels of success with MOET can be achieved with indigenous animals.

At present, with embryo transfer, but without molecular genetics, ONBS and MOET have theoretical advantages which if adapted successfully to the conditions of developing countries, could offer a new approach to livestock improvement. They also offer a vehicle which, if successfully established, will be suitable for conveying expected benefits of future molecular engineering research and development in embryo manipulation, gene transfer and designer transgenic animals which combine higher productivity and adaptation.

NOTE: Parts of this paper were previously published by FAO (Hodges, 1988)

REFERENCES

Bindon, B.M. (1984). Reproductive biology of the Booroola Merino sheep. *Australian Journal of Biological Science*, **37**, 163–189.

Christensen, L.G. and Liboriussen, T. (1986). Embryo transfer in the genetic improvement of dairy cattle. In: *Exploiting New Technologies in Animal Breeding: Genetic Developments* (eds. C. Smith, J.W.B. King and J.C. McKay), pp. 37–46. Clarendon Press, Oxford.

FAO (1987). *Crossbreeding* Bos indicus *and* Bos taurus *for milk production in the tropics.* Animal Production and Health, Paper No. 68.

Hodges, J. (1986). Biotechnology and domestic animals. *World Animal Review*, **59**, 2–10.

Hodges, J. (1988). Biotechnology applicable to animal production and health in Asia. *FAO Proceedings, Regional Workshop, Bangkok,* October 1988.

Nicholas, F.W. and Smith, C. (1983). Increased rates of genetic change in dairy cattle by embryo transfer and splitting. *Animal Production*, **36**, 341–353.

Palmiter, R.D., Brinster, R.L., Hammer, R.E., Trumbauer, M.E., Rosenfeld, M.G., Birnberg, N.C. and Evans, R.M. (1982). Dramatic growth of mice that develop from eggs micro injected with metallothionein growth hormone fusion genes. *Nature*, **300**, 611–615.

Polge, E.J.C. (1991). The role of embryo transfer technology. In *The Application of Biotechnology in Developing Countries* (ed. A.G. Hunter), pp. 40–41. Centre for Tropical Veterinary Medicine, University of Edinburgh.

Robertson, A. (1985). Molecular biology and animal improvement. *Review of Rural Science*, **6**, 3–9.

Smith, C. (1984). Rates of genetic change in farm livestock. *Research and Development in Agriculture*, **1**, 79–85.

Smith, C. (1988a). Applications of embryo transfer in animal breeding. *Theriogenology*, **29.1**, 203–212.

Smith, C. (1988b). Genetic improvement of livestock in developing countries using nucleus breeding units. *World Animal Review*, **65**, 2–10.

Smith, C. and Simpson, S.P. (1985). The use of genetic polymorphisms in livestock improvement. Summary 36th Annual meeting, European Association of Animal Production, Thessaloniki, Greece. October. Vol. 1, p.112.

Soller, M. and Beckmann, J.S. (1982). Restriction fragment length polymorphisms and genetic improvement. *Proceedings of the 2nd World Congress on Genetics Applied to Livestock Production, Madrid*, October 6, 396–404.

Soller, M. and Beckmann, J.S. (1985). Restriction fragment length polymorphisms and animal genetic improvement. *Review of Rural Science*, **6**, 10–18.

Woolliams, J.A. and Smith, C. (1988). The value of indicator traits in the genetic improvement of dairy cattle. *Animal Production*, **46**, 333–345.

2.4

Biotechnology and Draught Animals?

R. A. PEARSON
*Centre for Tropical Veterinary Medicine,
University of Edinburgh, Scotland*

INTRODUCTION

It seems a contradiction in terms to talk about biotechnology together with draught animals, as the former is regarded as 'high' technology and the latter is spoken of as 'low' or 'appropriate' technology. However, as this is a conference concerned with the application of biotechnology to livestock in developing countries and one of the important uses of large ruminant and equine livestock is animal traction, then it seems 'appropriate' to discuss the subject here. Jones (1988) points out that one of the greatest changes in the distribution of grazing herbivores in the developed countries was caused when steam and internal combustion engines replaced horses and oxen as the main sources of power for agriculture and transport. This dramatic change has not occurred in most developing countries where draught animals still provide 75–90% of power used in agriculture. Many cultivated hill areas in the world are inaccessible to tractors and other forms of mechanical power. Increasing fuel prices and difficulties in repairing machinery in these and other areas suggest that animal power will continue to be important in developing countries in the future. For this reason it is worth taking a long-term approach to the application of biotechnology to draught animal power.

Many draught animals are multipurpose, supplying fuel and fertilizers as well as power. Milk and replacement work animals or beef animals can also be obtained when female animals are kept for work. Hence it is often impossible to isolate the use of animals for work from their other productive functions. Healthy, well-nourished animals usually perform close to their genetic potential whether it be in the production of meat, milk or work. Obviously any advances in biotechnology that improve health, nutrition, body condition and reproductive capacity of large ruminants and equines in the developing countries will be good for draught animal power. With the increased understanding of the physiological processes involved in exercise in man, the horse and ruminants, it is possible to speculate where more specific applications of biotechnology might occur. Some areas where biotechnology might have application, namely in the selection, feeding and maintenance of animals for work, are discussed in this paper. Benefits to draught animals in the future have been considered, since, as suggested above, draught animals will probably continue to have a role in tropical and subtropical agriculture and transport for some time to come.

SELECTION OF DRAUGHT ANIMALS

The main problem in selecting animals for draught purposes is that there is no simple objective criterion that can be used to test the value of an animal for work purposes. Specific tasks often require specific characteristics.

Historically, the only systematic selection for draught that has taken place has been selection for size. In Europe the large draught breeds of horses (e.g. Shire and Clydesdale in Britain, Percheron in France and Ardennes and Belgium Draught in Belgium) and cattle (e.g. Charolais and Limousin in France, Chianina in Italy) are evidence of this selection procedure. Large size is not the only attribute required by a draught animal, and can sometimes be a disadvantage. For example on steep land and on small fields and terraces small agile animals are often easier to work than large animals (Pearson, Lawrence and Ghimire, 1989). Some tasks require speed rather than great strength and the type of animal produced reflects this; different types of camels have been produced for riding and for pack transport, which reflect the requirement for speed and smoothness of gait in the former and strength rather than speed in the latter (Wilson, 1984). The long legs of the Hariana cattle mean that they can pull carts rapidly and hence they are often the preferred draught oxen for transporting goods on the plains of India and Nepal. Temperament, disease resistance, ability to tolerate heat and survive on high roughage diets are other factors that need to be considered in the selection of animals for work. The relative importance of each characteristic in a selection programme depends very much on the jobs required of the animal and the terrain, environment and nutrition likely to be experienced.

Although it is possible to speculate that techniques in genetic engineering and associated molecular biotechnology may be able to provide the means to amalgamate the attributes required for a specific task or region into a 'super' draught animal, in some areas this has already been at least partly achieved by crossbreeding. One of the best examples of this is in the Himalaya. Yaks are often crossed with hill Zebu cattle to produce a male animal, the Zhopkyos (Epstein 1977), which is temperamentally more suitable to draught work than the yak (which is a better pack animal), physiologically more able to cope with the cold at altitude than the ox and physically larger than either the local yak or ox, providing the farmers with a more powerful and much sought after draught animal. Given that some species are more suited to particular tasks than others, and preferences for speed rather than for power may determine the species or type of animal used for work, it may be useful in the future to be able to identify animals which are more predisposed for work physiologically than others.

Considerable effort has been spent in attempting to identify the 'elite' performers in horse racing and human athletics. Although researchers are no nearer picking the next Derby winner (Dunbar, 1985; Tudge, 1989), a great deal more is now understood about equine exercise physiology and the effects of training on performance (e.g. Snow, Persson and Rose, 1983; Gillespie and Robinson, 1987). The consequences of exercise and work on ruminants have also received some attention (Bird, Chandler and Bell, 1981; Upadhyay and Madan,1985; Pethick, Harman and Chong, 1987; Pearson and Archibald, 1989). However, perhaps understandably, not to the same extent as the racehorse in which the financial rewards of successful performance are that much greater.

Attempts have been made to relate gross anatomy to performance. For example Gunn (1987) compared muscle, bone and fat proportions and muscle distribution in Thoroughbreds and other horses less specialised for athletic performance. He observed taht total muscle weight occupied a significantly greater proportion of liveweight in adult Thoroughbreds than in other adult horses and, relative to liveweight and total muscle mass, the weight of the hindlimb muscle groups (the main propulsive muscles) in Thoroughbreds was greater than in other horses. Although total bone weight formed a greater proportion of liveweight in Thoroughbreds there was little difference between the two types of horse. The percentage of fat was much more variable than that of other tissues, nevertheless Thoroughbreds had less fat. Gunn (1987) concluded that the identification of gross attributes of Thoroughbreds which have excelled in different athletic events should be of value to trainers and breeders. The disadvanrtage of these gross anatomical studies is that they require the animal or its close relatives to be sacrificed. Relationships between conformation in live animals and performance traits have been studied. For example, von Butler (1988) studied the relationship between performance traits and body measurements (e.g. height at the withers, girth and cannon bone circumference) in four different breeds of horse (German Saddle, Trakehnen, Arab and South German Coldblood). He was unable to show any significant correlation of pace length with body measurements in these breeds.

Biochemical and physiological techniques developed in the study of the horse have been more successful in relating animals and performance. Probably the most interesting studies from a selection point of view have been those concerned with the identification of different muscle fibre types. Skeletal muscle is composed of fibres which possess different contractile and metabolic properties (Saltin and Gollnick, 1983). Techniques of muscle biopsy sampling combined with histochemical and biochemical studies of the tissues (e.g. Lindholm and Piehl, 1974; Snow and Guy, 1976) have enabled different fibre types to be identified, namely slow twitch type I and fast twitch type IIA and type IIB. Slow twitch type I fibres have a contractile time about three times longer than fast twitch fibres. Histochemically they are rich in mitochondria and oxidative enzymes, and designed for a high rate of aerobic energy production. They are high in myoglobin content and have extensive capillaries which facilitate oxygen diffusion. The high energy yield and utilisation of oxygen give the type I fibres great endurance qualities. Histochemical staining has identified three types of type II myosin ATPase in fast-contracting muscle which are designated type IIA, IIB and IIC (Brooke and Kaiser, 1970). Type IIA has fast-contracting properties but is also well-equipped for oxidative energy production and therefore has good endurance properties. Type IIB fibres yield high rates of energy from intramuscular stores, having a high rate of energy release but limited endurance capacity. Type IIC fibres are present in only a small proportion, being more evident in very young animals. They seem to be a transitional stage in the development of new fibres and contain both fast and slow myosin (Snow, Billeter and Jenny, 1981). Functionally, the different fibre types are selectively recruited in a specific pattern according to the gait, speed and duration of exercise. In the horse, as speed increases, fibres are recruited in the order, type I through type IIA to type IIB (Hodgson, Rose and Allen, 1983; Valberg, 1986). It has been suggested that as a result the metabolic profile and time of recruitment of type IIB fibres must be of crucial importance for racing performance in both standardbred and thoroughbred horses (Valberg and Essen-Gustavsson, 1987). Studies of glycogen depletion patterns during draught work by standardbred horses indicated that similar fibre recruitment patterns occur to those seen in racing. As intensity and duration of draught work continues then muscle fibres are depleted in order from type I, through type IIA to IIB (Gottlieb, 1989).

Snow and Guy (1980) studied the fibre composition in six limb muscles of different breeds of horse. They found the percentage of fast twitch fibres in the middle gluteal muscle (the major propulsive muscle in the horse's hindlimb) varied significantly amongst breeds and these differences were related to the sprinting speed of the breed. The Quarter horse, which has been bred for speed over 400 m, had the highest percentage, followed by the thoroughbred, with the donkey and heavy hunter having the lowest proportion. Similarly some of the muscle enzyme activities could be related to the performance for which the animals were best suited. The Quarter horse had the highest activity of the glycolytic and glycolytic related enzymes (lactic dehydrogenase, aldolase and glycerol-3-phosphate dehydrogenase) and among the lowest activities of aerobic enzymes (citrate synthatase. 3-hydroxyacyl CoA dehydrogenase) reflecting its high dependence on anaerobic metabolism for 400 m racing. The Thoroughbred and Arab had the highest activities of aerobic enzymes when compared with the other breeds and in general the donkey had the lowest activities for all enzymes examined and the lowest concentrations of glycogen (Snow and Guy, 1981). Within a breed (the Thoroughbred) it was also possible to identify animals more suited to sprinting (1,000–1,600 m) or staying (2,400–7,000 m), the percentages of slow twitch fibres being significantly higher in the staying group than the sprinting group (Snow and Guy, 1981). There are close links between fibre composition and metabolic responses to exercise in horses. Horses with different muscle fibre composition show different metabolic responses to standardized near-maximum exercise (Valberg, Essen-Gustavsson, Lindholm and Persson, 1985). In addition, Valberg and Essen-Gustavsson (1987) observed that in both Standardbredand Thoroughbred horses the oxidative capacity and capillarization of fibre types strongly influenced the metabolic response to racing.

One can speculate that in the future, similar techniques may be applied to the selection of better draught animals. The emphasis in animals for draught power would usually be on staying rather than sprinting attributes, since most of the work required of these animals is of a low intensity, lasting several hours and is usually within the limits of aerobic metabolism (e.g. Gottlieb, 1989; Pearson and Archibald, 1989).

Although characterization of muscle fibre types seems to be a useful tool in the identification of animals for particular tasks, it is not without problems. The different fibre types occur in different proportions in the various skeletal muscles (Lindholm and Piehl, 1974; Gunn, 1978: Snow and Guy, 1976,1980). In addition the proportions of fibre types in a particular muscle vary between individual animals. The proportion of type I and type II fibres appears to be genetically determined and not altered by normal physiological adaptations. However training effects a transformation of some type IIB fibres to the highly oxidative type IIA fibres (Lindholm and Piehl, 1974; Guy and Snow, 1977; Essen, Lindholm and Thornton, 1980; Henckel, 1983) so that fast twitch fibres may by adaptation develop good endurance qualities whilst retaining their high speed of contraction. Snow and Guy (1980) did not find changes in fibre type with depth of sampling. However, more recently, variation in the relative proportion of fibre types has been observed throughout the middle gluteal muscle of several breeds of horses (Raub, Bechtel and Lawrence, 1985; van den Hoven, Wensing, Brukink, Meijer and Kruip , 1985; Bruce and Turek, 1985 and Kline, Lawrence, Novakofski and Bechtel, 1987). This suggests that care should be taken when sampling and interpreting data obtained from muscle biopsy studies. Nevertheless they may perhaps be usefully applied to the selection of draught animals in the future.

THE 'FUEL' SUPPLY – NUTRIENT INTAKE

A draught animal could be considered as a 'machine' which converts chemical energy into mechanical energy. Conversion of chemical energy to mechanical energy is accomplished by muscle tissues. The success with which the animal carries out this process will depend on its ability to supply energy to the tissues and use it. The immediate source of energy for muscle contraction is ATP. The energy released is used directly by the contractile mechanism. The concentration of ATP in skeletal muscle is very limited and if muscle contraction is to continue for more than a second or two ATP must be resynthesized. This is achieved by aerobic and anaerobic oxidation of substrates. These substrates originate from the absorbed products of digestion of the feed, which are modified by the gut epithelium and the liver. The circulating substrates that are available for muscle metabolism are acetate, ketone bodies, long chain fatty acids (LCFA) and glucose (Leng, 1985; Pearson, 1985). Additional sources of energy that can be mobilized include the triacylglycerol of adipose tissue and glycogen and triacylglycerol present in almost all tissues including skeletal muscle. Amino acids from muscle protein may be mobilized, but represent a minor source of energy (Leng, 1985).

Studies of substrate utilization by resting and exercising muscle in equines and in ruminants (e.g. Bird, Chandler and Bell, 1981; Oddy, Gooden, Hough, Teleni and Annison, 1985; Pethick, Harman and Chong, 1987) have shown that glucose oxidation in muscle is obligatory, although an increase in LCFA and ketone body utilization occurs as work continues (Rose, Purdue and Hensley, 1977; Pethick, 1984). Equine muscle has a high capacity for glycogen storage (over 126 mmol/l) which provides considerable glucogenic reserves (McMiken, 1983) and most circulating glucose is absorbed directly from the gut in the horse. In the ruminant, however, glucose availability is more limited (Leng, 1970), largely because the ruminant is dependent on hepatic gluconeogenesis of volatile fatty acids to provide most of the circulating glucose and glycogen reserves (Judson, Filsell and Jarrett, 1976). This does mean that the ruminant can survive on relatively low-energy diets whereas the horse, particularly when working, requires high-energy feeds if it is to maintain performance. In a mature male working ruminant that has finished growing all the absorbed amino acids will be metabolized (largely in the liver) to give rise to acetate, ketone bodies or glucose precursors (Preston and Leng, 1987) and so sufficient glucogenic precursors are likely to be available to meet requirements. This may not be the case in the female animal. In lactating animals there is competition for glucose and glucogenic precursors between work and lactation, which may be detrimental to milk production.

The tendency in many places where there is a chronic feed shortage is to replace male work animals with females (Matthewman, 1987). This trend is likely to continue in the future as feed resources for draught animals are unlikely to become more abundant. Hence the effect of work on the other productive functions of the female animal warrant closer investigation.

Matthewman (1989) has studied the effect of exercise on lactational performance in cattle. In a series of three experiments, each with Hereford x

Friesian suckler cows in the final third of lactation, he assessed the effect of exercise (equivalent to an energy demand of about 13 MJ per day) on lactational performance when food intake was fixed (experiments I and II) and when part of the diet (straw) was available *ad libitum* (experiment III). In the first two experiments, during exercise milk yield fell as did the yields of lactose and protein, but levels recovered following two days of rest (e.g. Fig. 1). These changes occurred even when cows were given a diet with an increased content of starch (in experiment II). This diet was offered to test the idea that the reduction in lactose and protein yield was the consequence of diet yielding an inadequate supply of glucogenic nutrients. Yield of milk fat remained unchanged with exercise in both experiments. The aim of the third

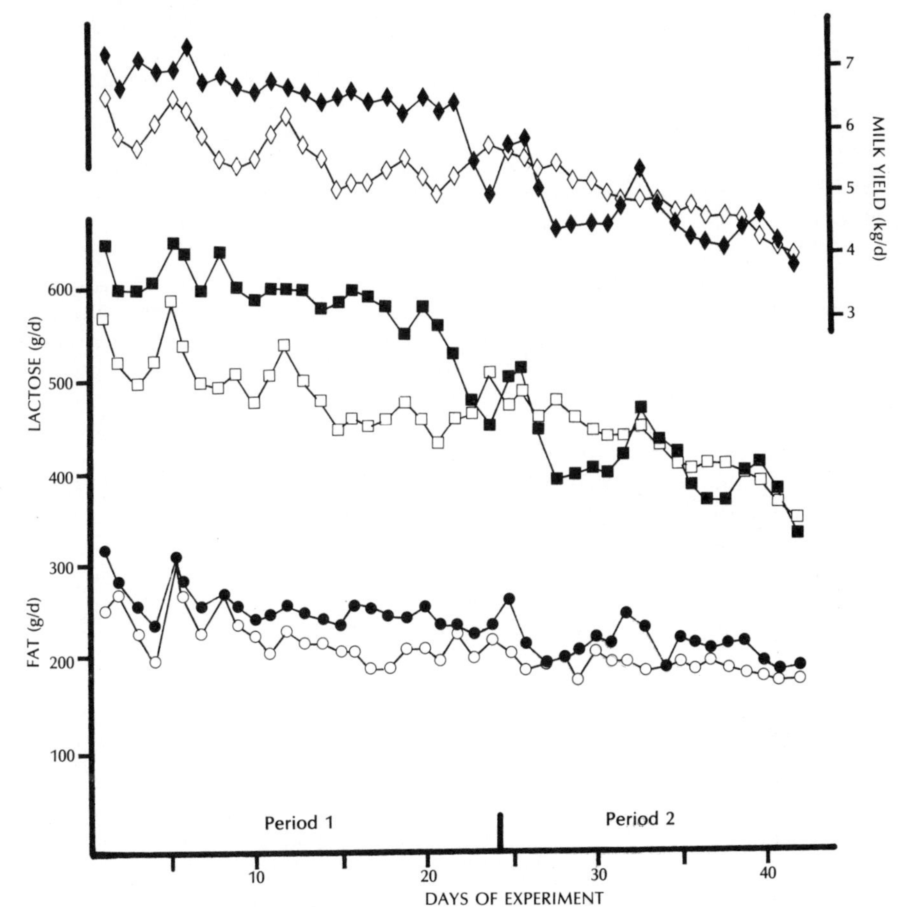

Fig. 1 *Milk yield and yield of lactose and fat during exercise and rest in two groups of cows. Group 1 (●, ■, ◆) rested in first period and exercised in second period. Group 2 (○, □, ◇) exercised in first period and rested in second period.*

experiment was to test the effect of exercise on intake of a poorly digested forage (straw) in the presence of supplements designed to be 'glucogenic' (based on barley), 'aminogenic' (based on fishmeal) or 'lipogenic' (based on sugarbeet). Exercise had little or no effect on straw intake and while the overall level of performance was greatest with the starch supplemented diet, the nature of the dietary supplement did not seem to have any substantial influence on the impact of exercise on lactational performance.

The main conclusion from these experiments was that the lactating cows dealt with a shortage of nutrients created through exercise by restricting secretion of protein and lactose whilst maintaining fat output. The latter was possible because there were sufficient tissue reserves of fat to be mobilized. It appeared that the nutrient shortage was not overcome by increased intake when the only food available was a poor quality forage.

Failure of draught animals to respond to the increased nutrient demands of work by increasing intake of roughages has been reported by others, for example, in cattle in Costa Rica consuming poor quality hay (Lawrence, 1985), in cattle in Nepal (e.g. Fig. 2) and buffaloes in Indonesia (Bamualim and Ffoulkes, 1988) consuming rice straw and field grasses and in working donkeys receiving hay or barley straw (Pearson and Merritt, 1990). Clearly if animals are not to lose weight when working over long periods of time and if cows are to work without milk yields being reduced then improvements in energy supply are needed. The staple diets of the majority of draught animals are crop residues and other forages, usually high in fibre and low in crude protein. Methods to improve fermentation and digestibility of these roughages by both ruminants and equines are needed in addition to other ways of cheaply increasing nutrient densities of diets available to draught animals. A recent example of manipulation of digestion is defaunation of ruminant animals (i.e. the reduction or elimination of protozoa from the rumen). This has been shown to improve the yield of glucogenic substrates from straw based feeds (Bird, Chaudhry and Leng, 1989). This would be advantageous to the lactating female draught animal. Other advances in feed biotechnology and manipulation of digestion may go some way towards solving the problems of 'fuelling' draught animals in the future.

DRAUGHT ANIMAL NUMBERS

A major problem in some tropical areas, particularly where pressure on land is high, is that of maintenance of draught animal populations. In several areas of Asia, for example, buffaloes and cattle are not reproducing at a high enough rate to replace work animals and the number of animals in the area is decreasing. In these areas turnover of animals is often high as they are used as a source of readily available money in financial emergencies and population pressures ensure good prices for meat as well as for trained work animals. This problem can be exacerbated by the use of female animals for work, particularly if they are not in good body condition. The increased demands on energy supply and additional stress of work can lead to reduced ovarian

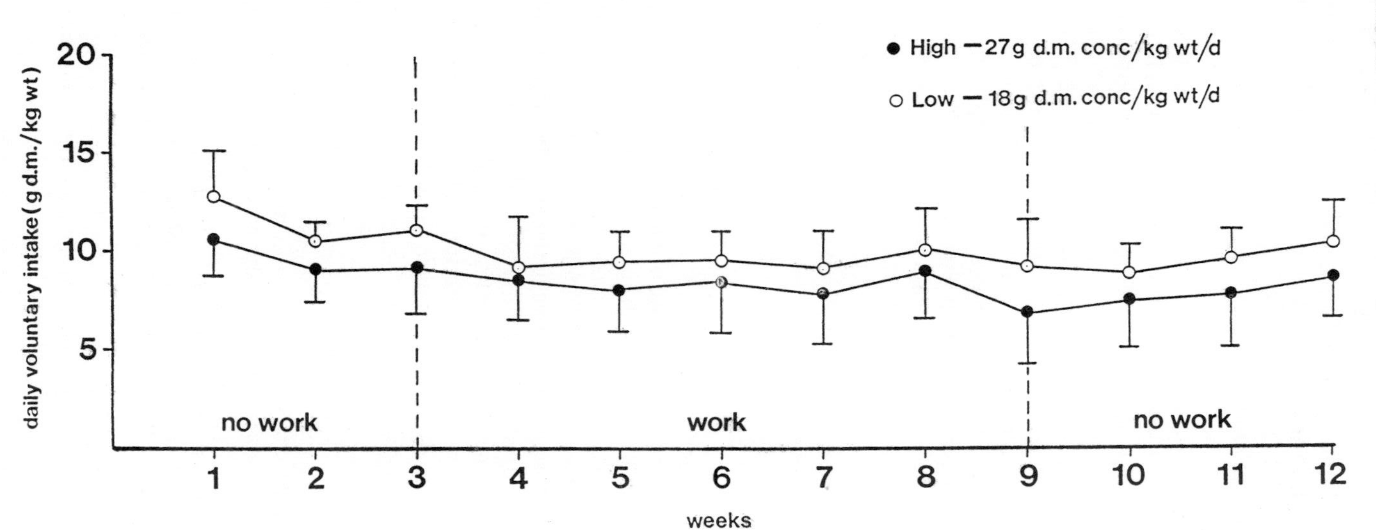

Fig. 2 *Mean ± s.d. (n = 6) daily intake of rice straw by draught cattle receiving one of two levels of concentrate supplement (high, low) and working on six days per week (work) or resting (no work). Energy expenditure on working days = 1.47 – 1.52 × maintenance.*

activity, and low conception rates. This coupled with a shortage of male animals, either through castration for work purposes or isolation of draught animals from potential breeding animals leads to long calving intervals. Castration of the better male animals for work can lead to a gradual downgrading of the draught animal population, as only the smaller weaker bulls are left for breeding. This is less of a problem with buffaloes than with cattle, as buffaloes are not usually castrated for use as draught animals.

Although the problem of maintaining draught animal numbers is confined largely to some intensively cropped regions in Asia, it is likely to become more widespread in the future where population pressures are increasing and grazing land available for livestock becomes more scarce. As long as traditional herds of cattle are maintained and traffic in cattle continues from regions of surplus to those of shortage as, for example, from India to Bangladesh and from Niger to Northern Nigeria then farmers' needs may be satisfied. However in areas like Indonesia where importation is difficult, but infrastructure for AI schemes already exist in dairy enterprises, then biotechnology in the form of reproduction techniques may be appropriate to draught animals in the future to increase reproductive rate and help solve shortages of working animals.

CONCLUSIONS

The problems in applying any technologies to draught animals are often financial and sometimes geographical. The 'low tech' value of animal traction means farmers as well as governments are often unwilling to spend money on their draught animals. The scatter of draught animals through some areas, often remote and inaccessible, can make schemes to promote health, nutrition and reproductive capacity difficult to implement. The aim of this paper has been to draw attention to some of the problems that are likely to be faced by farmers using draught animal power in the future and which may benefit from the attentions of biotechnologists. While some of the applications of biotechnology may seem rather fanciful, others may have more immediate application to draught animals in the world.

REFERENCES

Bamualim, A. and Ffoulkes, D. (1988). Effect of work and level of feed intake on nutritional parameters and bodyweight change of swamp buffalo cows. *DAP Project Bulletin,* **7**, 2-8.

Bird, S. Chaudhry, U.B. and Leng, R.A. (1989). In: *Draught Animals in Rural Development*, ACIAR Proceedings Series No. 27 (eds. D. Hoffman, J. Nari and R.J. Petheram), pp. 181-184. Canberra. ACIAR.

Bird, A.R., Chandler, K.D. and Bell, A.W. (1981). Effects of exercise and plane of nutrition on nutrient utilization by the hind limb of the sheep. *Australian Journal of Biological Science,* **34**, 541-550.

Brooke, M.H. and Kaiser, K.K. (1970). Muscle fibre types: how many and what kind? *Archives of Neurology,* **23**, 369–379.

Bruce, V. and Turek, R.J. (1985). Muscle fibre variation in the gluteus medius of the horse. *Equine Veterinary Journal,* **17**, 317–321.

Dunbar, R. (1985). The race to breed faster horses. *New Scientist,* **1459**, 44–47.

Epstein, H. (1977). *Domestic Animals of Nepal.* Holmes and Meier Publishers, New York.

Essén, B., Lindholm, A. and Thornton, J. (1980). Histochemical properties of muscle fibre types and enzyme activities in skeletal muscles of standardbred trotters of different ages. *Equine Veterinary Journal,* **12**, 174–180.

Gillespie, J.R. and Robinson, N.E. (eds.) (1987). *Equine Exercise Physiology 2.* ICEEP Publications, Davis, California.

Gottlieb, M. (1989). Muscle glycogen depletion patterns during draught work in standardbred horses. *Equine Veterinary Journal,* **21**, 110–115.

Gunn, H.M. (1978). Differences in the histochemical properties of skeletal muscles of different breeds of horses and dogs. *Journal of Anatomy,* **127**, 615–634.

Gunn, H.M. (1987). Muscle, bone and fat proportions and muscle distribution of Thoroughbreds and other horses. In: *Equine Exercise Physiology 2* (eds. J.R. Gillespie and N.E. Robinson), pp. 253–264. ICEEP Publications, Davis, California.

Guy, P.S. and Snow, D.H. (1977). The effect of training and detraining on muscle composition in the horse. *Journal of Physiology,* **269**, 33–51.

Henckel, P. (1983). Training and growth induced changes in the middle gluteal muscle of young standardbred trotters. *Equine Veterinary Journal,* **15**, 134–140.

Hodgson, D.R., Rose, R.J. and Allen, J.R. (1983). Muscle glycogen depletion and repletion patterns in horses performing various distances of endurance exercise. In: *Equine Exercise Physiology* (eds. D.H. Snow, S.G.B. Persson and R. Rose), pp. 229–325. Granta Editions, Cambridge.

Jones, R.J. (1988). The future for the grazing herbivore. *Tropical Grasslands,* **22**, 97–115.

Judson, G.J., Filsell, O.H. and Jarrett, I.G. (1976). Glucose and acetate metabolism in sheep at rest and during exercise. *Australian Journal of Biological Science,* **29**, 215–222.

Kline, K.H., Lawrence, L.M., Novakofski, J. and Bechtel, P.J. (1987). Changes in muscle fibre type variation within the middle gluteal of young and mature horses as a function of sampling depth. In: *Equine Exercise Physiology 2* (eds. J.R. Gillespie and N.E. Robinson), pp. 271–277. ICEEP Publications, Davis, California.

Lawrence, P.R. (1985). A review of the nutrient requirements of draught oxen. In: *Draught Animal Power for Production,* ACIAR Proceedings Series No. 10 (ed. J.W. Copland), pp. 59–63. ACIAR, Australia.

Leng, R.A. (1970). Formation and production of volatile fatty acids in the rumen. In: *Physiology of Digestion and Metabolism in the Ruminant* (ed. A.T. Phillipson), pp. 406–421. Oriel Press, Newcastle Upon Tyne.

Leng, R.A. (1985). Muscle metabolism and nutrition in working ruminants. In: *Draught Animal Power for Production,* ACIAR Proceedings Series No. 10 (ed. J.W. Copland), pp. 69–83. Canberra, ACIAR, Australia.

Lindholm, A. and Piehl, K. (1974). Fibre composition, enzyme activity and concentration of metabolites and electrolytes in muscles of standard bred horses. *Acta Veterinaire Scandinavica,* **15**, 287–309.

McMiken, D.F. (1983). An energetic basis of equine performance. *Equine Veterinary Journal,* **15**, 123–133.

Matthewman, R.W. (1987). The role and potential of draught cows in tropical farming systems: A review. *Tropical Animal Health and Production,* **19**, 215–222.

Matthewman, R.W. (1989). The effects of exercise on lactational performance. *PhD Thesis, University of Edinburgh.*

Oddy, V.H., Gooden, J.M., Hough, G.M., Teleni, E. and Annison, E.F. (1985). Partitioning of nutrients in Merino ewes. II. Glucose utilization by skeletal muscle, the pregnant uterus and the lactating mammary gland in relation to whole body glucose utilization. *Australian Journal of Biological Science,* **38**, 95–108.

Pearson, R.A. (1985). Physiological changes associated with work: some lessons from the horse. In: *Draught Animal Power for Production,* ACIAR Proceedings Series No. 10 (ed. J.W. Copland), pp. 51–56. Canberra, ACIAR.

Pearson, R.A. and Archibald, R. (1989). Biochemical and haematological changes associated with short periods of work in draught oxen. *Animal Production,* **48**, 375–384.

Pearson, R.A., Lawrence, P.R. and Ghimire, C. (1989). Factors influencing the work done by draught oxen: a study in the Eastern hills of Nepal. *Animal Production*, **49**, 345–353.

Pearson, R.A. and Merritt, J.B. (1990). Intake, digestion and gastrointestinal transit time in resting donkeys and ponies and exercised donkeys given *ad libitum* hay and straw diets. *Equine Veterinary Journal* (in press).

Pethick, D.W. (1984). Energy metabolism in skeletal muscle. In: *Ruminant Physiology: Concepts and Consequences* (eds. S.K. Baker, J.M. Gawthorne, J.B. Mackintosh and D.B. Purser), pp. 277–287. University of Western Australia, Perth.

Pethick, D.W., Harman, N. and Chong, J.K. (1987). Non esterified long chain fatty acid metabolism in fed sheep at rest and during exercise. *Australian Journal of Biological Science,* **40**, 221–234.

Preston, T.R. and Leng, R.A. (1987). *Matching Ruminant Production Systems with Available Resources in the Tropics and Subtropics.* Perambul Books, Armidale, Australia.

Raub, R.R., Bechtel, P.J. and Lawrence, L.M. (1985). Variation in the distribution of muscle fibre types in equine skeletal muscles. *Journal of Equine Veterinary Science,* **5**, 34–37.

Rose, R.J., Purdue, R.A. and Hensley, W. (1977). Plasma biochemistry alterations in horses during an endurance ride. *Equine Veterinary Journal,* **9**, 122.

Saltin, B. and Gollnick, P.D. (1983). Skeletal muscle adaptability: signifi-

cance for metabolism and performance. In: *Handbook of Physiology, Section 10, Skeletal Muscle* (eds. L.D. Peachy, R. Adrian and S.R. Geiger), pp. 555–631. The Williams and Wilkins Company, Baltimore.
Snow, D.H., Billeter, R. and Jenny, E. (1981). Myosin types in equine skeletal muscle fibres. *Research in Veterinary Science,* **30**, 381–382.
Snow, D.H. and Guy, P.S. (1976). Percutaneous needle biopsy in the horse. *Equine Veterinary Journal,* **8**, 150–155.
Snow, D.H. and Guy, P.S. (1980). Muscle fibre type composition of a number of limb muscles in different types of horse. *Research in Veterinary Science,* **28**, 137–144.
Snow, D.H, and Guy, P.S. (1981). Fibre type and enzyme activities of the gluteus medius in different breeds of horse. In: *International Series on Sports Sciences, 11B. Biochemistry of Exercise 1VB.* University Park Press, Baltimore.
Snow, D.H., Persson, S.G.B. and Rose, R.J. (1983). Equine Exercise Physiology. *Proceedings of the First International Conference, Oxford,* September 22–24, 1982. Cambridge Granton Editions.
Tudge, C. (1989). They breed horses, don't they? *New Scientist*, **1667**, 66–67.
Upadhyay, R.C. and Madan, M.L. (1985). Studies on blood acid-base status and muscle metabolism in working bullocks. *Animal Production,* **40**, 11–16.
Valberg, S. (1986). Glycogen depletion patterns in the muscle of standardbred trotters after exercise of varying intensity and duration. *Equine Veterinary Journal,* **18**, 479–484.
Valberg, S. and Essén-Gustavsson, B. (1987). Metabolic response to racing determined to pools of type I, IIA, IIIB fibres. In: *Equine Exercise Physiology 2* (eds. J.R. Gillespie and N.E. Robinson), pp. 290–301. ICEEP Publictions, Davis, California.
Valberg, S., Essén-Gustavsson, B., Lindholm, A. and Persson, S. (1985). Energy metabolism in relation to skeletal muscle fibre properties, during treadmill exercise. *Equine Veterinary Journal*, **17**, 439–444.
van den Hoven, R., Wensing, T., Brukink, H.J., Meijer, A.E.F.H. and Kruip, T.A.M. (1985). Variation of fibre types in the triceps brachii, longissinius dorsi, gluteus medius and biceps femoris of horses. *American Journal of Veterinary Research,* **15**, 939–941.
von Butler, I. (1988). What is the role of external conformation in horses? Relationships between performance traits and body measurements. *Tierzuchter,* **40**, 340–341.
Wilson, R.T. (1984). *The Camel.* Longman, London.

2.5

The Detection and Manipulation of Oestrus in Farm Animals

J. S. MACFARLANE
Centre for Tropical Veterinary Medicine,
University of Edinburgh, Scotland

INTRODUCTION

In nature it is the general rule that animals breed once annually and parturition occurs at the time most favourable for the progeny. In the northern and southern hemispheres at latitudes greater than 20° the young are born in the spring, the period of increasing light and warmth and a time when food for the mother is most abundant ensuring an adequate milk supply for the new born animal. In those areas of the world that are situated between the Tropics of Cancer and Capricorn (latitudes $<23°$) parturition usually takes place at any time throughout the year in humid wet zones, which have no marked seasonal variation of rainfall or ambient temperature, but in drier, seasonal rainfall areas parturition is usually restricted to the wet season.

For an animal to breed it must be mated and hence must attract the male and be sexually receptive: 'on heat', or oestrus. All domestic species show recurring periods of sexual receptivity which are normally associated with the maturation and shedding of one or more ova. Under the conditions of feeding and housing provided by domestication the breeding season tends to be lengthened and in commercial animal production, especially intensive production, breeding now occurs throughout the whole year and in those species with relatively short gestation periods, such as small ruminants and pigs, economic factors have encouraged breeding more than once a year.

The husbandry methods employed in commercial animal production have not only extended the natural breeding season, but have in many instances excluded the male from regular contact with the female. This is particularly so in dairy herds employing artificial insemination for breeding and in intensive pig breeding. Thus to an ever increasing extent oestrus detection is becoming dependent on the skill of the stockman, irrespective of whether the subsequent mating is carried out by natural or artificial means. Unfortunately, the detection of oestrus by the average stockman falls far short of the success rate achieved by the male animal who normally, but not invariably, approaches an accuracy of 100%. For many reasons, such as poor appreciation of the signs of overt oestrus, lack of time or opportunity to observe the signs and poor expression of the signs in some species, breeds and individuals, most stockmen obtain a detection rate of 60 to 80% depending on species and method of husbandry. This difficulty experienced in observing the signs of oestrus has resulted in the development of a proliferation of aids for the detection of oestrus, a few of considerable value, but most of doubtful practical use in the field situation.

IMPORTANCE OF OESTRUS DETECTION

It is a *sine qua non* of animal production that the female animal should, during its life span, produce offspring as frequently as biologically possible. This requires early observance of oestrus *post partum*, or following the attainment of sexual maturity, and successful mating. Where natural mating is practised, employing a sufficiency of fertile males of good libido to run with the herd or flock, oestrus detection is not a problem for the stockman, but where hand mating or artificial insemination is used, oestrus detection is entirely dependent upon the skill of the stockman and poor detection will mean delays in service and consequent economic loss.

The successful use of artificial insemination is almost totally dependent on good oestrus detection. For large dairy or beef herds wishing to use artificial insemination in order to optimize genetic gain, the burden of heat detection is substantial. In seasonally calving herds the task requires a concentrated effort over a short period of time. When oestrus detection is poor the result is extended calving to conception intervals, low conception rates, a scattered calving pattern and a high culling rate for infertility. The present trend towards intensification in dairy, beef and pig units has resulted in less individual contact between stockman and animal. These changed husbandry systems may also have modified the animal's behaviour making oestrus detection more difficult (O'Farrell, 1984).

Many dairy farmers are satisfied with their herds' reproductive performance provided the cows have reasonable conception rates and do not show obvious signs of reproductive diseases. They fail to realise the deleterious effects that delays to service have on calving intervals and thus on profitability. For most dairy herds an average calving interval close to 365 days, with minimal spread, is ideal. Under U.K. conditions an increase over this figure has been calculated to cost the producer as much as £3 per cow per day (MAFF, 1984). Ball (1987) states the cost to the farmer of one missed oestrus is approximately £40. In the seasonal rainfall areas of the tropics missed heats may result in serious financial loss and nutritional deprivation amongst subsistence cow keepers as cycling animals become anoestrus with the onset of the dry season and concomitant grazing shortage, and the cow misses a year of production.

To achieve a calving interval of 365 days a cow must be seen in heat, served and conceived within 12 weeks of calving. Studies based on milk progesterone profiles have shown that a high proportion of cows, if they are well fed and managed, are likely to be undergoing normal ovarian activity well within this 12 week period (Lamming, Wathes and Peters, 1981). In a survey of 533 dairy cows in four herds using a milk progesterone assay Bullman and Wood (1980) found that 47.8% of the cows had resumed normal cyclical ovarian activity within 20 days of calving and by 40 days this had increased to 92.4% of the cows. The resumption of ovarian activity may be delayed in cows that suckle their calves, in some cases in excess of 100 days (Lamming *et al*, 1981). However, the main problem causing delays to mating is a failure to observe oestrous behaviour at the correct time. When a herd of Boran and Tanzanian Shorthorn cows (*Bos indicus*) was observed continuously for 24 hours a day, all the cows were seen in oestrus at least once during a three week period, although the stockmen in their routine observations detected only 50% (Hutchison and Macfarlane, 1958a). On the other hand, milk progesterone profiles have revealed that 20% of cows are reported in oestrus at times other than around the time of ovulation (Appleyard and Cook, 1976). If cows are inseminated as a result, the cost is wasted and reproductive problems such as endometritis (Rowsan, Lamming and Fry, 1953) and abortion of pregnant cows can occur. Oestrous behaviour during pregnancy has been observed in all species, but is most commonly seen in the cow (Fraser, 1968). Hutchison and Macfarlane (1958a) using raddled (see 'Teaser bulls' below), vasectomized bulls to detect oestrus, recorded 7.2% of pregnant Zebus exhibiting signs of oestrus mainly during the first trimester of gestation.

OESTRUS DETECTION RATE

As the accuracy and efficiency of oestrus detection has a direct effect on conception rates it is important to be able to determine its contribution to overall herd reproductive performance. Detection efficiency may be calculated by determining the mean interoestral interval in days. An interval of 21 days indicates 100% detection and 42 days 50% detection rate. This is rather crude since it ignores genuine long or short return intervals. Another method is to calculate the proportion of all returns which are normal (19 to 24 days), short (less than 18 days), or long (more than 24 days). However, this is again subject to the same drawbacks as the previous method. In seasonally calving herds the submission rate to service is a good indicator of oestrus detection efficiency. The submission rate is expressed as the percentage of available animals which are served in the first 21 days of the breeding season. While a low submission rate may be indicative of poor heat detection there may also be a high level of anoestrus in the herd. Richardson, Bailie and McNab (1982) have developed a mathematical method for determining the level of anoestrus in a herd taking into account the submission rate and heat detection efficiency. These fertility tables can be used for investigating infertility in cattle and allow the investigator to calculate the true herd conception rate and oestrus detection efficiency. The most accurate method of determining heat detection efficiency would be by comparing the stockman's results with progesterone profile data. However, progesterone levels should not always be taken as infallible since it was found in one trial that three out of four cows, determined to be in oestrus by tail paint, conceived though unconfirmed by progesterone assay (Fulkerson, Sawyer and Crothers, 1983).

The writer has found that in herds which he regularly attends to undertake pregnancy diagnosis, a useful indicator of heat detection efficiency is the number of cows pregnant amongst those offered for checking at 42 days. If all are pregnant this indicates 100% efficiency in detecting cows returning to service at 21 days, but of course gives no indication of detection efficiency overall as the stockman may pay particular attention to possible returns amongst served animals. A further complicating factor is the tendency for Zebu cows to come on heat once only *post partum* and, if they do not conceive, pass into anoestrus. Bulman and Lamming (1978) found that 5.1% of dairy cattle in the U.K. resumed cyclic ovarian activity within a few weeks of calving and then became anoestrous, but the writer is of the opinion, based on recorded observation in the field, that it may be as high as 20% amongst *Bos indicus* cows in semi-arid areas.

It is generally assumed that in the U.K. oestrus detection rates in cows are rarely better than 60% (Esslemont, 1973). Although it is possible to achieve results greater than 80% and in small herds 100% may be approached. In the tropics, especially with *Bos indicus* cows, oestrus detection rates may be as low as 40% (Plasse, Warnick and Koger,1970).

Poor oestrus detection may be due to:

- Poor accommodation inhibiting cows from exhibiting overt signs of oestrus.
- Poor lighting or identification of animals.
- Poor herding practices.
- Lack of education or motivation of stockmen.
- Inadequate and too brief observation periods.
- Minimal and brief overt oestrus behaviour in *Bos indicus*.

The economic and husbandry aspects of oestrus manifestation and detection are covered excellently by Esslemont (1973) for cattle and English, Smith, and Maclean (1982) for pigs.

BEHAVIOURAL SIGNS OF OESTRUS

The view has been expressed (Rowell, 1963) that the term oestrus should be reserved to describe behaviour and not physiology. The normal mating state of the female obviously has both behavioural and physiological elements.

Presumably it was the behavioural aspect of the condition which was first recognized and named. The behaviour of intense 'heat' in cattle can be taken to simulate the frenzy occasioned by irritation from the gadfly (*Oestrus* spp). It is thus that the term appears to have been derived metaphorically (Fraser, 1968). This might justify the exclusive use of the term oestrus for the behavioural characteristics of the state. The recognition that, in many cases, the ovaries can undergo oestrous changes without the subject showing signs of oestrous behaviour, further encourages separate recognition of the two aspects of the female mating state. It must however be appreciated that the overt behaviour of the animal at oestrus is an expression of the animal's physiological state at that time and thus the behavioural and physiological components cannot be entirely divorced except, perhaps, in the case of some rare and somewhat obscure cranial lesions and psychoses (Garm, 1949).

Cows

In cows there are great variations amongst individuals in the intensity of oestrous behaviour and the form it takes. Heifers tend to be more overt in their behaviour than cows. However, it is generally agreed that the most reliable criterion that a cow or heifer is in oestrus is that she will stand to be mounted by another (Foote, 1975). The cow mounting her will invariably be a nonpregnant cow that is within a few days of heat herself and the two animals will undergo a mild degree of bonding, standing more closely together than is normal for herd mates, in between bouts of mounting. It is unusual for pregnant cows to take part in oestrous mounting and if most of the cows in a large herd are pregnant, little mounting behaviour will be seen when an animal is in oestrus. Occasionally the cow in oestrus will attempt to mount her bonded partner in a haphazard, nonaligned manner, the other cow taking avoiding action. A cow in full, standing oestrus will not only stand perfectly still to be mounted by her partner, but will turn her head round to look at her; this diagnostic sign has been termed the 'bulling look' (Isbister, 1984). A positive mounting response lasts about seven seconds and may occur every 15 minutes in *Bos taurus* cows (Esslemont and Bryant, 1976) but the frequency of mounting is considerably less in *Bos indicus* cattle and their crosses (Galina, McCloskey and Calderon, 1982). The oestrous cow is restless and more active (Lewis and Newman, 1984). There is a reduction in the time spent eating, resting and ruminating and frequently a reduction in milk yield (Horrell, Kilgour, Macmillan and Bremner, 1984). Water intake is quite markedly reduced, in many cases the oestrous cow not drinking at all (Macfarlane, 1967). There is frequent genital discharge of transparent mucus whose elasticity causes it to hang in complete, clear strands from the vulva (bulling string). It also adheres to the tail and flanks. The clear mucus becomes a cloudy white towards the end of oestrus. The vulva is slightly swollen and congested and there is a small elevation of body temperature. The tail may be slightly raised and the hair of the tail-head is often ruffled with the skin sometimes excoriated due to the mounting by other cows. The oestrous cow usually bellows a lot. Between 24 and 48 hours after heat, irrespective of service, many cows show a sanguineous discharge, the blood coming mainly from the uterine caruncles.

Ewes

Oestrous ewes are restless. They seek the ram and together form a following 'harem'. The ram examines members of this group for receptivity by pawing with a forefoot, by rubbing his head along the ewe's side and by nipping her wool. A nonreceptive ewe moves off, but if in oestrus she stands and waggles her tail in a lateral movement. The vulva is slightly swollen and congested and there is often a slight discharge of clear mucus. The number of services received by an oestrous ewe is from four to five. In British breeds of sheep overt oestrus lasts about 30 hours (Hunter, 1982).

Goats

In goats the detection of oestrus in a doe is difficult in the absence of a male goat according to Arthur, Noakes and Pearson (1989), however, Fraser (1968) considers, and the present writer concurs, that the doe of any breed shows more conspicuous oestrous behaviour than any other domestic ungulate. For the one to two days of oestrus the female demonstrates a rapid tail waving; the upright tail quivers vigorously from side to side in frequent bursts of flagging. There is repeated bleating throughout oestrus, the animal eats less than usual and has an even greater tendency than normal to roam.

Sows

In sows overt oestrus may last from one to three days. As oestrus approaches, the vulva swells and becomes congested and these signs are most noticeable in maiden gilts. Other signs of heat include mounting of other sows or allowing themselves to be mounted, pricking of ears in prick-eared breeds, restlessness, notably standing when others are sleeping and will often issue characteristic barks associated with heat. They will also show the 'standing' reflex in the presence of the boar or when the stockman firmly presses the loin of the sow with the palms of both hands, the oestrous sow standing motionless with pricked-up ears. This is a diagnostic sign that the sow is in oestrus and ready for service (Burger, 1952). The smell of the boar is a major factor in inducing sows to exhibit the standing reflex. The substance responsible for boar odour has been identified as 5d-andost-16 ene-3 one and is secreted by the salivary glands (Signoret and Du Mesnil Du Buisson, 1961). In the form of an aerosol it can be sprayed in the vicinity of sows to promote the standing reaction of oestrus. The boar's preputial fluid, when smeared on the sows snout has a similar effect. Apart from boar odour, sight, sound and contact with the boar is important and the writer has induced a standing reaction in a sow by playing a recorded tape of a boar vocalizing while serving a sow. Silent heats occur in 2% of porcine cycles (Arthur *et al*, 1989).

FACTORS AFFECTING OESTROUS BEHAVIOUR

Genotype

It is an established fact that there are significant differences in the expression of oestrous signs between *Bos taurus* and *Bos indicus* cows, both in duration and intensity and completely separate from environmental influences. Aside from the problem of inexperience of many owners and herdsmen in detecting heat in tropical countries, is the fact that Zebus usually show overt oestrus for a shorter period of time and show less intensity of oestrous signs than do temperate-type breeds. That this is a breed effect rather than a climatic effect is exemplified by the Zebu cows kept at the Centre for Tropical Veterinary Medicine in Edinburgh, which show minimal signs when in oestrus compared to Jersey x Limousin herd mates. The seminal work on Zebu oestrous behaviour was undertaken by Anderson (1944) working in Kenya at a reasonably temperate station, Naivasha, situated at an altitude of 2,000 m. He reported that the mean duration of oestrus was 4.78 hours in the Zebu and 7.40 hours in grade cattle. Anderson's work has subsequently lead to misconceptions about the length of oestrus in Zebus. Anderson was referring to standing, overt oestrus only and not to pro-oestrous behaviour. Later, Rollinson (1955), working with small East African Zebu and Nganda cattle in Uganda, found that cows were attracted to the bull for some hours before and after the standing oestrus reported by Anderson and in a subsequent trial (Rollinson, 1963) reported that the mean length of time Uganda Zebus remained attractive to bulls was about 26 hours. The percentages of oestruses occurring during the night and daylight were 34.8 and 65.2 respectively. Irrespective of the length of overt oestrous behaviour in *Bos indicus* cows it is generally accepted that the intensity of signs manifested are less than in *Bos taurus* cows (Plasse *et al*, 1970; Galina *et al*, 1982). Relative differences in the intensity of oestrous behaviour between breeds of *Bos taurus* cows have been reported (Lagerlof, 1951; Brackell, Rife and Salisbury, 1952). It is almost certain that similar breed differences exist in *Bos indicus* cows, but little information has been published. There is considerable idiosynchrosy of oestrous behaviour between individual cows, but both heritability and repeatability are very low (Rottensten and Touchberry, 1957). Virtually nothing appears in the literature as to genotype effects on oestrus expression in small ruminants and pigs, although in a recent review, Aboul-Naga (1985) states that in subtropical sheep breeds, of which the fat-tailed constitute a major part, the signs of oestrus are weak during the spring months. Spring is the period of rainfall in the subtropics so that this might be a climatic effect rather than genotype *per se*.

Climate

Thermal stress lengthens oestrous cycles and makes oestrus shorter and more difficult to detect (Dale, Ragsdale and Chang, 1959). There is a high incidence of oestrus with minimal overt signs (silent heat) associated with thermal stress (Labhsetwar, Tyler and Casida, 1963). However, the most consistent observation during thermal stress exposure is a reduction in length of oestrus from 18 hours, considered normal, to about 10 hours or less (Gangwar, Branton and Evans, 1965; Monty and Wolff, 1974; Vaught, 1976; Gwazdouskas, Thatcher, Kiddy, Paape and Wilcox, 1981). Abilay, Johnson and Madan (1975), working with Guernsey heifers, kept at environmental temperatures of 18.2 and 33.5° C found the duration of oestrus to be, in hours, 17.0 ± 0.7 and 12.5 ± 1.0 (Standard error of the mean) respectively ($P<0.05$). This attenuation of overt oestrus implies a response through the hypothalamo-pituitary-gonad axis resulting in lowered oestrogen secretion. Madan and Johnson (1973) reported a lower luteinizing hormone surge at oestrus at high ambient temperatures which may contribute to depressed oestrogen secretion and short, relatively quiescent, oestrus expression. Climatic effects can act indirectly by restricting available grazing in the dry season and more directly, through thermal stress, reducing food intake. In both cases the animal loses condition resulting in diminished signs of oestrus and eventually anoestrus. The writer has observed complete absence of overt oestrus in cycling Friesians during the summer months in Saudi Arabia where shade temperatures often rise to 45° C in July and August. Jersey cattle in similar conditions continued to exhibit overt signs of oestrus, albeit somewhat attenuated and requiring close observation by the stockmen to identify them. In many of the large dairy herds in Saudi Arabia, teams of trained observers are employed solely on heat detection 24 hours per day (Hudson, 1989 personal communication). Increasing ambient temperature will make it difficult for an animal to dissipate heat and hyperthermia will tend to develop. Discomfort due to climatic heat can be aggravated by heat increments within the animal as a result of physical activities. Clearly, it is physiologically appropriate that there be limitations on behaviour during hyperthermia, even at a subacute level and moderating the more physical components of oestrous behaviour is beneficial to the animal's well-being. During periods of heavy rainfall in the wet season all overt signs of oestrus are in abeyance.

Management

The management system under which the herd or flock is kept will affect oestrous behaviour and its detection. Systems which exclude the male from the female will place the onus for detection entirely upon the stockman and with sheep and pigs will curtail overt behaviour by the female. With cows, where the full expression of oestrous behaviour is not dependent on the presence of the male, this expression is facilitated in situations which allow the cow to interact with suitable herd mates, provides sufficient space and freedom of movement to display her repertoire of behavioural signs and gives freedom from factors, such as slippery underfoot conditions, or bullying from dominant cows; psychological factors suppress oestrous behaviour (Boyd, 1977). The writer has observed that in Britain, calls to artificial insemination centres for service, can drop by 50% on frosty winter mornings. A reflection of the icy conditions underfoot causing cows to curtail their mounting behaviour for fear of slipping and falling. Similar situations can arise in cubicle housing with wet and slippery floors.

The importance of the management practices on oestrous behaviour and its detection is emphasized from results reported by Beardon (1957). The sixty- to ninety-day nonreturn rates to first service were 64.1%, 69.5%, 70.4% and 68.3% for cows not turned out from their chained stanchions, for cows turned out once daily, for cows turned out twice daily and cows loose in pens, respectively. It is essential that the stockman should set aside enough time each day to observe his cows for oestrus. With *Bos taurus* cows there is a need for three or more observation periods of 30 minutes duration spread over the 24 hour day (Donaldson, Little and Hansel, 1968). With *Bos indicus* cows longer periods of observation are required because of their lower frequency of mounting behaviour (Galina *et al*, 1982). Hurnick, King and Robertson (1975) and Foote (1979) suggest that the onset of oestrus occurs most frequently at night, however, Hall, Branton and Stone (1959) found that oestrous behaviour was distributed evenly throughout the 24 hour period, as did Hutchinson and Macfarlane (1958a) working with *Bos indicus* cows. Physiologically the cow may come into oestrus at any period of the 24 hours, but it is possible that with *Bos taurus* dairy cattle under intensive management, only at night are the cows sufficiently undisturbed to display oestrous behaviour. Similarly, in areas of intense day-time heat, but relatively cool nights, as is found during the summer months throughout the countries of the Middle East, oestrous behaviour will mainly occur during the hours of darkness when the cows heat increment from the sun is dissipated.

As mentioned previously, the resumption of ovulation and/or oestrous behaviour are delayed in cows that suckle their calves. Vandeplassche (1982) attributes this to elevated levels of prolactin depressing the secretion and discharge of gonadotrophin releasing hormone (GnRH) from the hypothalamus, or that the pituitary may be less responsive to GnRH during suckling. Hanzen (1986) considers that suckling probably inhibits luteinizing hormone (LH) and GnRH release and their action, rather than their synthesis, as both the hypothalamic concentration of GnRH and the pituitary concentration of LH are similar in milked and suckled cows. He also points out that the social interaction of cow and calf and teat stimulation are involved in suckling anoestrus.

AIDS TO OESTRUS DETECTION

The increasing cost of labour, both in developed and developing countries, has resulted in fewer stockmen having to look after increasingly greater numbers of livestock and behavioural oestrus of individual animals may go unobserved. Also, in the developing countries, subsistence farmers often own too few animals to allow the necessary social interaction required for the expression of overt, behavioural oestrus and this is compounded by the owner's ignorance of oestrous cycles and oestrous behaviour. Several devices and methods have, therefore, been developed that aid visual recognition of oestrus. Foote (1975) and Boyd (1984) have produced excellent reviews on the subject. Aids to oestrus detection are mainly used for cattle, however, vasectomized males fitted with a suitable marking harness may be used with sheep and goats and a boar pheromone aerosol spray used with pigs.

Teaser bulls

These are epididectomized or vasectomized bulls, bulls with a surgically deviated or amputated penis, a preputial stenosis (pen-o-block), or a penis which is anchored posteriorly or ventrally to the scrotum, and castrates injected with oestrogen or testosterone. Androgenized cows are occasionally used, but in the writer's experience are not very reliable. Vasectomized bulls must be carefully monitored for libido which may decline with time (Weaver and Hinton, 1973; Macfarlane and Abbiss, 1975). Because they actually serve the cow, vasectomized bulls can transmit venereal diseases. Bulls with a deviated penis offer a safer alternative since they mount cows without intromission. However, this can lead to cessation of mounting behaviour caused by frustration and the writer has observed such bulls that learnt to overcome their frustration by mounting at an angle to obtain intromission. Three or four teasers should be used per 100 cows. They should be worked in groups with frequent rest. Bulls within a group should be moved frequently to avoid the collection of a favourite harem.

Teaser bulls are usually fitted with a device that deposits a coloured mark on the back or rump of each cow mounted. The cheapest to use is a homemade mixture of tallow and red oxide power (Raddle) smeared on the bulls brisket daily. Although cattle like tallow and may lick it, the writer has never experienced deleterious effects from its use with cattle. More sophisticated and expensive chinball markers or harnesses (Elmore, Aderibigbe and Garverick, 1986) using a crayon that leaves a strip of paint on the back of the cow after mounting may be used, but possess no advantage over the cheaper, raddle. The crayons must be replaced regularly and are commercially available in hard consistency for the hot tropics or, soft consistency for temperate areas. A more recently introduced device is a marking web (Broadbent, Alfuraiji, Macdonald and Dolman, 1989), which in trials on groups of heifers, both indoors and at pasture, gave 41% and 14% respectively of false positives, but no false negatives. In the writer's experience, home prepared raddle is almost 100% accurate if care is taken when interpreting the extent and position of the raddle marks on cows.

Tail paint In the tail-paint-mark system, a strip of paint is applied to the tail head of the cow: when the cow is mounted the paint becomes scuffed or cracked. Special paints and pastes are commercially available, but ordinary high gloss enamel paint is cheaper and equally efficacious. It should be applied twice a week. Smith and MacMillan (1980) reported 99% accuracy, however, Ducker, Haggett, Fisher, Bloomfield and Morant (1983) concluded from their trials that tail paint was not an effective or reliable aid to oestrus detection.

Hormonal changes

Radio-immunoassay (RIA) and enzyme-linked immunosorbent assay (ELISA) enables prompt monitoring of endocrine events. The characteristic changes in blood or milk progesterone levels can give an accurate indication of the time of oestrus (Dobson, Midmer and Fitzparich, 1975). Some ELISA techniques take as little as five minutes to yield results and commercial kits are available. Very recently an instant dip-stick test for use with milk has been made available by the English Milk Marketing Board. Progesterone assay tests on milk are mostly used for dairy cattle, but Macfarlane, Booth, Deas and Lowman (1977) successfully employed it for suckled beef cattle. To measure hormonal changes samples must be taken frequently and the results require knowledgeable interpretation. These requirements invalidate the technique for general use by livestock owners in the field.

Other methods

There are a considerable variety of methods to aid oestrus detection which have been suggested over the years, but are not in common use, either because of their lack of accuracy, or because of their sophistication and cost. They are listed in Table 1.

There is an obvious need to explore novel methods for the detection of oestrus and in the age of the microchip and electronic technology it would seem possible that miniature sensing devices, implanted subdermally in the cow to detect changes in electrical resistance, temperature or activity at oestrus, could become a practical reality. Coupled with new electronic

TABLE 1 *Aids to oestrus detection in cattle.*

Method	Source
Heat mount detectors	Ball (1987)
Closed circuit television	Boyd (1984)
Movement detectors	Kiddy (1977)
Cervical/vaginal mucus crystallisation	Goel and Rao (1971)
Cervical mucus glucose content	Symington and Hale (1967)
Cervical/vaginal mucus resistance	Leidl and Stolla (1976)
Cervical/vaginal mucus viscosity	Glover and Scott-Blair (1953)
Vaginal smears	Cuq and Pessinabe (1979)
Vaginal pH	Schilling and Zust (1968)
Rectal, vaginal and milk temperatures	Ball, Marant and Cant (1978)
Peroxidase concentration in cervical mucus	Linford (1974)
Pheromones and sniffer dogs	Kiddy (1979)

methods for identifying cows, there would seem much scope for development in this area (Britt, 1979; Booth, 1990). It should always be remembered that the most important aids to oestrus detection are accurate animal identification and accurate records.

THE MANIPULATION OF OESTRUS

The manipulation of oestrus is not synonymous with oestrous synchronization although embracing it. Synchronization is to have two or more animals exhibiting oestrus at the same time, but manipulation is to bring about oestrus in an individual animal at a precise time; a time usually dictated by husbandry or managerial requirements.

Historical background

The manipulation of oestrus is a practice that has been undertaken by owners of farm livestock for many years. Early techniques employed were based on empiricism and utilized husbandry practices such as 'flushing' ewes before exposing them to the ram and the abrupt weaning of a sow's piglets to induce heat (Fream, 1895). Fleming (1877) described enucleation of the corpus luteum *per rectum* in cows to produce oestrus four to five days later. Although this technique is not without hazard from haemorrhage and ovarian bursal adhesions, it was commonly employed in veterinary practice until the fairly recent advent of prostaglandins. The method is still favoured by the writer on the grounds of cost in developing countries to bring individual cows into oestrus. Corpus luteum removal was itself based on empiricism when originally proposed by Fleming, and not until Marshall (1903) established the function of the corpus luteum in ewes followed by Hammond's seminal work on the oestrous cycle of the rabbit (Hammond, 1925) and the cow (Hammond, 1927) was an understanding of oestrous cycle endocrinology sufficient to enable the manipulation of oestrus on a scientific basis.

Recent and current background

Early work on the synchronization of oestrus in cattle involved parenteral injection of natural progesterone; *Bos taurus* cattle in the United States (Christian and Casida, 1948) and *Bos indicus* cattle in Tanganyika (Hutchison and Macfarlane, 1958b). Treatment was expensive and conception rates low. Progesterone analogues and synthetic progestogens that were orally active became available in the 1960s; medroxyprogesterone acetate (MAP), chlormadinone acetate (CAP) and melengestrol acetate (MGA). Response to such oral treatments could be more accurately described as the 'grouping' of oestrus rather than synchronization and, especially in *Bos indicus* cattle, conception rates to first service were unacceptably low (Macfarlane and Saleka, 1971). The use of orally active progestogens to synchronize oestrus is reviewed by Hansel (1961) for cattle, Lamond (1964) for cattle and sheep and Nellor (1960) for pigs.

The discovery that progestogens would be released into biological tissues from silicone rubber (silastic) impregnated implants (Dziuk and Cook, 1966) presented another possible method for treating animals with these compounds, however, the problem of diminished fertility at the synchronized oestrus was still encountered (Dziuk, Cmarik and Greathouse, 1966). More recently progestogens has been administered intravaginally by means of impregnated sponge pessaries in sheep and goats (Robinson, 1965) and silastic coated coils in cattle (Roche, 1975).

The discovery of the role played by prostaglandins, particularly $PGF_{2}\alpha$, in bringing about regression of the cyclic corpus luteum (Lauderdale, 1972) in cattle and the subsequent availability of natural and synthetic prostaglandins has given renewed impetus to attempts to synchronize oestrus in ruminants (they have limited application in the sow). Since events following treatment with prostaglandins imitates closely part of the natural luteolytic process therefore avoiding the diminished fertility encountered with progestogens (Rowsan, Tervit and Brand, 1972) they have become the drug of choice for pharmacological manipulation of oestrus.

Recently several other pharmacological agents have been investigated for possible use in the manipulation of oestrus. Cooke and Knifton (1981) have induced oestrus in cycling goats using injections of oxytocin and the function of oxytocin as a luteolytic agent in ruminants is discussed by Homeida (1986). Macfarlane (1985) drew attention to a progesterone blocking agent epostane (3a-hydroxy-steroid dehydrogenase inhibitor) and suggested its use for both oestrous synchronization and induction of parturition. Current work on the role of endogenous opioid peptides secreted in the brain in suppressing the release of luteinizing hormone has concentrated interest on the use of the opioid antagonist naloxone to induce oestrus, especially in the lactational anoestrus of suckled cows (Myers, Myers, Gregg and Moss, 1989). The physiology of the neuro-peptide y-opioid-LHRH axis is discussed by Kahra, Allen, Sahu, Kahra and Crowley (1988).

Photoperiodicity and seasonal breeding

As well as the manipulation of overt oestrus within the oestrous cycle, seasonal breeders such as sheep and goats whose cyclicity is influenced by day-length can be brought into oestrus outwith their normal breeding season by controlling the ratio of light to darkness (Fraser and Laing, 1969) or by the injection of pregnant mare serum gonadotropin (PMSG) subsequent to progestogen priming (Evans and Robinson, 1980). More recently exogenous melatonin, administered as vaginal and subcutaneous implants, or orally, incorporated in the food, has proved sucessful in bringing about oestrus out of season in ewes (Kennaway, Dunston and Staples, 1987). Seasonal breeding and its manipulation using melatonin is reviewed by Rodway (1988). The influence of photoperiod on oestrus and cyclicity of sheep and goats is slight at latitudes within the tropics and subtropics, but can be a temporary problem in animals imported from latitudes above 35° (Macfarlane, 1969).

Lactational anoestrus

Suckling delays post-partum ovarian activity resulting in lengthened calving intervals, especially in seasonal rainfall areas where it is imperative to get a cow pregnant before nutritional anoestrus sets in as the dry season advances. Weaning calves in the first week after birth reduces the time from calving to the onset of ovarian activity (Moore and Rocha, 1983). Such early weaning is not practicable with ranched beef cattle and various techniques for reducing the effect of suckling on the post-partum cows have been devised (Moore, 1984). The most popular are weaning the calf: (1) at one month, three months or five months after calving, or (2) restricted suckling during a 48- or 72-hour period at one month after calving, or (3) reducing the suckling frequency by allowing the calf access to its dam only at night during the breeding season. The latter method, sometimes termed 'controlled nursing', the writer has found to be of considerable value in promoting an early return to oestrus of suckled Boran cattle on ranches in East Africa. The effect of suckling on the cow appears to be more closely related to the frequency of suckling than to the nutrient drain on the cow (Bastidas, Troconiz, Verde and Silva, 1984). Thus controlling the suckling stimulus can hasten post-partum return to oestrus without affecting the growth of the calf. Fonseca, Chow, Norte and Lima (1981) found 50 and 30% better conception rates in Gir cows when restricted suckling was applied during the dry and rainy seasons respectively indicating seasonal effects and Randel (1981) demonstrated that this effect was particularly beneficial in heifers calving for the first time. Despite the foregoing discussion, it should be noted that Lishman and Harwin (1985) failed to see an effect of early weaning on length of the anoestrous period, on the time from calving to ovulation, or on conception rate. As mentioned previously, the opioid antagonist naloxone may prove of value in overcoming lactational anoestrus (Myers *et al*, 1989), but this is still very much an experimental approach at present.

Prevention of oestrus

The manipulation of oestrus embraces the suppression of oestrus and the oestrous cycle. Mounting behaviour, reduced feed intake and lower weight gains caused by oestrous activity amongst beef heifers in large-scale feed-lot conditions in North America and Eastern Europe can be prevented by spaying (Dinusson, Andrews and Beeson, 1950). In the 19th century oophorectomy of cows and heifers being fattened for slaughter was standard farm practice in Britain (Fream, 1893). Such refinements in the fattening process are of doubtful commercial viability in developing countries, but there is a need to prevent oestrus and curtail breeding amongst scrub cows and animals of low genetic merit in those areas of the world where animal slaughter is prohibited for religious reasons as in the Hindu areas of India. Oophorectomy requires skill and must be carried out under suitable anaesthesia and is not without risks in the field situation. Roy and Rowsan

(1955) described a simple technique for preventing the establishment of pregnancy in cattle. A small spring clip was inserted into the cervical canal using a transvaginal technique similar to the recto-vaginal method used for artificial insemination. By keeping the cervical canal patent ovulation and conception was not interfered with, but there was early embryo death through failure to implant. Roy and Rowsan, who inserted the spring clip during oestrus when the uterus was under the influence of oestrogen, found no signs of uterine infection in treated cows on *post-mortem* examination, but the writer has encouraged a low grade, chronic endometritis, with retention of the corpus luteum and prevention of oestrus, by inserting the spring clip during the luteal phase of the cycle when the uterus is under the influence of progesterone (Rowsan, Lamming and Fry, 1953). The endometritis, while low grade and causing no discomfort in the cow, possibly interferes with prostaglandin synthesis and luteolysis of the corpus luteum does not occur and oestrus is effectively suppressed.

The manipulation of oestrus and the oestrous cycle in farm livestock using progestagens and prostaglandin $F_{2}\alpha$ is reviewed in detail by Gordon (1983) and a recent update on the use of prostaglandin $F_{2}\alpha$ and its analogues for controlling oestrus in cattle is provided by Fulgensio (1989).

REFERENCES

Abilay, T.A., Johnson, H.D. and Madan, M. (1975). Influence of environmental heat on peripheral plasma progesterone and cortisol during the bovine estrous cycle. *Journal of Dairy Science*, **58**, 1836–1840.

Aboul-Naga, A.M. (1985). Crossbreeding for fecundity in subtropical sheep. In: *Genetics of Reproduction in Sheep* (eds. R.B. Land and D.W. Robinson), pp. 55–62. Butterworths, London.

Anderson, J. (1944). The periodicity and duration of oestrus in zebu and grade cattle. *Journal of Agricultural Science*, **34**, 57–68.

Appleyard, W.T. and Cook, B. (1976). The detection of oestrus in dairy cattle. *The Veterinary Record*, **99**, 253–256.

Arthur, G.H., Noakes, D.E. and Pearson, H. (1989). *Veterinary Reproduction and Obstetrics* (6th edit.). Baillière Tindall, London.

Ball, J.H., Morant, S.V. and Cant, E.J. (1978). Measurement of milk temperature as an aid to estrus detection in dairy cattle. *Journal of Agricultural Science*, **91**, 593–597.

Ball, P. (1987). Oestrus detection in dairy cattle. In: *Practice*, **9** (6), 223–228.

Bastidas, P., Troconiz, J., Verde, O. and Silva, O. (1984). Effect of restricted suckling on ovarian activity and uterine involution in Brahman cows. *Theriogenology*, **21**, 525–532.

Bearden, H.J. (1957). The effect of some winter management practices and herd size on the 60- to 90-day nonreturns in artificial breeding. *Journal of Dairy Science*, **40**, 638.

Booth, J. (1990). Electronic identification. *Proceedings of the World Association for Transport Animal Welfare and Studies*. Inaugural Meeting Wolfson College, Oxford.

Boyd, H. (1977). Anoestrus in cattle. *The Veterinary Record*, **100**, 150–153.

Boyd, H. (1984). Aids to oestrus detection – A Review. In: *Dairy Cow Fertility* (eds. R.G. Eddy and M.J. Ducker), pp. 60–67. BVA, London.

Brackel, W.J., Rife, D.C. and Salisbury, S.M. (1952). Factors associated with the duration of gestation in dairy cattle. *Journal of Dairy Science*, **36**, 179–194.

Britt, J.H. (1979). New concepts in managing dairy cattle production. In: *Animal Reproduction* (BARC Symposium 3) (ed. H. Hawke), pp. 63–75. Allanheld, Osmun, Montclair.

Broadbent, P.J., Alfuraiji, M.M., MacDonald, D.C. and Dolman, D.F. (1989). Evaluation of a marking web device as an aid to detection of oestrus in cattle. *Animal Production*, **48**, 660.

Bulman, D.C. and Lamming, G.E. (1978). Milk progesterone levels in relation to conception, repeat breeding and factors influencing acyclicity in cows. *Journal of Reproduction and Fertility*, **54**, 447–458.

Bulman, D.C. and Wood, P.D.P. (1980). Abnormal patterns of ovarian activity in dairy cows and their relationship with reproductive performance. *Animal Production*, **30**, 177–188.

Burger, J.F. (1952). Sex physiology of pigs. *Onderstepoort Journal of Veterinary Research*, **25**, Supplement 2, 3–218.

Christian, R.E. and Casida, L.E. (1948). The effects of progesterone in altering the estrous cycle of the cow. *Journal of Animal Science*, **7**, 540 (Abstract).

Cooke, R.G. and Knifton, A. (1981). Oxytocin-induced oestrus in the goat. *Theriogenology*, **16**, 95–97.

Cuq, L. and Pessinabe, I.V. (1979). Cytohormonal diagnosis of estrus cycle phases by differential staining and detection of lipids in vaginal smears and urinary sediments in zebu. *Recueil de Médecin Vétérinaire*, **155**, 57–66.

Dale, H.D., Ragsdale, A.D. and Cheng, C.S. (1959). Effect of constant environmental temperatures of 50 and 80° F on appearance of puberty in beef calves. *Journal of Animal Science*, **18**, 1263 (Abstract).

Dinusson, W.E., Andrews, F.N. and Beeson, W.M. (1950). The effects of stilbestrol, testosterone, thyroid alteration and spaying on growth and fattening beef heifers. *Journal of Animal Science*, **9**, 321.

Dobson, H., Midmer, S.E. and Fitzparick, R.J. (1975). Relationship between progesterone concentration in milk and plasma during the bovine oestrus cycle. *The Veterinary Record*, **96**, 222–223.

Donaldson, L.E., Little, D.A. and Hansel, W. (1968). The duration of oestrus and the time of ovulation in cattle of three breed types with and without synchronization of oestrus with a progestagen. *Australian Veterinary Journal*, **44**, 364–366.

Ducker, M.J., Haggett, R.A., Fisher, W.J., Bloomfield, G.A. and Morant, S.V. (1983). An evaluation of tail paint as an aid or alternative to oestrus detection. *Animal Production*, **37**, 221–227.

Dziuk, P.J. and Cook, B. (1966). Passage of steroids through silicone rubber. *Endocrinology*, **78**, 208–211.

Dzuik, P.J., Cmarik, G. and Greathouse, T. (1966). Estrus control in cows by an impregnated progestogen. *Journal of Animal Science*, **25**, 1266 (Abstract).

Elmore, R.G., Aderibigbe, A.A. and Garverick, M.J. (1986). The use of heat detection aids in estrus synchronization programs. *Theriogenology*, **26**, 239–244.

English, P., Smith, W. and Maclean, A. (1982). *The Sow – Improving Her Efficiency* (2nd ed.). Farming Press Limited, Surrey.

Esslemont, R.J. (1973). Economic and husbandry aspects of the manifestation and detection of oestrus in cows in large herds. *PhD Thesis, University of Reading.*

Esslemont, R.J. and Bryant, M.J. (1976). Oestrous behaviour in a herd of dairy cows. *The Veterinary Record*, **99**, 472-475.

Evans, G. and Robinson, J.T. (1980). The control of fertility in sheep: Endocrine and ovarian responses to progestagen-PMSG treatment in the breeding season and in anoestrus. *Journal of Agricultural Science*, **94**, 69–88.

Fleming, G. (1877). *Veterinary Obstetrics.* Baillière, Tindall and Cox, London.

Fonseca, V.O., Chow, L.A., Norte, A.L.do. and Lima, O.P. (1981). Effect of suckling on the reproductive efficiency of zebu cows. *Arquivos da Escola de Veterinaria da Universidade Federal de Minas Gerais*, **33**, 165–171.

Foote, R.H. (1975). Estrus detection and estrus detection aids. *Journal of Dairy Science*, **58**, 248–256.

Foote, R.H. (1979). Time of AI and fertility in dairy cattle. *Journal of Dairy Science*, **62**, 355–358.

Fraser, A.F. (1968). *Reproductive Behaviour in Ungulates.* Academic Press, London.

Fraser, A.F. and Laing, A.H. (1969). Oestrus induction in ewes with standard treatments of reduced natural light. *The Veterinary Record,* **84**, 427–430.

Fream, W. (1893). *Youatt and Freams Complete Grazier* (13th ed.). Crosby Lockwood and Son, Edinburgh.

Fulkerson, W.J., Sawyer, G.J. and Crothers, I. (1983). The accuracy of several aids in detecting oestrus in dairy cattle. *Applied Animal Ecology*, **10**, 199–208.

Fulgensio, J. (1989). The role of prostaglandin F2α and its analogues in the management of cattle fertility and its application to cattle breeding in Uganda. *MSc Dissertation, University of Edinburgh.*

Galina, C.S., McCloskey, M. and Calderon, A. (1982). Detection of signs of estrus in the Charolais cow and its Brahman cross under continuous observation. *Theriogenology*, **17**, 485–498.

Gangwar, P.D., Branton, C. and Evans, D.L. (1965). Reproductive and physiological responses of Holstein heifers to controlled and natural climatic conditions. *Journal of Dairy Science*, **48**, 222–227.

Garm, O. (1949). A study of bovine nymphomania with special reference to etiology and pathogenesis. *Acta Endocrinology Copenhagen*, **2**, (Suppl. 3), 144.

Glover, F.A. and Scott-Blair, G.W. (1953). The flow properties of cervical

secretions in the cow as related to certain physiological conditions. *Journal of Endocrinology*, **9**, 160.
Goel, V.G. and Rao, M.V.N. (1971). Studies on the reproductive behaviour of zebu and crossbred farm animals. *Annual Report 1971*, National Dairy Research Institute, Karmal, India.
Gordon, I. (1983). *Controlled Breeding in Farm Animals.* Pergamon Press, Oxford.
Gwazdauskas, F.C., Thatcher, W.W., Kiddy, C.A., Paape, M.S. and Wilcox, C.J. (1981). Hormonal patterns during heat stress following PGF2α-tham salt induced luteal regression in heifers. *Theriogenology*, **16**, 271–285.
Hall, J.G., Branton, C. and Stone, E.J. (1959). Estrus, estrous cycles, ovulation time, time of service and fertility of dairy cattle in Louisiana. *Journal of Dairy Science*, **42**, 1086–1094.
Hammond, J. (1925). *Reproduction in the Rabbit.* Oliver and Boyd, Edinburgh.
Hammond, J. (1927). *The Physiology of Reproduction in the Cow.* Cambridge.
Hansel, W. (1961). Estrous cycle and ovulation control in cattle. *Journal of Dairy Science*, **44**, 2307–2314.
Hanzen, Ch. (1986). Endocrine regulation of post partum ovarian activity in cattle. *Reproduction, Nutrition and Development*, **26**, 1219–1239.
Homeida, A.M. (1986). Role of oxytocin during the oestrous cycle of ruminants with particular reference to the goat. *Animal Breeding Abstracts*, **54**, 263–268.
Horrell, R.I., Kilgour, R., Macmillan, K.L. and Bremner, K. (1984). Evaluation of fluctuations in milk yield and parlour behaviour as indicators of oestrus in dairy cows. *The Veterinary Record*, **114**, 36–39.
Hunter, R.H. (1982). *Reproduction of Farm Animals.* Longman, London.
Hurnick, J.F., King, G.J. and Robertson, H.A. (1975). Estrous and related behaviour in post partum Holstein cows. *Applied Animal Ecology*, **2**, 55–68.
Hutchinson, H.G. and Macfarlane, J.S. (1958a). Variation in gestation periods of zebu cattle under ranch conditions. *East African Agricultural Journal*, **24**, 148–152.
Hutchinson, H.G. and Macfarlane, J.S. (1958b). A Preliminary Report on the Progesterone Trial. *Government of Tanganyika Report*. Government Printers, Dar-es-Salaam.
Isbister, J. (1984). The recognition of cows in heat. Scottish Milk Marketing Board Information Sheet.
Kahra, S.P., Allen, L.G., Schu, A., Kahra, P.S. and Crowley, W.R. (1988). Gonadol steroids and neuro-peptide y-opioid-LHRH axis: interactions and diversities. *Journal of Steroid Biochemistry*, **30**, 185–193.
Kennaway, D.J., Dunston, E.A. and Staples, L.D. (1987). Photoperiodic control of the onset of breeding activity and fecundity in ewes. *Journal of Reproduction and Fertility*, Supplement 34, 187–199.
Kiddy, C.A. (1977). Variation in physical activity as an indication of estrus in dairy cows. *Journal of Dairy Science*, **60**, 235–243.

Kiddy, C.A. (1979). Estrus detection in dairy cattle. In: *Animal Reproduction* (BARC Symposium 3) (ed. H. Hawke), pp. 77–89. Allanheld, Osmun, Montclair.

Labhsetwar, A.P., Tyler, W.J. and Casida, L.E. (1963). Genetic and environmental factors affecting quiet ovulations in Holstein cattle. *Journal of Dairy Science*, **46**, 843–845.

Lagerlof, N. (1951). Hereditary forms of sterility in Swedish cattle breeds. *Fertility and Sterility*, **2**, 230–239.

Lamming, G.E. Wathes, D.C. and Peters, A.R. (1981). Endocrine patterns of the post partum cow. *Journal of Reproduction and Fertility*, Supplement 30, 155–165.

Lamond, D.R. (1964). Synchronization of ovarian cycles in sheep and cattle. *Animal Breeding Abstracts*, **32**, 269–285.

Lauderdale, J.W. (1972). Effects of PGF2α on pregnancy and oestrous cycles of cattle. *Journal of Animal Science*, **35**, 246 (Abstract).

Leidl, W. and Stolla, R. (1976). Measurement of electric resistance of the vaginal mucus as an aid for heat detection. *Theriogenology*, **6**, 237.

Lewis, G.S. and Newman, S.K. (1984). Changes throughout estrous cycles of variables that might indicate estrus in dairy cows. *Journal of Dairy Science*, **67**, 146–152.

Linford, E. (1974). Cervical mucus: an agent or a barrier to conception. *Journal Reproduction and Fertility*, **37**, 239–250.

Lishman, A.W. and Harwin, G.O. (1985). Failure to induce ovulation by short-term calf removal in lactating beef cows on dry-lot. *South African Journal of Animal Science*, **15**, 21–22.

Macfarlane, J.S. (1967). The effect of oestrus on 'free' water intake in zebu-type heifers. *The Veterinary Record*, **80**, 361.

Macfarlane, J.S. (1969). Oestrus induction in ewes. *The Veterinary Record*, **85**, 104.

Macfarlane, J.S. and Saleka, R. (1971). Synchronization of oestrus and ovulation in *Bos indicus* heifers using an orally active progestogen. *East African Agricultural and Forestry Journal*, **36**, 353–355.

Macfarlane, J.S. and Abbiss, T.P. (1975). Seminal fructose levels as a parameter of libido in entire and vasectomized zebu bulls. *Tropical Animal Health and Production*, **7**, 51–55.

Macfarlane, J.S., Booth, J.M., Deas, D.W. and Lowman, B.G. (1977). Pregnancy test and evaluation of embryonic and fetal mortality based on progesterone concentrations in fore-milk. *The Veterinary Record*, **100**, 565–566.

Macfarlane, J.S. (1985). The effect of a progesterone blocking agent (epostane) on embryo survival in ewes and reversal of this effect with exogenous progesterone. *MSc Dissertation, University of Edinburgh.*

Madan, M.L. and Johnson, H.D. (1973). Environmental heat effects on bovine luteinizing hormone. *Journal of Dairy Science*, **56**, 1420–1423.

MAFF (1984). *Dairy Herd Fertility.* Reference Book 259. London, H.M.S.O.

Marshall, F.H.A. (1903). The oestrous cycle and the formation of the corpus luteum in the sheep. *Philosophical Transactions B*, **196**, 47–50.

Monty, D.E. and Wolff, L.K. (1974). Summer heat stress and reduced fertility in Holstein-Friesian cows in Arizona. *American Journal of Veterinary Research*, **35**, 1495–1500.

Moore, C.P. and Rocha, C.M.C. da. (1983). Reproductive performance of Gyr cows: the effect of weaning age of calves and post partum energy intake. *Journal of Animal Science*, **57**, 807–814.

Moore, C.P. (1984). Early weaning for increased reproduction rates in tropical beef cattle. *World Animal Review*, **49**, 39–50.

Myers, T.R., Myers, D.A., Gregg, D. and Moss, G.E. (1989). Endogenous opioid suppression of release of luteinizing hormone during suckling in post partum anoestrous beef cows. *Domestic Animal Endocrinology*, **6**, 183–190.

Nellor, J.E. (1960). Control of estrus and ovulation in gilts by orally effective progestational compounds. *Journal of Animal Science*, **19**, 412–420.

O'Farrell, K.J. (1984). Oestrous behaviour, problems of detection and relevance of cycle lengths. In: *Dairy Cow Fertility* (eds. R.G. Eddy and M.J. Ducker), pp. 47–59. *Proceedings of a Joint BVA/BSAP Conference, Bristol University, U.K.*

Plasse, D., Warnick, A.C. and Koger, J. (1970). Reproductive behaviour of *Bos indicus* females in a subtropical environment. *Journal of Animal Science*, **30**, 63–72.

Randel, R.D. (1981). Effect of once-daily suckling on post partum interval and cow-calf performance of first-calf Brahman x Hereford heifers. *Journal of Animal Science*, **53**, 755–757.

Richardson, A., Bailie, J.H. and McNab, A.F. (1982). Mathematical method for investigating causes of infertility in cattle. *The Veterinary Record*, **110**, 387.

Robinson, T.J. (1965). Use of progestagen-impregnated sponges inserted intravaginally or subcutaneously for the control of the oestrous cycle in the sheep. *Nature* (London), **206**, 39–41.

Roche, J.F. (1975). Synchronization of oestrus in cows using intravaginal silastic coils containing progesterone. *Annals de Biologie Animale, Biochimie et Biophysique*, **15**, 301–302.

Rodway, R.G. (1988). Melatonin and Seasonal Breeding. *Proceedings 1987–88 of the Society for the Study of Animal Breeding, U.K.* pp. 23–25.

Rollinson, D.H.L. (1955). Oestrus in Zebu cattle. *Nature*, **176**, 352.

Rollinson, D.H.L. (1963). Reproductive habits and fertility of indigenous cattle to artificial insemination in Uganda. *Journal of Agricultural Science*, **60**, 279–284.

Rollinson, D.H.L. (1963). Reproductive habits and fertility of indigenous cattle to artificial insemination in Uganda. *Journal of Agricultural Science*, **60**, 279–284.

Rottensten, K. and Touchberry, R.W. (1957). Observations on the degree of expression of estrus in cattle. *Journal of Dairy Science*, **40**, 1457–1465.

Rowell, T.E. (1963). Behaviour and female reproductive cycles of rhesus macaques. *Journal of Reproduction and Fertility*, **6**, 193–203.

Rowsan, L.E.A., Tervit, R. and Brand, A. (1972). The use of prostaglandins for synchronization of oestrus in cattle. *Journal of Reproduction and Fertility*, **29**, 145 (Abstract).

Rowsan, L.E.A., Lamming, G.E. and Fry, R.M. (1953). The relationship between ovarian hormones and uterine infection. *The Veterinary Record*, **65**, 335–340.

Roy, A. and Rowson, L.E.A. (1955). A method of inducing sterility in the cow. *The Veterinary Record*, **67**, 177–179.

Schilling, E. and Zust, J. (1968). Diagnosis of estrus and ovulation in cows by pH measurements intra vaginam and by apparent viscosity of vaginal mucus. *Journal of Reproduction and Fertility*, **15**, 307.

Signoret, J.P. and Du Mesnil Du Buisson, F. (1961). Etude du comportement de la truie en oestrus. *Proceedings IVth International Congress on Animal Reproduction*, 171–175.

Smith, J.F. and Macmillan, K.L. (1980). Tail paint as an aid to estrus detection. *9th International Congress on Animal Reproduction and Artificial Insemination, Madrid, Spain*. p. 41.

Symington, R.B. and Hale, D.H. (1967). Test of ovarian function of zebu cattle. *Rhodesia, Zambia and Malawi Journal of Agricultural Research*, **5**, 3–7.

Vandeplassche, M. (1982). Reproductive efficiency in cattle: A Guideline for Projects in Developing Countries. F.A.O. Animal Production and Health Paper, No. 25. F.A.O., Rome, Italy.

Vaught, L.K. (1976). Some effects of high environmental temperatures on reproductive, endocrine and physiologic characteristics of lactating and nonlactating Holstein-Friesian cows in Arizona. *Dissertation Abstracts International*, **37**, 1982.

Weaver, A.D. and Hinton, M. (1973). The use of vasectomized bulls. *The Veterinary Record*, **93**, 27.

2.6

Methods of Making Transgenic Livestock and their Role in Developing Countries

I. WILMUT[1] and J. JERE[2]
[1]*AFRC Institute of Animal Physiology and Genetics Research, Roslin, Scotland*

[2]*University of Edinburgh, Centre for Tropical Veterinary Medicine, Present address: Ministry of Agriculture, Chitedze Agricultural Research Station, P.O. Box 15, Lilongwe, Malawi*

INTRODUCTION

Conventional genetic selection depends upon a measurement of performance to identify the best animals and their use as parents of the next generation. While able to cause change in many aspects of animal performance these aspects and the rate of progress are limited by the naturally occurring variation within that species. New techniques have been developed recently for the isolation of a gene from one animal, its multiplication and modification in the laboratory and transfer to another animal of the same or a different species. In this way, it is becoming possible to make changes in livestock that cannot be achieved by genetic selection. The new opportunities arise from fundamental research in two different areas of biology: molecular biology and reproductive physiology, and continuing research can be expected to create further opportunities and these will be outlined in the appropriate sections.

The present procedures of gene transfer are expensive and have so far only been applied in developed countries. In this paper there is no intention of providing a catalogue of applications that are being developed, rather, the objective is to describe the methods that are available and consider possible future developments, in order to allow those working in developing countries to consider potential applications of the technology in their environment.

Exploitation of the procedures for gene transfer depends, 1) upon efficient methods for the transfer or modification of the gene and, 2) upon the ability to design genes that are only expressed in specific tissues at particular stages of development and at desired levels. These aspects are considered in the first two sections of this paper. First, a description of the present procedures for gene transfer. Second, an outline of the mechanisms controlling gene expression and consideration of some factors that affect expression of transgenes in particular. As discussed by Smith and Daborn (this volume) two of the main limitations to animal production in tropical countries are the low digestibility of the forage and the occurrence of tick-borne diseases. In the final section of the paper, the potential routes for overcoming the problem of poor forage quality by gene manipulation will be considered briefly.

METHODS OF GENE TRANSFER

At present transfer of a gene in mammals is usually achieved by direct injection of several hundred copies of the gene into a nucleus in an early embryo that has been recovered from a donor animal. Surviving embryos are transferred to recipient females and allowed to develop to term. Gene transfer by direct injection was first described in mice (Gordon, Scangos, Plotkin, Barbosa and Ruddle, 1980), and has subsequently been used extensively for fundamental research in this species (Palmiter and Brinster, 1986 for an early review). Three factors make gene transfer in livestock more difficult than in mice: fewer eggs are available, there is greater variability in stage of embryo development and the oocyte contains cytoplasmic vesicles that obscure the view of the nuclei. Despite these problems, the procedures have been modified for pigs, sheep and cattle (Hammer, Pursel, Rexroad, Wall, Bolt, Ebert, Palmiter and Brinster, 1985; Simons, Wilmut, Clark, Archibald, Bishop and Lathe, 1988; Biery, Bondioli and De Mayo, 1988).

The treatments that are used to control the time of oestrus and induce superovulation in the different farm species are as follows. At Edinburgh, donor ewes are induced to superovulate by repeated injection of equine follicle stimulating hormone (FSH) during treatment with an intravaginal progestogen sponge. As the pronuclear stage of development lasts only a few hours it is helpful to control the time of ovulation. This is achieved by injection of gonadotropin releasing hormone (GnRH) 24 hours after withdrawal of the sponge. In order to maximize the proportion of eggs that are fertilized, intra-uterine insemination is carried out by laparoscopy. In Edinburgh, the insemination is carried out 16 hours after GnRH injection, this is some eight hours before the expected time of ovulation, but the routines of laboratories differ in detail.

Between 40 and 46 hours following GnRH injection, the reproductive tract is exposed by mid-ventral laparotomy and the eggs are recovered by passing sterile saline through the oviduct. The eggs are identified under a dissecting microscope and transferred to an inverted microscope fitted with a fixed stage, differential interference contrast optics and micromanipulators. Each egg in turn is secured upon the tip of a holding pipette and examined for the presence of pronuclei. There are differences between species in the clarity of the cytoplasm. Experience has shown that in sheep over 90% of pronuclei suitable for injection can be seen in untreated eggs using differential interference contrast optics (I. Wilmut and J.P. Simons, unpublished observations). By contrast the eggs of pigs and cattle must be centrifuged before the pronuclei can be seen. Fortunately, the majority of these embryos are able to develop normally after this treatment (Wall, Pursel, Hammer and Brinster, 1985).

A pipette is introduced into one pronucleus to allow direct injection of the gene of interest. These pipettes are very fine (less than 0.5 μm diameter) and are tapered at a very fine angle (less than 5°) in order to minimize damage to the cells. Distension of the pronucleus provides confirmation that a few hundred copies of the gene have been deposited in the pronucleus. The injected eggs are incubated for a period before transfer to a recipient to allow the occurrence of serious damage to become apparent. Surviving eggs are transferred as deeply as possible into the oviducts of recipients that have ovulated and been observed in oestrus at a similar time to the donor ewe. In practice, the enormous variability in response to the treatment to induce superovulation, leads to the use of less well-synchronized recipients on those days when a particularly large number of embryos suitable for injection are recovered.

The number of eggs transferred to each recipient can have a significant impact upon the outcome of the project. The proportion of embryos developing to term is reduced by the process of injection. As a result, if the number of eggs transferred is similar to the number of ovulations, only a small proportion of recipients become pregnant. There are additional species-specific problems in cattle and pigs. In pigs there is a need for a minimum of four embryos for the establishment of pregnancy. As heifer calves born as twins to a bull calf are almost always infertile (freemartins), unless the embryos have been sexed or cloned it is only appropriate to transfer one embryo to each recipient. Three approaches have been adopted to increase the efficiency of the use of recipients. In cattle, the injected eggs are allowed to develop for six days in the oviduct of a temporary recipient, usually a sheep. Only those eggs that develop to morulae or blastocysts are transferred to recipient heifers. In pigs a small number of control eggs that have not been injected are transferred, in order to increase the probability that pregnancy is established and to allow the survival to term of even one viable injected egg. In sheep and pigs an increased number of injected eggs are transferred to each recipient. Unfortunately, this leads to the occasional birth of large litters and some very small young that are not viable.

The proportion of injected eggs that develop to become transgenic offspring is small, being 1% or less in farm animals. In the first three years of the project at Edinburgh the proportion was 0.84% which is very similar to the production of 20 transgenic piglets from 2,035 injected pig eggs (Hammer *et al*, 1985). This low success rate reflects the facts that many eggs are killed by the act of injection and that integration of genes is an infrequent event. Pregnancy diagnosis by ultrasound has shown that foetal death of injected eggs continues to occur throughout pregnancy (unpublished observations), making it extremely unlikely that a test can be devised to detect the viable eggs.

The mechanism of integration of the gene is not known, but it does not involve site directed mutation with an homologous gene in the injected egg. Rather the consensus of opinion from experiments in mice is that the site of integration is probably random. In some cases there is damage to endogenous genes. A recent estimate is that, in mice, insertional mutation occurred in 5 to 10% of lines studied. It has been suggested that integration is a result of damage to the chromosomes during injection and inadvertent incorporation of the gene into one of these sites during repair (Palmiter and Brinster, 1986). Typically the transgene is incorporated in head to tail concatemers, arrays that may contain many copies of the gene. The same repair enzymes that incorporate the gene into the chromosome are assumed to link together the free copies of the gene before integration takes place (Palmiter and Brinster, 1986).

There are several possible means of reducing the costs or increasing the efficiency of gene transfer that are the subject of active research projects at the present time. These include the use of tissue culture to produce embryos cheaply, the identifiction of those embryos in which the gene has integrated, isolation and manipulation of embryo stem cells and the use of retroviral vectors. These opportunities will be considered in turn.

Tissue culture may provide an alternative source of eggs suitable for injection. Procedures have been described for the maturation of sheep and cattle oocytes recovered from the ovaries of slaughtered animals, in medium supplemented with serum and hormones (Staigmiller and Moor, 1984; Lu, Gordon, Gallagher and McGovern, 1987). Fertlization may then be achieved by capacitation of semen with specialized media and the co-culture of sperm and oocytes (Parrish, Susko-Parrish, Leibfried-Rutledge, Critser, Eyestone and First, 1986). While this procedure has the potential to provide large numbers of fertilized eggs, at the present time not all of the eggs have a normal potential for development. In one major trial in a very experienced laboratory, some 28.6% of pronuclear cattle eggs developed to become morulae or blastocysts (191 of 668) suitable for transfer to recipients (Lu, Gordon, McGovern and Gallagher, 1988). This proportion would be reduced still further by injection of DNA. Perhaps even more important, the ability of these transferred embryos to develop to term was lower than that of eggs recovered from donor animals. As a result the saving in animals and surgery by the elimination of the need for donors may be more than counterbalanced by the need for more recipients. The ability to produce large numbers of normal embryos cheaply would be of considerable value in commerce and research. This area should clearly continue to have high priority either for fundamental research, to discover the nature of the regulatory factors, or for developmental projects.

Projects are in hand to develop methods for the identification, at the morula or blastocyst stage of development, of those eggs in which the injected gene has integrated. In this way it may be possible to transfer only those eggs that have the potential to develop to transgenic animals. The polymerase chain reaction allows the detection in a very small number of cells of genes that are present as single copies (Saiki, Gefland, Stoffel, Scharf, Higughi, Horn, Mullis and Erlich, 1988). The proposal is to remove cells from early embryos and probe for the presence of the gene. Only embryos carrying the gene would be transferred to final recipients. The value of these procedures will depend upon the proportion of injected eggs that are lost in the temporary recipient used to support development of the injected eggs, the proportion of biopsied transgenic eggs that are able to develop to term and the frequency of false positive tests. In principle it may also be possible to transfer nuclei from transgenic embryos at the morula and blastocyst stages of development and produce several copies of the animal, however, experience shows that the consecutive use of several different manipulative procedures is difficult.

In view of the costs of gene transfer it is perhaps surprising that relatively little research has been carried out to increase the frequency of gene integration. It is apparently necessary to cause a certain amount of damage to the chromosomes if integration is to occur at a reasonable frequency. Treatment to cause damage to chromosomes in the pronuclei may increase the frequency of integration. This could be achieved by use of ultra violet light or of enzymes expected to cut chromosomal DNA relatively infrequently. In mice the frequency of integration was affected by the ionic composition of the buffer, DNA concentration and the use of linear rather than circular DNA (Brinster, Chen, Trumbauer, Yagle and Palmiter, 1985). In farm animals, the cost of embryos and the low frequency of integration have made it unrealistic to consider such experimentation, however the development of methods for *in vitro* fertilization, embryo culture from the time of injection to the morula stage and the detection of genes in early embryos would create this opportunity. In addition to such specific studies in farm animals, there may be some benefit in using mice as models for other studies.

Retroviral vectors might be expected to provide another means of achieving gene transfer. Retroviruses infect cells and then incorporate their genome into the chromosomes of the host cell (Varmus, 1988). It has been suggested that recombinant viruses be produced that retain the ability to insert themselves into the chromosomes, but from which the mechanisms of reproduction and dispersal have been removed. In principle this should create a vector that is capable of achieving a very high frequency of integration, with only one site of insertion in each cell, but which could not spread throughout the animal population. In early experiments genes have been integrated into mice, but the frequency of integration was not greater than after microinjection (Jaehner, Kirsten, Mulligan and Jaenisch, 1985). The potential for this technique remains to be determined, but it should remain an area for active research.

Finally, the isolation of stem cells from the embryos of farm animals would provide an alternative means of achieving gene transfer. Cells have been isolated from mouse embryos in culture in such a way that they divide, but do not differentiate (Evans and Kaufman, 1981). When they are injected into the blastocoel cavity of another embryo they sometimes colonize that embryo and contribute to all of the tissues of the offspring, including the germline (Bradley, Evans, Kaufman and Robertson, 1984). Manipulation of such stem cells in culture before transfer has led to the production of transgenic animals (Lovell-Badge, Bygrave, Bradley, Robertson, Evans and Cheah, 1985), although in this early case the transgene was not passed through the germline. One advantage of this approach is that by selection it is possible to transfer only cells in which the desired change has been made. However, any transgenic young that are born are chimeric, that is they are derived from two embryos. Before the effect of the gene can be assessed a second generation of animals must be produced. While in mice this requires only a few weeks, in farm animals the delay could be several years.

There is the possibility in farm animals of using nuclear transfer to avoid the chimeric generation (Wilmut and Smith, 1988). In sheep and cattle, but not mice, young have been born following the transfer of nuclei from cells of the inner cell mass to enucleated oocytes (Smith and Wilmut, 1989; Marx, 1988). Mouse embryo stem cells are derived from the inner cell mass and, despite the occurrence of several cell divisions, still bear a considerable resemblance to them (Beddington and Robertson, 1989). There is then the possibility, that if embryo stem cells can be isolated from farm animals, it will be possible to transfer nuclei from them. In this way, gene transfer could be confirmed before nuclear transfer, several genetically identical transgenic animals could be made and the chimeric generation would be avoided. This possibility is the subject of active research.

The development of embryo stem cells would also make it practicable to use site directed techniques of gene manipulation. The present method of direct injection is inefficient, sometimes causes damage to the existing genes and, as will be discussed later, leads to very variable patterns of gene expression. By contrast, site directed techniques make specific changes. They have been used extensively in tissue culture cells, but the frequency of success is so low (1 in 1,000 to 10,000 cells are changed) that it is impracticable to apply them directly to embryos. By contrast, site directed mutation in mouse embryo stem cells is being used to study the congenital human disorder Lesch Nyhann disease (Hooper, Hardy, Handyside, Hunter and Monk, 1987) and the role of homeobox genes in development (Joyner, Skarnes and Rossant, 1989; Zimmer and Gruss, 1989). In principle, it would be possible to use such techniques not only to make specific changes to endogenous genes, but also to insert genes in sites where efficient expression could be achieved.

Recently, an entirely new approach to gene transfer was described (Lavitrano, Camaioni, Fazio, Dolci, Farace and Spadafora, 1989). It was reported that transgenic mice were produced following the addition of DNA to mouse spermatozoa that were subsequently used to fertilize eggs *in vitro*.

In the absence of confirmation of the original observation at the time of the conference, despite extensive trials in many different laboratories, it seems that research with livestock should await further developments in studies with mice.

In summary, the method of gene transfer by direct injection can be used to achieve gene transfer in farm animals at present. However, this approach is expensive. There are likely to be developments in the field of embryo culture and manipulation that will make the present procedures seem very primitive.

CONTROL OF GENE EXPRESSION

Exploitation of gene transfer depends upon understanding the mechanisms that regulate gene expression. Many genes are expressed in all cells, producing proteins that are required for 'housekeeping' functions. By contrast, some proteins are produced only in particular cells at specific stages of development. There are DNA sequences that encode each protein and in many cases it is now known that sequences adjacent to the protein coding sequences govern the tissue specific expression of the gene. Just as an understanding of these mechanisms is essential for exploitation of gene transfer, transgenes are in turn revealing a great deal about the mechanisms of regulation.

Initiation of gene expression involves two stages. In the inert chromosome, the DNA is tightly bound to histones and so inaccessible to the polymerase enzymes that synthesize RNA. The chromosomes are secured by a scaffold which determines their basic form. Little is known of the nature of this nucleoskeleton or of the binding sites that constitute this primary mechanism. The secondary differences in form are believed to reflect the effect of transcription factors that bind to specific regions of the DNA (enhancers) and facilitate binding of the polymerase to the gene (La Thangue and Rigby, 1988; Hatzopoulos, Schlokat and Gruss, 1988 for recent reviews of the factors and binding sites respectively).

The nature of the enhancers associated with a particular gene can be studied by transfer of the gene with different lengths of flanking DNA. In turn, these regulatory mechanisms must be known if expression of the gene is to be regulated effectively after transfer. Studies after transfer of the rat gene for the digestive enzyme elastase were among the first to use this means of defining the regulatory sequences (Swift, Hammer, MacDonald and Brinster, 1984; Palmiter and Brinster, 1986). Elastase is one of the digestive enzymes produced by the pancreas and other tissues have only very small quantities of the protein. In four of the five transgenic lines produced, the rat elastase gene was expressed in the acinar cells at a level equal to or greater than that of the gene in rats. Except in one line, expression in other tissues was very low, and it is assumed that in the exceptional case the DNA adjacent to the transgene caused the expression. A similar level of expression was observed following the transfer of the coding sequences with only 205 base pairs of flanking

DNA. By contrast, 72 base pairs of flanking DNA present in the transgene was not effective in inducing expression of the transgene. An important regulatory element apparently lies in the region omitted (72 to 205 base pairs upstream.)

In some cases the regulatory element lies some distance from the structural sequences while in others it may lie within the gene. One particularly complex system regulates the expression of the human β-globin genes (Grosveld, Assendelft, van Greaves and Kollias, 1987). This system is being studied intensively because mutations in this region cause a number of genetic diseases, many of which are associated with early death. The human gene has been found to have regulatory elements, both stimulatory and inhibitory, immediately upstream of the coding sequences, within the gene and downstream of the gene. Following transfer to mice of genes carrying these elements, expression is never equivalent to that of the endogenous mouse gene and is variable from one line to another. In very exciting recent research, regulatory elements have been revealed at much greater distances from the gene. Two new sites have been defined, one approximately 50,000 base pairs upstream the other 20,000 base pairs downstream. High levels of expression that was position independent and equivalent to that of the mouse gene was obtained, for the first time, when genes carrying these distant sites and the neighbouring sequences were transferred. In addition, the level of expression was directly related to the number of copies of the gene in the different lines. The authors suggested that the distant sites have a dominant role in inducing expression of the cluster of globin genes. Within their domain of influence there are several genes that are expressed at particular stages of development. It is envisaged that specific factors, probably proteins, are then able to act upon the regulatory elements of the specific genes to induce expression of the individual genes at the appropriate time. It seems very likely that very high levels of expression of different genes could be achieved in bone marrow by transfer of a fusion gene containing the dominant and specific regulatory elements of the globin gene. This gene family is the only one for which such dominant elements have been revealed and it remains to be determined whether or not there are others. The existence of such elements for the cell type of interest would be of enormous benefit for those seeking to exploit gene transfer.

Expression of transgenes

An additional, fundamental observation underlying many applications of gene transfer is that production of a protein in a particular, novel manner can often be achieved by fusion of the regulatory sequences from one gene to the DNA sequences that encode the protein of interest. When the 205 base pair regulatory region of elastase was fused to the coding sequences for human growth hormone, the acinar cells synthesized growth hormone (Ornitz, Palmiter, Hammer, Brinster, Swift and MacDonald, 1985). Growth hormone has been produced in the liver of farm animals by fusion of the regulatory sequences of a gene that is expressed particularly in the liver, metallothionein, to the structural sequences for a growth hormone gene (Pursel, Miller, Bolt, Hammer, Palmiter and Brinster, 1989). In an analogous manner, a human protein that is usually produced in the liver, is being produced in the milk of sheep (Clark, Brown, Harris, Lathe, McClenaghan, Prowse, Simons, Whitelaw and Wilmut, 1989). The regulatory sequences of the sheep milk protein β-lactoglobulin have been fused to the structural sequences of the human gene. This fusion gene was introduced into sheep and some secrete human protein in their milk.

There are several additional factors that are now known to influence the expression of transgenes. The most important are the effects of the site of integration and the presence of introns in the transgene. One consistent observation in the studies of transgenic animals is the variation between lines of animals carrying the same transgene (Palmiter and Brinster 1986 for an early review). In a recent review of experiments with transgenic pigs, the transgene was expressed in 55% of lines (26 of 47 lines carrying one of several different genes; Pursel *et al*, 1989). The proportion was not influenced by the number of copies of the gene in each cell (range 1 to more than 100). There is great variation in the concentration of hormone produced in animals carrying fusion genes containing the human growth hormone structural sequences. At birth the concentration varied from less than 10 to over 900 ng/ml (Hammer *et al*, 1985; Miller, Bolt, Pursel, Hammer, Pinkert, Palmiter and Brinster, 1989), while during the first six months of life a peak of 8,710 ng/ml was recorded (Miller *et al*, 1989).

Most mammalian genes that code for mRNA contain noncoding sequences interspersed within the coding region, that are known as introns. In some cases these are longer than the exons, the regions that are represented in the mRNA. As a result, some genes span several hundred kilobases. A comparison has been made of the production of growth hormone in transgenic mice from genes with and without introns (Brintster *et al*, 1988). Regulatory sequences from mouse metallothionein were linked to rat growth hormone coding sequences with or without introns. The presence of introns had two effects upon the pattern of expression. First, the transgene containing introns was expressed in seven of nine mice compared with four of 20 of those without introns. Second, accumulation of mRNA from the gene without introns was 1% of the level with introns. A similar difference was observed with several other genes. The apparent requirement for introns poses major problems for the exploitation of gene transfer. Many genes are larger than the present limit to the size of gene that it is possible to transfer by direct injection and transfer of genes without introns had been seen as a means of overcoming this problem. Clearly a different solution must be found. There is very little information available at present on the role of introns or the effect of a small number of introns. It may be possible to prepare genes that contain a proportion of the introns, but which are still within the size range that can be transferred. The introns may be important because they contain binding sites for the nucleoskeleton and it may be possible to design shorter segments that contain these sites and are small enough to be transferred. There is a need for fundamental knowledge concerning the regulation of gene structure and function to provide a solution to these problems.

POTENTIAL APPLICATION

In considering the use of gene transfer it is necessary to:

- Identify a protein that it would be useful to produce in a novel situation
- Clone the gene
- Select regulatory sequences appropriate for the pattern of tissue specific expression that is required
- Clone that gene and identify the regulatory sequences
- Create the fusion gene and study its expression in a model system, such as a tissue culture cell or mice
- Transfer the gene to the species of interest.

Many of these stages involve only the routine application of the techniques of molecular biology or reproductive physiology. By contrast, the selection of suitable proteins for production in a novel situation and of effective regulatory mechanisms are very difficult.

The fibre content of forage in developing countries is often very high and a significant increase in productivity could be obtained if their digestion could be increased. There are three approaches to this problem. First, chemical treatments have been developed to modify the composition of the food before consumption (Ørskov, this volume). These are effective, but as they can only be applied to conserved food their use in many rural situations is limited. Fibre digestion is achieved by enzymes released by microorganisms in the digestive tract and the other two routes to increase efficiency involve genetic manipulation to induce the production of such enzymes by microorganisms, that would be placed in the digestive tract of livestock, or by transgenic livestock. There are advantages and disadvantages to each of these approaches.

Recombinant DNA techniques applied to microorganisms can be expected to be successful, although work with rumen organisms is difficult (Teather, 1985; Hespell, 1987), but there are two causes for concern. First, there is the need for caution in releasing recombinant microorganisms into the environment. Second, there is very great selection pressure within the rumen and it may be necessary to reinoculate the animal with the recombinant organism from time to time. While this is of great benefit to the company selling the product, there are practical and financial problems in such repeated applications in developing countries.

The studies of the elastase gene already discussed provide an example of the way in which this problem could be approached in transgenic animals. A short segment of the flanking DNA of this gene is capable of directing tissue specific expression to the acinar cells of the pancreas (Ornitz *et al*, 1985). This sequence could be used to introduce additional enzymes to the intestine and a project to study this approach in mice is in progress (Hazlewood, Mann and Gilbert, 1989). Once the principle is established, there are several stages in considering the production of enzymes in transgenic livestock. First, the selection of suitable enzymes, second the identification of the most appropriate site for production, having in mind the pH optimum of the enzyme and the potential effects of the enzyme on microorganisms in that region, and third the cloning of a gene that is expressed in a tissue specific manner in that tissue to provide regulatory sequences. There is a need for study of gene expression in the rumen in order to obtain suitable regulatory sequences.

There are several factors to have in mind when considering the use of gene transfer in this situation. Gene transfer in livestock is extremely expensive and if possible it would be wise to assess the effect of the protein by administration in the appropriate site. Once achieved the change is permanent and can be dispersed readily by conventional breeding or artificial insemination. As the effects of the gene may vary in different breeds of livestock a careful choice of animal should be made before beginning the project. The release of transgenic livestock should be under regulation, but is intrinsically less dangerous than release of recombinant microorganisms as they will only affect their own species and they can be identified and contained or destroyed if necessary.

In view of the great costs involved and the demand for resources for other applications it would be wasteful for individual developing countries to invest large sums in their own projects. Rather, this would be a prime area for international cooperation. When appropriate, a number of centres could be started to establish the expertise necessary not only for gene transfer, but also for other uses of embryo transfer and manipulation. Such centres of excellence could serve as sources of skilled personnel and places of contact with scientists from other countries. They could also be the site for production of elite animals in breeding schemes which might ultimately use embryo transfer (McGuirk, 1989). They might also attract funds from the international bodies. In view of the differences in climate, breed of livestock and political outlook, such a centre might be necessary in each region. It would be a pity to squander resources because of national pride.

CONCLUSIONS

The techniques of gene transfer are very new and crude, but great improvements can be expected. In time it may be possible to modify endogenous genes as well as transfer genes in a more precise and effective manner. These are just some of the new methods of embryo manipulation that are now being developed (Wilmut and Smith, 1988). Present knowledge of gene structure and function is limited, but growing rapidly. Similarly, our understanding of the genes that govern animal performance is meagre. Experience has shown that the efficient application of new techniques, such as artificial insemination or embryo transfer, does not occur immediately. In these circumstances it seems very likely that the best potential applications for gene transfer in any environment have yet to be conceived, and this seems particularly likely to be true for the developing countries.

REFERENCES

Beddington, R.S.P. and Robertson, E.J. (1989). An assessment of the development potential of embryonic stem cells in the midgestation mouse embryo. *Development,* **105**, 733–737.

Biery, K.A., Bondioli, K.R. and De Mayo, F.J. (1988). Gene transfer by pro-nuclear injection in the bovine. *Theriogenology,* **29**, 224 (Abstr.).

Bradley, A., Evans, M., Kaufman, M.H. and Robertson E. (1984). Formation of germ-line chimaeras from embryo-derived teratocarcinoma cell lines. *Nature, London,* **309**, 255–256.

Brinster, R.L., Chen, H.Y., Trumbauer, M.E., Yagle, M.K. and Palmiter, R.D. (1985). Factors affecting the efficiency of introducing foreign DNA into mice by microinjecting eggs. *Proceedings of the National Academy of Science, USA,* **82**, 4438–4442.

Brinster, R.L., Allen, J.M., Behringer, R.B., Gelinas, R.E. and Palmiter, R.D. (1988). Introns increase transcriptional efficiency in transgenic mice. *Proceedings of the National Academy of Science,* **85**, 836–840.

Clark, A.J. Bessos, H., Bishop, J.O., Brown, P., Harris, S., Lathe, R., McClenaghan, M., Prowse, C., Simons, J.P., Whitelaw, C.B.A. and Wilmut, I. (1989). Expression of human anti-hemophilic factor IX in the milk of transgenic sheep. *Biotechnology,* **7**, 487–492.

Evans, M.J. and Kaufman, M.H. (1981). Establishment in culture of pluripotential cells from mouse embryos. *Nature, London,* **292**, 154–156.

Gordon, J.W., Scangos, G.A., Plotkin, D., Barbosa, J.A. and Ruddle, F.H. (1980). Genetic transformation of mouse embryos by microinjection of purified DNA. *Proceedings of the National Academy of Science, USA,* **77**, 77380–77384.

Grosveld, F., Assendelft, G.B. van Greaves, D.R. and Kollias, G. (1987). Position independent, high level expression of the human beta-globin gene in transgenic mice. *Cell,* **51**, 975–985.

Hammer, R.E., Pursel, V.G., Rexroad, C.E. Jr., Wall, R.J., Bolt, D.J., Ebert, K.M., Palmiter, R.D. and Brinster, R.L. (1985). Production of trangenic rabbits, sheep and pigs by microinjection. *Nature, London,* **315**, 680–683.

Hatzopoulos, A.K., Schlokat, U. and Gruss, P. (1988). Enhancers and other *cis*-acting regulatory sequences. *Transcription and Splicing* (eds. B.D. Hames and D.M. Glover), pp. 43–36. IRL Press, Oxford.

Hazlewood, G., Mann, S. and Gilbert, H. (1989). Improving forage digestion by genetic engineering. *AFRC News Royal Show Supplement,* pp.12–13.

Hespell, R.B. (1987). Biotechnology and modifications of the rumen microbial ecosystem. *Proceedings of the Nutrition Society,* **46**, 407–413.

Hooper, M.L., Hardy, K., Handyside, A., Hunter, S. and Monk, M. (1987). HPRT-deficient (Lesch-Nyhan) embryos derived from the germline colonization by culture cells. *Nature,* **326**, 292–295.

La Thangue, N.B. and Rigby, P.W.J. (1988). Transacting protein factors and the regulation of eukaryotic transcription. *Transcription and Splicing,* (eds. B.D. Hames and D.M. Glover), pp. 1–42. IRL Press, Oxford.

Lu, K.H., Gordon, I. Gallagher, M. and McGovern, H. (1987). Pregnancy established in cattle by transfer of embryos derived from *in vitro* fertilization of oocytes matured *in vitro. Veterinary Record,* **121**, 259–260.

Lu, K.H., Gordon, I., McGovern, H. and Gallagher, M. (1988). Production of cattle embryos by *in vitro* maturation and fertilization of follicular oocytes and their subsequent culture in sheep. *Theriogenology,* **29**, 272 (Abs.).

Jaehner, D., Kirsten, H., Mulligan, R. and Jaenische, R. (1985). Insertion of the bacterial gpt gene into the germ line of mice by retroviral infection. *Proceedings of the National Academy of Science, USA,* **82**, 6927–6931.

Joyner, A.L., Skarnes, W.C. and Rossant, J. (1989). Production of a mutation in mouse *En-2* gene by homologous recombination in embryonic stem cells. *Nature,* **338**, 153–156.

Lavitrano, M., Camaioni, A. Fazio, V.M., Dolci, S., Farace, M.G. and Spadafora, C. (1989). Sperm cells as vectors for introducing foreign DNA into eggs: genetic transformation of mice. *Cell,* **57**, 717–723.

Lovell-Badge, R.H., Bygrave, A.E., Bradley, A., Robertson, E., Evans, M.J. and Cheah, K.S.E. (1985). Transformation of embryonic stem cells with the human type-II collagen gene and its expression in chimeric mice. *Cold Spring Harbor Symposium on Quantitative Biology,* **50**, 707–711.

Marx, J.L. (1988). Cloning in sheep and cattle embryos. *Science,* **239**, 463–464.

McGuirk, B. (1989). The relevance of MOET programmes to developing countries. *Theriogenology,* **31**, 29–40.

Miller, K.F., Bolt, D.J., Pursel, V.G., Hammer, R.E., Pinkert, C.A., Palmiter, R.D. and Brinster, R.L. (1989). Expression of human or bovine growth hormone gene with mouse metallotionein I promoter in transgenic swine alters the secretion of porcine growth hormone and insulin-like growth factor-1. *Journal of Endocrinology* (in press).

Ornitz, D.M., Palmiter, R.D., Hammer, R.E, Brinster, R.L., Swift, G.H. and MacDonald, R.J. (1985). Specific expression of an elastase-human growth hormone fusion gene in pancreatic acinar cells of trangenic mice. *Nature, London,* **313**, 600–603.

Ørskov, E.R. and Flint, H.J. (1991). Manipulation of rumen microbes or feed resources as methods of improving feed utilization. In *The Application of Biotechnology in Developing Countries* (ed. A.G. Hunter), pp. 123–138. Centre for Tropical Veterinary Medicine, University of Edinburgh.

Palmiter, R.D. and Brinster, R.L. (1986). Germline transformation of mice. *Annual Review of Genetics,* **20**, 465–499.

Parrish, J.J., Susko-Parrish, J., Leibfried-Rutledge, M.L., Critser, E.S., Eyestone, W.H. and First, N.L. (1986). Bovine *in vitro* fertilization with frozen thawed semen. *Theriogenology,* **25**, 591–600.

Pursel, V.G., Miller, K.F., Bolt, D.J., Hammer, R.E., Palmiter, R.D. and Brinster, R.L. (1989). Insertion of growth hormone genes into pig embryos. *Biotechnology in Growth Regulation* (eds. R.B. Heap, C.G. Prosser and G.E. Lamming), pp. 181–188. Butterworths, London.

Saiki, R.K., Gefland, D.H., Stoffel, S., Scharf, S.J., Higughi, R., Horn, G.T., Mullis, K.B. and Erlich, H.A. (1988). Primer-directed enzymatic amplification of DNA with a thermostable DNA polymerase. *Science,* **239**, 487–491.

Smith, A.J. and Daborn, C. (1991). Constraints to animal production and health in the tropics. In *The Application of Biotechnology in Developing Countries* (ed. A.G. Hunter), pp. 2–18. Centre for Tropical Veterinary Medicine, University of Edinburgh.

Simons, J.P., Wilmut, I., Clark, A.J., Archibald, A.L., Bishop, J.O. and Lathe, R. (1988). Gene transfer into sheep. *Biotechnology,* **6**, 179–183.

Smith, L.C. and Wilmut, I. (1989). Influence of nuclear and cytoplasmic activity on the development *in vivo* of sheep embryos after nuclear transfer. *Biological Reproduction,* **40**, 1027–1035.

Staigmiller, R.B. and Moor, R.M. (1984). Competence of ovine oocysts matured outside the follicle. *Gamete Research,* **9**, 221–229.

Swift, G.H., Hammer, R.E., MacDonald, R.J. and Brinster, R.L. (1984). Tissue specific expression of the rat pancreatic elastase I gene in transgenic mice. *Cell,* **38**, 639–646.

Teather, R.M. (1985). Application of gene manipulation to rumen microflora. *Canadian Journal of Animal Science,* **65**, 563–574.

Varmus, H. (1988). Retroviruses. *Science,* **240**, 1427–1435.

Wall, R.J., Pursel, V.G., Hammer, R.E. and Brinster, R.L. (1985). Development of porcine ova that were centrifuged to permit visualization of pronuclei and nuclei. *Biology of Reproduction,* **32**, 645–651.

Wilmut, I. and Smith, L.C. (1988). Biotechnology and the bovine embryo: at present and in the future. *Proceedings of the 4th Scientific Meeting European Embryo Transfer Association,* pp. 19–31. Foundation Marcel Merieux, Lyons.

Zimmer, A. and Gruss, P. (1989). Production of chimaeric mice containing embryonic stem (ES) cells carrying a homeobox *Hoxl-1* allele mutated by homologus recombination. *Nature,* **338**, 150–153.

DISCUSSION OF SESSIONS 1 AND 2

HASNAIN, YEMEN ARAB REPUBLIC *Are the constraints in Dr. Smith's paper listed in order of priority?*

SMITH No. The relative importance of the various constraints will vary from region to region and possibly change with time.

SSENYONGA, UGANDA *Would Dr. Turton comment on the continuous use of vectors (e.g. vaccinia viruses) in vaccines as there is concern that repeated injections can immunize animals against the vectors?*

TURTON Vaccinia DNA is not altered by insertion of foreign antigen in recombinant vaccinia vaccines and thus both the vaccinia and insertion components are immunogenic. It seems unlikely, however, that vaccinia antibodies will interfere with the inserted antigen DNA at primary vaccination or revaccination.

TEALE, KENYA Bacteria are potentially important vectors of immunogenic components of vaccines e.g. *Salmonella* spp.

WIDJI WIDODO, EAST JAVA, INDONESIA *Would Dr. Hodges like to comment on the role of blood typing in breeding with imported purebred cattle?*

HODGES The possible genetic relationships between blood constituents and performance (for growth or milk) have been extensively researched without success. That's why performance recording is still the basis of identifying genetic merit.

RASTOGI, TRINIDAD AND TOBAGO *Could Dr. Hodges explain how his diagram showed that the open nucleus herd overcomes the effect of inbreeding.*

HODGES The diagram showed an 'open' system which will avoid inbreeding through continuous introduction of new genes from two sources. One is the ongoing search for elite females from the base population for a temporary stay in the nucleus herd. The second is the use of semen in the nucleus herd from bulls tested in other populations.

RANGNEKAR, INDIA *The open nucleus herd approach may be difficult to operate as an alternative to field recording and progeny testing for improvement of livestock. Animals would have to be selected for the herd, and record keeping and farmer cooperation would be necessary. A combination of field progeny testing and the open nucleus herd approach might be tried.*

HODGES If the infrastructure in the field will support progeny testing, then of course it should be used in association with an open nucleus breeding system (ONBS). In the absence of an adequate infrastructure, it is likely to be more successful to use ONBS where activities can be focussed in one location, rather than trying to establish a field testing programme. In the absence of an organized testing programme, then the owner's own knowledge of the performance of his females can be used to identify the superior individuals to bring into the nucleus herd temporarily. Their performance can be verified there. Because the owner loans rather than sells his best cows to the nucleus herd, he is discouraged from promoting poor performers.

ADEBAMBO, NIGERIA *Will FAO be in a position to help animal breeders in the application of an ONBS?*

HODGES The establishment of an ONBS with all facilities new will be very expensive, but many developing countries have Ministry of Agriculture livestock stations with facilities which could be adapted. No general promises can be made, but FAO is willing to consider applications from governments for essential new equipment if national facilities are made available and if the government proposals can be seen to benefit general animal populations. We are also running training courses on ONBS for animal breeders and extension workers and will shortly publish an operating manual.

TEALE, KENYA *Are there any comments on the use of markers, particularly DNA polymorphisms, in breed improvement?*

WOOLLIAMS If we could identify on the DNA all genes affecting a quantitative trait and their impact on performance, we would certainly make better progress! The use of markers is an approximation to this but its efficacy depends heavily on the existence of genes of significant effect and our ability to detect them using linkage maps. As a result it is unlikely that their usage will be feasible until complete genome maps of the species concerned can be constructed to a degree of coverage that depends on the size of gene effects that we wish to detect. The efficient construction of the genome maps currently entails the availability of genetically distinct populations and many man-years of work.

WIDJI WIDODO, EAST JAVA, INDONESIA *With regard to selection programmes, could you comment on the relation between progress and generation interval?*

WOOLLIAMS Maximum selection progress is an optimum compromise between how much information you can obtain on the breeding value of an animal (the more the better) and how long you take to get it (the quicker the better). This compromise will depend very much on the species, recording facilities and selection objectives.

WANAPAT, THAILAND *Which forms of biotechnology could be practised by farmers who own draught animals?*

PEARSON I don't think draught animal farmers themselves would have much use for the specialised techniques involved, but they can benefit from the advances of biotechnology in a practical way by making use of improved feed crops, better health care, vaccines and breeding schemes.

RANGNEKAR, INDIA *Farmers have been selecting for size, speed and stronger hooves, especially for hard soils or paddy growing areas. Crossing between indigenous breeds for a draught animal with strength and speed has also been common.*

Is there a case for biotechnological intervention in draught animals in India?

PEARSON I don't believe it should be the case of the biotechnologist intervening, rather the other way round. Livestock officers and animal scientists should be aware of what biotechnologists are doing and should themselves consider which biotechnological techniques and advances can be applied to their particular farming systems.

SSENYONGA, UGANDA *You mentioned an experiment in buffalo in Nepal. Has a similar experiment been done at low altitude?*

PEARSON The experiment was done at 200 m which would be considered low in altitude.

AFOLAYAN, NIGERIA *Visual detection of heat is less efficient than physiological methods using milk progesterone which usually detect heats missed by farmers. It is hoped that a simple test to detect heat could be developed which could be used by farmers in developing countries.*

MACFARLANE I quite agree. The ELISA field kit for measuring milk progesterone levels is useful but quite expensive (U.S. $5.00 per test) and probably too sophisticated for the average small subsistence farmer. Research should be directed to develop a simple and cheap test, possibly identifying hormones (e.g. oestrogen) in urine by a simple colour change. Unlike the mare, however (Cuboni's test for urine oestrogens), oestrogen is not present in cows in a chemical form easy to identify.

MEPHAM, U.K. *What progress has been made in the production of transgenic animals secreting milk with reduced lactose content? What effects are envisaged in terms of milk yield, given that lactose is the major osmole of milk and thus the principal determinant of yield.*

WILMUT Although it is several years since this work was first proposed by Mercier, I am not aware of any groups actually carrying out the necessary work. The proposal was to use antisense RNA to reduce lactose production which might be expected to reduce milk volume.

RASTOGI, TRINIDAD AND TOBAGO *I wish to comment that it is essential to develop capabilities for genetic engineering for potential use in developing countries.*

WILMUT I agree that at some time each country or region should aim to establish this technology. The time should depend upon the development of other techniques e.g. artificial insemination, and use of vaccines etc.

SINGH, INDIA *What is your view regarding the priority of developing, for example, animal breeding, health care, and vaccines rather than genetic engineering?*

WILMUT There obviously is a priority for each country to establish some basic practices such as vaccinations, fencing and the necessary breeding programmes. Because of these priorities, it may be appropriate for regions to collaborate in the establishment of centres of excellence necessary for embryo transfer, embryo manipulation and gene transfer. These centres could carry out good projects themselves and act as a point of contact for developed countries. The appropriate time to start such work would vary depending on the prior establishment of other basic practices.

SMITH, U.K. Are there examples of transgenic work on tick-borne diseases?

WILMUT Not to my knowledge.

IRVIN, U.K. *What is known about the expression of transferred genes in the offspring of transgenic animals?*

WILMUT Inheritance of transgenes is usually quite normal but there are exceptions, particularly in transmission from the foundation generation. The gene should be passed to 50% of the offspring, but sometimes is not. Expression is the same in all generations. However, the effect of the gene may vary in different genetic backgrounds.

3.

ANIMAL PRODUCTION, NUTRITION AND PHYSIOLOGY

Chairmen: J.D. Oldham
School of Agriculture
Edinburgh

and

R.W. Matthewman
CTVM
Edinburgh

3.1

Biological Routes to Improved Digestibility of Animal Feeds

J.C. MASON, P.F.G. SIMS and P. BRODA*
Department of Biochemistry and Applied Molecular Biology
University of Manchester Institute of Science and Technology, Manchester
*To whom correspondence should be addressed

INTRODUCTION

Lignocellulose, a major component of animal feeds such as grasses, hay and straw, is a complex of three polymers, cellulose, hemicellulose and lignin. Its precise composition varies between species and varieties of plant, and also in its proportion of the total material during the life cycle of the plant. For example, during growth of ryegrass in the U.K. between April and September the lignocellulose content of the plant increases from 31% to 64% of dry matter (Waite and Gorrod, 1959). The three components constitute a complex that is of poor nutritional value, but because of the enormous quantities available it nevertheless represents a potentially valuable material for future biotechnological exploitation (Eggeling, 1983). Whereas cellulose can be degraded by microorganisms (for example in the ruminant gut, or in composts and silage) the hemicelluloses have an as yet undefined nutritional role. The lignin component is especially recalcitrant to microbial degradation and constitutes a physical barrier to the extraction and utilization of the other components.

The recalcitrance of lignin is a result of its unique structure; it is formed by a chemical polymerization of three aromatic monomers (coumaryl, coniferyl and sinapyl alcohols) to form an heterogeneous three dimensional polymer that lacks chirality. The predominant types of linkages between monomers are alpha and beta aryl ether bonds, but a large number of other bond types also exist (Higuchi, 1980). An organism that can remove a significant amount of lignin from lignocellulose must therefore be able to cleave a high proportion of the total number of bonds. The challenge to biotechnologists therefore is to develop microbial systems that will improve the digestibility of animal feeds by either wholly or partially degrading the lignocellulose, particularly the recalcitrant lignin component. To this end, our own research has involved studies on the nature of the substrate and its degradation products and on the biochemistry and molecular genetics of organisms, particularly the white rot fungus *Phanerochaete chrysosporium* and the actinomycete *Streptomyces cyaneus*, that are capable of degrading lignocellulose.

LIGNOCELLULOSE SUBSTRATES

Studies designed to screen for organisms that are capable of degrading and/or utilizing lignin have employed either synthetic or natural substrates. Synthetic model compounds of lignin include ethoxy and/or methoxy substituted phenols and aromatic alcohols joined together to form dimers either linked via an oxygen (ether bond) or directly through the beta group (Enoki, Goldsby and Gold, 1980; Enoki and Gold, 1982; Kirk, Nakatsubo and Reid, 1983; Nakatsubo, Kirk, Shimada and Higuchi, 1981; Kawai, Umezawa and Higuchi, 1985). Studies utilizing such model compounds have concentrated on the ability of organisms to cleave the dimer into monomers; most investigations have been with white-rot fungi. In an attempt to reflect the complexity of the lignin molecule, the degradation of model compounds of polymers obtained from the polymerization of radiolabelled aromatic alcohols (e.g. coniferyl alcohol; Connors, Sarkanen and McCarthy, 1980; Tanahashi and Higuchi, 1981; Tanahashi, Akoi and Higuchi, 1982) have also been investigated (Hammel, Kalyanaraman, and Kirk, 1986); the molecular weights of these compounds are in the range 2 to 10×10^3. These studies have been designed to measure the mineralization of such polymeric substrates to $^{14}CO_2$ during incubation with the organisms (Haider and Trojanowski, 1975; Trojanowski, Haider, and Sundman, 1977; Haider, Trojanowski and Sundman, 1978; Haider, Kern and Ludger, 1985; Kirk, Tien, Johnsrud and Eriksson, 1986). The use of synthetic rather than natural substrates (see below) for lignin degradation studies results in both advantages and disadvantages. Such relatively simple compounds lend themselves to accurate and technically straightforward measurement of conversion of the substrate to products; thus the enzymatically catalyzed reactions, while not without their complications (see discussion on peroxidases below), are at least susceptible to investigation. However, none of the synthetic substrates, although representing one or other of the structural aspects of lignin, can possibly reflect its true complexity in native lignocellulose.

Radiolabelled natural substrates have been used to overcome these shortcomings; these substrates have been prepared either from cereal grasses (e.g. wheat and barley) grown in the presence of [^{14}C] phenylalanine (McCarthy, MacDonald, Paterson and Broda, 1984; Mason, Birch and Broda, 1990), or [^{14}C] cinnamic acid (Benner, Maccubbin and Hodson, 1984), or by dipping cut stems of woody plants in a buffer containing [^{14}C] ferulic acid (Crawford and Crawford, 1978). In each case the radiolabelled acids provide a precursor for lignin biosynthesis. The removal of nonlignocellulose materials using inorganic and then organic solvents results in a lignocellulose substrate which contains 85% of the radioactivity in the lignin component of the complex, and is therefore sometimes referred to as [^{14}C lignin] lignocellulose (such determinations are based on the Klason definition of lignin, namely the material that is insoluble in 72% H_2SO_4; Effland, 1977). The proportion of [^{14}C] lignin may be improved to 90% by the removal of some residual proteinaceous material using proteases (Odier, Janin and Monties, 1981). The resulting substrates have a specific activity (approximately 10^3 dpm/mg) sufficient to allow the screening of organisms for the ability to degrade lignin (Phelan, Crawford and Pometto, 1979; Haider and Trojanowski, 1980; McCarthy and Broda, 1984; Agosin, Daudin and Odier, 1985). The use of such substrates has revealed two quite different actions: one is the solubilization of the [^{14}C] lignin, giving rise to soluble radiolabelled products in culture supernatants of actinomycetes (McCarthy and Broda, 1984; Mason, 1988; Mason, Richards, Zimmermann and Broda, 1988), and the other is the complete degradation of the [^{14}C] lignin to $^{14}CO_2$ as exhibited by cultures of *P. chrysosporium* (McCarthy, MacDonald, Paterson and Broda, 1984; Agosin, Daudin and Odier,1985).

Given the complexity of lignocellulose and indeed lignin itself, it is likely that both solubilization and degradation require that a number of enzymes act synergistically (see below). As a result of this synergism, factors affecting the composition of the lignocellulose substrate, such as plant maturity, will determine the contribution that each enzyme makes in the fate of lignin from lignocellulose. For example in a recent study (Mason, Birch and Broda, 1990) it was found that substrates derived from immature spring barley plants were particularly susceptible to solubilization of the lignocellulose by polysaccharidases from *P. chrysosporium* and *S. cyaneus*. Substrates derived from older but still immature crops resulted in lignocellulose material almost totally resistant to polysaccharidase actions but which is susceptible to lignocellulose solubilization by an as yet uncharacterized enzymic activity (see below). Fully mature crops were solubilized at comparatively very low levels by both organisms. Thus despite these complications the complementary use of natural and synthetic substrates has allowed the identification of efficient lignin-degrading organisms and then the resolution of some of the different activities involved in the degradation of lignocellulose in the natural state (for recent reviews see McCarthy, 1987; Kirk, 1987; Broda, Sims and Mason, 1989a).

WHITE-ROT FUNGI

The most studied organism involved in lignocellulose degradation is *P. chrysosporium*. It will only degrade lignin if it is depleted for carbon or nitrogen sources; since lignin contains no nitrogen, it is likely that the primary function of lignin solubilization and degradation is to allow the fungus to obtain previously inaccessible nutrients. Studies of the extracellular enzymes of *P. chrysosporium* (Tien and Kirk, 1983; Glenn, Morgan, Hayfield, Kuwahara and Gold, 1983) have resulted in the discovery of lignin peroxidases; these have the ability to cleave model dimers representative of some of the different bond types present in lignin if provided with exogenous H_2O_2. *P. chrysosporium* produces a number of such enzymes; all are glycosylated, contain a haem group and have a molecular weight of about 40K. The key catalytic reaction of these enzymes is the one-electron oxidation of aromatic nuclei, generating short-lived aryl cation radicals which are further modified by a number of reactions (Kirk 1987). Such radicals would then interact with the lignin polymer, resulting in its partial depolymerization. It has been shown that a peroxidase-type catalytic cycle is involved. The enzymes, now termed lignin peroxidases, convert the alcohol functional group of veratryl alcohol (the simplest compound that has structural similarities to the lignin structure) to an aldehyde. This conversion can be followed spectrophotometrically and has formed the basis of an assay specific for this family of enzymes. The situation has been complicated by the subsequent identification of a second class of enzymes, the manganese-dependent peroxidases, which also produce radical intermediates but do not oxidise veratryl alcohol (Glenn and Gold, 1985).

While the use of veratryl alcohol and model dimers as substrates have allowed the characterization and isolation of lignin peroxidases and the cloning of the corresponding genes (see below), evidence that these enzymes by themselves can degrade lignin itself is less strong (Kirk, 1987). Thus degradation of lignin has not been demonstrated using either isolated lignin peroxidases or crude extracellular mixtures of the enzymes that are secreted during the ligninolytic phase. An important objective is therefore to identify the full complement of components needed for degradation of lignin *in vitro*.

Efforts to fully understand lignin degradation by *P. chrysosporium* have also included studies on its molecular genetics. It has been shown that control of the ligninolytic system is likely to be mediated via cyclic adenosine monophosphate (CAMP) which is in turn regulated by adenylate cyclase (MacDonald, Paterson and Broda 1984, MacDonald, Ambler and Broda, 1985). It was also shown that the production of extracellular enzymes during the organism's ligninolytic phase was correlated with differences observed in mRNA populations extracted from primary and idiophase mycelia (Haylock, Liwicki and Broda, 1985). The hypothesis that ligninolytic activity is controlled at the level of transcription provided a rationale for the cloning of genes which encode proteins unique to the idiophase, and indeed this is exactly how our own study progressed.

Following partial restriction of genomic DNA and creation of a gene library with inserts of about 15 kilobases, 38 clones were identified as containing sequences that were expressed only during idiophase. These accounted for 1% of the total clones containing active genes (Raeder,

Thompson and Broda, 1987). Upon detailed analysis of the idiophase-specific clones using cross-hybridization studies they were assigned to 17 distinct classes. One of the classes (consisting of five clones) was of particular interest because the related sequences that they contained were expressed strongly during idiophase and because genetic mapping (Raeder and Broda, 1986) had located four of the clones to a single cluster unlinked to the fifth clone. Complete sequencing of one of these putative genes and partial sequencing of three others revealed considerable homology with a cDNA sequence of a lignin peroxidase identified in another strain of *P. chrysosporium* (Tien and Tu, 1987). It was concluded that a number of lignin peroxidase-related sequences had been isolated (Brown, Sims, Raeder and Broda, 1988). Genomic and/or cDNA sequences for lignin peroxidases from different strains of *P. chrysosporium* have now been determined by several different groups. Although all of the sequences show similarities at least three different cDNA sequences and six distinct genomic sequences have been identified. Five of the latter have been found in a single strain.

We have also studied cellulases from *P. chrysosporium*. Although cellulase activity can be induced during both primary growth and the idiophase, it is likely that cellulases play an important role in lignin degradation. Thus lignin is always found in intimate association with cellulose, as described above, and its degradation from within lignocellulose involves a poorly understood synergism of enzymic activities which almost certainly includes cellulases. Moreover, at least some of the H_2O_2 required by lignin peroxidases comes from the glucose that is derived from cellulose degradation. Recently we have isolated a clone which carries a gene, inducible with cellulose, that on the basis of its sequence encodes a 516 residue protein, with 54% homology to the exo-cellobiohydrolase I (CBHI) of *Trichoderma reesei* (Sims, James and Broda, 1988). We have isolated a second CBHI-like gene from *P. chrysosporium* and identified further distinct but closely related sequences (unpublished results). Thus, as in the case of the lignin peroxidase related sequences, *P. chrysosporium* appears to have a number of closely related sequences that could code for cellulases. The recent demonstration that *P. chrysosporium* has extensive restriction fragment length polymorphisms (RFLPs) has been exploited to construct a genetic map (Broda, Birch, Brown, James, Raeder, Thompson and Sims, 1989b), and has allowed the mapping of the lignin peroxidase-related and cellulase genes.

ACTINOMYCETE BACTERIA

There have also been studies on the role of actinomycete bacteria in lignocellulose biodegradation. Actinomycetes, which have the same invasive habit as fungi, are common in decaying lignocellulose systems such as compost. Early studies (Phelan *et al*, 1979) showed that a *Streptomyces* strain, in addition to being able to degrade the cellulose from lignocellulose and thereby contributing to a substantial weight loss of the substrate, is also able to degrade lignin, although to a much lesser extent. We began a research programme by screening candidate actinomyces for ligninolytic activity (McCarthy and Broda, 1984). The use of isolation media incorporating lignocellulose and lignin related phenolic compounds allowed the isolation of candidate strains. Organisms of several genera, *Streptomyces, Micromonospora, Thermomonospora* and *Actinomadura,* were identified as being able to grow on grass lignocellulose (McCarthy and Broda, 1984). Whereas in liquid cultures of *P. chrysosporium* 30–40% of the [^{14}C] lignocellulose was converted to $^{14}CO_2$, the levels achieved by actinomycetes were much lower (typically 10%, McCarthy and Broda, 1984). However, in addition, some strains solubilize up to 30% of the total lignin content; that part which is not mineralized to CO_2 accumulates in the supernatant of cultures, and may represent an end product of lignin degradation (Phelan *et al*, 1979; Antai and Crawford, 1981; Crawford, Barder, Pometto and Crawford, 1982; McCarthy and Broda, 1984; McCarthy, Paterson and Broda, 1986; Mason, 1988).

This soluble product has been termed acid precipitable polymeric lignin or APPL (Crawford, Pometto and Crawford, 1983; Pometto and Crawford, 1986) because it is insoluble when the pH of the medium is lowered. It has been partially characterized using high performance liquid chromatography (HPLC) (Borgmeyer and Crawford, 1985; Mason, 1988) and nuclear magnetic resonance (NMR) spectroscopy (McCarthy *et al*, 1986). HPLC analysis revealed that APPL is a mixture of high molecular weight components (1 to 3×10^5) and that the proportions and size distribution of the APPL products are specific for each organism cultured on ball milled straw (Mason, 1988). The production is accompanied by an increase in the levels of extracellular proteins during growth (Mason *et al*, 1988).

Preparations of cell-free supernatants are able to solubilize amounts of ^{14}C-lignocellulose (up to 30%) similar to those solubilized by the cultures from which they were derived (McCarthy *et al*, 1986; Mason *et al*, 1988). Using partially purified extracellular enzymes from *Streptomyces cyaneus*, the proteins were further purified on gel filtration columns. Fractions of the eluate from columns were tested for their enzymic activities using cellulose-azure, xylan and ^{14}C labelled lignocellulose as substrates (Figure 1). In the case of lignocellulose that had not been pretreated with polysaccharidases during its preparation, the ability to solubilize lignin from lignocellulose was mainly due to the activities of xylanases (molecular weights 100K and 45K), a cellulase (molecular weight 30K) and a previously unidentified enzymic activity (molecular weight 20K). With preparations of substrate that had been exhaustively pretreated with polysaccharidases the solubilizing activity was associated principally with the 20K enzyme (Mason *et al*, 1988).

FUTURE DEVELOPMENTS AND AVENUES FOR BIOTECHNOLOGICAL EXPLOITATION

During the earlier studies on lignin biodegradation there was an understandable desire on the part of researchers for a simple explanation of the process and the expectation that there might be a simple route to biotechnological

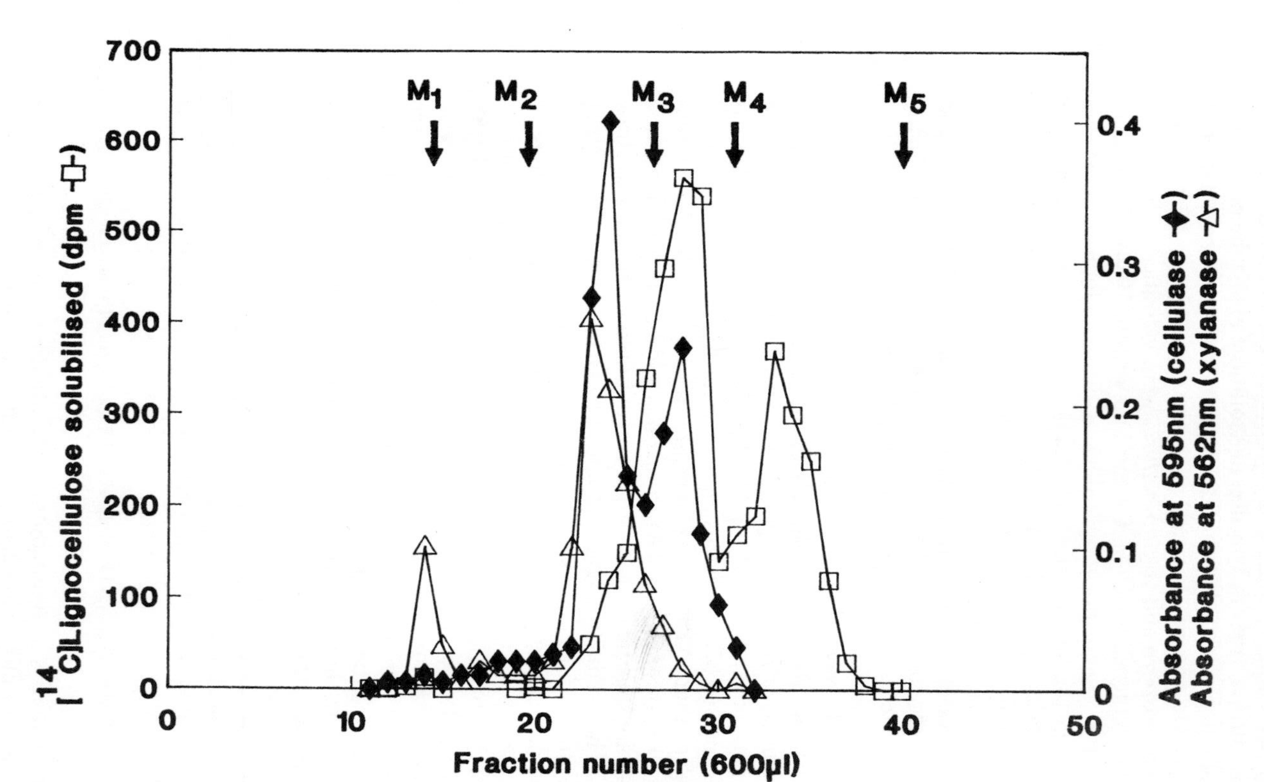

Fig. 1 *Gel filtration, on columns of Superose 12 (Pharmacia), of extracellular proteins from cultures of* Streptomyces cyaneus *grown on media containing 0.5% (w/v) ball-milled straw (Mason* et al*, 1988). Radioactivity solubilized as a result of incubating*[14] *C-labelled lignocellulose with aliquots of the eluate is represented by the symbols (□), cellulose activity (cellulose-azure method, Rinderknecht Wilding and Haverback, 1967) is represented by the symbols (◆) and xylanase activity (measurement of reducing sugars, Gruninger and Fiechter, 1986; Mopper and Gindler, 1973; Sinner and Puls, 1978) is represented by the symbols (△). The column was equilibrated with buffer, 0.1M (Tris/HC1 pH 7.0 and was calibrated with the molecular weight markers M1, Blue Dextran; M2, albumin molecular weight 66K; M3, carbonic anydrase molecular weight 29K; M4, chymotrypsinogen molecular weight 25K; M5, cytochrome C molecular weight 12K*

exploitation. However, as has been described above, the complex chemical nature of lignocellulose has meant that a wide variety of approaches have been needed for us to achieve our present understanding. Thus, studies have utilized various organisms and mutants (e.g. brown-rot fungi, white-rot fungi and actinomycetes), synthetic and natural substrates (the latter from both grasses and woody plants) and have screened for a range of enzymic activities (such as cellulases, xylanases, and lignin peroxidase, solubilizing and degradation activities on lignin). The result has been a bewildering array of data which, although generally consistent within particular studies, have nevertheless been very difficult to relate to each other.

The parallel studies of lignin degradation with the white-rot fungi and actinomycetes have provided interesting comparisons and suggested avenues of exploitation utilizing the important differences that exist between lignin degradation mediated by these organisms. The degradation of lignin, as measured by the production of $^{14}CO_2$, is more complete when *P. chrysosporium* is used. If the aim is the complete destruction of the lignin component of lignocellulose then the choice of a fungal system would seem obvious. However, as described above, such degradation of lignin only occurs during the idiophase, following severe nitrogen and carbon depletion. In contrast, with actinomycetes lignin solubilization occurs during primary growth and has no requirement for the presence of H_2O_2; thus although lignin degradation may be more limited, it may have the advantage in making available solubilized products of lignin degradation (APPL) rather than its total destruction to CO_2. Moreover, it may be of significance that the products of lignin solubilization are different for each of the actinomycetes that have been tested.

Irrespective of the organism under study it is evident that lignocellulose solubilization and degradation are due to synergistic enzymic activities. This gives rise to the possibility of emphasizing particular aspects of the overall reaction for biotechnological exploitation. Thus, the rate and extent of the lignocellulose degradation might be manipulated either by strain improvement (followed by use of the organism itself or total extracellular protein preparations), or by purification of the extracellular enzymes, allowing mixtures containing different proportions of the components to be formulated for optimum action on particular lignocellulose substrates. Strain improvement of organisms may be achieved both by genetic crosses (in the case of *P. chrysosporium*) and by using *in vitro* genetic manipulation methods. However, a reliable transformation system is a prerequisite for the reintroduction of engineered DNA sequences. In the case of *P. chrysosporium* we have sought to develop systems that utilize phleomycin resistance, tryptophan biosynthesis and nitrate reductase as selectable markers.

Establishment of such a transformation system might allow the *in vitro* construction of strains able to degrade lignin during primary growth rather than only when severely depleted for nitrogen and carbon. A number of strains, obtained by mutagenesis or genetic crosses in which the expression of lignin peroxidases and cellulase are increased or decreased have already been identified. One class of mutants that would be of immediate interest would be lignin degraders that are cellulase-negative since an obvious requirement in seeking to improve the nutritional value of animal feedstuffs is to degrade the lignin while sparing the cellulose component of lignocellulose. The ruminant gut is well-equipped with micro-organisms that can convert the cellulose component, freed from lignocellulose, to glucose. In this case the energy source for the lignin degrading organisms would be provided by the utilization of the hemicellulose components.

The progress made in this area means that we can now begin to assemble a specification for a useful organism to exploit particular lignocellulose resources. One objective of particular relevance to the U.K. is to maximize the efficiency of the use of silage as an animal feedstuff. In this case, one can envisage an organism that degrades lignin and hemicellulose efficiently but has no activity against cellulose, with the ability to grow in the low pH and high temperature commonly encountered in silage. Alternatively, one might use enzyme preparations from such an organism grown under industrial fermentation conditions. However, it is still too early to predict which group of micro-organisms e.g. white-rot fungi or actinomycetes, will produce the best candidate for exploitation in this manner.

REFERENCES

Agosin, E., Daudin, J.J. and Odier, E. (1985). Screening of white-rot fungi on (^{14}C) lignin-labelled and (^{14}C) whole-labelled wheat straw. *Applied Microbiology and Biotechnology*, **21**, 6811–6817.

Antai, S.P. and Crawford, D.L. (1981). Degradation of softwood, hardwood and grass lignocelluloses by two *Streptomyces* strains. *Applied and Environmental Microbiology*, **42**, 378–380.

Benner, R., Maccubbin, A.E. and Hodson, R.E. (1984). Preparation, characterization and microbial degradation of specifically radio-labelled ^{14}C-lignocelluloses from marine and freshwater macrophytes. *Applied and Environmental Microbiology*, **47**, 998–1004.

Borgmeyer, J.R. and Crawford, D.L. (1985). Production and characterization of polymeric lignin degradation intermediates from two different *Streptomyces* spp. *Applied and Environmental Microbiology*, **49**, 273–278.

Broda, P., Sims, P.F.G. and Mason, J.C. (1989a). Lignin biodegradation: a molecular biological approach. In: *Essays in Biochemistry 24* (eds. R.D. Marshall, and K.F. Tipton), pp. 82–114. Academic Press.

Broda, P., Birch, O., Brown, A., James, C., Raeder, U., Thompson, W. and Sims, P.F.G. (1989b). The genetics of *Phanerochaete chrysosporium*: A model for strain improvement? In: *Enzyme Systems for Lignocellulose Degradation* (ed. M.P. Coughlan), pp. 121–134. Elsevier Science Publishers Ltd.

Brown, A., Sims, P.F.G., Raeder, U. and Broda, P. (1988). Multiple ligninase genes from *Phanerochaete chrysosporium*. *Gene*, **73**, 77–85.

Connors, W.J., Sarkanen, S. and McCarthy, J.L. (1980). Gel chromatography and association complexes of lignin. *Holzforschung*, **34**, 80–85.

Crawford, R.L. and Crawford, D.L. (1978). Radioisotopic methods for the study of lignin biodegradation. *Developments in Industrial Microbiology*, **19**, 35–49.

Crawford, D.L., Barder, M.J., Pometto, III, A.L. and Crawford, R.L. (1982). Chemistry of softwood lignin degradation by *Streptomyces viridosporus*. *Archives of Microbiology*, **131**, 140–145.

Crawford, D.L., Pometto III, A.L. and Crawford, R.L. (1983). Lignin degradation by *Streptomyces viridosporus*: isolation and characterization of a new polymeric lignin degradation intermediate. *Applied and Environmental Microbiology*, **45**, 898–904.

Eggeling, L. (1983). Lignin – an exceptional biopolymer ... and a rich resource? *Trends in Biotechnology*, **1**, sp. 123–127.

Effland, M.J. (1977). Modified procedure to determine acid-insoluble lignin in wood and pulp. *TAPPI*, **60**, 143–144.

Enoki, A. and Gold, M. (1982). Degradation of the diarylpropane lignin model compounds 1-(3',4'-diethoxyphenyl)-1-,3-dihydroxy-2-(4"-methoxyphenyl)-propane and derivatives by the basidiomycete *Phanerochaete chrysosporium*. *Archives of Microbiology*, **132**, 123–130.

Enoki, A., Goldsby, G.P. and Gold, M. (1980). Metabolism of the lignin model compound verarylglycerol-β-guaiacyl ether and 4-ethoxy-3-methoxyphenol-glycerol-β-guaiacyl ether by *Phanerochaete chrysosporium*. *Archives of Microbiology*, **125**, 227–232.

Glenn, J.K. and Gold, M.H. (1985). Purification and characterization of an extracellular Mn(II)-dependent peroxidase from the lignin-degrading basidiomycete *Phanerochaete chrysosporium*. *Archives of Biochemistry Biophysics*, **242**, 329–241.

Glenn, J.K., Morgan, M.A., Hayfield, M.B., Kuwahara, M. and Gold, M.H. (1983). An extracellular H_2O_2 requiring enzyme preparation involved in lignin biodegradation by the white-rot basiodiomycete *Phanerochaete chrysosporium*. *Biochemical Biophysical Research Communications*, **114**, 1077–1083.

Gruninger, H. and Fiechter, A. (1986). A novel highly thermostable D-xylanase. *Enzymes and Microbial Technology*, **8**, 309–314.

Haider, K. and Trojanowski, J. (1975). Decomposition of specifically ^{14}C-labelled phenols and dehydropolymers of coniferyl alcohol as models for lignin degradation by soft and white rot fungi. *Archives of Microbiology*, **105**, 33–41.

Haider, K., Trojanowski, J. and Sundman, V. (1978). Screening for lignin degrading bacteria by means of ^{14}C-labelled lignins. *Archives of Microbiology*, **119**, 103–106.

Haider, K. and Trojanowski, J. (1980). A comparison of the degradation of ^{14}C-labelled DHP and cornstalk lignins by micro and macrofungi and by bacteria. In: *Lignin Biodegradation: Microbiology, Chemistry and Potential Applications*, **1** (eds. T.K. Kirk, T. Higuchi, and H.M. Chang), pp. 111–134. CRC Press.

Haider, K., Kern, H.W. and Ludger, E. (1985). Intermediate steps of microbial lignin degradation as elucidated by ^{13}C NMR spectroscopy of specifically ^{13}C-enriched DHP-lignins. *Holzforschung,* **39**, 23–32.

Hammel, K.E., Kalyanaraman, B. and Kirk, T.K. (1986). Oxidation of polycyclic aromatic hydrocarbons and dibenzo p-dioxins by *Phanerochaete chrysosporium* ligninase. *Journal of Biological Chemistry,* **261**, 16940–16952.

Haylock, R.A., Liwicki, R. and Broda, P. (1985). The isolation of mRNA from the basidiomycete fungi *Phanerochaete chrysosporium* and *Coprinus cinereus* and its *in vitro* translation. *Journal of Microbiology Methods,* **41**, 55–62.

Higuchi, T. (1980). Lignin structure and morphological distribution in plant cell walls. In: *Lignin Biodegradation: Microbiology, Chemistry and Potential Applications,* **1**, (eds. T.K. Kirk, T. Higuchi and M.M. Chang), pp. 1–20. CRC Press.

Kawai, S., Umezawa, A. and Higuchi, T. (1985). Metabolism of a non-phenolic-0-4 lignin substructure model compound by *Coriolus versicolor. Agricultural and Biological Chemistry,* **49**, 2325–2330.

Kirk, T.K. (1987). Lignin-degrading enzymes. *Philosophical Transactions Royal Society of London,* **321**, 3461–474.

Kirk, T.K., Nakatsubo, F. and Reid, I.D. (1983). Further study discounts role for singlet oxygen in fungal degradation of lignin model compounds. *Biochemical and Biophysical Research Communications,* **3**, 200–204.

Kirk, T.K., Tein, M., Johnsrud, S.C. and Eriksson, K.E. (1986). Lignin degrading activity of *Phanerochaete chrysosporium* Burds: comparison of cellulase-negative and other strains. *Enzymes and Microbial Technology,* **8**, 75–80.

McCarthy, A.J. (1987). Lignocellulose-degrading actinomycetes. *FEMS Microbiology Reviews,* **46**, 145–163.

McCarthy, A.J. and Broda, P. (1984). Screening for lignin-degrading actinomycetes and characterization of their activity against [^{14}C]-lignin-labelled wheat lignocellulose. *Journal of General Microbiology,* **130**, 2905–2913.

McCarthy, A.J., MacDonald, M.J., Paterson, A. and Broda, P. (1984). Degradation of ^{14}C lignin-labelled wheat lignocellulose by white-rot fungi. *Journal of General Microbiology,* **130**, 1023–1030.

McCarthy, A.J., Paterson, A. and Broda, P. (1986). Lignin solubilization by *Thermomonospora mesophila. Applied Microbiology and Biotechnology,* **24**, 347–352.

MacDonald, M.J., Paterson, A. and Broda, P. (1984). Possible relationship between cyclic AMP and iodiophasic metabolism in the white-rot fungus *Phanerochaete chrysosporium. Journal of Bacteriology, 180*, 470–472.

MacDonald, M.J., Ambler, R. and Broda, P. (1985). Regulation of intracellular cAMP levels in the white-rot fungus *Phanerochaete chrysosporium* during the onset of iodiophase metabolism. *Archives of Microbiology,* **142**, 152–156.

Mason, J.C. (1988). HPLC analysis of solubilized products from lignocellulose degradation by actinomycetes. *Biotechnology Techniques,* **2**, 95–100.

Mason, J.C., Richards, M., Zimmermann, W. and Broda, P. (1988). Identification of extracellular proteins from actinomycetes responsible for the solubilization of lignocellulose. *Applied Microbiology and Biotechnology*, **28**, 276–280.

Mason, J.C. Birch, O.M. and Broda, P. (1990). Preparation of [^{14}C] radiolabelled lignocelluloses from spring barley of differing maturities and their solubilization by *Phanerochaete chrysosporium* and *Streptomyces cyaneus*. *Journal of General Microbiology*. In press.

Mopper, K. and Gindler, E.M. (1973). A new noncorrosive dye reagent for automatic sugar chromatography. *Analytical Biochemistry*, **56**, 440–442.

Nakatsubo, F., Kirk, T.K., Shimada, M. and Higuchi, T. (1981). Metabolism of a phenylcoumaran substructure lignin model compound in ligninolytic cultures of *Phanerochaete chrysosporium*. *Archives of Microbiology*, **128**, 416–420.

Odier, E., Janin, G. and Monties, B. (1981). Poplar lignin decomposition by gram-negative aerobic bacteria. *Applied and Environmental Microbiology*, **41**, 337–341.

Phelan, M.B., Crawford, D.L. and Pometto III, A.L. (1979). Isolation of lignocellulose-decomposing actinomycetes and degradation of specifically ^{14}C-labelled lignocelluloses by six selected *Streptomyces* strains. *Canadian Journal of Microbiology*, **25**, 1270–1276.

Pometto III, A.L. and Crawford, D.L. (1986). Catabolic fate of *Streptomyces viridosporus* T7A-produced, acid precipitable polymeric lignin upon incubation with ligninolytic *Streptomyces* species and *Phanerochaete chrysosporium*. *Applied and Environmental Microbiology*, **51**, 171–179.

Raeder, U. and Broda, P. (1986). Meiotic segregation analysis of restriction site polymorphisms allows rapid genetic mapping. *EMBO Journal*, **5**, 1125–1127.

Raeder, U., Thompson, W. and Broda, P. (1987). Establishing molecular genetics for *Phanerochaete chrysosporium*. *Philosophical Transactions Royal Society, London*, **A321**, 405–422.

Rinderknecht, H., Wilding, P., Haverback, B.J. (1967). A new method of the determination of D-amylase. *Experientia*, **23**, 1805.

Sims, P., James, C. and Broda, P. (1988). The identification, molecular cloning and characterization of a gene from *Phanerochaete chrysosporium* that shows strong homology to the exocellobiohydrolase I gene from *Trichoderma reesei*. *Gene*, **74**, 411–422.

Sinner, M. and Puls, J. (1978). Non-corrosive dye reagent for detection of reducing sugars in borate complex ion-exchange chromatography. *Journal of Chromatography*, **156**, 197–204.

Tanahashi, M.and Higuchi, T. (1981). Dehydrogenative polymerization of monolignols by peroxidase and H_2O_2 in a dialysis tube. I. Preparation of highly polymerized DHPs. *Wood Research*, **67**, 29–42.

Tanahashi, M., Aoki, T. and Higuchi, T. (1982). Dehydrogenative polymerization of monolignols by peroxidase and H^2O^2 in a dialysis tube. II. Estimation of molecular weights by thermal softening method. *Holzforschung*, **36**, 117–112.

Tien, M. and Kirk, T.K. (1983). Lignin degrading enzyme from the hymenomycete *Phanerochaete chrysosporium* Burds. *Science,* **211**, 661-663.

Tien, M. and Tu, C.P.D. (1987). Cloning and sequencing of a cDNA for a ligninase from *Phanerochaete chrysosporium. Nature,* **326**, 520-523 and Corrigendum, *Nature,* **328**, 742.

Trojanowski, J., Haider, K. and Sundman, V. (1977). Decomposition of ^{14}C-labelled lignin and phenols by a *Nocardia* sp. *Archives of Microbiology,* **114**, 149-153.

Waite, R. and Gorrod, A.R.N. (1959). The structural carbohydrates of grasses. *Journal Science Food Agriculture,* **10**, 308-316.

3.2

Manipulation of Rumen Microbes or Feed Resources as Methods of Improving Feed Utilization

E. R. ØRSKOV and H. J. FLINT
The Rowett Research Institute, Aberdeen, Scotland

INTRODUCTION

It is possible to envisage an increase in utilization of feed resources either through manipulation of the rumen microflora or by manipulating the quality of the resources. It might be possible to engineer organisms capable of making more substrate available from lignocellulosic material or of detoxifying plant materials presently underutilized. On the other hand it may be possible to manipulate the quality of resources by genetic manipulation or upgrading by external treatment. In the following, progress made in these fields of study will be briefly discussed.

MANIPULATION OF THE RUMEN MICROFLORA

Naturally occurring strains

The microbial community present in the rumen at any given time is determined in a complex manner by the inoculum received at various times after birth, by dietary composition, by interactions between microbes and by the animal's behaviour, gut anatomy, secretions and movements. The most significant inoculum is likely to be that received by the young animal via saliva from the mother, but there is also evidence for transmission of obligately anaerobic rumen bacteria between adult animals (Hungate, 1966). It is not clear to what extent the nature of the available inoculum normally influences rumen function. It could be argued that dissemination of oxygen intolerant rumen species of bacteria would be severely limited, leading to wide geographic, interspecies, interherd or interanimal variation in the rumen microflora. With some exceptions, however, the same major bacterial, protozoal and fungal species have been found in a wide range of ruminants in diverse locations (reviewed Hungate, 1966; Dehority and Orpin, 1988). It is still possible that significant strain variation, or variation in minor species, exists and that deliberate transfer between animals of strains having certain desired characteristics may be beneficial. A clear example of functionally significant geographic variation in the rumen microflora is that of 3 hydroxy 4(IH) pyridone (3,4DHP) degrading microbes (Jones and Megarrity, 1986). In this case the ability to detoxify 3,4 DHP, which is derived from the nonprotein amino acid mimosine present in *Leucaena* forage, was conferred on ruminants in Australia by an inoculum derived from animals in Hawaii.

Introduction of manipulated bacteria

The idea that it may be possible to enhance aspects of rumen function through the introduction of genetically manipulated bacterial strains has been the subject of several recent reviews (Smith and Hespell, 1983; Forsberg, Crosby and Thomas 1986; Armstrong and Gilbert, 1985). As yet it is still unclear whether this approach will find application, particularly with respect to agriculture in developing countries, but the long-term possibilities are both novel and wide-ranging.

The rapid progress in molecular biology and in genetic manipulation techniques that has occurred in recent years has involved a small number of bacterial and fungal species only. Development of gene transfer techniques in new species is not a trivial undertaking and demands considerable research effort, particularly where, as with the predominant rumen species, the organisms concerned are oxygen sensitive. Alternative approaches based on mutagenesis and protoplast fusions have been used to derive strains of rumen anaerobes with enhanced cellulolytic activity *in vitro* (Taya, Ohmiya, Kobayashi and Shimizu, 1983) or to obtain fusants with an enhanced rate of degradation *in vitro* of the lignin model compound dehydrodivanillin (DDV) (Chen, Ohmiya and Shimizu, 1987). Progress is now being made with the development of techniques for gene transfer in certain abundant and ubiquitous species of noncellulolytic rumen anaerobes (Flint, Thomson and Bisset, 1988; Thomson and Flint, 1989; Lockington, Attwood and Brooker, 1988) which should lead to the ability to introduce foreign genes that could be maintained in self-replicating plasmids or through incorporation into the host chromosome. Meanwhile techniques are developing rapidly for several groups of facultative anaerobes (e.g. *Streptococci, Lactobacilli*) that may prove applicable to related rumen species.

Little is known about the likely survival of manipulated strains in the rumen – for example whether it is reasonable to expect that a single strain would survive well in diverse locations and in different animals. Approaches have been developed for monitoring the survival of introduced strains (Flint, Bisset and Webb, 1989; Attwood, Lockington, Xue and Brooker, 1988) that would allow these questions to be examined. It seems probable that most manipulated strains will be at some selective disadvantage compared to indigenous competitors. This would make long-term survival unrealistic, but need not prevent large transient populations being established through reinoculation. In some cases dietary supplementation might be used to promote the survival of introduced strains (Wallace, 1989).

Proposals to release engineered organisms for use in the gut will have to satisfy risk assessment criteria. In most cases it can be argued that no significant risk of environmental or health damage would result from the types of well-defined alterations proposed to nonpathogenic gut bacteria, particularly if onward transfer of manipulated traits can be minimized and survival time in the rumen is limited.

Two possible areas for the application of inoculants based on naturally occurring or manipulated strains are considered below.

Prospects for enhancing ruminal fibre degradation Relatively little is known about the enzyme systems involved in the degradation of plant cell wall polysaccharides by rumen bacteria, although the existence of multiple cellulase and xylanase genes has been demonstrated in the major cellulolytic species (Crosby, Collier, Thomas, Teather and Erfle, 1984; Howard and White, 1988; Flint, McPherson and Bisset, 1989). A model system may be provided by the nonrumen anaerobe *Clostridium thermocellum* where complex cell surface structures (cellulosomes) containing many distinct polypeptides are involved in degradation (Bayer and Lamed, 1986). Introduction of fibre degrading activity into noncellulolytic bacteria, which has been proposed as a means of enhancing numbers of cellulolytic bacteria in the rumen or of achieving fibre degradation at pHs lower than those tolerated by the existing cellulolytic species (Russell and Wilson, 1988; Forsberg *et al,* 1986), would presumably require the creation of systems at least as efficient as the cellulosome.

Proposals for enhancing the fibre degrading activities of cellulolytic rumen bacteria themselves have included the introduction of new metabolic pathways (e.g. for pentose utilization) or of 'key' degradative activities (Forsberg *et al*, 1986; Russell and Wilson, 1988). It is often assumed that greater degradation of lignin could enhance the overall extent of fibre degradation in the rumen, but cleavage of bonds joining phenolic residues in core lignin does not appear to occur at any significant rate in any system in the absence of oxygen (Vicuna, 1988). Another possibility is that increased cleavage of bonds between polysaccharide chains and lignin would enhance fibre degradation. The rate determining enzyme reactions have yet to be identified conclusively, so that the consequences of introducing novel activities cannot be predicted with confidence at this stage.

Mutational approaches require little detailed knowledge of the system to achieve manipulation, provided suitable selection methods are available, and significant activity changes may be obtainable through the isolation of regulatory mutants. It is intriguing to speculate whether strains selected as showing enhanced degradation of particular complex substrates *in vitro* could be used to inoculate animals being fed such substrates. This selection must already occur naturally in the rumen, but in the case of mutations where the spontaneous mutation rate is low the appearance of new forms *in vivo* could be a slow and unpredictable process.

There may also be scope for exploring the effectiveness of inoculants based on cellulolytic species in enhancing fibre degradation under conditions (e.g. dietary transitions) where the numbers of rumen cellulolytic microbes are limiting. This would not require strain manipulation, but would require overcoming the problem of administering inocula of oxygen sensitive microbes or of finding suitable oxygen tolerant species.

Degradation of toxic compounds A great variety of toxic compounds and antinutritional factors is found widely distributed among plant species, in particular in the tropics, and these often limit or prevent the use of otherwise suitable plant material as ruminant feed. Use of specially manipulated microbes for the detoxification of these substances appears one of the most promising areas to explore for applications of microbial inoculants and gene manipulation techniques in the rumen (Table 1).

Many plant toxins are potentially degradable to harmless derivatives through one or a few enzyme steps. In several cases (e.g. oxalic acid, some pyrrolizidine alkaloids) detoxification by rumen bacteria is known to occur naturally, but may require a lengthy period of adaptation or, as in the case of 3 hydroxy 4(IH) pyridone degradation, may be geographically limited (Allison, 1978). In many other cases detoxification does not occur but the necessary degradative activities may exist in microbes that cannot establish successfully in the rumen. Here it should prove possible to isolate and transfer the genes to a microbe capable of survival in the rumen. The degradative

TABLE 1 *Effects of rumen microorganisms on the toxicity of dietary components.*

		Potential for improvement
Detoxification	– rapid, widespread	–
	– requiring 'adaptation' [e.g. heliotrine, oxalic acid]	+
	– geographically localized [e.g. 3 hydroxy 4 (IH) pyridone]	+
Toxin production	[e.g. 3 methyl indole, 3 Hydroxy 4 (IH) pyridone, thiaminase]	+
No effect		+

enzymes may or may not require to be exported from the cell depending on whether the toxic substance is taken up by the bacterium.

Effective detoxification may only require a relatively small proportion of the total rumen population to be degraders. This broadens the range of bacterial species that might be considered as hosts to include some of the normally less numerous facultatively anaerobic species (e.g. *Lactobacilli, Enterococci*). Introduction of degradative activities into oxygen tolerant species would have the advantage of greatly simplifying inoculation (e.g. through addition of freeze dried cultures). The ability to degrade the toxic plant product may sometimes provide an energy source uniquely available to the introduced strain, giving a potential positive selection. In some cases where the ruminal concentrations of the toxic agent are slightly inhibitory to rumen microbes, a selective advantage might derive from the degrading microbe being resistant. There may be no need to try to establish the introduced microbe as a permanent member of the rumen flora. Rather it might be used in a prophylactic manner shortly before a shift to a diet containing the toxic compound.

Alternative approaches to detoxification of course exist, but may not always be satisfactory. Isolation of genes encoding detoxifying enzymes might, for example, allow the large-scale production of these enzymes. Pretreatment of feed with such enzymes seems unlikely to succeed unless simple procedures could be found to achieve release of the toxin without otherwise adversely affecting the nutritive value of the feed. Addition of such enzymes to the rumen would be successful only where they were able to function under rumen conditions and were not subject to degradation by rumen proteases. Finally, plant breeding may be used to create plant varieties that do not synthesize the toxins in question. The role of these toxins may often be a defence mechanism, however, and their removal could create serious problems of susceptibility to pests.

MANIPULATION OF FEED RESOURCES

In the last section the possibilities of manipulating or improving nutritive value of resources by genetic manipulation of the rumen microflora were discussed. In the following section methods of improving the nutritive value of resources by plant genetic manipulation or breeding and by appropriate upgrading treatments will be discussed in more detail with emphasis here on cereal straws.

It should first be pointed out that the rapid progress and accumulation of information in this field owes much to the development of reliable biological laboratory based methods for assessment of nutritive value. Chemical analyses of fibre content have been very unreliable in assessment both of differences between varieties and of differences between types of roughage. They are most useful in analysing differences in nutritive value that result from differences in stage of maturity. Ramanzin, Ørskov and Tuah (1986) found no differences in chemical fibre and lignin content between straws varying greatly in nutritive value. The most reliable method is probably the nylon bag procedure described by Ørskov and McDonald (1979) using a mathematical description of the data obtained. Feeds characterized in this way have also been shown to indicate voluntary consumption (Ørskov, 1988b; Ørskov, 1989). While the nylon bag method requires the use of rumen fistulated animals, biological methods such as use of cellulase enzymes show promising results (Dowman and Collins, 1982).

Manipulation of nutritive value by selection or genetic engineering

In the following the progress in identifying genetic variation will be discussed in some detail. Reports on variation in nutritive value between varieties are relatively recent for the reasons mentioned above. Kernan, Coxworth, Crowle and Spurr (1984) reported differences between varieties of wheat straw. Bainton, Plumb, Capper and Juliano (1987) worked with rice straw and Tuah, Lufadeju and Ørskov (1986) and Capper, Thomson, Rihawi, Termanini and Macrae (1986) reported variations in nutritive value of barley straws. In the following some data have been prepared from work by Shand, Ørskov and Morrice (1988) and Tuah *et al*, (1986) to illustrate the differences. In the tables the degradability at 48 hours, which is generally close to *in vivo* digestibility, the potential nutritive value of the dry matter and the rate constant of disappearance of the digestible, but insoluble, fraction have been used. As mentioned before these characteristics of straw are very important in identifying nutritive value and voluntary intake (Ørskov *et al*, 1988b).

In a series of trials Tuah *et al* (1986) collected samples of varieties of spring barley, oats and winter wheat. In Table 2 some of the varieties of spring barley straw are given. It can be seen that there was a large variation between varieties in nutritive value expressed here as the total potential for digestion, and in the 48 hours degradability. In Table 3 some representative varieties of oat straw are given. The variability between the varieties of oats was not as

TABLE 2 *Differences between varieties of spring barley on degradation characteristics of dry matter.*

Variety	48 hr degradability %	Potential %	Rate constant fraction/hr
Celt	46.0	56.4	0.0371
Delta	38.5	59.6	0.0193
Doublet	60.7	71.7	0.0419
Golden Promise	40.2	48.5	0.0337
Corgi	58.7	68.8	0.0392
Triumph	50.1	65.7	0.0320

From: Tuah *et al* (1986)

TABLE 3 *Differences between varieties of oat straw in degradation characteristics of dry matter.*

Variety	48 hr degradability %	Potential %	Rate constant fraction/hr
Ballad	36.7	49.6	0.0240
Cabana	38.7	49.0	0.0272
Dula	38.3	53.4	0.0212
Leanda	36.7	50.8	0.0218
Matra	40.7	56.0	0.0215
Trafalgar	37.6	49.3	0.0250

From: Tuah *et al* (1986)

TABLE 4 *Differences between varieties of wheat in degradation characteristics of dry matter.*

Variety	48 hr degradability %	Potential %	Rate constant fraction/hr
Aquilla	42.5	57.9	0.0251
Boxer	39.0	47.7	0.0401
Brigand	41.7	52.0	0.0340
Longbow	43.5	53.7	0.0335
Renard	42.1	58.3	0.0264
Stetson	48.0	58.9	0.0300

From: Tuah *et al* (1986)

great as with spring barley straws but was still substantial and significant. Wheat straw varieties in Table 4 also show great variability.

Nakashima *et al* (1988) showed substantial differences between four varieties of rice straw but the largest comparison between varieties of rice straw is probably that recently by Soebarinoto, Sarwiyono, Chuzaemi and Van Bruchem (1989) from Indonesia shown in Table 5. Again large differences here in the organic matter digestibility measured *in vivo*.

Causes of differences between varieties

Some of the variation in nutritive value between varieties can no doubt be attributed to differences in botanical fractions. For all of the temperate cereals the leaf is more digestible than stems. Some representative average values for leaf and stems mainly from Shand *et al* (1988) are given in Table 6.

TABLE 5 *Organic matter digestibility and intake of digestible organic matter of rice straw grown at two locations, Malang (Ma) and Mojosari (Mo).*

Variety	Organic matter digestibility (%)		Voluntary intake (g digestible organic matter/kg $W^{0.75}$)	
	MA	MO	MO	MO
IR36	39.0	46.1	10.4	18.0
Batang	47.1	45.7	16.5	18.3
IR54	42.2	41.4	13.8	11.5
IR64	45.7	45.7	12.2	11.8
Citandui	42.2	45.4	13.9	14.8
Progo	48.6	48.3	16.9	13.5
Cisadana	46.9	36.7	13.7	12.7
Kvueng Aceh	53.1	47.3	17.5	19.2
Kapuas	48.7	46.4	18.9	16.5
Tuntang	46.8	46.8	18.8	16.1

From: Soebarinoto *et al* (1989)

TABLE 6 *Effect of botanical fractions of different cereals on degradation characteristics of dry matter.*

Type of straw	Fraction	48 hr degradation %	Potential %	Rate constant fraction/hr
Oats	Leaves	50.1	60.7	0.0353
Oats	Stem	27.1	42.1	0.0152
Wheat	Leaves	61.5	73.4	0.0423
Wheat	Stem	33.0	44.8	0.0259
Spring barley	Leaves	70.5	85.3	0.0383
Spring barley	Stem	28.4	37.7	0.0248
Rice	Leaves	43.5	52.5	0.0341
Rice	Stem	59.6	68.3	0.0487

From: Shand *et al* (1988)

It can be seen clearly that differences between varieties in the leaf to stem ratio can result in differences in nutritive value. On the other hand when Ramanzin *et al* (1986) analyzed two varieties which were very different in degradability most of the differences could be attributed to differences in nutritive value of leaf and stems and only about 25% due to differences in the leaf stem ratio. It is interesting to note from Table 6 that for rice straw the stem is more digestible than leaf.

There is no doubt that location can influence nutritive value of straw. There is also a large year-to-year variation in nutritive value which is particularly noticeable in the water soluble fraction probably due to differences in the extent to which the soluble sugars have been transported to the grain or the extent to which the water soluble materials may have been washed out due to exposure of mature straw to wet weather.

While there may well be variety by location or variety by year interaction Ørskov and Shand (1987) found on the whole that while year-to-year variation in nutritive value was large the ranking of the varieties according to nutritive value was relatively constant. Table 7 shows some spring barley varieties grown in a similar locality for three consecutive years. It can be seen that in spite of large year-to-year variation the ranking was similar indicating that the character of nutritive value can be selected for.

TABLE 7 *Differences in degradability of spring barley straw among varieties and years.*

	48 hr degradability (%)		
Variety	**Year 1**	**Year 2**	**Year 3**
Celt	46.4	39.6	45.5
Corgi	58.9	46.2	52.7
Doublet	61.1	45.9	57.9
Golden Promise	40.3	34.4	41.5
Golf	46.9	37.7	42.6
Heriot	54.4	42.1	50.6
Klaxon	48.8	34.3	39.9

From: Ørskov and Shand (1987)

In all instances referred to above no correlations between nutritive value of straw and yield and quality of grain have been reported again indicating that quality of crop residues can be selected for without sacrificing cereal yield. For countries like India and Bangladesh where up to 90% of the feed for cattle is based on straw, differences of 10% in digestibility of straws can have enormous implications for resource availability and animal production as they affect not only digestibility but intakes as well.

The consequences for intake are given in Table 8 from Ørskov *et al* (1988a) in which five straws varying in degradation characteristics were fed *ad libitum* to steers which received also 1.5 kg of concentrate/d. The differences in intake and performance were greater still than differences in degradability. This was also apparent in the work reported by Soebarinoto *et al* (1989). While differences in digestibility varied from 367 to 531 g/kg the voluntary intake varied by about two-fold (Table 5).

TABLE 8 *Effect of degradation characteristics on straw intake and performance of steers.*

Type	Variety	48 hr degrad-ability	Potential	Rate constant	Intake kg/d	Live weight gain g/d
Winter barley	Gerbel	33.4	38.9	0.0337	3.43	106
Winter barley	Igri	37.4	43.3	0.0391	3.56	126
Spring barley	Corgi	47.3	52.1	0.0483	5.16	400
Spring barley	Golden Promise	44.3	55.5	0.0303	4.43	198
Wheat	Norman	40.8	48.6	0.0345	4.57	273

From: Ørskov *et al* (1988a)

Manipulation of nutritive value by external treatment

In recent years a multitude of methods of increasing availability of the cellulose to microbes has been reported. It is possible to remove some of the barriers imposed by lignified material by several means including acid, alkalis oxidative methods and enzymes. It is not intended here to discuss all these methods in detail. Only treatment with alkali has been adopted on any scale in practice. While sodium hydroxide application has been used for large-scale treatment and industrial application due to the rapid treatment time, on farm treatment has made much greater use of ammonia either in the form of anhydrous ammonia (Sundstøl, Coxworth and Mowat, 1978) or aqueous ammonia. For small-scale farmers particularly in tropical and subtropical regions when the environmental temperature is high urea has been used as a source of ammonia. The ammonia is released with the action of the enzyme urease which is normally present in organisms in the straw but which require a temperature of about 20° C for the process to be initiated.

The advantage of using ammonia as the alkali is that in general sufficient NH_3 will adhere to the straw to satisfy the need of the rumen microbes. While the action of alkali is to cause swelling of the cell walls thus increasing the access of microbes to cellulose the action of oxidative agents such as ozone and peroxide is to oxidize lignin selectively. Using a technique developed by Gould (1985) it was shown that hydrogen peroxide at alkaline pH was effective in increasing the digestibility. Adebowale, Ørskov and Hotten (1989) recently attempted to spray hydrogen peroxide in different concentrations on barley straw and subsequently expose straw to ammonia treatment. The result on degradation characteristics of wheat straw is given in Fig. 1. It can be clearly seen that it is possible by this combined method to ensure the release of a great deal of energy from straw or make straw similar in quality to high quality hay or silage.

The possibility of using mixtures of cellulase enzymes to treat straw has

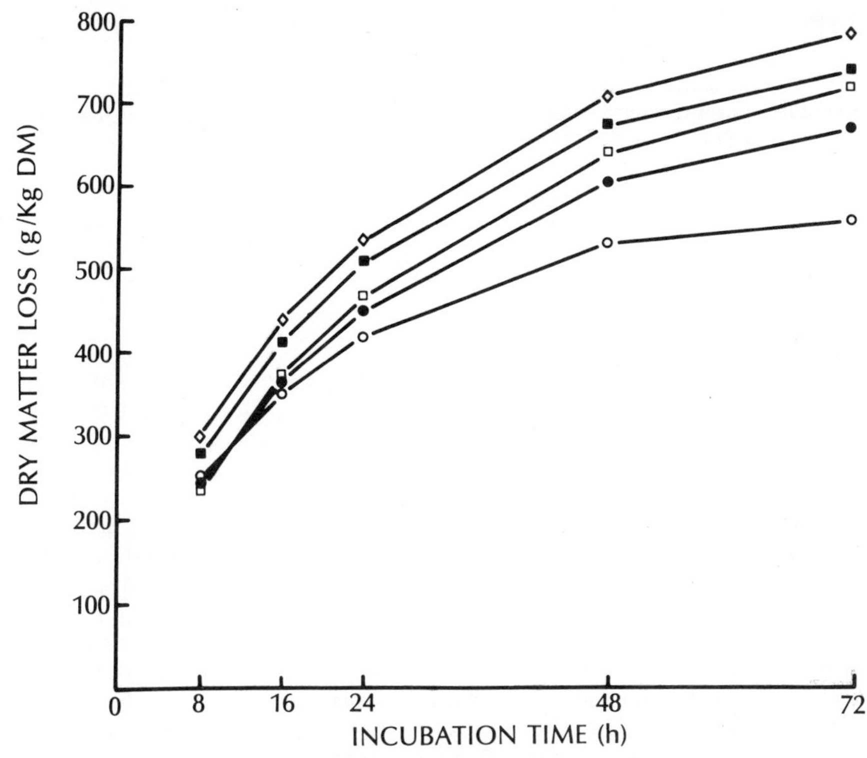

Fig. 1 *Effect of ammonia treatment on untreated and H_2O_2 treated wheat straw on dry-matter loss from samples incubated in nylon bags in the rumens of sheep; untreated (○), ammonia-treated (●), 10 g H_2O_2 per kg straw + NH_3 (□), 50 g H_2O_2 per kg straw + NH_3 (■), 100 g H_2O_2 per kg straw + NH_3 (◇).*

been reported by Nakashima *et al* (1988) and Nakashima and Ørskov (1988). They showed that straw incubated with cellulase enzymes increased in solubility due to release of sugars. The released sugars were subsequently fermented to yield mainly lactic and volatile acids. The acid content in the moist straw was sufficient for adequate preservation. In general the potential nutritive value was not changed. Note in Table 9 that the potential is similar but the solubility and thus the 24 hour degradation was greater. The effect of these treatments on food intake is not known. Nakashima and Ørskov (1988) subsequently showed that if fermentation of the released sugar was prevented by adding propionic acid to the straw then the potential value of the straw was increased by enzyme treatment. It was also evident that the leaves from straw appear to benefit more than stems from enzyme treatment while the opposite is true for ammonia treatment (Ramanzin *et al*, 1986).

It should finally be pointed out that animals differ in their ability to utilize poor quality resources. This is due to stomach structure, size and animal

TABLE 9 *Effect of cellulase enzymes on solubility, 24 hr dry matter (DM) loss, the potential and the rate constant.*

Cellulase concentration g/kg DM	Solubility %	24 hr degradation %	Potential %	Rate constant fraction/hr
0	15.2	47.7	62.4	0.0498
5	19.6	53.3	62.1	0.0677
10	21.2	56.6	62.8	0.0817

From: Nakashima *et al* (1988)

behaviour. There are large differences within breeds (Ørskov *et al*, 1988a) and between breeds (Mould, Saadullah, Haque, Davis, Dolberg and Ørskov, 1982). The former authors also showed that differences between animals were consistent and could be selected for. Mould *et al* (1982) showed that Zebu cattle in Bangladesh had gut volumes considerably greater than exotic animals relative to body weight. Differences between animals and breeds in their ability to utilize poor quality resources should be taken into account when exotic animals are imported. Failure to do this has resulted in many disappointments. Similarly adding yield or growth potential to an animal by use of hormones such as bovine somatotropin is unlikely to be beneficial if resource quality rather than potential is limiting production. Animals with an ability to select the most nutritious part of the plant, e.g. leaves, can be used to advantage when quantity of resources is plentiful, e.g. sheep and goats versus cattle. A better understanding of animal resource interaction is another method of increasing the use of poor quality renewable resources and which should receive much more attention in future formulation of livestock policies.

CONCLUSIONS

It is difficult at the moment to predict how effectively fibre digestion could be enhanced in the rumen by the introduction of novel strains or manipulated organisms. Progress in this area requires further understanding of the enzymology of fibre breakdown, further developments in the genetics of rumen microbes and a greater knowledge of the factors governing strain survival in the rumen. It is however possible to envisage great progress in the use of organisms to detoxify toxic plant materials thus greatly increasing the resources available for feeding. This can be envisaged by at least two routes, either by transferring adapted organisms from one area to another or by introducing genes for detoxification into already adapted rumen organisms.

There appear to be immense possibilities for manipulating or increasing the nutritive value of crop residues by means of breeding. An understanding of the genes involved may well speed up the process. In the work reported so far nutritive value of straw has not been correlated with yield and quality of grain. It is also possible that a separation of botanical fractions into leaf and stem may be of interest in some areas as the stem is an excellent product for pulp for paper industries and for hardboard while, as mentioned before in the case of temperate cereals, the leaves provide far better nutritive value than stems. It is interesting also to note (Ørskov and Shand, 1987) that the nutritive values of leaves and stems are only poorly correlated which may suggest that good quality strong fibre for industry could be selected for at the same time as high quality leaf for feeding. In spite of the documented evidence plant breeders have so far taken little or no note of the possibilities. The progress in treatment of straw has also been rapid and there now seems to be possibilities for combining different treatments, each with different actions on the lignin barriers, to produce from straw very high quality products suitable not only for ruminants but for monogastric animals as well.

REFERENCES

Adebowale, E.A., Ørskov, E.R. and Hotten, P.M. (1989). Rumen degradation of straw. 8. Effect of alkaline hydrogen peroxide on degradation of straw using either sodium hydroxide or gaseous ammonia as source of alkali. *Animal Production*, **48**, 553–559.

Allison, M.J. (1978). The role of ruminal microbes in the metabolism of toxic constituents from plants. In *Effects of Poisonous Plants on Livestock* (eds. R.F. Keeler, K.R. van Kampen, and L.F. James), pp. 101–120. Academic Press.

Armstrong, D.G. and Gilbert, H.J. (1985). Biotechnology and the rumen: a mini review. *Journal of the Science of Food and Agriculture*, **36**, 1039–1046.

Attwood, G.T., Lockington, R.A., Xue, G-P. and Brooker, J.D. (1988). Use of a unique gene sequence as a probe to enumerate a strain of *Bacteroides ruminicola* introduced into the rumen. *Applied and Environmental Microbiology*, **54**, 534–539.

Bainton, S.J., Plumb, V.E., Capper, B.S. and Juliano, B.O. (1987). Botanical composition, chemical analysis and cellulose solubility of rice straw from different varieties. *Animal Production*, **44**, 481 (abstract).

Bayer, E.A. and Lamed, R. (1986). Ultrastructure of the cell surface cellulosome of *Clostridium thermocellum* and its interaction with cellulose. *Journal of Bacteriology*, **167**, 828–836.

Capper, B.S., Thomson, E.F., Rihawi, S., Termanini, A. and Macrae, R. (1986). The feeding value of straw from different genotypes of barley when given to Awassi sheep. *Animal Production*, **42**, 337–342.

Chen, W., Ohmiya, K. and Shimizu, S. (1987). Intergeneric protoplast fusion between *Fusobacterium varium* and *Enterococcus faecium* for enhancing dehydrodivanillin degradation. *Applied and Environmental Microbiology*, **53**, 542–548.

Crosby, B., Collier, B., Thomas, D.Y., Teather, R.M. and Erfle, J. (1984). Cloning and expression in *Escherichia coli* of cellulase genes from *Bacteroides succinogenes*. In *5th Canadian Bioenergy R & D Seminar* (ed. S. Hasnain), pp. 573–576. Elsevier, Amsterdam.

Dehority, B.A. and Orpin, C.G. (1988). Development of, and natural fluctuations in, rumen microbial populations. In *The Rumen Microbial Ecosystem* (ed. P.N. Hobson), pp. 151–183. Elsevier Applied Sciences, London and New York.

Dowman, M.G. and Collins, F.C. (1982). The use of enzymes to predict the digestibility of animal feeds. *Journal of Agricultural Science, Cambridge*, **33**, 689–696.

Flint, H.J., Thomson, A.M. and Bisset, J. (1988). Plasmid associated transfer of tetracycline resistance in *Bacteroides ruminicola*. *Applied and Environmental Microbiology*, **54**, 855–860.

Flint, H.J., Bisset, J. and Webb, J. (1989). Use of antibiotic resistance mutations to track strains of obligately anaerobic bacteria introduced into the rumen of sheep. *Journal of Applied Bacteriology*, **67**, 177–183.

Flint, H.J., McPherson, C.A. and Bisset, J. (1989). Molecular cloning of genes from *Ruminococcus flavefaciens* encoding xylanase and β (1,3–1, 4) glucanase activities. *Applied and Environmental Microbiology*, **55**, 1230–1233.

Forsberg, C.W., Crosby, B. and Thomas, D.Y. (1986). Potential for manipulation of the rumen fermentation through the use of recombinant DNA techniques. *Journal of Animal Science*, **63**, 310–325.

Howard, G.T. and White, B.A. (1988). Molecular cloning and expression of cellulase genes from *Ruminococcus albus 8* in *Escherichia coli* bacteriophage δ. *Applied and Environmental Microbiology*, **54**, 1752–1755.

Hungate, R.E. (1966). *The Rumen and Its Microbes*. Academic Press Inc., New York.

Gould, J.M. (1985). Studies on the mechanism of alkaline peroxide delignification of agricultural residues. *Biotechnology and Bioengineering*, **27**, 225–231.

Jones, R.J. and Megarrity, R.G. (1986). Successful transfer of DHP degrading bacteria from Hawaiian goats to Australian ruminants to overcome the toxicity of Leucaena. *Australian Veterinary Journal*, **63**, 259–262.

Kernan, J.A., Coxworth, E.C., Crowle, W.L. and Spurr, D.T. (1984). The nutritional value of crop residue components from several wheat cultivars grown at different fertilizer levels. *Animal Feed Science and Technology*, **11**, 301–311.

Lockington, R.A., Attwood, G.A. and Brooker, J.D. (1988). Isolation and characterisation of a temperate bacteriophage from the ruminal anaerobe *Selenomonas ruminantium*. *Applied and Environmental Microbiology*, **54**, 1575–1580.

Mould, F.L., Saadullah, M., Haque, M., Davis, C., Dolberg, F. and Ørskov, E.R. (1982). Investigation of some of the physiological factors influencing intake and digestion of rice straw by native cattle in Bangladesh. *Tropical Animal Production*, **7**, 174–181.

Nakashima, Y., Ørskov, E.R., Hotten, P.M., Ambo, K. and Takase, Y. (1988). Rumen degradation of straw. 6. Effect of polysaccharidase enzymes on degradation characteristics of ensiled rice straw. *Animal Production*, **47**, 421–427.

Nakashima, Y. and Ørskov, E.R. (1988). Rumen degradation of straw. 7.

Effects of chemical pre-treatment and addition of propionic acid on degradation characteristics of botanical fractions of barley straw treated with a cellulase preparation. *Animal Production*, **48**, 543–551.

Nakashima, Y. and Ørskov, E.R. (1990). Rumen degradation of straw. 9. Effect of cellulase and ammonia treatment on different varieties of rice straw and their botanical fraction. *Animal Production*, **50**, 309–317.

Ørskov, E.R. and McDonald, I. (1979). The estimation of protein degradability in the rumen from incubation measurements weighted according to rate of passage. *Journal of Agricultural Science, Cambridge*, **92**, 499–503.

Ørskov, E.R., Ojwang, I. and Reid, G.W. (1988a). A study on consistency of differences between cows in rumen outflow rate of fibrous particles and other substrates and consequences for digestibility and intake of roughages. *Animal Production*, **47**, 45–51.

Ørskov, E.R., Reid, G.W. and Kay, M. (1988b). Prediction of intake by cattle from degradation characteristics of roughages. *Animal Production*, **46**, 1, 29–34.

Ørskov, E.R. (1989). Recent advances in evaluation of roughages as feeds for ruminants. In *Advances in Animal Nutrition in Australia 1989*. (ed. D.J. Farrell), pp. 102–108. Department of Biochemistry, Microbiology and Nutrition, University New England, Armidale, Australia.

Ørskov, E.R. and Shand, W.J. (1987). *The Effect of Type and Variety of Cereals on Nutritive Value of Straw*, pp. 17–30. Pira Paper Board Division, Letherhead, Surrey.

Ramanzin, M., Ørskov, E.R. and Tuah, A.K. (1986). Rumen degradation of straw. 2. Botanical fractions of straw from two barley cultivars. *Animal Production*, **43**, 271–278.

Russell, J.B. and Wilson, D.B. (1988). Potential opportunities and problems for genetically altered rumen microorganisms. *Journal of Nutrition*, **118**, 271–272.

Shand, W.J., Ørskov, E.R. and Morrice, L.A.F. (1988). Rumen degradation of straw. 6. Botanical fractions and degradability of different varieties of oat and wheat straws. *Animal Production*, **47**, 387–392.

Smith, C.J. and Hespell, R.B. (1983). Prospects for development and use of recombinant deoxyribonucleic acid techniques with ruminal microorganisms. *Journal of Dairy Science*, **66**, 1536–1546.

Soebarinoto, Sarwiyono, Chuzaemi, S. and Van Bruchem, J. (1989). Nutritive value of rice straw varieties in Indonesia as related to location and urea treatment. Paper given at Meeting on Tropical Animal Production. Agricultural University, Wageningen, September 1989.

Sundstøl, F., Coxworth, S. and Mowat, D.N. (1978). Improving the nutritive value of straw and other low-quality roughages by treatment with ammonia. *World Animal Revue*, **26**, 13–21.

Taya, M., Ohmiya, K., Kobayashi, T. and Shimizu, S. (1983). Enhancement of cellulose digestion by mutants from an anaerobe, *Ruminococcus albus*. *Journal of Fermentation Technology*, **61**, 197–199.

Thomson, A.M. and Flint, H.J. (1989). Electroporation induced transformation of *Bacteroides ruminicola* and *Bacteroides multiacidus* by plasmid DNA. *FEMS Microbiology Letters*, **61**, 101–104.

Tuah, A.K., Lufadeju, E. and Ørskov, E.R. (1986). Rumen degradation of straw. 1. Untreated and ammonia-treated barley, oat and wheat straw varieties and triticale straw. *Animal Production*, **43**, 261–269.

Vicuna, R. (1988). Bacterial degradation of lignin. *Enzyme and Microbial Technology*, **10**, 646–655.

Wallace, R.J. (1989). Identification of slowly metabolised sugars and sugar derivatives that could be used to establish new or modified microbial species in the rumen. *Current microbiology*, **19**, 271–274.

3.3

Biotechnology in Monogastric Nutrition

C.A. MORGAN
Edinburgh School of Agriculture, Edinburgh, Scotland

INTRODUCTION

This paper will consider four specific areas where biotechnology is having an influence on monogastric nutrition, using information on pigs and poultry.

- The nutrition and health of young pigs
- The requirements for nutrients
- The enhancement of food value
- Biology combined with computer technology

THE NUTRITION AND HEALTH OF YOUNG PIGS

The unweaned pig suckles its mother about once an hour thereby obtaining nutrients on a little and often basis. Its digestive system can easily cope with the specific nutrients in milk supplied in this way; the milk clots in the stomach and the limited gastric acid (HCl) secretion is augmented by lactic acid produced by fermentation of milk lactose by *Lactobacilli* (Easter, 1988). Thus the pH is lowered to the level required for efficient protein hydrolysis and for suppression of harmful bacteria. Nutrients are released from the clot in a steady controlled way into the intestine. The ability of the piglet to reduce stomach pH increases with age (Cranwell, 1985) and when the pig is weaned at 21 days of age this is a critical factor in the maintenance of health. At weaning the nutrient supply is switched from milk to solid food. This may be eaten in larger meals on a less regular basis, it may contain nutrients in a form which are not readily digestible and may have a high buffering capacity as a result of the ingredients used (e.g. limestone). Ideally cooked cereals,

TABLE 1 *Effects of adding acid to water of piglets.*

	Control	Lactic acid	Propionic acid	Calcium propionate	Calcium acrylate
Food intake (kg/d)	1.009	1.027	0.927	0.931	0.868
Growth rate (kg/d)	0.372	0.409	0.355	0.345	0.310
Food utilization (kg food/kg gain)	2.72	2.53	2.68	2.70	2.82

From: Cole *et al* (1968)

TABLE 2 *Effects of adding acid to food of piglets.*

	Nursed by sow	Control diet	Lactic acid diet	High casein diet
No. pigs	6	7	6	6
No. scouring	4	7	3	6
Mean days scouring/pig	1.2	6.0	1.0	3.5

From: White *et al* (1969)

skimmed milk and fish meal should be used in such diets (Fowler, 1980), with a gradual progression to raw starch and vegetable protein to coincide with digestive enzyme development (Aumaitre, 1972). In practice the acid conditions required in the stomach may not be achieved and pathogenic bacteria can proliferate. Nutrients may be released into the intestine in large irregular doses and are not fully digested, leading to further bacterial activity. The end result is digestive upset and diarrhoea. Two remedies are now being investigated which aim to alleviate the problem by augmenting the acid production in the stomach and ensuring that the population of bacteria in the gut is benign.

Firstly acids have been added to water or food and the effectiveness of such treatments can be seen in the early work of Cole, Beal and Luscombe (1968) and White, Wenham, Sharman, Jones, Rattray and McDonald (1969) in Tables 1 and 2. Kirchgessner and Roth (1982) reviewed the use of fumaric acid as a feed additive and, in addition to describing the effects on gastrointestinal health, they also reported improvements in food consumption, growth rate, food efficiency and digestibility and metabolizability of dietary nitrogen and energy. Easter (1988) discussed the problems of replicating the effects of added acids in the American situation. In general the effects were small but improvements were observed in gain and food conversion ratio. For example in the work of Giesting and Easter (1985) the

TABLE 3 *Effects of addition of fumaric acid to the diet on digestibility over the whole gut; pigs 5–10 kg liveweight.*

Fumaric acid (g/kg)	Digestibility of DM	GE	N	N retained/ N intake
0	0.856	0.859	0.852	0.615
10	0.867	0.872	0.873	0.644
20	0.873	0.877	0.877	0.656

From: Kirchgessner and Roth (1980)

TABLE 4 *Effects of addition of fumaric acid to the diet on digestibility to ileum; pigs 4 to 8 weeks of age.*

Protein source	Soya bean meal		Skimmed milk	
Fumaric acid	–	+	–	+
Digestibility of				
DM	0.688	0.694	0.738	0.740
N	0.677	0.705	0.740	0.740

From: Giesting (1986)

addition of 30 or 40 g fumaric acid/kg diet for pigs from 10 to 18.7 kg liveweight resulted in gains of 0.297 kg/d and a food conversion of 1.67, compared with 0.261 kg/d and 1.92 on the unsupplemented diet. The response depends on the ingredients used in the diet, being greater for maize/soya bean meal diets than those based on maize and skimmed milk (Giesting, 1986). The consequences of the limited digestive capacity of the young pig to deal with vegetable protein compared with milk protein was referred to earlier and it is likely that the addition of acid assisted in this. Kirchgessner and Roth (1980) demonstrated that fumaric acid significantly ($P < 0.05$) increased the digestibility of dry matter, energy and nitrogen and nitrogen balance in pigs from 5 to 10 kg liveweight (Table 3). Using pigs fitted with a cannula in the terminal ileum, Giesting (1986) confirmed these observations although the effects were nonsignificant (Table 4). The response declined as the digestive tract matured.

The second method of establishing the correct conditions in the gut involves the use of a Probiotic i.e. "a live microbial feed supplement which benefically affects the host animal by improving its intestinal microbial balance" (Fuller and Cole, 1989). The digestive tract is sterile at birth but contact with the sow and the environment results in colonization by a variety of microorganisms. These complement the digestive ability of the host by providing extra digestive enzymes and provide a barrier against invading pathogens (Sissons, 1988). Times of stress, such as weaning, tend to upset the balance of the microflora, resulting in digestive upsets. It is common practice to use antibiotics to control the proliferation of harmful bacteria but these also destroy the desirable nonpathogenic species. An alternative is to promote colonization by the desirable bacteria by feeding live bacterial cells. Pollmann (1986) and Sissons (1988) outlined the ways in which the desirable bacteria such as *Lactobacilli,* express their effects:

- adhesion to digestive tract wall to prevent colonization by pathogens
- neutralization of toxins
- bactericidal activity
- prevention of amine synthesis
- enhanced immune competence

Sissons (1988) gave a detailed discussion of these modes of action. In brief it is suggested (Sissons, 1988; Thacker, 1988) that there is definite evidence to support the competitive attachment theory. *E. coli* need to become attached to the intestinal wall to exert their harmful effects and *Lactobacilli* successfully compete for attachment sites. There is some evidence for the neutralization of enterotoxins but the specific substance has yet to be identified. *Lactobacilli* exert a bacteriocidal effect by the fermentation of lactose to lactic acid and reduction of pH, described earlier. They also produce hydrogen peroxide. Coliforms decarboxylate amino acids, producing amines which have been shown to coincide with the occurrence of diarrhoea. Thus desirable bacteria may reduce amine production if the coliforms are prevented from proliferating. Finally, oral inoculation with *Lactobacilli* has resulted in elevated levels of total serum protein and increased white blood cell counts and thus could be important in the development of the immune system of young pigs.

The responses of pigs of different ages to various probiotic treatments were reviewed by Pollmann (1986) and his summary is shown in Table 5. On balance probiotics were effective for young pigs but for growing-finishing pigs they are unlikely to be of use (Pollmann, 1986; Thacker, 1988). Even with young pigs the effects are small with increases in growth rate from −8.5 to +14.1%. Sissons (1988) pointed to the conflict between commercial claims for

TABLE 5 *Summary of experiments with probiotics for pigs.*

Period	No. of pigs	Number of Trials Positive	Number of Trials Negative
Starter	3,207	13	5
Grower-finisher	1,393	3	5

From: Pollmann (1986)

probiotics and scientific trials which have often failed to show a benefit from their use. If the organism does not attach itself to the gut epithelium or it cannot grow rapidly in the conditions existing in digesta and cannot tolerate contact with acid and bile, then it will not be useful as a probiotic agent (Fuller, and Cole, 1989).

In conclusion it should be realized that the addition of acids or probiotics to the diet of early weaned pigs will not cure diarrhoea. They can only be considered as aids to prevent diarrhoea occurring in the first instance and ingredient formulation of diets is critical.

THE REQUIREMENTS FOR NUTRIENTS

Advances in genetics and the manipulation of the physiology of growth of pigs and poultry have resulted in animals with increased production potential, and an increased demand for nutrients.

Selection in pig breeding has increased the lean (protein) deposition rate and decreased the amount of fat deposited. The consequences of this are that animals can be fed *ad libitum* to slaughter without becoming too fat, providing the increased demand for protein (amino acids) is recognized when diets are formulated. Typical recommendations for bacon pigs in the mid-1970s suggested that the diet should contain 0.68 g lysine/ MJ digestible energy (DE) between 20 and 50 kg liveweight and 0.56 g/ MJ DE between 50 and 90 kg liveweight (MAFF, 1977). The Agricultural Research Council (ARC, 1981) recommended 0.84 and 0.60 g lysine/ MJ DE, respectively, and the feed industry are now using even higher levels of 0.87 and 0.72 g lysine/ MJ DE (Hanrahan, 1989).

The current research on the incorporation of genes responsible for litter size from Chinese pigs, such as the Meishan, into European breeds in an attempt to increase the litter size will require that the sow's nutrient requirements are reviewed. It is unlikely that the increased burden of foetuses will demand much of an increase in nutrient supply but once the piglets are born the demand to supply the needs of lactation could be significant. Using the early data of Elsley (1971), Black, Campbell, Williams, James and Davies (1986) derived the following equation to predict daily milk yield (y, kg) from litter size (x).

$$y = 1.81 + 0.58\ x$$

i.e. an increase of 0.58 kg of milk per day per piglet. The production of this amount of milk requires 4.9 MJ DE and 47 g digestible crude protein (DCP) (ARC, 1981), so an increase in litter size of two piglets will require the equivalent of 0.75 kg barley for the DE or 0.25 kg soya bean meal for the DCP. It should be remembered that selective breeding has resulted in the modern sow already having a yield potential in excess of the Elsley data, thereby increasing nutrient requirements. In the mid-1970s it was suggested that sow diets contain 12.5 MJ DE and 140–150 g crude protein (CP)/ kg (MAFF, 1977) but Whittemore and Yang (1989), using a diet with 13.2 MJ

TABLE 6 *Effects of cimaterol in pigs and poultry.*

	Control	Cimaterol
Pigs growing from 31 to 110 kg liveweight		
Growth rate (g/day)	694	708
Food utilization (kg food/kg gain)	3.50	3.47
Killing out %	78.1	79.8
Weight of ham joint (kg)	13.1	13.7
Leaf fat weight (kg)	1.48	1.21
Fat area (cm^2)	16.1	14.0
L. dorsi area (cm^2)	41.4	46.8
Average backfat depth (mm)	26.0	24.8
Broilers growing to 35 days of age		
35 day weight gain (g)	1,190	1,229
35 day food intake (g)	2,416	2,430
Food utilization (g gain/g food)	2.03	1.98

From: Hanrahan *et al* (1986)

DE and 162 g CP/kg, reported substantial losses of body fat and protein in sows suckling ten piglets.

The recent significant research in physiology and animal production concerns the application of repartitioning agents – β agonists and exogenous growth hormone – to manipulate growth and development so as to improve performance and carcass quality (i.e. reduce fat). Hanrahan, Quirke, Bomann, Allen, McEwan, Fitzsimons, Kotzian and Roche (1986) reviewed the effects of β agonists on growth and carcass quality and the effects in pigs and poultry can be seen in Table 6, using cimaterol as an example. In both cases growth rate and efficiency of food utilization were increased. In pigs fat weight and area were decreased and the cross sectional area of the *longissimus dorsi* was increased. Similar effects on performance were recorded with broilers. Hanrahan *et al* (1986) suggested that β agonists exert their effects by interacting with cell membrane receptors, increasing intracellular cyclic adenosine monophosphate (AMP), resulting in reduced lipogenesis and increased lipolysis. Protein degradation in muscle is reduced and the fractional rate of protein synthesis is increased. Thus nutrients are diverted from fat to muscle deposition. Problems have been recorded with the use of cimaterol (Goihl, 1988) in that a withdrawal period of seven days resulted in an increase in food intake and fat deposition. Low levels of cimaterol and shorter withdrawal periods overcame the problem.

Although the results with β agonists in pigs have been encouraging, the greatest and most consistent responses have been achieved with exogenous growth hormone – porcine somatotropin (pST). This stimulates protein

TABLE 7 *Effects of exogenous pST on performance in pigs; energy intake.*

Energy intake (MJ/d)	20.1		24.3		*ad lib*	
pST (mg/kg per day)	0	0.1	0	0.1	0	0.1
Daily gain (kg)	0.543	0.681	0.670	0.842	0.905	1.051
Food/gain (kg/kg)	2.54	1.92	2.45	1.92	2.57	1.96
Body composition (g/kg)						
Protein	163	173	154	169	146	162
Fat	196	141	231	153	258	188

From: Campbell *et al* (1987)

TABLE 8 *Effects of exogenous pST on performance in pigs; genotype and sex.*

	pST (mg/kg per day)	Gain (kg/day)	Accretion rate (g/d) Protein	Fat
Genotype and pST				
Strain A	0	1.180	153	275
	0.1	1.520	251	134
B	0	0.992	110	355
	0.1	1.290	189	188
Sex and pST				
Boar	0	1.185	196	316
	0.1	1.341	238	202
Female	0	1.010	148	410
	0.1	1.237	232	185
Castrate	0	1.057	139	462
	0.1	1.224	234	222

From: Campbell (1988)

deposition in muscle and inhibits lipogenesis in adipose tissue. Examples of these responses were recorded by Campbell, Caperna, Steele and Mitchell (1987), shown in Table 7. The increases in protein deposition rate obtained with the use of pST are independent of genotype as the unpublished data of Campbell *et al*, presented by Campbell (1988), showed that two strains of pigs gave similar proportional responses in spite of very different initial rates of deposition (Table 8). However, there is an interaction with sex; again Campbell (1988) presented data which showed that the increases in protein deposition were greater for castrates and gilts than boars, resulting in similar levels of deposition for all animals (Table 8).

The significance of the responses to pST in terms of nutrient requirements is demonstrated in experiments which have also examined the protein content of the diet. Fowler, Kay, Thikey, Livingstone, Pennie and Hart (1989) treated pigs with 0, 1.75, 3.50 or 7.00 mg/day and used two diets, 165 g CP/kg or 190 g CP/kg. Pigs given the diet with 165 g CP/kg gained 877, 892, 937 and 908 g/d, respectively and those on the 190 g CP/kg diet 864, 983, 995 and 1,040 g/d. Carcass CP (g/kg) was 177, 185, 196, 192 and 185, 194, 203 and 206 and carcass lipid (g/kg) was 243, 214, 181, 177 and 219, 183, 156, 123, respectively. The diet with the higher CP content allowed the pigs to express a greater response to the administered pST. Campbell, Johnson, King and Taverner (1989) employed two levels of pST with six levels of dietary crude protein (Table 9). In pigs of 30 to 60 kg liveweight rate of protein deposition increased and fat deposition was reduced, with increasing dietary CP up to 175 g/kg and the administration of pST further enhanced the protein deposition at the higher levels of dietary CP. However, at the two lowest levels of CP the pST had no effect on protein deposition but fat deposition was reduced at all levels. For pigs growing from 60 to 90 kg liveweight similar responses were seen (Table 9) but they were proportionately larger than in the lighter pigs and continued up to the highest CP level. Campbell *et al* (1989) concluded that the responses in protein anabolism to pST were dependent on dietary CP content but the effects on lipogenesis were independent of CP and the effect on protein deposition. Taking the results of the two experiments together, it appeared that for pST-treated animals, the level of dietary CP required to support maximum protein deposition was related to liveweight. In the lighter animals, treated and untreated animals reached a maximum response at similar levels of dietary CP but in the heavier pigs the response continued up to the highest level of CP used.

ENHANCEMENT OF FOOD VALUE

The three methods of enhancing food value considered here are by plant breeding, by the addition of enzymes to the diet and by the supplementation of the diet with synthetic amino acids.

Selective plant breeding has resulted in improved cereal composition, the reduction of toxic factors in foods and has produced new food varieties. The cereals maize and barley provide energy for farm animal diets, especially for pigs and poultry. They also provide a significant proportion of the protein supply but the balance of amino acids in cereal protein (i.e. their biological value) tends to be poor. For example, the lysine content of the crude protein in maize and barley is 30 and 34 g/kg respectively, but the lysine in ideal protein for the pig is 70 g/kg (ARC, 1981). In an attempt to improve this situation, plant breeders have produced varieties with increased amino acid content. In the case of maize, which is particularly deficient in lysine and tryptophan, the variety Opaque-2 has an increased lysine content and is nutritionally superior to normal maize, but only in methionine-supplemented diets (McDonald, Edwards and Greenhalgh, 1988). The newer variety, Floury-2, has improved lysine and methionine contents and is superior to Opaque-2 (McDonald *et al*, 1988). Similar attempts are being made to

TABLE 9 *Effects of pST and dietary crude protein.*

pST (mg/kg per day)	Dietary CP (kg/kg)	Daily gain (g)	Protein (g/d)	Fat (g/d)	Backfat thickness (mm)
Pigs growing from 30 to 60 kg liveweight					
0	83	605	72	234	-
	114	712	108	203	-
	145	776	122	210	-
	176	871	144	200	-
	207	790	146	192	-
	238	866	139	187	-
0.09	83	583	71	186	-
	114	750	111	175	-
	145	908	152	162	-
	176	977	166	133	-
	207	1007	173	123	-
	238	1004	174	98	-
Pigs growing from 60 to 90 kg liveweight					
0	70	628	-	-	20.5
	103	803	-	-	19.8
	137	862	-	-	18.6
	171	823	-	-	20.2
	204	887	-	-	17.2
	238	860	-	-	18.4
0.09	70	588	-	-	17.0
	103	760	-	-	15.0
	137	961	-	-	12.4
	171	1108	-	-	14.2
	204	1204	-	-	14.0
	238	1338	-	-	13.1

From: Campbell *et al* (1989)

improve the amino acid content of barley protein. The methods used are in three areas:

- decreasing the amount of low-lysine storage protein
- manipulating the protein fractions of the grain to increase those with high-lysine content
- selecting for mutant varieties with increased pools of free amino acids by manipulating plant enzyme activity (Armstrong, 1986).

There have been great successes by plant breeders developing low glucosinolate rapeseed varieties. Glucosinolates present in the seeds are converted by the accompanying thioglucosidase enzyme into thiocyanates and goitrogens, thus severely limiting the use of rapeseed meal in diets for monogastrics. The development of low glucosinolate varieties (double-low) was initiated in Canada, resulting in the production of canola meals and now European double-low varieties are available for use in monogastric diets. Varieties of rapeseed with lower tannin and fibre content (triple-low) are currently under development (Edwards, 1989).

Selective breeding has also resulted in glandless varieties of cotton which lack the toxic material gossypol present in normal varieties, but little of the new varieties are grown (Aherne and Kennelly, 1982), presumably due to difficulties in crop production or yield.

Plant breeding techniques have provided new food varieties for animals, an example of which is triticale. This is a cross between wheat and rye and has an ability to grow in areas that are marginal for wheat and has a higher amino acid content (Farrell, Chan and McCrae, 1983). Typical lysine contents are around 4.4 g/kg compared with 3.1 g/kg for wheat. Although the determined DE of triticale was similar to that of wheat, pigs do not always perform as well as with wheat-based diets and this was attributed to the presence of an anti-trypsin factor (Farrell *et al*, 1983).

Another new variety of cereal is naked oats which loses the husk during threshing. Naked oats were used successfully in diets for early weaned pigs when they replaced expensive cooked oatflakes (Davies, 1987) but Evans, Fowler and Fordyce (1985) found that the extra amino acid content relative to other cereals was not used as efficiently as those contributed by skimmed milk or fish meal.

With current advances in biotechnology active enzyme preparations can be produced in large quantities and relatively inexpensively. Thus supplementation of a diet as a means of improving food value is a practical possibility. Early experiments involving the addition of enzymes to diets yielded variable and confusing responses, mainly because they were impure materials (Chesson, 1987). The use of enzymes falls into one of three categories (Chesson, 1987; Rotter, Marquardt and Guenter, 1989). Firstly to increase the bioavailability of polysaccharides and proteins. Early work with crude enzyme preparations of α amylase increased weight gains in poultry fed maize/soya bean meal diets but the pure enzyme gave little response. Digestion of starch by the host animal's α amylase is generally very effective and the response to the crude preparations was probably due to some other enzyme activity (Chesson, 1987).

Secondly, enzymes are used to break down antinutritive properties in foods and thus increase the value of poor food ingredients. The major application in this category has been the use of β glucanase in barley-based diets for poultry. The polysaccharide β glucan present in barley is poorly digested and forms a viscous gum in the digestive tract, hindering the digestion and absorption of

TABLE 10 *Effect of β glucanase on performance of broilers.*

Diet type	Intake (g)	Gain (g)	Food/ gain	Vent pasting (%)
Wheat	2,910	1,527	1.90	10.0
Barley	2,941	1,473	2.00	73.8
Barley + enzyme	2,992	1,638	1.83	18.9

From: Rotter *et al* (1989)

other nutrients. In poultry this results in poor performance and sticky droppings (Rotter *et al*, 1989). The β glucan content of barley depends on the variety, date of harvest and growing conditions (Chesson, 1987). β glucanase treatment of barley improved the time taken for broilers to reach 1.8 kg from 43.2 days without the enzyme to 40.6 days, similar to the value of 39.1 days for a wheat/maize diet (Campbell, Classen and Salmon, 1984). Rotter *et al* (1989) demonstrated similar improvements in performance of broiler chicks and the inclusion of enzyme reduced litter problems (Table 10). These authors also presented data which showed that the metabolizable energy (ME) value of a barley-based diet was increased by the addition of β glucanase and was similar to that of a diet based on wheat. Chesson (1987) presented a table showing improvements of up to 30% in liveweight gain and 22% in food conversion efficiency. With pigs, Graham, Aman and Lowgren (1988) found that the inclusion of β glucanase in a barley-based diet resulted in improved ileal and faecal digestibilities of nutrients. Other foods which would potentially benefit from the application of enzymes are linseed and guar, both of which contain gel forming polysaccharides.

The third potential benefit from the application of enzymes is in the breakdown of the fibrous constituents of foods. Mammals and birds do not produce digestive enzymes capable of attacking fibrous plant cell wall components and these are usually broken down by microbial fermentation in the gut. If enzymes could be added to food to break down fibre, then more of the nutrients in the food would be released and the fermentation products of fibre could also be used as nutrients. Again Chesson (1987) presented a table summarizing the response of poultry and pigs to the supplementation of diets with plant cell wall degrading enzymes. In both species there were small responses of 5 to 10% improvement in liveweight gain and about 10% in food conversion efficiency, or no response at all. Chesson (1987) pointed out that several reports do not give adequate details of the enzyme preparations used, making interpretation of results difficult. The activity of cell wall degrading enzymes is constrained by several factors such as the noncarbohydrate fraction (e.g. lignin).

The reasoning behind the supplementation of diets with enzymes has been to complement the host animal's enzymes and convert foods from a low to a high energy content. To be effective the enzyme must be carefully chosen. Originally enzymes were those from the human food and detergent industries and were not applicable. The enzyme should be selected on the basis of its target substrate and careful consideration must be given to its delivery to the site of action. Unlike industrial processes, the gut has a wide range of pH and the enzyme must be able to survive such fluctuations, be resistant to the proteolytic activity of the stomach and be active at the conditions prevailing in the appropriate part of the gut. Also in practice it is most convenient to add an enzyme at the feed mill and therefore it must survive pelleting.

Previous mention has been made of the efforts of plant breeders to improve the amino acid content of cereals. An alternative approach, which allows the efficient use of protein foods, is to supplement the diet with synthetic amino acids produced industrially or from microorganisms. It is now common practice to supplement poultry diets with DL-methionine and pig diets with L-lysine hydrochloride. Recently significant quantities of L-threonine production have made it feasible to supplement diets with this amino acid. As lysine, methionine and threonine are the first limiting amino acids in barley/soya bean meal diets for pigs (Madsen, Mortensen and Hall, 1987), synthetic amino acids are now a real option in formulating diets with a reduced total crude protein content. The pig cannot use amino acids that are surplus to requirement for protein deposition and these are metabolized for yielding energy, the associated excretion of waste nitrogen being a process requiring energy (Whittemore, 1983). Thus supplements of amino acids can be used to balance those from the other diet ingredients, ensuring efficient use of protein.

Batterham (1974) reported that the utilization of free lysine was poorer with once daily compared with frequent feeding and Cole and Bong (1989) presented results showing a similar effect with free threonine. Low (1980) examined the data of Batterham (1974) and concluded that improvements in the utilization of free amino acids as a result of frequent feeding were small. Since there is a trend towards feeding rapidly growing modern pigs *ad libitum,* this aspect should not be a problem.

An example of the potential to reduce the level of protein supplement used and the CP content of the diet can be seen where barley and soya bean meal are used to formulate a diet with 10 g lysine/kg. This requires a mix of 744 g barley and 256 g soya bean meal/kg and the mix has 189 g CP/kg. By using 2 g L-lysine hydrochloride, the same dietary lysine content can be achieved with 803 g barley and 195 g soya bean meal and the mix has 169 g CP/kg.

Inborr and Suomi (1988) fed pigs growing from 31 to 105 kg liveweight one of two diets containing the same amounts of lysine, methionine and threonine. The first diet contained 170 g CP/kg while the second had a reduced level of soya bean meal and increased levels of free lysine, methionine and threonine such that it contained 155 g CP/kg. The pigs on the lower CP diet showed a better performance and carcass quality (Table 11).

It is with young pigs that the opportunity to reduce CP level in the diet is

TABLE 11 *Performance of pigs given diets differing in CP content but with the same content of lysine, methionine and threonine.*

	Diet CP (g/kg)	
	170	**155**
Daily weight gain (g)	743	788
Food/gain (kg/kg)	2.95	2.84
Protein/gain (kg/kg)	0.50	0.44
Carcase quality % of carcases in		
E+	33.3	58.3
E	33.3	16.7
I	33.4	25.0
R	0.0	0.0

From: Inborr and Suomi (1988)

greatest. Gatel and Fekete (1987) recorded improvements in growth rate and food utilization in piglets growing from 10 to 28 kg liveweight when they were offered a diet with 177 g CP/kg containing free lysine and threonine (gain 626 g/day; 1.71 kg food/kg gain) compared with those offered a diet where all the supplementary amino acids came from soya bean meal and contained 238 g CP/kg (gain 595 g/day; 1.74 kg food/kg gain). Inborr and Suomi (1988) obtained similar performance from piglets growing to eight weeks of age when they were offered diets with the same lysine, methionine and threonine contents but with 183 g CP/kg or with a reduced level of soya bean meal and 167 g CP/kg.

The experiments of Gatel and Fekete (1987) and Inborr and Suomi (1988) involved the multiple supplementation of diets with amino acids; lysine and threonine in the former and lysine, threonine and methionine in the latter. As more amino acids are produced, either industrially or by microorganisms, the opportunity to reduce further the level of protein supplementation and increase efficiency of utilization of protein will become more widespread. However, there will always come a point where the next amino acid becomes limiting and protein supplementation must be sustained to satisfy the requirement until cheap sources of that amino acid are available. For example, Morgan and Whittemore (unpublished) supplemented diets for young pigs growing from 10 to 20 kg liveweight with free lysine, methionine, threonine and tryptophan but peformance was poorer than on a diet where the amino acids were supplied by herring meal (Table 12). Whereas the requirements (ARC, 1981) for these four amino acids were adequately met in all three diets, the diets WA and WAF were deficient in the other essential amino acids when expressed as a ratio to lysine (Table 12). The reduced

TABLE 12 *Performance of piglets on amino acid and herring meal supplemented diets.*

	Diet			
	WF[1]	WA[2]	WAF[3]	ARC (1981)
Ingredient (g/kg)				
Micronized wheat	758	867	825	–
Herring meal	208	-	80	–
L-lysine HCl	–	14.5	8.9	–
DL-methionine	–	7.0	5.5	–
L-threonine	–	7.4	5.2	–
DL-tryptophan	–	1.7	1.2	–
Maize oil	11	50	34	–
Minerals etc.	23	52.4	40.2	–
Composition (g/kg)				
DE (MJ)	14.8	14.8	14.8	–
CP	224	132	165	–
Lysine	13.2	14.0	13.2	–
Methionine	4.8	10.5	9.9	–
Threonine	7.5	8.9	8.5	–
Tryptophan	1.8	2.0	2.0	–
Performance (10 to 20 kg liveweight)				
Daily gain (kg)	0.404	0.235	0.366	–
Food kg/kg gain	1.568	2.236	1.666	–
Ratio of amino acids to lysine (= 100)				
Isoleucine	68	34	45	55
Leucine	117	59	80	100
Histidine	58	35	48	33
Phenylalanine plus tyrosine	122	66	86	96
Valine	76	36	55	70

[1]WF Wheat and herring meal diet
[2]WA Wheat and synthetic amino acids diet
[3]WAF Wheat, herring meal and synthetic amino acids diet

From: Morgan and Whittemore (unpublished)

performance on diets WA and WAF was due to lower food intake, a response typical of a dietary imbalance of amino acids (Harper and Rogers, 1965).

Free amino acids do have a most useful role in diet formulation in promoting the more efficient use of dietary protein, but their use must not be to the extent that they jeopardize the levels of the other essential amino acids.

BIOLOGY AND COMPUTER TECHNOLOGY

The advances in biotechnology described in the previous three sections have the potential to increase productivity in monogastric animals of both developed and developing countries. Whereas their efficacy requires demonstration by animal experimentation, their application to individual farm systems must also be ensured. This necessitates adequate models of the production system to predict response. Such models have been developed for growing poultry by Emmans (1981) and for pigs by Whittemore (1983) and Black *et al* (1986). The models require adequate description of the food and the animal and ever more sophisticated points of detail are being developed, so that the models necessarily become more and more complex. Recent advances in computer technology, which have produced the powerful personal microcomputer, offer the animal nutritionist the ability to take into account these complex points of detail.

In the case of the description of the food, accurate knowledge of its energy content is essential for prediction of response. In the practical situation the ingredient composition of the food may not be known and a prediction of energy value is required. Morgan, Whittemore, Phillips and Crooks (1987) developed several equations to predict the DE of pig foods from their chemical analysis, the best being

$$\text{DE (MJ/kg DM)} = 17.49 - 14.9\ \text{NDF} + 15.7\ \text{OIL} + 7.8\ \text{CP} - 32.5\ \text{ASH}$$

where NDF is neutral detergent fibre and OIL is petroleum spirit extract and all components are expressed as kg/kg DM. Although NDF is the major negative contributor to prediction equations for DE, fibre is digested by microflora in the hind gut of the pig and the end products (volatile fatty acids) are absorbed by the pig as a source of nutrients (ARC, 1981). This is an active area of research and recent work by Close, Longland and Low (1989) has indicated that the nutrients yielded from fibre are used very efficiently. It is likely that a better description of the fibre component of the diet, and its effect on dietary energy, will be obtained from more complex analytical methods such as the profile of the nonstarch polysaccharides (Englyst and Cummings, 1984).

In the case of protein nutrition of pigs, current requirements are expressed in terms of the balance of the total dietary amino acids (ARC, 1981). This balance was defined as that in pig lean tissue and thus assumed that digestibility and efficiency of utilization of each amino acid are the same for all amino acids in all foods. There is now cause to reconsider these assumptions. The most accurate measure of digestibility of amino acids is that determined at the terminal ileum. Bacteria in the hind gut ferment undigested food, including protein, interconverting the amino acids and forming bacterial protein. The consequence is that the pattern of amino acids appearing in the faeces is more like that of bacteria than the undigested protein. Also Zebrowska (1973 – quoted by Low, 1980) showed that all of the nitrogen from amino acids infused into the large intestine of pigs on a protein-free diet and which was absorbed, was excreted in the urine. Therefore the large intestine does not have a role in the amino acid nutrition of the pig. Hence digestibility of amino acids should be determined at a point after small intestine absorption and before interference by the hind gut bacteria i.e. at the terminal ileum.

It is now recognized that different foods have differing ileal digestibilities of amino acids and the digestibility differs for each amino acid within a food (Sauer and Ozimek, 1986). Once the amino acids have been digested they may be utilized with differing efficiencies. For example, Batterham (1989) found that even when diets were formulated to equal ileal digestibility, pigs performed less well on a diet containing cottonseed meal than one with soya bean meal. Whittemore (1983) suggested that the efficiency of utilization of digested amino acids was between 0.85 and 0.9 and Stranks, Cooke, Fairbairn, Fowler, Kirby, McCracken, Morgan, Palmer and Peers (1988) used a value of 0.85. Black *et al* (1986) used the concept of amino acid availability (i.e. digestible, absorbable and utilizable amino acids), based mainly on ileal digestibility but with a correction for individual feed ingredients. Due to lack of information, availability of lysine was applied to all amino acids, but again individual utilization values are required for each amino acid. In conclusion requirements are most accurately described in terms of the balance of digestible and utilizable amino acids (or available amino acids) and foods should also be described in this way (Batterham, 1989).

The animal should also be described in a manner which will allow the prediction of response to technological advances. For meat production systems, the rate of lean (protein) deposition is a key factor and the potential of the animal is most accurately decribed by a Gompertz relationship (Emmans, 1981)

$$Pr = B.Pt.\ln(Ptm/Pt)$$

where Pr is the potential protein deposition rate, B is the rate of decline of the relative growth rate, Ptm is the mature protein mass and Pt is the current protein mass. Advances in animal breeding and the application of repartitioning agents require to be expressed in a form which can use this description of the animal.

Current models of nutrition are being refined to examine the detail of nutrient requirement (e.g. Moughan, 1989) and supply (e.g. Batterham, 1989; Close *et al,* 1989). In the near future the capacity and speed of microcomputers will make it possible to model the whole food-nutrient-animal system at the biochemical level as described by Gill, Thornley, Black, Oldham and Beever (1984).

CONCLUSIONS: APPLICATION OF BIOTECHNOLOGY IN MONOGASTRIC NUTRITION IN DEVELOPING COUNTRIES

This review has highlighted areas undergoing rapid change as a result of advances in biotechnology.

With the introduction of weaning of pigs as young as four weeks of age, the application of acidified foods and probiotics may prove useful against digestive upsets in piglets. Availability and relative cost will dictate their usage.

Genetic improvement of breeds will require more attention to the supply of nutrients if these improvements are to be realized and diet formulation will require careful selection of home-produced foods, balanced by imported materials. Again, although the remarkable responses to repartitioning agents offer an instant increase in animal protein production, availability of these materials will be a key factor governing their use. Responses of pigs to pST in terms of reduced fat deposition will not be desirable in those countries where fat remains of value. Careful diet formulation with high energy ingredients should allow the benefits of pST to be achieved without detriment to the deposition of fat if this is required.

In the field of enhancement of food value, enzymes may upgrade feedstuffs, providing the enzymes are selected carefully for the activity required. The feasibility of introducing new plant food varieties will depend on the growing conditions prevailing in any particular developing country. It is the availability of synthetic amino acids that will dictate their use.

The complexity of computer models in describing the animal/food system allows information on animals and foods to be presented at a level subsequent to the information collation and interpretation phases of the decision making process. Therefore, it is presented in a more simple way which enables prediction of response and optimum use of resources.

REFERENCES

Agricultural Research Council (1981). *The Nutrient Requirements of Pigs.* C.A.B., Slough.

Aherne, F.X. and Kennelly, J.J. (1982). Oilseed meals for livestock feeding. In *Recent Advances in Animal Nutrition, 1982* (eds. W. Haresign), pp. 39–89. Butterworths, London.

Armstrong, D.G. (1986). The potential implications of biotechnology in animal nutrition. In *Recent Advances in Animal Nutrition, 1986* (eds. W. Haresign and D.J.A. Cole), pp. 89–103. Butterworths, London.

Aumaitre, A. (1972). Development of enzyme activity in the digestive tract of the suckling pig: nutritional significance and implications for weaning. *World Review of Animal Production,* **8**, 54–68.

Batterham, E.S. (1974). The effect of frequency of feeding on the utilization of free lysine by growing pigs. *British Journal of Nutrition,* **31**, 237–242.

Batterham, E.S. (1989). Advances in the use of cottonseed meal in diets for growing pigs. In *Recent Advances in Animal Nutrition in Australia, 1989* (ed. D.J. Farrell), pp. 164–171. University of New England.

Black, J.L., Campbell, R.G., Williams, I.H., James, K.J. and Davies, G.T. (1986). Simulation of energy and amino acid utilization in the pig. *Research and Development in Agriculture,* **3**, 121–145.

Campbell, G.L., Classen, H.L. and Salmon, R.E. (1984). *Feedstuffs*, May 7, 1984, 26–27.

Campbell, R.G. (1988). Nutritional constraints to lean tissue accretion in farm animals. *Nutrition Research Reviews,* **1**, 233–253.

Campbell, R.G., Caperna, T.J., Steele, N.C. and Mitchell, A.D. (1987). Effects of porcine pituitary growth hormone (pGH) administration and energy intake on growth performance in pigs from 25–55 kg body weight. *Journal of Animal Science,* **65**, Supplement 1, p. 244.

Campbell, R.G., Johnson, R.J., King, R.H. and Traverner, M.R. (1989). Interactions between porcine growth hormone administration and dietary protein. In *Recent Advances in Animal Nutrition in Australia, 1989* (ed. D.J. Farrell), pp. 141–146. University of New England.

Chesson, A. (1987). Supplementary enzymes to improve the utilization of pig and poultry diets. In *Recent Advances in Animal Nutrition, 1987* (eds. W. Haresign and D.J.A. Cole), pp. 71–89. Butterworths, London.

Close, W.H., Longland, A.C. and Low, A.G. (1989). Energy metabolism studies on pigs fed diets containing sugar beet pulp. *Animal Production,* **48**, 625–626.

Cole, D.J.A., Beal, R.M. and Luscombe, J.R. (1968). The effect on performance and bacterial flora of lactic acid, propionic acid, calcium propionate and calcium acrylate in the drinking water of weaned pigs. *Veterinary Record,* **83**, 459–464.

Cole, D.J.A. and Bong, L. (1989). Ideal protein in pig nutrition with special reference to threonine. Paper presented to a *Symposium on Amino Acids in Animal Production.* Forum Chemicals Limited, Redhill, Surrey.

Cranwell, P.D. (1985). The development of acid and pepsin (EC3.4.23.1) secretary capacity in the pig; effects of age and weaning. 1. Studies on anaesthetized pigs. *British Journal of Nutrition,* **54**, 305–320.

Davies, O.D. (1987). Naked oats in the diets of young pigs. *Animal Production,* **44**, 487–488.

Easter, R.A. (1988). Acidification of diets for pigs. In *Recent Advances in Animal Nutrition, 1988* (eds. W. Haresign and D.J.A. Cole), pp. 61–71. Butterworths, London.

Edwards, S.A. (1989). The potential for new varieties of oilseed rape in pig and poultry diets. *The Feed Compounder, August 1989*, 24–26.

Elsley, F.W.H. (1971). Nutrition and lactation in the sow. In *Lactation* (ed. I.R. Falconer), pp. 393–411. Butterworths, London.

Emmans, G.C. (1981). A model of the growth and feed intake of *ad libitum* fed animals, particularly poultry. In *Computers in Animal Production* (eds. G.M. Hillyer, C.T. Whittemore and R.G. Gunn), pp. 103–110. Occasional Publication No. 5, British Society of Animal Production.

Englyst, H.N. and Cummings, J.H. (1984). Simplified method for the measurement of total nonstarch polysaccharides by gas-liquid chromatography of constituent sugars as alditol acetates. *Analyst,* **109**, 937-942.

Evans, J.B., Fowler, V.R. and Fordyce, R. (1985). Naked oats and other cereals in the diets of early weaned pigs. *Animal Production,* **40**, 549.

Farrell, D.J., Chan, C. and McCrae, F. (1983). A nutritional evaluation of triticale with pigs. *Animal Feed Science and Technology,* **9**, 49-62.

Fowler, V.R. (1980). The nutrition of weaner pigs. *Pig News and Information,* **1**, 11-15.

Fowler, V.R., Kay, M. Thikey, H.M., Livingstone, R.M., Pennie, K. and Hart, I.C. (1989). The effect of recombinant porcine somatotrophin on the growth of pigs given different concentrations of protein in the diet. *Animal Production,* **48**, 625.

Fuller, R. and Cole, C.B. (1989). The scientific basis of the probiotic concept. In *Probiotics. Theory and Application* (eds. B. A. Stark and J.M. Wilkinson), pp. 1-14. Chalcombe Publications, Buckinghamshire.

Gatel, F. and Fekete, J. (1987). Reduction du taux azote des aliments pour porcelets sevres. Contribution a l'étude du besoin en threonine. *Journées Recherche Porcine,* **19**, 265-270.

Giesting, D.W. (1986). Utilization of soy protein by the young pig. *PhD Thesis. University of Illinois, Urbana.*

Giesting, D.W. and Easter, R.A. (1985). Response of starter pigs to supplementation of corn-soybean meal diets with organic acids. *Journal of Animal Science,* **60**, 1288-1294.

Gill, M., Thornley, J.H.M., Black, J.L. Oldham, J.D. and Beever, D.E. (1984). Simulation of the metabolism of absorbed energy-yielding nutrients in young sheep. *British Journal of Nutrition,* **52**, 621-649.

Goihl, J. (1988). Repartitioning agents show promise in finishing swine. *Feedstuffs,* October 10, 1988, 17.

Graham, H., Aman, P. and Lowgren, W. (1988). Enzyme supplementation of pig feeds. *Proceedings of the 4th Symposium on Digestive Physiology in the Pig,* pp. 371-376. Jablonna, Poland.

Hanrahan, J.P., Quirke, J.F., Bomann, W., Allen, P. McEwan, J.C., Fitzsimons, J.M., Kotzian, J. and Roche, J.F. (1986). β-agonists and their effects on growth and carcass quality. In *Recent Advances in Animal Nutrition, 1986* (eds. W. Haresign and D.J.A. Cole), pp. 125-138. Butterworths, London.

Hanrahan, T.J. (1989). Response of growing pigs to lysine. Paper presented to a *Symposium on Amino Acids in Animal Production.* Forum Chemicals Limited, Redhill, Surrey.

Harper, A.E. and Rogers, Q.R. (1965). Amino acid imbalance. *Proceedings of the Nutrition Society,* **24**, 173-190.

Inborr, J. and Suomi, K. (1988). Industrial amino acids in diets for piglets and growing pigs. *Journal of Agricultural Science in Finland,* **60**, 673-683.

Kirchgessner, M. and Roth, F.X. (1980). Digestibility and balance of protein, energy and some minerals in diets for piglets supplemented with furmaric acid. *Zeitschrift für Tierphysilogie, Tierernahrung und Futtermittelkunde,* **44**, 239-246.

Kirchgessner, M. and Roth, F.X. (1982). Fumaric acid as a feed additive in pig nutrition. *Pig News and Information,* **3**, 259–264.

Low, A.G. (1980). Amino acid use by growing pigs. In *Recent Advances in Animal Nutrition, 1980* (ed. W. Haresign), pp. 141–156. Butterworths, London.

Madsen, A., Mortensen, H.P. and Hall, D.D. (1987). *Beretning fra Statens Husdryrbrugsforsog, No. 627.* National Institute of Animal Science, Denmark.

M.A.F.F. (1977). *Nutrient Allowances for Pigs.* A.D.A.S. Advisory Paper No. 7., 2nd edn. M.A.F.F., Pinner, Middlesex.

McDonald, P., Edwards, R.A. and Greenhalgh, J.F.D. (1988). *Animal Nutrition.* 4th edn. Longman Scientific and Technical, Harlow, Essex.

Morgan, C.A., Whittemore, C.T., Phillips, P. and Crooks, P. (1987). The prediction of the energy value of compounded pig foods from chemical analysis. *Animal Feed Science and Technology,* **17**, 81–107.

Moughan, P.J. (1989). Simulation of the daily partitioning of lysine in the 50 kg liveweight pig – a factorial approach to estimating amino acid requirements for growth and maintenance. *Research and Development in Agriculture,* **6**, 7–14.

Pollmann, D.S. (1986). Probiotics in pig diets. In *Recent Advances in Animal Nutrition, 1986* (eds. W. Haresign and D.J.A. Cole), pp. 193–205. Butterworths, London.

Rotter, B.A., Marquardt, R.R. and Guenter, W. (1989). Enzymes in feed – they really can be made to work. Paper presented to *Alltech European Lecture Tour 1989, Biotechnology in the Feed Industry.* Alltech U.K., Clwyd.

Sauer, W.C. and Ozimek, L. (1986). Digestibility of amino acids in swine: results and their practical application. A Review. *Livestock Production Science,* **15**, 367–388.

Sissons, J.W. (1988). The potential of probiotic organisms to prevent diarrhoea and promote digestion. *Proceedings of the 4th Symposium on Digestive Physiology in the Pig,* pp. 357–370. Jablonna, Poland.

Stranks, M.H., Cooke, B.C., Fairbairn, C.B., Fowler, N.G., Kirby, P.S., McCracken, K.J., Morgan, C.A., Palmer, F.G. and Peers, D.G. (1988). Nutrient allowances for growing pigs. *Research and Development in Agriculture,* **5**, 71–88.

Thacker, P.A. (1988). Novel approaches to growth promotion in the pig. In *Recent Advances in Animal Nutrition, 1988* (eds. W. Haresign and D.J.A. Cole), pp. 73–84. Butterworths, London.

White, F., Wenham, G., Sharman, G.A.M., Jones, A.S., Rattray, E.A.S. and McDonald, I. (1969). Stomach function in relation to a scour syndrome in the piglet. *British Journal of Nutrition,* **23**, 847–858.

Whittemore, C.T. (1983). Development of recommended energy and protein allowances for growing pigs. *Agricultural Systems,* **11**, 159–186.

Whittemore, C.T. and Yang, H. (1989). Physical and chemical composition of the body of breeding sows with differing body subcutaneous fat depth at parturition, differing nutrition during lactation and differing litter size. *Animal Production,* **48**, 203–212.

3.4

Manipulation of Animal Growth

R.B. HEAP
AFRC Institute of Animal Physiology and Genetics Research, Cambridge, U.K.

INTRODUCTION

Advances in biotechnology arising from the application of molecular biology techniques have signalled a new era of investigation into the regulation of growth in animals, including man. Many of these developments were described at recent international symposia including 'Biotechnology in Growth Regulation' held at this Institute in Cambridge in September, 1988 (Heap, Prosser and Lamming, 1989) and 'Bioscience in Animal Production' held at the University of Warwick, Coventry in June 1989 (Heap, 1989). The purpose of this paper will be to highlight new findings which emerged at both these meetings and in subsequent publications in respect of the hormonal and immunological manipulation of growth. A number of these findings are relevant to enhancing the efficiency of milk secretion in dairy animals and are discussed in detail by Dr. T.B. Mepham in this volume.

GROWTH HORMONE (GH)

A primary objective of research into the control of growth processes in domestic animals is to identify ways of increasing protein accumulation within the body, a vertebrate equivalent of nitrogen fixation in plants. Increasing the efficiency of protein accretion has economic and environmental implications since it relates to improved use of valuable nitrogenous sources from plants grown in developed or developing countries.

Growth hormone (or somatotropin, ST) is an endocrine agent that acts to promote cell growth in several tissues of the body by a range of different mechanisms. It stimulates the synthesis of proteins and the polypeptide growth factor, insulin-like growth factor I (IGF-I), and exerts a variety of metabolic effects on carbohydrate metabolism and lipid mobilization. GH is a single polypeptide chain of 190 amino acids found in some form in all vertebrate groups with the possible exception of primitive jawless fishes. Although variant forms of the hormone have been reported, amino acid sequences show that its primary structure is very similar in various nonprimate species, though markedly different in humans. A hypothetical GH sequence has been derived for the common ancestor of placental mammals which reveals that the closest similarity is found in the pig followed by horse, rat, cow, sheep/goat, human (Wallis, 1989). The relationship of GH to placental lactogens is more complex, and although in man these hormones share a similar sequence, in nonprimates the placental lactogens are more closely related to prolactin than to GH (Schuler and Hurley, 1987).

Structure-function studies of GH are increasingly important for understanding the multiple ways by which growth hormone has its effects in the body. The tertiary structure of recombinant porcine (p)ST has been recently reported and it reveals that about 55% of the polypeptide chain is in the form of an α-helix, folded to give four helices in an antiparallel, twisted helical bundle (Abdel-Meguid, Shieh, Smith, Dayringer, Violand and Bentle, 1987). It remains a matter of debate whether all the actions of this molecule stem from one primary event such as its interaction with a single membrane receptor, or whether different receptors in various tissues are involved in recognizing different parts of the tertiary structure of the hormone to produce a multiplicity of effects.

The importance of GH receptors in mediating the effects of the hormone is evident from studies of human dwarfs which lack liver GH receptors and serum GH binding protein. When a specific monoclonal antibody was used to locate the normal distribution of GH receptors, antibody was concentrated in target tissues such as the growth plate chondrocytes of long bones. Messenger RNA for the cloned receptor was also present in cells of GH target tissues (Waters, Spencer, Leung, Hammonds, Cachianes, Henzel, Wood, Barnard, Quirk and Hamlin, 1989). Gluckman and Breier (1989) have reported that hepatic GH membrane receptor may exist in at least two affinity states, and that the capacity of the high affinity site is correlated with growth rate in ruminants. Gluckman's laboratory, as well as that of others, demonstrated that nutrition has a substantial effect on the GH receptor in the bovine. In animals on high nutritional intake, GH secretion was low and high affinity GH binding sites were present on liver cells which were enhanced after oestradiol administration. At maintenance nutritional intake, GH secretion was increased but high affinity binding sites could not be detected (Breier, Gluckman and Bass, 1988). Thus, in the ruminant it appears that GH receptors are regulated by endocrine and nutritional mechanisms and this finding has important implications for the application of recombinant products where the nutritional status of animals is low.

Availability of recombinant ST has made it possible to produce large amounts of pure GH for experimental studies. (The abbreviation ST will be used to indicate recombinantly-derived GH, though the structures of pituitary and recombinant GH are virtually identical apart from minor modifications of the N-terminal sequence.) Treatment of lambs with bST (bovine ST, 0.1 mg/kg/day) from 9 to 20 weeks of age produced a 36% increase in weight compared with control lambs. The lambs were fed a 16% crude protein diet with an intake of 40 g per kg liveweight. The treatment produced a decrease in the amount of visceral fat (−30%) and an increase in intestines (+15%), liver (+12%) and certain skeletal muscles. Lipid synthesis was inhibited in subcutaneous and visceral adipose tissue, whereas protein synthesis rate in certain muscles was increased (Pell, 1989). Decreased lipid synthesis and enhanced lipolysis, which have been observed in several studies of the action of GH on adipocytes, also depend on the energy balance of the animal. Decreased lipogenesis is more important in positive energy balance while enhanced lipolysis is apparent if the animal is in negative energy balance (Vernon and Flint, 1989).

Efficiency of growth performance is substantially increased in growing pigs treated with pST. The magnitude of the response varies with reported increases ranging from 10 to 20% in average daily weight gain, 15 to 35% in improved feed efficiency, up to 50% in protein deposition with a reduction in adipose tissue mass and lipid accretion rates of 50 to 80%. These effects were associated with a stimulation of satellite cell proliferation in skeletal muscle (Dodson, Allen and Hossner, 1985), inhibition of glucose utilization by adipocytes due to a decrease in glucose transport, fatty acid synthesis and inhibition of several lipogenic enzymes, and antagonism of the stimulatory effects of insulin on glucose utilization in adipose tissue (Etherton, 1989). Administration of pST stimulated plasma IGF-I concentration and the production of the 150 kDa IGF-I-binding protein in plasma (Etherton, 1989).

The potential impact of bST on efficiency is strikingly illustrated by its effects on milk secretion (Bauman, Eppard, DeGeeter and Lanza, 1985; Peel and Bauman, 1987). The galactopoietic response in cows treated with pituitary or recombinant bST amounted to increased milk yields ranging from about 10 to 30% with significant improvements in gross efficiency of milk production. The response was associated with rises in mammary blood flow, efficiency of milk secretion, and mammary uptake of glucose and acetate (Heap, Fleet, Fullerton, Davis, Goode, Hart, Pendleton, Prosser, Silvester and Mepham, 1989). As one of the first major products of recombinant DNA technology for the animal industries, bST has been rigorously tested in large numbers of cows under various management conditions in different countries. It has been shown to be effective in capital intensive systems and in simpler systems using flat rate feeding of concentrates and grazing pasture, and promises to provide a valuable product for enhancing the efficiency of dairy animals (Peel, Eppard and Hard, 1989).

Growth factors

Whether or not growth hormone acts directly on tissues to produce cell proliferation and protein accretion remains a topic of scientific investigation. GH has long been recognized as the main stimulator of longitudinal bone growth and there is evidence for a direct effect on the proliferation and maturation of the proximal cells in the growth plate column (Schlechter, Russell, Greenberg, Spencer and Nicoll, 1986; Isaksson, Janson and Gause, 1982). Recently it has been shown that some actions of GH on bone marrow (erythropoiesis and granulopoiesis) are mediated by IGF-I (Hochberg, Maor, Lewinson and Silbermann, 1989), supporting the hypothesis that GH does not always produce its effects directly. This argument was further strengthened by experiments in hypophysectomized and diabetic rats in which infusions of recombinant IGF-I for 18 days were as effective as human (h)ST in increasing body weight. Adipose deposits were reduced by hIGF-I even more than by hST (Guler, Zapf, Binz and Froesch, 1989).

Attention is now being given to the possibility that IGF-I may also be used to manipulate animal growth. Serum levels of IGF-I parallel body size in poodles of different breeds, so that mini-poodles have low IGF-I levels compared to king poodles (Eigenmann, Patterson and Froesch, 1984). Infusions of hIGF-I, however, failed to enhance the growth rate of endocrine-competent mini-poodles (Guler *et al*, 1989). Other studies in hypophysectomized rats showed a significant response in body weight change, but only at a high dose (Skottner, Clark, Robinson and Fryklund, 1987). Differences of opinion remain, therefore, about the role of IGF-I as a growth promoter. IGF-I in circulation is largely bound by high-affinity binding proteins which are believed to diminish the biological activity of the growth factor. It could be that IGF-I which is locally produced in tissues has a more important role in growth regulation of certain cell types than IGF-I in circulation. If this is the case, the paracrine (cell to cell) effects of the growth factor may be more significant than its endocrine (systemic circulation) actions. Indeed, exogenous administration of the growth factor would be thought less likely to produce an effect because of plasma protein binding in circulation.

Evidence for a direct effect of IGF-I on the mammary gland, however, has been observed when the growth factor was infused directly into the pudic (mammary) artery of goats for six hours. This resulted in an increase in the rate of milk secretion by $30 \pm 5\%$ compared with that in the adjacent noninfused gland ($15 \pm 4\%$, $P < 0.05$). Mammary blood flow in the infused gland also increased substantially during IGF-I infusion but not during a control saline infusion (Prosser, Fleet and Heap, 1989). As stated earlier, there is an increase in mammary blood flow during treatment of lactating cows with bST. Treatment with bST also produces a raised level of IGF-I in systemic circulation and in milk (Prosser, Fleet and Corps, 1989) so that IGF-I may be responsible for increased mammary blood flow and milk secretion in cows treated with bST. The explanation of these findings may reside in an increase of free IGF-I reaching the mammary gland initially. Receptors for IGF-I, IGF-II and insulin are present on mammary epithelial cells during growth, differentiation and lactation. It will be important to test the efficacy of truncated forms of IGF-I since these compounds possess high biological activity in respect of mammary growth probably because they are bound less effectively by plasma IGF-I-binding proteins (Collier, Ganguli, Menke, Buonomo, McGrath, Kotts and Krivi, 1989) and therefore partially escape the neutralizing effect of plasma protein binding.

Among other polypeptide growth factors, IGF-II may prove to have considerable influence on fetal and neonatal growth. There is a notable interaction between different polypeptide growth factors in the regulation of cell growth and this means that individual compounds should not be studied in isolation. Due regard should be given to growth factor synergism which has been demonstrated using defined cell cultures *in vitro*.

IMMUNOLOGICAL MANIPULATION

Among the manipulative procedures described so far, all require frequent administration by skilled staff which inevitably limits their practical application. Two alternative techniques offer the prospect of longer term effects, one by an immunological approach and the other by germline modification achieved through transgenesis.

Antibodies which look and act like bST can be produced by raising anti-idiotypic mimics. Monoclonal antibodies to bST (idiotypic antibodies) can be injected into rabbits to produce a second set of polyclonal antibodies (anti-antibodies or anti-idiotypes). This second set of antibodies contains mimics that bind to bST receptors but not to receptors for other hormones such as prolactin or insulin. Further studies have shown that bST or bST mimics stimulated growth in rats which were deficient in their own growth hormone (Flint, Stevenson, Gardner, Crilly and Beattie, 1989). The idea has been proposed that monoclonal idiotypic antibodies could be used to vaccinate cows to produce anti-idiotypic mimics. The attraction of the procedure is that frequent administration would be unnecessary. The potential disadvantage rests in the difficulty of identifying the ideal idiotypic immunogen to provide the correct specificity of sufficient duration to promote an effective anti-idiotypic response.

Another approach adopted for immunization against pregnancy (Wang, Heap and Taussig, 1989) concerns the use of anti-idiotypic antibodies as 'surrogate antigens' to stimulate an idiotypic response. Administration of certain anti-GH monoclonal antibodies has been shown to enhance bovine growth hormone activity *in vivo* (Holder, Aston, Preece and Ivanyi, 1985; Holder, Blows, Aston and Bates, 1988; Aston, Holder, Preece and Ivanyi, 1986; Aston, Holder, Ivanyi and Bomford, 1987; Holder and Aston, 1989), and further work is required to establish whether similar potentiation can be achieved with appropriate anti-idiotypes.

TRANSGENESIS

The introduction of copies of cloned genes into the early embryo offers the potential to manipulate animal growth by germline modification. In 1982 Palmiter and colleagues published their striking results in mice whereby growth rate was dramatically increased by injection of fertilized eggs with a metallothionein-growth hormone fusion gene (Palmiter, Brinster, Hammer, Trumbauer, Rosenfeld, Birnberg and Evans, 1982). Later studies in sheep and pigs have produced less convincing results since growth rate has not been consistently increased nor feed efficiency enhanced. One of the problems seems to relate to the unregulated expression of GH which results in excessively high concentrations of the hormone in circulation with attendant problems of joint pathology, reproductive disorders and decreased appetite (Pursel, Miller, Bolt, Pinkert, Hammer, Palmiter and Brinster, 1989). Considerable reduction in the deposition of fat was noted in these studies (Vize, Michalska, Ashman, Lloyd, Stone, Quinn, Wells and Seamark, 1988; Pursel *et al*, 1989).

In the light of these findings research has concentrated on understanding how the expression of a foreign growth hormone gene can be targeted to specific tissues, and how the expression can be induced or switched-off at particular stages of development and growth. Current work in Cambridge has shown the integration of a bovine prolactin-growth hormone fusion gene into pigs following microinjection into the pronuclei of fertilized ova. This gene is found to be expressed at a low level but can be induced by a dopamine antagonist or by thyrotrophin hormone-releasing hormone. The results show that the foreign gene is regulated through its promoter by the normal feedback mechanisms that control prolactin secretion. The activity can be controlled and the prospect exists of manipulating expression at specific periods of the growth phase (Polge, Barton, Surani, Miller, Wagner, Rottman, Camper, Elsome, Davis, Goode, Foxcroft and Heap, 1989).

ACCEPTABILITY

The advances reviewed in this paper raise important issues regarding acceptability both in terms of the target species and the consumer, and applicability in developing and developed countries. Potential problems that are receiving close attention include the impact of biotechnological innovations on animal welfare. Metabolic disease in animals already operating at high metabolic rates, as in high-yielding dairy animals, is an obvious aspect of concern (Kronfeld, 1988; Webster, 1988). Yet results obtained so far with bST over a range of treatments have failed to identify such problems even in cows given large doses for prolonged periods (Peel *et al*, 1989). Nevertheless, the importance of adequate nutrition and good husbandry practice remains if these techniques are to become acceptable in animal husbandry. Limitations in animal nutrition will restrict the application of these techniques in certain developing countries, and parallel advances are required in the control of disease and improvements in fertility.

Mepham (1989) has discussed other important concerns about perceived biological risks alleged to be associated with biotechnological applications. For the treated animal these concerns relate not only to the physiological responses but also behaviour and disease susceptibility. For the consumer they include questions about concentrations of biologically-active constituents in food, and for the agricultural industry a range of socioeconomic consequences arising from increased production. Research findings with bST demonstrate that the functional activity of porcine or bovine GH in the human is low, partly on account of gastrointestinal proteolytic degradation and partly because of structural dissimilarities (Wallis, 1989). In respect of socioeconomic consequences, the relatively rapid reduction in surpluses in the U.K. with the introduction of quotas and 'set aside' will probably increase the requirement for increased efficiency in animal performance leading to savings in valuable resources. Biotechnological advances may therefore prove most timely in their impact on agricultural practice.

This paper was presented in part to a Royal Agricultural Society of England International Symposium on 'Bioscience in Animal Production', 27 June–3 July, 1989 held at the University of Warwick, Coventry.

REFERENCES

Abdel-Meguid, S.S., Shieh, H.-S., Smith, W.W., Dayringer, H.E., Violand, B.N. and Bentle, L.A. (1987). Three-dimensional structure of a genetically engineered variant of porcine growth hormone. *Proceedings of the National Academy of Sciences, U.S.A.*, **84**, 6434–6437.

Aston, R., Holder, A.T., Ivanyi, J. and Bomford, R. (1987). Enhancement of bovine growth hormone activity *in vivo* by monoclonal antibodies. *Molecular Immunology*, **24**, 143–150.

Aston, R., Holder, A.T., Preece, M.A. and Ivanyi, J. (1986). Potentiation of the somatogenic and lactogenic activity of human growth hormone with monoclonal antibodies. *Journal of Endocrinology*, **110**, 381–388.

Bauman, D.E., Eppard, P.J., DeGeeter, M.J. and Lanza, G.M. (1985). Responses of high producing dairy cows to long-term treatment with pituitary somatotropin and recombinant somatotropin. *Journal of Dairy Science*, **68**, 1352–1362.

Breier, B.H., Gluckman, P.D. and Bass, J.J. (1988). The somatotrophic axis in young steers: influence of nutritional status and oestradiol-17β on hepatic high- and low-affinity somatotrophic binding sites. *Journal of Endocrinology*, **116**, 169–177.

Collier, R.J., Ganguli, S., Menke, P.T., Buonomo, F.C., McGrath, M.F., Kotts, C.E. and Krivi, G.G. (1989). Changes in insulin and somatomedin receptors and uptake of insulin, IGF-I and IGF-II during mammary growth, lactogenesis and lactation. In *Biotechnology in Growth Regulation* (eds. R.B. Heap, C.G. Prosser and G.E. Lamming), pp. 153-163. Butterworths, London.

Dodson, M.V., Allen, R.E. and Hossner, K.L. (1985). Ovine somatomedin, multiplication-stimulating activity, and insulin promote skeletal muscle satellite cell proliferation *in vitro*. *Endocrinology*, **117**, 2357–2363.

Eigenmann, J.E., Patterson, D.F. and Froesch, E.R. (1984). Body size parallels insulin-like growth factor I levels but not growth hormone secretory capacity. *Acta Endocrinologica*, **106**, 448–453.

Etherton, T.D. (1989). The mechanisms by which porcine growth hormone improves pig growth performance. In *Biotechnology in Growth Regulation* (eds. R.B. Heap, C.G. Prosser and G.E. Lamming), pp. 97–105. Butterworths, London.

Flint, D., Stevenson, L., Gardner, M., Crilly, P. and Beattie, J. (1989). Antibodies as alternatives to bovine somatotropin (bST). AFRC News July 1989, pp. 4–5.

Gluckman, P.D. and Breier, B.H. (1989). The regulation of the growth hormone receptor. In *Biotechnology in Growth Regulation* (eds. R.B. Heap, C.G. Prosser and G.E. Lamming), pp. 27–33. Butterworths, London.

Guler, H.P., Zapf, J., Binz, K. and Froesch, E.R. (1989). Growth promotion using recombinant insulin-like growth factor-I. In *Biotechnology in Growth Regulation* (eds. R.B. Heap, C.G. Prosser and G.E. Lamming), pp. 119–122. Butterworths, London.

Heap, R.B. (1989). Manipulation of growth and lactation. In RASE Bioscience in Animal Production 7th Royal Show International Symposium, 27 June–3 July, 1989. *Monograph Series* No. 9, pp. 69–77. Stoneleigh, Warwickshire.

Heap, R.B., Prosser, C. and Lamming, G.E. (eds.) (1989). *Biotechnology in Growth Regulation.* Butterworths, London.

Heap, R.B., Fleet, I.R., Fullerton, F.M., Davis, A.J., Goode, J.A., Hart, I.C., Pendleton, J.W., Prosser, C.G., Silvester, L.M. and Mepham, T.B. (1989). A comparison of the mechanisms of action of bovine pituitary-derived and recombinant somatotropin (ST) in inducing galactopoiesis in the cow during late lactation. In *Biotechnology in Growth Regulation* (eds. R.B. Heap, C.G. Prosser and G.E. Lamming), pp. 73–84. Butterworths, London.

Hochberg, Z., Maor, G., Lewinson, D. and Silbermann, M. (1989). The direct effects of growth hormone on chondrogenesis and osteogenesis. In *Biotechnology in Growth Regulation* (eds. R.B. Heap, C.G. Prosser and G.E. Lamming), pp. 123–128. Butterworths, London.

Holder, A.T. and Aston, R. (1989). Antigen-antibody complexes that enhance growth. In *Biotechnology in Growth Regulation* (eds. R.B. Heap, C.G. Prosser and G.E. Lamming), pp. 167–177. Butterworths, London.

Holder, A.T., Aston, R., Preece, M.A. and Ivanyi, J. (1985). Monoclonal antibody-mediated enhancement of growth hormone activity *in vivo*. *Journal of Endocrinology*, **107**, R9–R12.

Holder, A.T., Blows, J.A., Aston, R. and Bates, P.C. (1988). Monoclonal antibody enhancement of the effects of human growth hormone on growth and body composition in mice. *Journal of Endocrinology*, **117**, 85–90.

Isaksson, O.G.P., Janson, J.O. and Gause, I.A.M. (1982). Growth hormone stimulates longitudinal bone growth directly. *Science*, **216**, 1237–1239.

Kronfeld, D.S. (1988). Biologic and economic risks associated with the use of bovine somatotropins. *Journal of the American Veterinary Medical Association*, **192**, 1693–1696.

Mepham, T.B. (1989). Criteria for the public acceptability of biotechnological innovations in animal production. In *Biotechnology in Growth Regulation* (eds. R.B. Heap, C.G. Prosser and G.E. Lamming), pp. 203–212. Butterworths, London.

Mepham, T.B. (1991). Control of milk production. In *The Application of Biotechnology in Developing Countries* (ed. A.G. Hunter), pp. 186–200. Centre for Tropical Veterinary Medicine, University of Edinburgh.

Palmiter, R.D., Brinster, R.L., Hammer, R.E, Trumbauer, M.E., Rosenfeld, M.G., Birnberg, N.C. and Evans, R.M. (1982). Dramatic growth of mice that develop from eggs microinjected with metallothionein-growth hormone fusion genes. *Nature*, **300**, 611–615.

Peel, C.J. and Baumann, D.E. (1987). Somatotropin and lactation. *Journal of Dairy Science,* **70**, 474–486.

Peel, C.J., Eppard, P.J. and Hard, D.L. (1989). Evaluation of sometribove (methionyl bovine somatotropin) in toxicology and clinical trials in Europe and the United States. In *Biotechnology in Growth Regulation* (eds. R.B. Heap, C.G. Prosser and G.E. Lamming), pp. 107–116. Butterworths, London.

Pell, J.M. (1989). Growth promoting properties of recombinant growth hormone. In *Biotechnology in Growth Regulation* (eds. R.B. Heap, C.G. Prosser and G.E. Lamming), pp. 85–96. Butterworths, London.

Polge, E.J.C., Barton, S.C., Surani, M.A.H., Miller, J.R., Wagner, T., Rottman, F., Camper, S.A., Elsome, K., Davis, A.J., Goode, J.A., Foxcroft, G.R. and Heap, R.B. (1989). Induced expression of a bovine growth hormone construct in transgenic pigs. In *Biotechnology in Growth Regulation* (eds. R.B. Heap, C.G. Prosser and G.E. Lamming), pp. 189–199. Butterworths, London.

Prosser, C.G., Fleet, I.R. and Corps, A.N. (1989). Increased secretion of insulin-like growth factor I into milk of cows treated with recombinantly derived bovine growth hormone. *Journal of Dairy Research,* **56**, 17–26.

Prosser, C.G., Fleet, I.R. and Heap, R.B. (1989). Action of IGF-I on mammary function. In *Biotechnology in Growth Regulation* (eds. R.B. Heap, C.G. Prosser and G.E. Lamming), pp. 141–151. Butterworths, London.

Pursel, V.G., Miller, K.F., Bolt, D.J., Pinkert, C.A., Hammer, R.E., Palmiter, R.D. and Brinster, R.L. (1989). Insertion of growth hormone genes into pig embryos. In *Biotechnology in Growth Regulation* (eds. R.B. Heap, C.G. Prosser and G.E. Lamming), pp. 181–188. Butterworths, London.

Schlechter, N.I., Russell, S.M. Greenberg, S., Spencer, E.M. and Nicoll, C.S. (1986). A direct growth effect of growth hormone in rat hindlimb shown by arterial infusion. *American Journal of Phsyiology,* **250**, E231–E235.

Schuler, L.A. and Hurley, W.L. (1987). Molecular cloning of a prolactin-related mRNA expressed in bovine placenta. *Proceedings of the National Academy of Sciences U.S.A.*, **84**, 5650–5654.

Skottner, A., Clark, R.G., Robinson, I.C.A.F. and Fryklund, L. (1987). Recombinant human insulin-like growth factor: testing the somatomedin hyopthesis in hypophysectomized rats. *Journal of Endocrinology*, **112**, 123–132.

Vernon, R.G. and Flint, D.J. (1989). Role of growth hormone in the regulation of adipocyte growth and function. In *Biotechnology in Growth Regulation* (eds. R.B. Heap, C.G. Prosser and G.E. Lamming), pp. 57–71. Butterworths, London.

Vize, P.D., Michalska, A.E., Ashman, R., Lloyd, B., Stone, B.A., Quinn, P., Wells, J.R.E. and Seamark, R.F. (1988). Introduction of a porcine growth hormone fusion gene into transgenic pigs promotes growth. *Journal of Cell Science*, **90**, 295–300.

Wallis, M. (1989). Species specificity and structure-function relationships of growth hormone. In *Biotechnology in Growth Regulation* (eds. R.B. Heap, C.G. Prosser and G.E. Lamming), pp. 3–14. Butterworths, London.

Wang, M.-W., Heap, R.B. and Taussig, M.J. (1989). Blocking of pregnancy in mice by immunization with anti-idiotype directed against monoclonal anti-progesterone antibody. *Proceedings of the National Academy of Sciences U.S.A.*, **86**, 7098–7102.

Waters, M.J., Spencer, S.A., Leung, D., Hammonds, R.G., Cachianes, G., Henzel, W.J., Wood, W.I., Barnard, R., Quirk, P. and Hamlin, G. (1989). Growth hormone receptors and binding proteins. In *Biotechnology in Growth Regulation* (eds. R.B. Heap, C.G. Prosser and G.E. Lamming), pp. 15–25. Butterworths, London.

Webster, A.J.F. (1988). Farm animal protection-somatotropin. In *Farm Animal Protection – The Practical Way Forward* (eds. V. Carter and H. Carter), pp. 80–88. European Conference Group on the Protection of Farm Animals, Horsham, U.K.

3.5

Improving the Nutrition of Livestock – The Low Technology Approach

J.H. TOPPS
School of Agriculture, University of Aberdeen, Scotland

INTRODUCTION

Livestock production in developing countries is limited by inadequate intakes of energy and protein. Deficiencies of other essential nutrients are rarely seen and tend to be of secondary importance. A practical or low technology approach to improve nutrition depends on the provision of foods or supplements that increase energy and protein intakes. This review considers some of the approaches which have been developed over the past 25 years and which appear to be more relevant than others. For this and other reasons they are more likely to achieve widespread success. Nevertheless this selection is arbitrary, but it may have some benefit from being contentious.

In addition, it has two distinct biases which are acceptable if the state of knowledge, including that of the author's from first-hand experience, is taken into account. Only ruminant livestock i.e. cattle, sheep and goats are considered. The nutrition and management of pigs and poultry can be improved but nearly all the measures used are relatively sophisticated and away from low technology. As a result there is a fairly common incidence of advanced production units in some developing countries, which are sustained by costly inputs. It has been argued that these units do not encourage the development of an appropriate livestock industry in some developing countries.

The other bias centres on selecting information from work carried out in Africa. This personal preference may be justified in helping to overcome the grim food solution for large parts of Africa which has been highlighted by Brumby (1986).

A straightforward definition of low technology will suffice for this review. A low technology approach is that which is understandable and can be applied by farmers and extension workers with a basic knowledge of livestock husbandry. This means that they can assess the likely responses of livestock to changes in feeding which are either quantitative or qualitative or both. Using this definition of low technology six areas of ruminant livestock nutrition which are especially relevant to the developing world are discussed.

DRY-SEASON FEEDING OF TRADITIONALLY MANAGED CATTLE

There is little need to emphasize the need to increase the intake of herbage by grazing cattle during the dry-season in many parts of the world. The quality of the material ingested slows the rate of rumen degradation which results in a low intake and submaintenance planes of nutrition. Supplements are required which enhance the rate of rumen degradation so causing an appreciable increase in intake and some improvement in digestibility or energy value. Three kinds of supplementation may be considered, the provision of liquid feeds or blocks, the introduction of pasture legume into natural grazing and the establishment of fodder banks.

Liquid and block supplements

Liquid supplements have been known for about 100 years and the most common, a mixture of urea (fertilizer grade) and molasses, has been widely used in developing countries. It usually has the merit of being cheap, convenient and easy to make as such or with the addition of minerals and vitamins. This addition is often unnecessary but if sodium chloride and a source of phosphate are available their incorporation may be worthwhile. However, the addition of some mineral sources to molasses can cause mixing problems (Topps, 1976). The relative proportions of urea and molasses are important for reasons of toxicity, palatability and efficiency of utilization of urea. An appropriate ratio of urea to molasses is close to 1:8 (Topps, 1971). Two problems are inevitably part of the feeding of urea and molasses. Over-consumption by some or all animals can occur which lowers efficiency of utilization and results in substitution rather than supplementation. Secondly a lack of consumption by some animals in the herd which may occur at the same time. These problems are seen with block supplements and will be considered later.

Block supplements had their origin 25 years ago in Southern Africa. Their success then depended on a viscous liquid by-product with strong cohesive properties but for low technology it depends on molasses which has similar properties. Specifications for making blocks based on molasses and urea for use in developing countries have been described by Sansoucy (1986). The hardness of the block is of prime importance and to ensure sufficient hardness several recipes include cement at a level of 5 or 10%. Some concern must be felt with this recommendation since all but a few special cements contain lead

TABLE 1 *Effect of providing a molasses urea block to grazing cows in Ethiopia on the length of the lactational anoestrous period.*

	Anoestrous period (days)	
	With block	**Without block**
Suckling calves	132	199
Restricted suckling	114	159

After: ILCA (1987)

in amounts that may be toxic. Tests need to be carried out to ascertain whether any of the lead is absorbed following ingestion of the block.

Appropriate management of blocks is essential if they are to be effectively utilized. Earlier a controlled experiment should be carried out to see whether consumption leads to an increase in intake of poor quality roughage and in digestibility of the diet. Details of the procedure have been given in an earlier review (Topps, 1976). Once this is established, the siting of the blocks in relation to the available grazing or supplies of roughage and the watering points should be judged using a mixture of experience and frequent observations. Frequent herding of the cattle may be necessary to ensure that all animals eat some of the supplement and that the dominant or greedy animals do not consume large amounts. A daily consumption of 500 g by an adult beast weighing 250 kg is close to optimum. For smaller and larger animals the recommended amounts can be calculated on a *pro rata* basis. Obviously young cattle have to be fully developed ruminants to make use of the urea.

It is difficult to find reports of work which show the benefits of using molasses urea blocks during the dry season with traditionally managed cattle. Their use in more intensive systems has been reported more frequently. A notable exception is that given in the International Livestock Centre for Africa (ILCA) Annual Report (1987), a summary of which is given in Table 1. A clear response was seen in an improvement of the fertility of beef cows on a ranch in Ethiopia under two management systems. Such a result is appropriate since any measure used with beef cows needs to be cheap and convenient as exemplified by the provision of block supplements.

Reinforcement of natural pasture with legumes

There have been many attempts to select legumes that could be grown successfully in grass-legume pastures under local conditions. Over the years a wide range of both temperate and tropical legumes have been tested. The earlier work relied on nursery plots which were cut and harvested at regular intervals and their production measured but then allowed to regrow for a long time. Success was achieved in that certain legumes persisted for several years

TABLE 2 *Effect of veld reinforcement with Silverleaf desmodium* (Desmodium unicatum) *on dry season performance of steers.*

	Proportion seeded with legume					
	0		0.33		0.67	
Stocking rate (Lu/Ha)	1.7	2.6	1.7	2.6	1.7	2.6
Initial weight (kg)	221	221	221	217	221	221
End of dry season (kg)	195	195	207	205	211	212
Loss (kg)	26	26	14	12	10	9
After 6 weeks rains (kg)	208	204	238	218	240	236
Gain (kg)	13	9	31	13	30	24

After: Clatworthy and Boultwood (1980)

and at several harvests yields of grass were greater from the plots containing legumes than from similar plots without legumes. This would have resulted only from the release of nitrogen from the legume probably as a result of root dieback. However, the results from this work were only an indication of those that could be obtained in a cut-and-carry system. The situation differed greatly from that of true grazing in which the defoliation would be more irregular, the time for regrowth would be shortened and other animal factors like trampling may have a pronounced effect.

Over the last 20 years the need for grazing trials in which animal performance especially during the dry season is the measure of the contribution of the legume has been widely recognized. Unfortunately the number of reports that have appeared giving useful results have been less convincing. Three research stations in Zimbabwe carried out a large amount of controlled experimentation which provided clear-cut results. This work has been reviewed by Clatworthy (1985). An example of it is given in the form of summarized results in Table 2 (Clatworthy and Boultwood, 1980). The results showed that at two stocking rates the reinforcement of veld grazing with *Desmodium uncinatum* (Silverleaf desmodium) reduced the weight loss of young steers during the dry-season, and enhanced their weight gain during the first six weeks of the rainy-season. The latter result was particularly encouraging since work with supplementary feeds during the dry season has shown that reducing the weight loss then may lead to a decrease in weight gain during the earlier part of the rainy season i.e. the effect of compensatory growth is reduced. However, the success of this trial needed to be qualified since later work at another research station (Clatworthy, 1984) gave poor results. They were ascribed to leaf shedding from the Silverleaf desmodium after frost and to a loss of herbage through trampling. This led to the suggestion that a legume with an erect growth habit may be more suitable. Hence even under well-managed conditions such as found on a commercial ranch either climatic or animal factors may interfere with the effect of legume reinforcement.

The situation becomes much more complex and difficult in communal grazing areas where there is a need for low technology to improve the performance of grazing animals and to reduce the effects of overgrazing. Farmers in such areas are aware of the role and importance of livestock in their farming systems and they are aware that their grazing areas are being depleted in terms of both area and productivity. They are keen to try new technologies, subject to certain conditions, that will improve their livestock and grazing. Their keenness is often greater following a drought. The introduction of forage legumes into communal grazing area or fallow land appears to be attractive since it has been clearly shown that improved productivity would result. However, if the grazing areas are to be reinforced some form of improved management will be necessary. A theoretical recommendation may include rotational grazing and reduced stocking rates. Traditionally movement of cattle, which has a similar effect to rotational grazing, depends on child labour to carry out herding duties. This may be scarce in some areas and the alternative of fencing is very expensive particularly for subsistence farmers. Reduced stocking rates are always difficult to achieve, they are often less after an adverse climatic change. In addition communal areas use draught cattle for crop production so any reduction in numbers may reduce the incidence of early ploughing and timely cultivations during the growing season. It may be possible to obtain a better distribution of stock over the whole grazing area through the strategic placement of watering points. If so this alternative should be seriously considered.

Legumes that are more suited to communal grazing areas are those with an erect growth habit. Farmers appear to be willing to grow such legume shrubs in hedge rows and along contours but not on fallow land. More development work is needed to assess the persistence and usefulness of legumes grown in this way. The species that may be used are relatively few. Older work (Mills, 1961) indicated that *Cajanus cajan* may provide browse during the earlier part of the dry-season. However, it has to be carefully managed to avoid excessive defoliation. An alternative is *Leucaena leucocephala* as an early dry season browse and some success has been achieved with this legume. However, this advance has to be linked to the application of another low technology. To avoid the deleterious effects of mimosine the rumen needs to be inoculated with strains of bacteria that breakdown mimosine and its main degradation product. Another species of legume with an erect growth habit is *Desmodium discolor*, sometimes called Horse marmalade. It yields well but it has not been thoroughly tested in the grazing situation.

Establishment of fodder banks

Fodder banks are concentrated units of forage legumes established and managed by pastoralists close to their homesteads for supplementation of selected animals during the dry-season. A description of their establishment and success in the subhumid zone of Nigeria has been written by Mohamed Saleem and Suleiman (1986). The establishment of fodder banks is not an easy task. Despite this difficulty the number has increased substantially over the last nine years. As well as technical there are social problems which delay their acceptance. Pastoralists in the subhumid zone tend to settle where crops are grown in order to use crop residues and to have access to marketing and other facilities. This makes it difficult to secure land for fodder banks especially if there is increasing demand for crop production. The land that is available is likely to be of low quality since the best areas are used for cropping by the farmers themselves. Furthermore the demands for land preparation for cropping and fodder banks may conflict. Herds may be kraaled at night to prepare land for the fodder bank but before the onset of the rains dung from night kraaling may be needed for crop production. Burning is another potential drawback. Annual burning of croplands and rangelands is still practised and if the fodder bank is accidentally burnt it is a serious deterrent to renewing their establishment.

Fodder banks are usually a few hectares in area. The block of land has to be fenced and then the seed-bed prepared by confining the herd at nights in the area before the onset of the rains. With the rains scarified seeds are broadcast. Since the fodder bank is there to provide supplementary feed during the dry-season, the management practices are designed to maximize legume composition and yield by the end of the growing season. One problem is that legumes are slow to grow initially and they do not compete effectively against fast growing grasses. Early grazing by cattle has been recommended but there is a risk of worm infection after night kraaling and this is known to the pastoralists. Other establishment methods have been developed therefore. Forage is allowed to accumulate by deferring grazing until the dry-season. At this time there is controlled use according to a determined stocking rate for about two hours per day. It is very important to ensure sufficient seed crop and stubble for regeneration in the following rainy-season. The legumes used are perennials, e.g. *Stylosanthes guianensis* and *Stylosanthes humata*. They should persist for many years, but this is not always seen in practice. Pastoralists tend to overstock their fodder banks and the stylo is selectively grazed to ground level during the dry season. In addition, ungrazed stumps may be attacked by termites. Nevertheless some success has been achieved with fodder banks. They are known to persist at a high level of production for at least five years. There are few data on improvements in animal performance. At first it was considered that fodder banks would be grazed by animals in a herd that are more vulnerable to nutritional stress during the dry season. For example, pregnant and lactating animals especially heifers in the first parity. However, pastoralists prefer to allow all animals in the herd to graze which may cause overstocking. Among the benefits mentioned by pastoralists are greater milk offtake, better animal condition, better calf survival and access to land. Perhaps the most telling measure of their success is the spontaneous adoption of fodder banks by pastoralists in a few areas.

FEEDING OF LIVESTOCK KEPT BY SMALLHOLDERS

In developing countries where the natural resources of soil and climate allow a certain level of crop production the land is divided into small areas which are owned or farmed by smallholders. Size of the holding is often 1–2 hectares but in some countries the average size is being reduced due to pressure of an increase in population. Systems of mixed farming have been established by smallholders in different parts of the world which are characteristic of the people and which have been successful. However, to accommodate the increase in population both locally and in the cities, the productivity per unit area from these farms of both the crop and animal enterprises has to increase. To accomplish this aim low technology has to be tried and the approaches that are most appropriate, which will be the most successful, adopted by the farmer. With livestock, their productive efficiency has to increase by improving the feeding in order to obtain more output, including work per animal and to reduce the number of animals where necessary. Three different sorts of approach to improved feeding have been examined extensively in recent years. They may be described under the headings of alley farming, semi-intensive milk production and improved utilization of crop by-products.

Alley farming

Alley farming, which is also called hedgerow intercropping, is a system which successfully integrates crop and livestock production. It is the planting of rows of trees or shrubs, which are usually leguminous, with food crops between the tree rows i.e. in the alleys. A modification of the system is to plant grass rather than human food crops between the tree rows. The trees are pruned at regular intervals at about 0.7 m above ground level for two purposes, to prevent shading of companion food crops and to provide mulch or animal feed. The trees are managed as shrubs therefore rather than being allowed to grow to a full stature. Being leguminous they will provide mulch rich in nitrogen to enhance soil fertility and a high quality feed which may be used as supplement for ruminant livestock. In addition the trees are likely to reduce or prevent soil erosion and after a modification of the management provide fuel for cooking.

Two tree species, *Leucaena leucocephala* and *Gliricidia sepium* have been widely used for alley farming. In some countries leucaena alone is used but in some parts of Africa a combination of alternative rows of leucaena and gliricidia is more common. The planting of two or more species is to be recommended since it reduces the risk of a pest or disease decimating the tree crop. An ominous example of this occurring is the psylled pest (*Heteropsylla cubana*) of leucaena in S.E. Asia and Australia. Indeed there is a need to establish two or three more species for widespread use as soon as possible.

Production from the tree depends upon environmental factors, especially rainfall and management. As a guide, foliage yields of 6–7 tonnes dry matter/ ha can be expected with tree rows 4 m apart and 0.25 m spacing within a row and a 6–8 week pruning interval with an adequate rainfall of about 1,250 mm. Alley farming is best suited to areas with a rainfall of over 1,200 mm with a bimodal distribution, a soil pH of at least 5.2 and where farms are small. Low input agriculture i.e. little or no mechanization is the norm and the major food crop is maize or cassava. A variety of people are able to manage well this system. Mulching with foliage from the trees will increase levels of nutrients in the soil and increases of crop yields of up to 40% have been obtained which are usually better than that obtained from a basic application of fertilizer. Incorporation of mulch into the soil gives a much better response than a surface application. With increased crop production it may be possible to leave fallow some of the land from time to time. This will improve subsequent crop production and any interruption in pruning will increase tree production in future harvestings. However, during the fallow period the plots can generate fodder and at times fuel wood.

Small ruminant livestock are common in areas where alley farming has had some success. The livestock management imposed has allowed the use of either free-roaming or confined animals. Where grass rather than a human food crop is planted between the tree rows, the grass and tree prunings can be used on a cut-and-carry basis in more intensive livestock operations, such as stall-fed beef or dairy cattle. More commonly, the use of the prunings as animal feed is considered an alternative outlet. It will mean that less material is available for mulch which will diminish the effect on crop production. Hence the amount of prunings available for feeding may be relatively small but it is invariably of high quality especially with respect to crude protein content. The material from leucaena or gliricidia often has a crude protein level in the dry matter greater than 200 g/kg. For these reasons a suitable use is as a supplement to poor quality roughage or grazing. The effect of leucaena, gliricidia and to a lesser extent other legumes provided for this purpose to small ruminants has been studied at several places in recent years. The results indicate a varied response and a full interpretation is difficult to make.

Foliage from legume trees often contains high amounts of polyphenolic compounds. They are commonly referred to as tannins, but this is a misleading name since polyphenolic compounds are diverse and some do not have the traditional characteristics of tannins. Any naturally occurring mixture of polyphenolics has an overall effect on the nitrogen utilization of ruminants. Part of this effect is a protection by polyphenolics of dietary protein from the degradation of microorganisms in the rumen which is likely to be beneficial. However, this may be offset by other effects in another part of the gut or the need to detoxify certain polyphenolics if they are absorbed from the gut. Certainly the foliage of some browse legumes differ in their effect on nitrogen metabolism of small ruminants as shown by the results of Ebong (1989) in a comparison of *Acacia nilotica* and *Acacia seyal.* Hence differences between polyphenolics in different legumes together with factors such as the amount fed, the nutritional status of the animal and the level of production are likely to be the cause of a varied response.

TABLE 3 *Effect of browse* supplementation on growth rate of lambs to weaning (12 weeks) and to 24 weeks from West African Dwarf sheep receiving* Panicum maximum ad libitum.

Browse Intake gDM/d		Growth Rate g/d	
Dam	Kid	Birth to Weaning	Birth to 24 weeks
1985/86			
0	0	39.0	25.5
110	27	43.5	33.2
212	71	58.7	38.3
390	111	57.9	44.3
1986/87			
129	38	49.1	28.2
275	79	56.4	31.4
495	155	73.1	44.6
741	250	84.0	50.3

**Leucaena leucephala* and *Gliricida sepium* (1:1 W/W)

After: Reynolds and Adediran (1988)

TABLE 4 *Effect of browse* supplementation on survival rates of lambs to 24 weeks from West African Dwarf sheep receiving* Panicum maximum ad libitum.

Browse Intake gDM/d Dam	Lamb	Number born	Litter size	Survival
1985/86				
0	0	8	1.33	0.50
110	27	8	1.00	0.62
212	71	11	1.37	0.55
390	111	8	1.33	0.87
1986/87				
129	38	8	1.00	0.62
275	79	12	1.20	0.83
495	155	10	1.00	0.90
741	250	9	1.12	1.00

**Leucaena leucephala* and *Gliricidia sepium* (1:1 W/W)

After: Reynolds and Adediran (1988)

To gain an insight into the response of sheep and goats to graded amounts of a mixture of leucaena and gliricidia, the work of Reynolds and Adediran (1988) and of Reynolds (1989) in West Africa is especially relevant. The results are summarized in Tables 3–6. They provide information on both dam and offspring and include data on viability of the latter as measured by survival rate. Increasing amounts of the legume mixture gave an increasingly better response in both sheep and goats with a tendency for the sheep to respond better than the goat. Unfortunately at the higher levels a substitution effect was seen with the animals eating less *Panicum maximum* which formed the basal diet. For this reason and others related to the amount of legume likely to be available and the time needed to collect or browse it, the higher levels used in these studies are likely to be impractical and unacceptable to smallholders.

Semi-intensive milk production

In the high potential areas of developing countries where there is a large demand for milk and an effective marketing system, semi-intensive milk production by smallholders is an acceptable and profitable enterprise. Smallholders farming close to cities and towns in countries such as Kenya have achieved a notable success in making a major contribution to dairy production within the country. In Kenya, milk production has kept up with a rapid increase in the population and the country continues to export dairy products.

The semi-intensive system is based on the growing of a forage which has an acceptable quality for all or most of the year. Other feeds, usually high quality by-products need to be available also if the milk potential of the genotype used is higher than 1,200–1,500 litres per year or lactation. The most effective use of the forage, and possibly of other feeds is made if the animals are housed and the forage is cut-and-carried. Hence the units, usually one to four cows in size sometimes with a heifer replacement, on the smallholdings are referred to as zero-grazing units. They have the advantage of day to day control over the animals and their feeding which can be manifested in careful management and pride in ownership. In addition, the units should be constructed so that the excreta are collected and the dung used for food crop and forage production on the farm with very little loss of nutrients. This is particularly important, otherwise forage production will quickly decline unless costly inputs of fertilizer are used.

An appropriate forage is one that has a vigorous growth, which is not affected by frequent cutting, and moreover the quality of material harvested should provide the animal with an acceptable intake of energy and protein. The level of nutrition from the forage alone should approach that needed for twice the maintenance requirements or be at least 1.5 times these requirements. A suitable species, which is now well used, is *Pennisetum purpureum*, commonly called Napier fodder or Elephant grass. It is a tall, vigorous, erect, deep-rooted perennial which resembles sugar cane in growth habit. It spreads

TABLE 5 *Effects of browse* supplementation on growth rate of kids to weaning (16 weeks) and to 24 weeks from West African Dwarf goats receiving* Panicum maximum ad libitum.

Browse Intake gDM/d		Growth Rate g/d	
Dam	Kid	Birth to Weaning	Birth to 24 weeks
143	39	17.4	14.0
254	83	28.7	20.1
554	160	25.9	20.9
719	246	31.9	28.3

**Leucaena leucephala* and *Gliricidia sepium* (1:1 W/W)

After: Reynolds (1989)

TABLE 6 *Effect of browse* supplementation on survival rates of kids to 24 weeks from West African Dwarf goats receiving* Panicum maximum ad libitum.

Browse gDM/d	Number born	Litter size	Survival
200 (75)	11	1.22	0.36
400 (150)	13	1.30	0.46
800 (300)	11	1.37	0.82
1,200 (450)	18	1.38	0.94

* *Leucaena leucocephala* and *Gliricidia sepium* (1:1 W/W)
( ) amount given to kids after weaning at 16 weeks

After: Reynolds (1989)

by short stout rhizomes to form large clumps which are up to 1 m across. Many varieties are known and there is considerable variation among them. In Kenya, a variety called Bana grass is especially suitable and is commonly grown.

Napier fodder grows best in deep, moisture-retentive soils of moderate to fairly heavy texture and it responds well to dung or fertilizer. It is drought-resistant for a grass of this type and is moderately frost tolerant. It is not very suitable for grazing but is relatively easy to harvest for zero-grazing. To ensure a digestibility of about 0.60 and a crude protein content in the dry matter of close to 100 g/kg the height at cutting should be no more than 1.5 m. Often this represents six weeks growth so eight cuts per year can be obtained and in some areas it can be as many as 10–12. To facilitate feeding, especially mixing with another dietary ingredient and reducing waste, the harvested material should be chopped into pieces a few centimetres in length. This practice is likely to enhance intake of the forage or at least help to maintain a consistently high intake from day to day. A low technology approach to the growing, feeding and management of Napier fodder in Kenya has helped to make a success of the crop and the milk production it supports.

With any success there is always some inclination to think that it will continue indefinitely but the heavy reliance of an enterprise on one particular forage needs to be considered seriously. A pest or disease, as for example that affecting leucaena, may strike Napier fodder and cause a substantial loss in production. Active interest of plant breeders and forage agronomists needs to be sustained to find alternatives either within the same species i.e. different varieties or in the form of other species. Any alternative needs to have characteristics similar to those of Napier fodder. In addition the introduction of a legume such as *Desmodium intortum* (Greenleaf desmodium) into plots of Napier fodder may produce a better quality forage and help to sustain the viability of the grass.

Another approach to reduce the dependence on Napier fodder is to consider the utilization of crops grown for food production as animal feeds. The maize crop is appropriate for this dual-purpose approach. Defoliation of the plant in the late stages of producing grain will give high quality leafy material and have only a small effect on yield of the grain which is left to mature. Work has been carried out in Kenya by Abate and Topps (unpublished results) on defoliated maize forage which has been ensiled and the silage fed to dairy cows. The maize was defoliated at two different times i.e. when the grain was at the doughy stage and about six weeks later. It was found that defoliation at the earlier stage resulted in a reduction in grain yield of 5–10%, the later defoliation had no effect. Each material was chopped and ensiled with molasses. The two different silages were each fed *ad libitum* with either 2 or 4 kg/day of dairy concentrate to a group of eight dairy cows. The cows were grade Friesian or Ayrshire or crossbreds of *Bos taurus* x *Bos indicus*; their performance was measured over six weeks. Two similar trials were carried out in consecutive years and the results are summarized in Table 7. In the first year the early stage was significantly better than the late silage in sustaining milk production, the same significant difference was seen between the two levels of concentrate. In the second year the differences between the two silages was smaller and not statistically significant, while that between the concentrate levels was larger and significant. However, in both years the difference between the silages was small. As a result it may not be worthwhile to defoliate the maize at the earlier stage. Similarly the response to additional concentrate was small and disappointing. Since there was little difference in silage intake between the groups the feeding daily of 4 rather than 2 kg concentrate resulted in increased weight gains of the cows. This partitioning of extra dietary energy more towards the body rather than milk appears to be a characteristic of cows in the tropics. In general the results of both trials show that silage made from defoliated maize fed with a small amount of

TABLE 7 *Milk yield (kg/d) of grade and crossbred cows on early and late defoliated maize silage with two levels of concentrate.*

	Concentrate (kg/d)		
	2	4	Mean
1987			
Early silage	11.7	12.3	12.0
Late silage	10.2	11.6	10.9
Mean	10.9	12.0	11.4
	SED = 0.44		
1988			
Early silage	10.5	11.7	11.1
Late silage	9.7	11.6	10.6
Mean	10.1	11.6	10.9
	SED = 0.46		

After: Abate and Topps (Unpublished results)

TABLE 8 *Milk yield (kg/d) of grade and crossbred cows on natural grazing following the feeding of silage with two levels of concentrate.*

	Concentrate (kg/d)		
	2	4	Mean
1987			
Early silage	10.3	11.5	10.9
Late silage	9.5	11.1	10.3
Mean	9.9	11.3	10.6
	SED = 0.42		
1988			
Early silage	10.1	11.2	10.7
Late silage	9.5	12.4	11.0
Mean	9.8	11.8	10.8
	SED = 0.63		

After: Abate and Topps (Unpublished results)

concentrate sustains a level of milk production of 10 to 12 kg/day. Immediately after each trial the cows were allowed to graze natural pastures but kept on the same level of concentrate. The production obtained is summarized in Table 8. The response to the greater amounts of concentrate was statistically significant but it remains relatively small.

Other food crops may produce foliage that can be used in zero-grazing units. Cassava tops for example are known to be rich in protein and acceptable to livestock. A better response to Napier fodder may be obtained by feeding it with certain protein concentrates. Recent work by Muinga, Thorpe and Topps (unpublished results) in the coastal region of Kenya has shown an appreciable response to copra cake fed with Napier fodder.

Improved utilization of crop by-products

Crop by-products, with a few exceptions, are either high quality concentrates e.g. maize bran or poor quality roughages such as cereal straws. With the former any simple improvement in their utilization is related to how much is fed and the nature of the other dietary ingredients. A little more care in devising diets for the more productive animals may well lead to a significant increase in growth, milk yield or work output.

An enormous amount of effort has gone into techniques to improve the utilization of cereal straw by ruminant livestock. Most of the procedures are not low technology nor are they appropriate for use in developing countries.

TABLE 9 *Teff straw* (Eragrostis tef) *botanical and chemical composition of eight varieties.*

	Range of values
Leaf:stem ratio	70 : 30–77 : 23
Crude protein content (g/kg DM)	19–22
Organic matter digestibility *in vitro* (%)	62–66
Neutral detergent fibre digestibility *in vitro* (%)	56–60

After: Blummel (1988)

TABLE 10 *Teff straw* (Eragrostis tef) *chemical composition of leaves of eight varieties.*

	Range of values
Crude protein content (g/kg DM)	21–25
Organic matter digestibility *in vitro* (%)	64–70
Neutral detergent fibre (g/kg DM)	77–82
Neutral detergent fibre digestibility *in vitro* (%)	58–64

After: Blummel (1988)

TABLE 11 *Teff straw* (Eragrostis tef) *chemical composition of stems of eight varieties.*

	Range of varieties
Crude protein content (g/kg DM)	11 - 14
Organic matter digestibility *in vitro* (%)	53 - 58
Neutral detergent fibre (g/kg DM)	85 - 87
Neutral detergent fibre digestibility *in vitro* (%)	46 - 53

After: Blummel (1988)

TABLE 12 *Teff straw* (Eragrostis tef) *variation in composition with planting date.*

	Range of values
Leaf:stem ratio	63 : 36–70 : 30
Crude protein content (g/kg DM)	49–83
Organic matter digestibility *in vitro* (%)	55–60
Neutral detergent fibre digestibility *in vitro* (%)	47–52

After: Blummel (1988)

Of the chemical treatments only that which uses urea to generate ammonia is safe, and relatively easy to handle. When used in hot climates in sealed containers it can be effective unless the presence of polyphenolics inhibits the activity of the urease. Nevertheless, a clear case has yet to be made to show that it gives a consistently better improvement than the addition of urea to straw as a source of nonprotein nitrogen.

A practical approach to improve straw utilization in developing countries is to use more effectively the better quality straws and to make use of the variation in quality in these straws. Teff (*Eragrostis tef*) is the traditional cereal food crop in Ethiopia and teff straw is an important feed for livestock on many small farms. Recent studies have revealed the nature of this by-product which in general is considerably better in nutritive value than other cereal straws. The work of Blummel (1988) exemplifies the difference and shows that there are useful variations among different teff straws. In Table 9 a range of values is given for eight varieties. All of them have high leaf:stem ratios but in some varieties it is much higher than others. This gives rise to a difference in digestibility. Similar data are given for leaves and stems in Tables 10 and 11 respectively. The ranges in values are small but if allowance is made for the selection shown by animals larger differences may be seen. For example animals eating mainly the leaf of the better varieties are likely to give a considerably higher level of production than those given

TABLE 13 *Teff straw* (Eragrostis tef) *variation in composition with site and altitude. (Five sites at altitudes of 1650, 1850, 2150, 2350 and 2440 m.)*

	Range of values
Leaf:stem ratio	65 : 35–77 : 23
Crude protein content (g/kg DM)	25–46
Organic matter digestibility *in vitro* (%)	56–63
Neutral detergent fibre digestibility *in vitro* (%)	48–57

After: Blummel (1988)

controlled amounts of the poorer straws. Such differences may be enhanced when planting date and site or altitude are taken into account as shown by the results in Tables 12 and 13 respectively.

In countries like Ethiopia where the by-product is important it is hoped that cereal breeders will be able to take account of straw quality. To help them in this aim the following relationships or factors need to be examined. The relationship, if any, between straw and grain yield, and whether varietal differences are persistent from year to year and the effect of the environment is secondary. In addition it is not entirely clear whether differences in nutritive value are inherent plant factors that are genetically controlled or whether they are mainly due to botanical characteristics which are influenced by agronomic practice. Without doubt we now have an array of chemical and biological methods for the evaluation of straw and grain which will help to answer these questions.

CONCLUSIONS

A wide range of low technology approaches are available to improve the nutrition of livestock in developing countries. Nevertheless in may situations it is doubtful whether there are more than one or two that fit the farming system. In cases where there are two or more it may be very difficult to make the final choice. In the majority of occasions it may be wise to favour the approach which gives a small but consistent effect e.g. chopping of Napier fodder on holdings with zero-grazing units rather than the more ambitious approach. The cost of any input is critical. It has to be low and this is likely to apply to labour as well as other inputs. It should not be assumed that farmers have spare time – they will 'find time' if the innovation interests them. Once they are well-briefed it should be recognized that they are likely to be a better judge of the results than the person who brought it to their attention. This is especially the case with livestock farmers.

REFERENCES

Blummel, M. (1988). The nutritive value of teff straw and methods used in its assessment. *MSc Thesis*, University of Aberdeen, Scotland.

Brumby, P.J. (1986). ILCA and food production in Africa. A brief review. *World Animal Review*, **60**, 33–37.

Clatworthy, J.N. (1984). Effects of reinforcement of native grass with Silverleaf desmodium (*Desmodium uncinatum*) on dry season performance of beef steers in Zimbabwe. *Tropical Grassland*, **18**, 198–205.

Clatworthy, J.N. (1985). Pasture research in Zimbabwe (1964–1984). *Proceedings of the IDRC/SADCC Workshop of Pasture Improvement Research in Eastern and Southern Africa*, pp. 25–28. Harare, Zimbabwe,

Clatworthy, J.N. and Boultwood, J.N. (1980). Effect of veld reinforcement with Silverleaf desmodium on dry season performance of steers. *Annual Report*. pp. 183–184. Division of Livestock and Pastures, Department of Research and Specialist Services, Zimbabwe.

Ebong, C. (1989). The nutritional effects of tannins and related polyphenols in bird resistant and non-bird resistant sorghum varieties and in legume browses. *PhD Thesis*. University of Aberdeen, Scotland.

International Livestock Centre for Africa (1987). *ILCA Annual Report 1986/87*. ILCA, Addis Ababa, Ethiopia. 82pp.

Mills, P.F.L. (1961). Pigeon pea as a pasture legume in the high rainfall sandveld regions of Southern Rhodesia. *Rhodesian Agricultural Journal*, **58**, 171–172.

Mohamed Saleem, M.A. and Suleiman, H. (1986). Nigeria and West Africa fodder banks. Dry season feed supplementation for traditionally managed cattle in the subhumid zone. *World Animal Review*, **59**, 11–17.

Reynolds, L. (1989). The effects of browse supplementation on the productivity of West African dwarf goats. In *African Small Ruminant Research and Development* (ed. R.T. Wilson and A. Melaku), pp. 237–247. ILCA, Addis Ababa, Ethiopia.

Reynolds, L. and Adediran, S.O. (1988). The effects of browse supplementation on the productivity of West African Dwarf sheep over two reproductive cycles. In *Goat Production in the Humid Tropics* (eds. O.B. Smith and H.G. Bosman), pp. 83–91. Pudoc, Wageningen, The Netherlands.

Sansoucy, R. (1986). The Sahel. Manufacture of molasses-urea blocks. *World Animal Review*, **57**, 50–48.

Topps, J.H. (1971). The use of non-protein nitrogen for ruminant grazing low protein pasture of Africa. *Report of an ad hoc consultation on the value of non-protein nitrogen for ruminant consuming poor herbages*, pp. 35–52. FAO, Rome.

Topps, J.H. (1976). Block and liquid feeding for supplementing pasture and roughages. In *Simplified Feeding for Milk and Beef*, pp. 47–60. U.S. Feed Grains Council, London, England.

3.6

Control of Milk Production

T.B. MEPHAM
Department of Physiology and Environmental Science,
University of Nottingham, U.K.

BIOTECHNOLOGICAL OBJECTIVES

The importance of milk production in developing countries was emphasized at the last conference in this series (Smith, 1985). Particular advantages of dairying, even on a small-scale, are that it facilitates generation of a regular cash income, while at the same time providing a range of nutritionally-valuable supplements to a predominantly vegetable diet and offering, in some measure, the many advantages of livestock farming, e.g. meat, draught power and fertilizer.

There are, however, two main problems relating to milk production in developing countries: there is not enough of it; and its composition is not ideal for many potential consumers. The object of this paper is to examine the capability of current and prospective biotechnological innovations to ameliorate these problems.

The social context

'Biotechnology' has acquired considerable kudos in the modern scientific community. Its undoubted successes have accentuated the tendency for seeking reductionist, rather than holist, approaches to explaining – and manipulating – biological processes. But cautionary voices have been raised. As Spedding (1986) put it: "Any subject is as complicated as the viewer wishes to make it; but the study of a cow in relation to milk production, e.g., is unlikely to be helped by viewing it in, say, molecular terms." It is thus important that changes induced by biotechnological means are evaluated by their overall effect on animal welfare and productivity. But, ultimately, the context is much wider: as for all technology, it is impacts on the welfare of people and the environment which are paramount. Biotechnology provides the means to achieve ends which are, invariably, social.

The present concerns may thus be defined as: 'identification of factors regulating milk secretion which are susceptible to biotechnological intervention, and are aimed at modulating milk yield and composition in ways which are economically and ethically acceptable'. These two constraints (economics and ethics) are clearly crucial: no one would wish to increase milk yields *regardless* of such factors.

Because of the extreme variation in socioeconomic and cultural norms, not only between developed and developing countries, but also within those categories, the most useful approach to these problems would seem to be one which concentrates on general principles and broad trends. Whether and how to exploit any of the biotechnological interventions to be discussed will require full systems analyses specific to different social groups. Other technologies might well be more beneficial.

PHYSIOLOGICAL CONTROL OF MILK SECRETION

In order to identify processes susceptible to biotechnological intervention, it will be useful to review briefly current theories of the physiological control of milk secretion. Milk yield, and the yields of individual milk components, are the product of two factors, viz. the number of mammary secretory cells; and the average secretory activity per cell. Agents controlling these factors are species-variable and interact in complex, often synergistic, ways which also vary with the stage of mammary development (e.g. Mepham, 1987a). Several phases of mammary development have been described: (i) mammogenesis (which occurs prepubertally, postpubertally, during pregnancy and during lactation); (ii) lactogenesis (initiation of lactation); (iii) established lactation. To a large degree, the proximate regulators of mammary function are humoral, and while, in the past, hormones (particularly those secreted from the pituitary gland, ovary and placenta) were ascribed a dominant role, latterly, 'locally-produced' factors have also been perceived to be significant. Thus, currently, mammary function is believed to be subject to autocrine and paracrine, as well as endocrine, influences (Forsyth, 1989).

These humoral agents, often acting in concert with neural signals in 'neuroendocrine' reflexes, effectively channel available energy supplies to the mammary glands in a manner which balances the immediate demands of the suckling young with the longer-term requirements of maternal survival. But milk production in high-yielding animals makes considerable demands on energy supply, so that, notwithstanding the role of humoral factors in partitioning nutrients in the body, it is usually the supply of metabolizable energy in the feed which is the major determinant of yield in any given animal. It follows that the physiological control of milk yield and composition consists of the interplay of genetically-determined regulators (nerves and humoral agents), working via the major organ-systems (such as the digestive and cardiovascular systems), on feed energy which is surplus to maintenance requirements.

Mammotrophic agents

In ruminant species major development of mammary tissue, and hence an increase in secretory cell number, occurs during pregnancy; but at least in goats (Knight, Wilde and Peaker, 1988) further significant growth also occurs during lactation. The principal hormones involved are the steroids, oestrogen, progesterone and corticosteroids, which act synergistically with growth hormone (GH) and lactogenic hormones. In sheep and goats the mammotrophic activity of prolactin (PRL) is augmented by that of placental lactogen (PL). In these species there is a good correlation between increasing blood PL concentrations (which are positively correlated with the number of fetuses *in utero*) and the extent of mammary lobulo-alveolar development, and, hence, the subsequent milk yield (Forsyth, 1983). In cattle, however, PL appears to play, at most, a subordinate role (Bremel and Shuler, 1988).

Yield might also be partially determined prepubertally. Thus, in prepubertal dairy heifers, mammary secretory tissue development has been shown to be positively correlated with blood GH concentrations, which are depressed at high planes of nutrition (Sejrsen, Huber and Tucker, 1983).

Insight into the mode of action of mammotrophic hormones has been provided by *in vitro* studies and by identification of hormone receptors. A significant finding is that GH receptors are absent from mammary cells (e.g. Forsyth, 1989). This discovery is consistent with the theory that GH action on mammary tissue is mediated by insulin-like growth factor 1 (IGF1, also called somatomedin C), mammary receptors for which *are* present. Furthermore, although mammary cells possess receptors for oestrogen, its mitogenic effects appear to be indirect, i.e. elicited via autocrine or paracrine factors, such as IGFs, epidermal growth factor (EGF) and transforming growth factor (TGF) (Dembinski and Shiu, 1988).

Galactopoietic agents

Galactopoietic agents, by definition, increase milk secretion rates. They might achieve this by increasing milk output per cell and / or by increasing cell number. Thus, where the two glands of goats are milked twice and three times daily, respectively, the increased yield of the latter is initially due to an increased mean secretion rate per cell, but subsequently to increased cell number (Knight *et al*, 1988).

The classical approach to determination of hormonal requirements, viz. endocrine gland ablation followed by hormone replacement therapy, indicated that milk secretion, like mammogenesis, is controlled by species-specific complexes of hormones, e.g. in goats the complex appeared to comprise an adrenal corticosteroid, triiodothyronine, GH and PRL. Interpretation of such experiments is, however, difficult; and less traumatic procedures lead to different conclusions. For example, administration of bromocriptine, a specific inhibitor of PRL secretion, showed that although PRL is necessary in most species for lactogenesis, once yield is established it appears not to be necessary for maintained lactation in goats and cows, though it remains so in sheep and most nonruminants (Forsyth, 1983). Identification of galactopoietic hormones has frequently resulted from experiments in which blood concentrations have been increased by exogenous administration. PRL, not surprisingly, has proved not to be galactopoietic in cows and goats, but increased yields are frequently reported in response to thyroid hormone and, most notably, GH administration (Forsyth,1983).

As for mammotrophic agents, *in vitro* studies on mammary tissue have provided clues as to the mechanisms of action of galactopoietic agents, but they are of limited value in defining the factors controlling milk secretion *in vivo* since extra-mammary factors are so important. This is because the major metabolic demands of lactation involve a significant reorientation of metabolic priorities in the body, which has come to be designated 'homeorhesis' (Bauman and Elliot, 1983). Essentially, the changes involved, which are largely coordinated by the endocrine system, result in an enhanced flux of substrates into the metabolic pools, their diminished utilization by tissues inessential to lactation, and augmentation of their supply to the mammary glands through increased mammary blood flow (MBF) and activation of appropriate transport systems on mammary cells (e.g. Mepham, 1987a). It is thus perhaps not surprising that hormones with well-recognized roles in regulating whole-body metabolism, thyroxine and GH, should profoundly affect lactation.

Three components of the galactopoietic response to increased blood concentrations of GH may be identified: (i) changes in whole-body nutrient utilization; (ii) cardiovascular changes; (iii) changes in the secretory activity of mammary tissue (Prosser and Mepham, 1989).

Changes in whole-body metabolism (i) are most readily apparent from the fact that while milk yield in cows increases almost immediately after GH administration, voluntary feed intake does not increase for at least the first five to seven weeks of treatment (Bauman, Eppard, De Geeter and Lanza, 1985). The need for increased mammary uptake of nutrients to support the higher yield is satisfied by mobilization of body stores, and, particularly in early lactation, the animal is likely to enter a period of negative energy balance. Such changes are consistent with the well-known diabetogenic, lipolytic and protein anabolic roles of GH (Wallis, 1989).

A notable feature of the response to GH in ruminants is increased MBF (ii, e.g. Heap, Fleet, Fullerton, Davis, Goode, Hart, Pendleton, Prosser, Silvester and Mepham, 1989). Since the effect is to increase nutrient supply to the mammary glands, it could act as a major element of repartitioning. Indeed, in studies on cows the mean percentage increases in milk yield and MBF were shown to be identical (Fullerton, Fleet, Heap, Hart and Mepham, 1989). But indications that MBF is not solely responsible for increased milk yields are provided by studies *in vitro* and on the metabolism of mammary glands *in vivo* (iii). For example, increased mammary arteriovenous concentration differences (Mepham, 1987a) for glucose, acetate, NEFA and triglycerides have been reported following GH treatment of cows (Prosser and Mepham, 1989). This stimulation of mammary activity is unlikely to be due to direct effects of GH because, as noted above, the mammary cells are devoid of GH receptors. There is much evidence that the action of GH in this respect is mediated by IGF1, blood concentrations of which are increased by GH injections, due to increased production in the liver and several other tissues (Wallis, 1989). Indeed, infusion of IGF1 directly into the artery supplying one mammary gland of goats induces a unilateral galactopoietic effect in the infused glands (Prosser, Fleet and Corps, 1989).

PROSPECTIVE BIOTECHNOLOGICAL INTERVENTIONS IN DAIRYING

For reasons which will become apparent, the above discussion has concentrated on endocrine control of milk production. But, because lactation has such a marked effect on the body's metabolism, changes affecting many other aspects of physiological control have repercussions for milk yield and composition. Fig. 1 summarizes the hierarchy of controls involved. Traditionally, improvements in dairying have been achieved by manipulation of factors at higher levels of organization, at the periphery of the diagram, e.g. by choice of phenotype and feeding regime, and by environmental and reproductive control. Biotechnology permits improvements in several of these inputs, but, by providing means for the large-scale production of biologically-active chemicals, it also presents the opportunity to radically intervene in animals' homeostatic processes and thereby alter their productivity.

The potency of biotechnology results from its ability to reprogram existing biological systems so that they channel energy in what are considered more desirable ways. (There is a sense in which *all* human desires amount to alternative ways of partitioning available energy supplies.) This is achieved most obviously at the genetic level by inserting foreign or extra DNA into the genome, but it also refers to more proximate modulators of metabolic activity, such as hormones and enzymes.

Prospective biotechnological procedures affecting lactation include (a) embryo transfer (ET, e.g. Polge, this volume); (b) production of transgenic animals (e.g. Wilmut and Jere, this volume), with a capacity to secrete more or different milk; (c) administration of genetically engineered hormones and other regulatory factors; (d) use of immunological techniques to modulate the activity of hormones and other regulatory factors; (e) manipulation of feed resources and rumen microbes to improve feed utilization (e.g. Ørskov and Flint, this volume); (f) use of various procedures in prevention, diagnosis and treatment of disease conditions (e.g. Lecocq, this volume). Many of these interventions are discussed elsewhere in this volume, so that the following discussion concentrates on procedures more specifically related to lactational

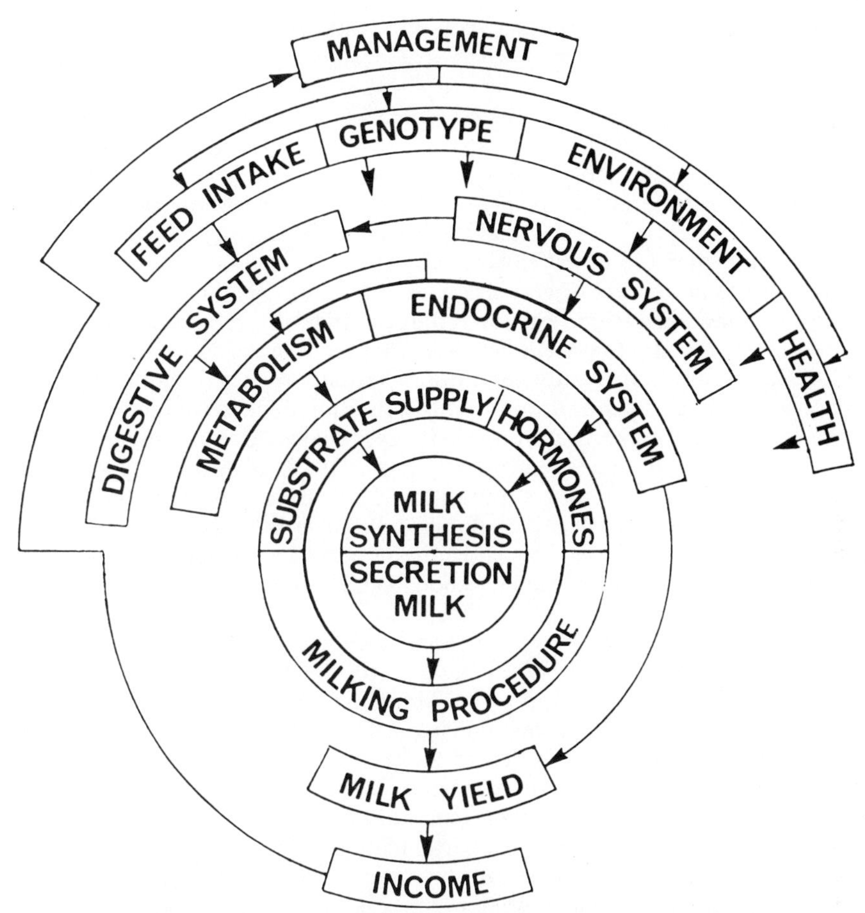

Fig. 1 A representation of the hierarchy of controls which regulate lactation in dairy animals. *Inputs are arranged in concentric layers in the upper semi circle of the digram; outputs in the lower semi circle. Arrows indicte casual relations: geneotype and health have widespread effects. This scheme, which facilitates concise representation of complex interrelationships, is based on that used, for other purposes, by Spedding (1986).*

control, viz. (c), (d) and, to a lesser extent, (b). This selection is made solely to avoid repetition: the *importance* of the other procedures is evident from the concluding section of this paper.

ADMINISTRATION OF EXOGENOUS RECOMBINANT GH

The prospective dairy biotechnology with by far the highest profile in developed Western countries is that involving administration of recombinant bovine (rb) GH (more frequently called 'bovine somatotropin', or bST) to lactating cows. As manufactured by four major pharmaceutical companies, it is proposed that the hormone would be injected subcutaneously, in a slow-release formulation, at intervals of at least two weeks. The commercially produced forms of bST are not strictly speaking 'natural', both because they represent single molecular species, whereas pituitary (p) GH is highly heterogeneous (Lewis, Singh, Lewis and Abadi, 1989), and because of slight modifications to the molecular structure (e.g. by addition of a methionyl group at the N terminus in one product). Such differences appear to result in certain differences in physiological and biochemical activity of rGH and pGH when administered to cows (Heap *et al*, 1989).

Despite some reports of very dramatic effects on yield in the short-term, long-term administration (e.g. for 200 days) under 'European management conditions' indicates that yield increases vary from over 25% to less than 5% (Chilliard, 1989). Since body condition is initially reduced, maintenance of increased yield and restoration of body condition depend on increased and appropriate feed intake, and it is often stressed that yield responses are highly subject to 'level of management' (Bauman, 1987). Even so, appreciable changes in milk yield and composition have been reported during the treatment period (e.g. Vérité, Rulquin and Faverdin, 1989), including an increase in the long-chain fatty acid content of milk fat when animals are in negative energy balance (Bitman, Wood, Tyrrell, Bauman, Peel, Brown and Reynolds, 1984).

Yield responses in other species have been smaller and less consistent, though this may be partly attributable to the use of nonspecific GH preparations, e.g. ovine GH in goats (Mepham, Lawrence, Peters and Hart, 1984) and bGH in sheep (Fleet, Fullerton, Heap, Mepham, Gluckman and Hart, 1988). A brief report indicated that bST is galactopoietic in buffaloes (Ludri, Upadhyay, Singh and Guneratne, 1988).

The observation that growth of mammary parenchyma is associated with raised GH concentrations in prepubertal heifers (Sejrsen *et al*, 1983) suggests the possibility that rbGH might be used to promote mammogenesis. However, the relationship between prepubertal mammary development and subsequent milk yield is, as yet, unclear. Moreover, the correlation between mammary cell number (indicated by mammary total DNA) and milk yield is poor (Mepham, 1983).

The majority of published reports suggest that exogenous GH treatment is efficacious and safe for both animals and consumers. There is, nevertheless, widespread opposition in Europe to its proposed introduction, particularly from farming and consumer organizations. Such concern centres on consumer reactions to technological processes which are seen to meddle with the 'purity' of food: and it is feared that the introduction of bST could seriously reduce dairy sales. The more substantive points relate to possible welfare issues for animals and consumers, effects on employment in the dairy industry and on the rural environment, and effects on less developed countries through greater reliance on imported feeds (Mepham, 1989a). The incidence and scale of such problems has not been carefully assessed, so that it is at present impossible to conduct a reliable cost/benefit analysis for bST use.

Moreover, assurances that milk from treated animals is perfectly safe for consumption are called into question by the observation that in treated animals there are significant increases in the milk concentration of IGF1, a peptide which is biologically active in humans. In the opinion of Norcross, Carnevale, Brown and Post (1989), of the Food Safety and Inspection Service, United States Department of Agriculture, this is "an issue of some concern". They continued: "This question regarding IGF1 must be resolved and is critical because of the potential for these shorter chain peptides to be absorbed through the gut, particularly in neonates."

GH secretagogues

As alternatives to exogenous GH administration, several approaches to increasing its endogenous concentration have been proposed (Flint, 1989). These include treatment with growth hormone releasing factor (GRF); stimulation of GRF release from the hypothalamus using e.g. α-adrenergic agents; and stimulation of GH release with several peptides based on met-enkephalin. At present, the mode of administration appears to preclude their practical application.

IMMUNOLOGICAL TECHNIQUES

The manipulative power of recombinant-DNA technology is matched by that of new immunochemical techniques. Antibodies (Abs) can be produced to either reduce (immunoneutralize) or enhance (immunopotentiate) the activity of biologically active molecules.

Immunoneutralization of somatostatin

Endogenous GH release from the pituitary gland is regulated by somatostatin (SRIF, somatotrophin release inhibiting factor), so that suppression of the activity of the latter increases blood GH concentrations. A study in goats showed that immunization against SRIF during pregnancy resulted in increased milk yield until peak lactation, after which there were no differences in yield between treated and control animals (Spencer, Garssen and Welling, 1985).

Monoclonal antibodies to GH

The usual immune response to an antigen is production of polyclonal Abs, which neutralize the antigen's activity. By contrast, the production of monoclonal (M) Abs to bGH (i.e. Abs of a single type to a specific epitope on the hormone molecule) *enhances* its galactopoietic activity, through formation of a GH-MAb complex. Injection of a GH-MAb complex into lactating sheep caused a larger increase in milk yield than the same dose of GH alone (Pell, Johnsson, Pullar, Morrell, Hart, Holder and Aston, 1989). Identification of the GH epitope associated with galactopoiesis would allow its use in vaccinating animals to increase yield, i.e. the hormone epitope would stimulate production of polyclonal Abs of restricted specificity. One or two injections of small amounts of GH-epitope might thus produce effects equivalent to repeated injections of large amounts of GH itself.

GH anti-idiotypes

Another approach involves production of GH anti-idiotypes, i.e. anti-Abs which resemble GH in molecular configuration (Flint, 1989). Thus, if cows are injected with bGH-Abs (raised e.g. in rabbits) their immune systems make the anti-Ab (or GH-mimic) which could have equivalent activity to GH itself. As for MAbs, the advantage lies in the requirement for very few injections, the animal being induced to manufacture the active agent itself.

Immunoneutralization of the autocrine inhibitor

In recent years it has become apparent that milk contains a chemical factor, which acts as an autocrine feedback inhibitor of milk secretion (Knight *et al*, 1988). Thus, more frequent milking, by removing the inhibitor, increases milk yield. Although the precise chemical nature of the inhibitor has not yet been reported, in goats' milk it has been located in a fraction containing small whey proteins (Knight *et al*, 1988). In theory, immunoneutralization of the autocrine factor might be used to enhance milk yield, without increasing milking frequency.

TRANSGENESIS

The most radical way of increasing GH activity is by reprogramming at the genetic level, inserting extra copies of the GH gene (or that for GRF) into the genome shortly after fertilization of the egg cell. Reviews of progress with this technique (e.g. Pursel, Pinkert, Miller, Bolt, Campbell, Palmiter, Brinster and Hammer, 1989), which has largely been directed to producing transgenic pigs with raised blood GH concentrations, reveal serious animal welfare problems, which would prohibit commercial application if not eliminated. GH transgenesis does not appear to have been investigated in dairy animals, but it would encounter additional problems in view of the need to limit gene expression to specific time periods in the animal's life.

Theoretically, a less-problematical objective of transgenesis is modification of milk composition to produce milk with e.g. less lactose (which limits raw milk consumption in lactose-malabsorbers: Paige and Davis, 1985) or higher protein content (Mercier, 1986). The production of transgenic sheep which express human anti-haemophilic factor IX in their milk has formed the basis of a major research effort (Clark, Bessos, Bishop, Brown, Harris, Lathe, McClenaghan, Prowse, Simons, Whitelaw and Wilmut, 1989) and there seems to be no scientific reason why such an approach should not be directed to nutritional as well as pharmaceutical objectives. Transgenic animals which merely secrete qualitatively different

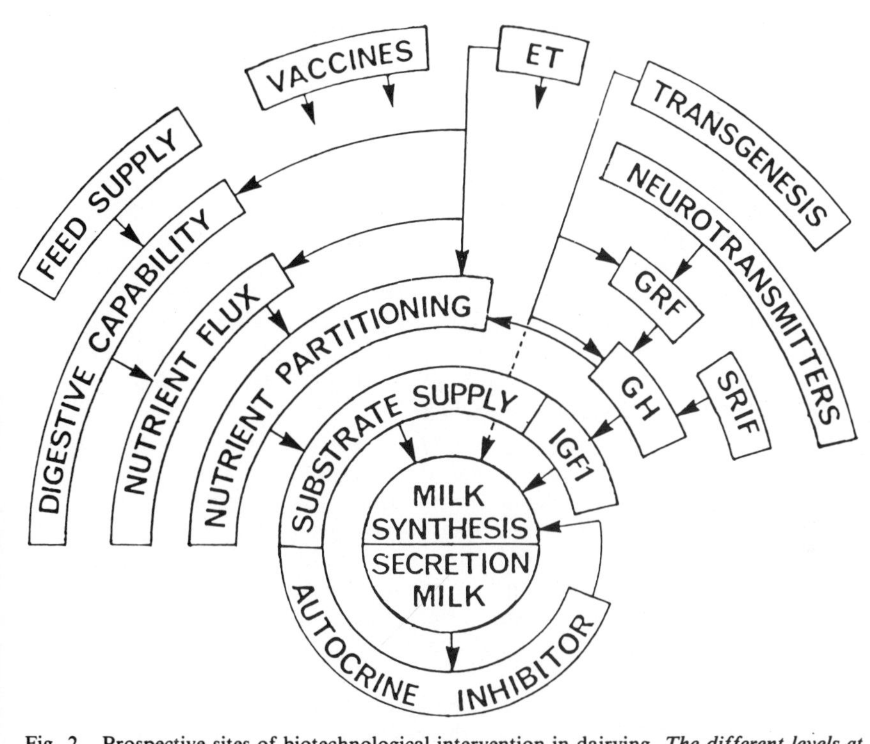

Fig. 2 Prospective sites of biotechnological intervention in dairying. *The different levels at which interventions might be applied are indicated by concentric circles, as in Fig. 1. Abbreviations: ET, embryo transfer; GRF, growth hormone releasing factor; SRIF, somatostatin; GH, growth hormone (somatotrophin); IGF1, insulin-like growth factor 1. Arrows indicate causal relations: ET and genetically engineered vaccines would have widespread effects. For details see text.*

milk should not be subjected to the major metabolic demands of increased milk yields.

Fig. 2 summarizes the possible sites of biotechnological intervention discussed above.

APPROPRIATE BIOTECHNOLOGY FOR DAIRYING IN DEVELOPING COUNTRIES

Virtually all biotechnology has originated in Western developed countries and has inevitably been conditioned by their prevailing socioeconomic norms: *biotechnology* implies *ideology*. There are thus likely to be significant problems in transferring this technology to the quite different socioeconomic and physical environments of developing countries (e.g. Uehara, 1989). There are two aspects to these problems: the nature of the needs and the transferability of the technology.

Granted that it is difficult to generalize about the needs of so many and diverse countries, one fact is overwhelmingly important: virtually all of the one billion people in the world suffering from starvation and malnunutrition live in developing countries. Their plight is not due to a global shortage of food but to the inability of the poorest people to command their share of it. In the opinion of the World Commission on Environment and Development (WCED, 1987) the long-term solution to this problem, attainment of 'sustainable livelihood security', lies in giving priority to the needs of the poor, i.e. a rejection of the 'trickle down' philosophy. Action Point 4 of the WCED report (1987) states that research priorities "should explicitly emphasize the generation of new knowledge and the adaptation of existing knowledge directed specifically to the amelioration and sustainability of agricultural production in the poor farm sector." (It is also implicit in the report that sustainable livelihood security requires that the profligate use of resources by Western developed countries be curbed.)

Consideration of technology transfer has to take account of major differences between developed and developing countries in respect of: political and legal constraints; GNP per capita; demographic indices; family size; proportion of population engaged in agriculture; land availability; educational standards; traditional practices; climate. More specifically, in relation to milk production: animal breed, genetic merit, feed availability, multiple uses of animals, exposure to heat stress and to disease conditions – are all important determinants of the likely success of any technological innovation.

Given these constraints, it is possible to construct a check list of attributes of biotechnological procedures, which would favour their adoption by resource-poor farmers. They should be:– (i) simple to use; (ii) inexpensive (possibly subsidized by government or aid agency funds in the interests of humanitarian, longer-term national and/or global benefits); (iii) reliably effective (since with small farming enterprises poor responses could have disastrous effects); (iv) sustainable, without adverse secondary effects; and (v) preferably, capable of producing a more nutritious product.

Clearly, biotechnology aimed at increasing milk yields can only do so effectively and sustainably if feed intake is adequate to meet increased requirements. But, in the humid and semi-arid tropics and in countries of the Mediterranean basin, the quality and quantity of herbage available is frequently a significant constraint on milk yield, and this is particularly true for poor farmers (e.g. Whyte, 1969; Smith, 1985). Consequently, the dominant prospective dairy biotechnologies in developed countries, which are designed to partition nutrients to the mammary glands by increasing blood GH concentrations, do not address the commonest limiting factor. Even with adequate feed supplies, responses to GH treatment in heat-stressed animals may be insignificant (Zoa-Mboe, Head, Bachman, Baccari and Wilcox, 1989) or, at ambient temperatures over 30° C, result in reduced yields (Zoa-Mboe *et al*, 1989). No doubt in intensively managed herds of taurine dairy cattle, housed in controlled environments and fed concentrates, yield increases to bST treatment could approach those observed in temperate conditions. This, however, would be to the detriment of poorer farmers, since milk sales are often confined to richer urban sectors (Karunaratne and Wagstaff, 1985): and in development terms, it is a strategy which ignores the WCED (1987) recommendations.

It would seem, then, that for resource-poor farmers, adoption of biotechnologies aimed at increasing yields and digestibility of forage, and improving the animals' digestive capabilities, might be the most profitable approaches, in that they seek to increase nutrient availability in the body's metabolic pools. For example, genetic manipulation might be employed to improve the quality of crop residues, while modified strains of rumen microbe might enhance cellulose degradation and promote detoxification (Ørskov and Flint, this volume).

Significant benefits are also likely to accrue from the application of biotechnology to vaccination programmes aimed at reducing the microbial and parasitic infestations to which tropical animals are prone (e.g. Lecocq, this volume) and which greatly reduce the efficient use of available feed energy.

Technologies involving transgenic animals secreting nutritionally-improved milk for adults (e.g. with reduced lactose) seem feasible; but given the damage wrought by misapplication of artificial babyfoods (Mepham, 1989c), a recent report of attempts to engineer cows to secrete a 'human-like' milk (Highfield, 1989) must be viewed with apprehension.

In essence, the most appropriate biotechnologies would seem to be those which promise a sustainable increase in the availability of dairying inputs (factors at the periphery of Fig. 1) for resource-poor farmers. The problems they face are largely due to the maldistribution of global energy supplies, which a Western-dominated biotechnology is likely to exacerbate. If the benefits of biotechnology are to be distributed more equitably, there must be a substantial shift in the assignment of priorities (Mepham, 1987a, 1987b, 1989b); a veritable repartitioning of nutrients, not just within animals but, principally, between societies. Since the poor themselves cannot do it, there is a need for national governments and international aid agencies to commission appropriate biotechnology: biotechnology which is sensitive to social needs and consistent with the objective of sustainable development.

> "New approaches must not be allowed to emerge merely under the impetus of their intellectual interest or their commercial potential. The technology of the future needs ideals as well as ideas – objectives as well as an intellectual framework – if the direction of its progress is to be in harmony with the long term needs of mankind" (Pacey, 1974).

The author is grateful to Professor D. Sastradipradja, University of Bogor, Indonesia for his helpful comments on the draft manuscript.

REFERENCES

Bauman, D.E. (1987). Bovine somatotropin: the Cornell experience. In *Proceedings of the National Invitational Workshop on Bovine Somatotropin*, pp. 45–56. USDA Extension Service, St. Louis, Missouri.

Bauman, D.E. and Elliot, J.M. (1983). Control of nutrient partitioning in lactating ruminants. In *Biochemistry of Lactation* (ed. T.B. Mepham), pp. 437–468. Elsevier, Amsterdam and New York.

Bauman, D.E., Eppard, P.J., De Geeter, M.J. and Lanza, G.M. (1985). Responses of high producing dairy cows to long-term treatment with pituitary somatotropin and recombinant somatotropin. *Journal of Dairy Science*, **68**, 1352–1362.

Bitman, J., Wood, D.L., Tyrrell, H.F., Bauman, D.E., Peel, C.J., Brown, A.C.G. and Reynolds, P.J. (1984). Blood and milk lipid responses induced by growth hormone administration in lactating cows. *Journal of Dairy Science*, **67**, 2873–2880.

Bremel, R.D. and Shuler, L.A. (1988). Bovine placental lactogen: structure and function. In *The Mammary Gland: Development, Regulation, Function* (eds. M.C. Neville and C.W. Daniel), pp. 439–457. Plenum, New York and London.

Chilliard, Y. (1989). Long-term effects of recombinant bovine somatotropin (rBST) on dairy cow performances: a review. In *Use of Somatotropin in Livestock Production* (eds. K. Sejrsen, M. Vestergaard and A. Neimann-Sorensen), pp. 61–87. Elsevier, London and New York.

Clark, A.J., Bessos, H., Bishop, J.O., Brown, P., Harris, S., Lathe, R., McClenaghan, M., Prowse, C., Simons, J.P., Whitelaw, C.B.A. and Wilmut, I. (1989). Expression of human anti-hemophilic factor IX in the milk of transgenic sheep. *Biotechnology*, **7**, 487–492.

Dembinski, T.C. and Shiu, R.P.C. (1988). Growth factors in mammary gland development and function. In *The Mammary Gland: Development, Regulation, Function* (eds. M.C. Neville and C.W. Daniel), pp. 335–381. Plenum, New York and London.

Fleet, I.R., Fullerton, F.M., Heap, R.B., Mepham, T.B., Gluckman, P. and Hart, I.C. (1988). Cardiovascular and metabolic responses during growth hormone treatment of lactating sheep. *Journal of Dairy Research*, **55**, 479–485.

Flint, D.J. (1989). Alternatives to growth hormone for the manipulation of animal performance. In *Use of Somatotropin in Livestock Production* (eds. K. Sejrsen, M. Vestergaard and A. Neimann-Sorensen), pp. 51–60. Elsevier, London and New York.

Forsyth, I.A. (1983). The endocrinology of lactation. In *Biochemistry of Lactation* (ed. T.B. Mepham), pp. 309–349. Elsevier, Amsterdam and New York.

Forsyth, I.A. (1989). Mammary development. *Proceedings of the Nutrition Society*, **48**, 17–22.

Fullerton, F.M., Fleet, I.R., Heap, R.B., Hart, I.C. and Mepham, T.B. (1989). Cardiovascular responses and mammary substrate uptake in Jersey cows treated with pituitary-derived growth hormone during late lactation. *Journal of Dairy Research* **56**, 27–35.

Heap, R.B., Fleet, I.R., Fullerton, F.M., Davis, A.J., Goode, J.A., Hart, I.C., Pendleton, J.W., Prosser, C.G., Silvester, L.M. and Mepham, T.B. (1989). A comparison of the mechanisms of action of bovine pituitary-derived and recombinant somatotropin (ST) in inducing galactopoiesis in the cow during late lactation. In *Biotechnology in Growth Regulation* (eds. R.B. Heap, C.G. Prosser and G.E. Lamming), pp. 73–84. Butterworths, London.

Highfield, R. (1989). Cows designed to produce 'human milk'. *Daily Telegraph (London)* 18.8.89 p. 1.

Karunaratne, G. and Wagstaff, H. (1985). Income and employment from dairy development. In *Milk Production in Developing Countries* (ed. A.J. Smith) pp. 73–90. Centre for Tropical Veterinary Medicine, Edinburgh.

Knight, C., Wilde, C.J. and Peaker, M. (1988). Manipulation of milk secretion. In *Nutrition and Lactation in the Dairy Cow* (ed. P.C. Garnsworthy), pp. 3-14. Butterworths, London.

Lecocq, J.P. (1991). Genetically engineered vaccines against rabies and parasites. In *The Application of Biotechnology in Developing Countries* (ed. A.G. Hunter), pp. 334-335. Centre for Tropical Veterinary Medicine, University of Edinburgh.

Lewis, U.J., Singh, R.N.P., Lewis, L.J. and Abadi, N. (1989). Multiple forms of growth hormone. In *Basic and Clinical Aspects of Growth Hormone* (ed. B.B. Bercu), pp. 43-55. Plenum, New York and London.

Ludri, R.S., Upadhyay, R.C., Singh, M. and Guneratne, J.R. (1988). Bovine somatotropin in buffaloes. *The Veterinary Record*, **122**, 495.

Mepham, T.B. (1983). Physiological aspects of lactation. In *Biochemistry of Lactation* (ed. T.B. Mepham), pp. 3-28. Elsevier, Amsterdam and New York.

Mepham, T.B. (1987a). *Physiology of Lactation.* Open University Press, Milton Keynes and Philadelphia.

Mepham, T.B. (1987b). Changing prospects and perspectives in dairy research. *Outlook on Agriculture*, **16**, 182-188.

Mepham, T.B. (1989a). Criteria for the public acceptability of biotechnological innovations in animal production. In *Biotechnology in Growth Regulation* (eds. R.B. Heap, C.G. Prosser and G.E. Lamming), pp. 203-212. Butterworths, London.

Mepham, T.B. (1989b). Questions of validity in mammary physiology: methodology and ethics. *Proceedings of the Nutrition Society*, **48**, 1-7.

Mepham, T.B. (1989c). Science and the politics of breastfeeding: birthright or birth rite? *Science and Public Policy*, **16** 181-191.

Mepham, T.B., Lawrence, S.E., Peters, A.R. and Hart, I.C. (1984). Effects of growth hormone on mammary function in lactating goats. *Hormone and Metabolic Research*, **16**, 248-253.

Mercier, J-C. (1986). Genetic engineering applied to milk producing animals. In *Exploiting New Technology in Animal Breeding* (eds. C. Smith, J.W.B. King and J.C. McKay), pp. 122-131. Commission of the European Communities/Oxford University Press, Oxford and London.

Norcross, M.A., Carnevale, R.A., Brown, E.A. and Post, A.R. (1989). Biotechnology and the control of growth and product quality in swine – safety of edible products. In *Biotechnology for Control of Growth and Product Quality in Swine: Implications and Acceptability* (eds. P. van der Wal, G.J. Nieuwhof and R.D. Politiek), pp. 169-182. Pudoc, Wageningen.

Ørskov, E.R. and Flint, H.J. (1991). Manipulation of rumen microbes or feed resources as methods of improving feed utilization. In *The Application of Biotechnology in Developing Countries* (ed. A.G. Hunter), pp. 123-138. Centre for Tropical Veterinary Medicine, University of Edinburgh.

Pacey, A. (1974). *The Maze of Ingenuity: Ideas and Ideals in the Development of Technology*, p. 320. Allen Lane, London.

Paige, D.M. and Davis, L.R. (1985). Nutritional significance of lactose: I. Nutritional aspects of lactose digestion. In *Developments in Dairy Chemistry* (ed. P.F. Fox) Vol 3, pp. 111-132. Applied Science Publishers, London and New York.

Pell, J.M., Johnsson, I.D., Pullar, R.A., Morrell, D.J., Hart, I.C., Holder, A.T. and Aston, R. (1989). Potentiation of growth hormone activity in sheep using monoclonal antibodies. *Journal of Endocrinology*, **120**, R15-R18.

Polge, E.J.C. (1991). The role of embryo transfer technology. In *The Application of Biotechnology in Developing Countries* (ed. A.G. Hunter), pp. 40-41. Centre for Tropical Veterinary Medicine, University of Edinburgh.

Prosser, C.G., Fleet, I.R. and Corps, A.N. (1989). Increased secretion of insulin-like growth factor 1 (IGF1) in milk during bovine growth hormone treatment in the goat. *Journal of Dairy Research*, **56**, 17-26.

Prosser, C.G. and Mepham, T.B. (1989). Mechanism of action of bovine somatotropin in increasing milk secretion in dairy ruminants. In *Use of Somatotropin in Livestock Production* (eds. K. Sejrsen, M. Vestergaard and A. Neimann-Sorensen), pp.1–17. Elsevier, London and New York.

Pursel, V.G., Pinkert, C.A., Miller, K.F., Bolt, D.J., Campbell, R.G., Palmiter, R.D., Brinster, R.L. and Hammer, R.E. (1989). Genetic engineering of livestock. *Science*, **244**, 1281–1287.

Sejrsen, K., Huber, J.T. and Tucker, H.A. (1983). Influence of amount fed on hormone concentrations and their relationship to mammary growth in heifers. *Journal of Dairy Science*, **66**, 845–855.

Smith, A.J. (1985). (ed.) *Milk Production in Developing Countries*. Centre for Tropical Veterinary Medicine, Edinburgh.

Spencer, G.S.G., Garssen, G.J. and Welling, A.M.A.W. (1985). Increased milk production by goats following immunization against somatostatin. *Animal Production*, **40**, 572–573.

Spedding, C.R.W. (1986). Animal production from grass: a systems approach. In *Bioindustrial Ecosystems* (vol. 21 of *Ecostystems of the World*) (eds. D.J.A. Cole and G.C. Brander), pp.107–120. Elsevier, Amsterdam and New York.

Uehara, G. (1989). Technology transfer in the tropics. *Outlook on Agriculture*, **18**, 38–42.

Vérité, R., Rulquin, H. and Faverdin, P. (1989). Effect of slow-released somatotropin on dairy cow performances. In *Use of Somatotropin in Livestock Production* (eds. K. Sejrsen, M. Vestergaard and A. Neiman-Sorensen), pp. 269–273. Elsevier, London and New York.

Wallis, M. (1989). Mechanism of action of growth hormone. In *Hormones and their Actions* (eds. B.A. Cooke, R.J.B. King and H.J. van der Molen) Part II, pp. 265–294. Elsevier, Amsterdam and New York.

Whyte, R.O. (1969). *Milk Production in Developing Countries*. Faber, London.

Wilmut, I. and Jere, J. (1991). Methods of making transgenic livestock and their role in developing countries. In *The Application of Biotechnology in Developing Countries* (ed. A.G. Hunter), pp. 91–104. Centre for Tropical Veterinary Medicine, University of Edinburgh.

World Commission on Environment and Development (1987). *Food 2000: Global Policies for Sustainable Agriculture*. p. 112. Zed Books, London and New York.

Zoa-Mboe, A., Head, H.H., Bachman, K.C., Baccari, F. and Wilcox, C.J. (1989). Effects of bovine somatotropin on milk yield and composition, dry matter intake, and some physiological functions of Holstein cows during heat stress. *Journal of Dairy Science*, **72**, 907–916.

3.7

Manipulation of Animal Fertility

A.R. PETERS
Hoechst U.K. Limited, Milton Keynes, U.K.

INTRODUCTION

Even in most developed countries, reproductive performance, particularly of domestic ruminants is poor. For example in the U.K., the calving rate of dairy cows to first insemination is of the order of only 55–60%. Furthermore, few herds meet the target optimum calving frequency of one calf per cow per year. In the developing countries, the problems are compounded by adverse climatic conditions, e.g. heat (Thatcher, 1974) and probably poor nutrition. In addition species indigenous to developing countries may have specific problems or at least more severe problems than in the developed world. Similarly the use of animals for draught purposes may have adverse effects on their reproductive performance (Jainudeen, 1985; Momongan, 1985). Also less may be known about the physiology of these species, e.g. *Bos indicus* and buffalo versus *Bos taurus* (e.g. Dobson and Kamonpatana, 1986).

The present paper will briefly review some of the functional reproductive problems in the female and the endocrine and pharmacological approaches being made to overcome these. It is important however to realize at the outset that there are at least two ways in which biotechnology will help to manipulate fertility. They are: 1) through a better understanding of the physiological control systems so that we can devise appropriate hormonal treatments, but equally important 2) by developing improved methods of drug delivery particularly from the point of view of controlled release and adjuvancy but possibly also drug targeting. A few comments will be made about drug delivery at relevant points in the paper.

CAUSES OF REPRODUCTIVE INEFFICIENCY

Functional reproductive problems, in the absence of infection, can be classified into four categories. They are:

- a failure to undergo ovarian cycles known as true anoestrus
- a failure to exhibit oestrus at the appropriate time – behavioural anoestrus
- a failure to conceive when mated or inseminated
- small litter size in litter-producing animals or low fecundity.

These four areas will be considered in turn with particular reference to the new ways in which biotechnology may be used to alleviate their effects if not entirely overcome them.

Anoestrus

Lack of ovarian activity or true anoestrus occurs in three states, viz: before puberty, *post partum* and in some species on a seasonal basis. The final endocrine pathway appears to be common in these three conditions i.e. suppressed gonadotropin secretion, particularly pulsatile luteinizing hormone (LH) release (Fig. 1). However, their causes and primary mechanisms appear to be different. Seasonal anoestrus will not be considered here but has been extensively reviewed relatively recently by Ellendorff and Elsaesser (1985). Considerable research effort has been expended in understanding the endocrine mechanisms involved in controlling the time of puberty (e.g. Foster, Yellon and Olster, 1985; Dodson, McLeod, Haresign, Peters and Lamming, 1988). As discussed above a failure of pulsatile LH secretion is involved but attempts to induce puberty in young heifers by restoring this using repeated injections of gonadotrophin releasing hormone (GnRH) or prolonged infusions have met with limited success (McLeod, Peters, Haresign and Lamming, 1985; Jagger, Peters, McLeod and Lamming, 1989). The attainment of puberty is known to be related closely to body weight (Sorenson, Hansel, Hough, Armstrong, McEntee and Bratton, 1959) with typical European breeds of cattle reaching puberty at around 250–300 kg usually at 7–12 months. Puberty appears to occur later in Zebu cattle and delays are also well recognized in buffalo (Dobson and Kamonpatana, 1986) all probably associated with poor weight gain during prepubertal life. There seems little prospect of immediate pharmacological answers to delayed puberty but resolution most likely lies with good management and improved nutrition.

Post-partum anoestrus

The post-partum period in farm animals is characterized by lactation and a lack of ovarian activity. In normal cattle this acyclic period is generally shorter in dairy animals than in suckled beef cows. For example, 95% of dairy cows under U.K. conditions had resumed ovarian cycles by day 50 *post*

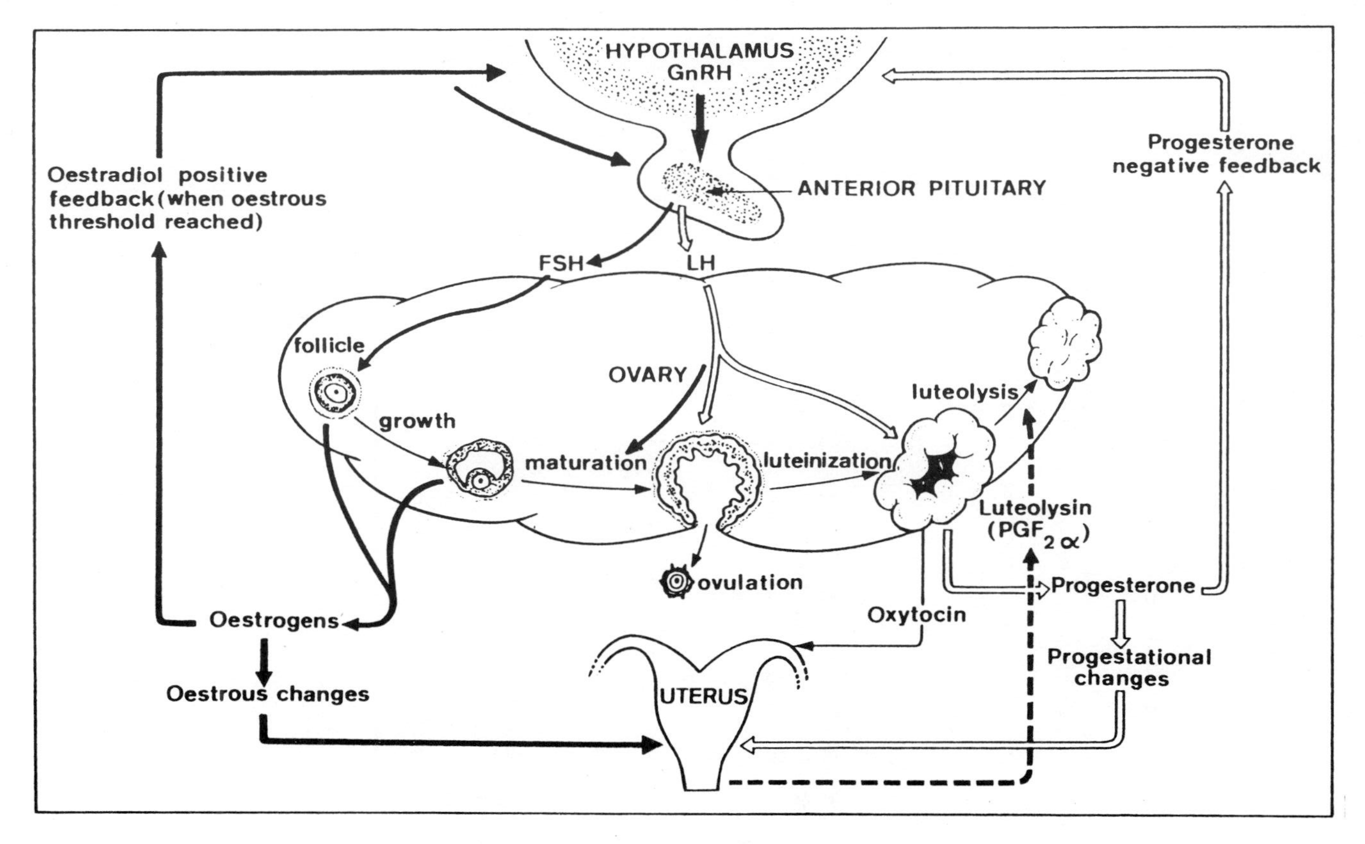

Fig. 1 *A summary of the hormonal control of the ovarian cycle.*

partum (Bulman and Lamming, 1978), whereas the equivalent figure for beef cows was 40% (Peters and Riley, 1982). In the sow lactation is associated with anoestrus for up to six weeks, with oestrus and ovulation occurring within three to ten days after weaning (Britt, Armstrong, Cox and Esbenshade, 1985). If ewes lamb in the breeding season the anoestrus period is likely to be three to six weeks (Hunter, 1968).

It is important to understand the physiological mechanisms controlling the restoration of ovarian activity in the normal animal so that this can be applied to the development of appropriate treatments for animals undergoing delay. A variety of genetic, environmental and husbandry factors may act on the pregnant and post-partum animal to influence ovarian activity *post partum*. These include nutrition, suckling, season, climate and disease. One or a combination of these factors may result in extended periods of ovarian acyclicity *post partum* possibly by common final endocrine mechanisms. However, despite intensive study the exact interactions of these factors with the neuroendocrine system are poorly understood. The author has recently reviewed the endocrine aspects of lactational anoestrus in farm animals (Peters and Lamming, 1990).

Inhibitory environmental factors in some way result in reduced hypothalamic GnRH secretion, a lack of LH secretion and consequent lack of ovarian follicle development (Fig. 1).

Over the years many workers have examined methods of inducing ovulation in anoestrus animals but none has yet been totally effective in deeply anoestrous animals. Our work has concentrated on the possibility of mimicking hypothalamic GnRH secretion by giving repeated intravenous injections of the exogenous decapeptide for up to 48 hours in post-partum beef cows (Riley, Peters and Lamming, 1981; Jagger, Peters and Lamming, 1987). This was moderately effective in inducing ovulation (Table 1).

In post-partum sheep, hourly injections of 100 ng GnRH for 48 hours induced preovulatory LH surges and ovulation, but luteal function was

TABLE 1 *Effect of GnRH administration in post-partum beef cows.*

Method of administration	Dose of GnRH µg/h	Number of cows Total	Number of cows Ovulating
Repeated injection	1.0	6	3
	2.5	6	4
	5.0	6	4
	1.0	5	0
Continuous infusion	2.5	5	5
	5.0	5	3

Data: Jagger *et al* (1987)

deficient (Wright, Geytenbeek, Clarke and Findlay, 1983). Using a modified treatment regimen Wright, Geytenbeek, Clarke and Findlay (1984) induced ovulation in 11/15 ewes by injecting GnRH three-hourly for 24 hours, two-hourly for 24 hours and hourly for 24 hours. Luteal function was normal in most ewes and the authors concluded that the ovary requires a period of stimulation by LH pulses before ovulation in order to ensure normal luteal function.

Oestrus and ovulation were induced in both lactating and weaned sows using hourly or two-hourly injections of GnRH (Cox and Britt, 1982; Armstrong and Britt, 1985). In the lactating sows, 3/6 receiving 2.5 μg GnRH per two hours and 6/6 receiving 1.5 μg per hour showed oestrus whereas none of the controls did so. Pulsatile administration of GnRH has also been used to induce ovulation in anoestrous mares (Johnsson, 1986).

If such a technique was consistently successful it would clearly have considerable potential in several species, however automatic pulsatile administration is currently impractical from a technical point of view. Therefore later studies have investigated the possibility of using continuous administration of GnRH to achieve the same result. This also raises the question of the physiological necessity of a pulsatile pattern of endocrine signalling.

To my knowledge continuous infusion of GnRH has not been reported for the post-partum ewe but it has been for the seasonally anoestrous ewe. Constant infusion of 125 or 250 ng GnRH per hour for 48 hours resulted in elevated plasma LH concentrations, eventual preovulatory surges and ovulation; however a period of progesterone pretreatment was required to ensure that viable corpora lutea were formed. Studies with continuous infusion of GnRH in sows are limited but Britt *et al* (1985) reported that lactating sows infused with 2.5 μg per hour for nine days did not exhibit oestrus until after weaning.

In our most recent experiments post-partum beef cows received 1.0, 2.5, or 5.0 μg GnRH per two hours for 48 hours either as 24 two-hourly repeated injections or by continuous infusion (Jagger *et al*, 1987). Preovulatory LH surges occurred in half the cows receiving repeated injections and 8/10 of the cows receiving the two highest doses by continuous infusion. The surges occurred about 30 hours after the start of treatment in the injected cows and after about 3.5 hours in the infused cows. Cows which showed preovulatory surges had significantly higher plasma oestradiol and lower plasma follicle-stimulating hormone (FSH) concentrations than those that did not. This suggested that cows that responded had more advanced follicular development as evidenced by higher oestradiol output. This was also reflected in lower FSH concentrations considered to be due to negative feedback influences of oestradiol or inhibin (Fig. 2). Similar results were obtained when prepubertal heifers were infused with GnRH (Jagger *et al*, 1989). The most notable difference between GnRH infused cows or heifers and those receiving repeated injections was in the relative timing of the preovulatory

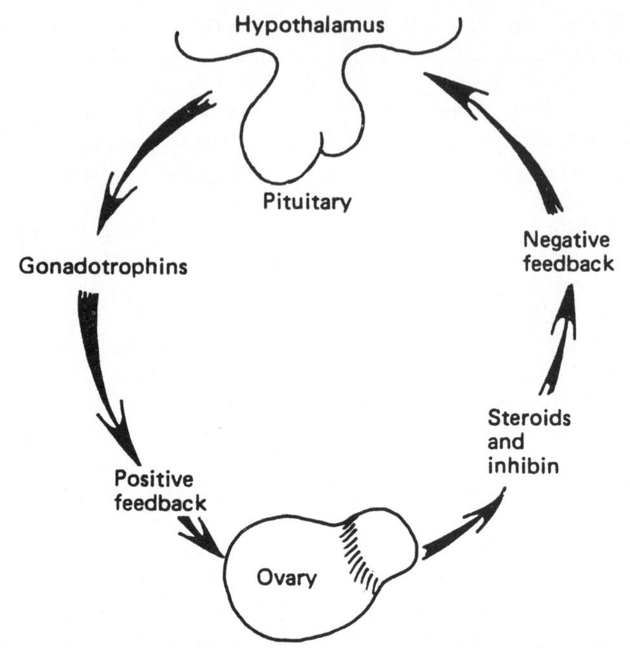

Fig. 2 *Relationship between ovarian hormones and gonadotrophins.*
From: Webb *et al* (1984)

gonadotrophin surges as mentioned above. This may suggest that the mechanism by which the surge is induced is different in the two situations. It also illustrates the small quantity of GnRH required to induce a preovulatory surge when infused into a sensitized animal.

It appears to date that low-dose GnRH treatments are more consistently successful in inducing ovulation in the sow (Britt *et al*, 1985) and ewe (Wright *et al*, 1984) than in the cow (Jagger *et al*, 1987), although this might simply reflect differences in the treatment regimen. If low-dose GnRH treatments are to be applied in practice then a subcutaneous delivery system would be necessary. Our recent experiments in heifers (Jagger *et al*, 1989) suggest that this is feasible.

It is considered unlikely that practical application of this type of work will progress unless a suitable subcutaneous delivery system becomes available. McLeod, Haresign, Peters, Humke and Lamming (1988) experimented with a number of controlled release vehicles for GnRH and found implant devices made from polyhydroxy-butyric acid to be most successful. On the other hand oil-based depot formulations were found to give insufficient control over release for these purposes.

Some uncertainty has surrounded the subject of continuous infusion of GnRH compared to repeated injections. Crowder, Herring and Nett (1986) showed that continuous intravenous infusion of 2.5 μg GnRH per hour in sheep resulted in a 50% decrease in pituitary GnRH receptor concentrations after 24 hours, although these were restored within six hours after the end of infusion. In cows, infusion of 20 μg of GnRH per hour resulted in an initial increase in plasma LH concentrations followed by a return to pretreatment levels after 48 hours (Lamming and McLeod, 1988). After 14 days of infusion the pituitary was still able to respond to a 10 μg GnRH challenge but at a reduced magnitude. This is also suggestive of a reduction of pituitary receptors or at least some form of desensitization. Nevertheless as shown above, continuous infusion has been used to induce ovulation successfully in some circumstances and it may be that such desensitization is more an effect of dosage rather than the mode of administration.

OESTRUS AND ITS DETECTION

As indicated above failure of oestrus is an important cause of poor fertility. However perhaps a more common phenomenon is the failure to detect oestrus. Any progress of biotechnology in this field is likely to come via the development of diagnostic kits. A number of enzyme-linked immunosorbent assay (ELISA) kits for progesterone are available commercially and may be applied to this problem. However this is a relatively imprecise method of pinpointing oestrus. Future progress may be made in detecting subtle hormonal or other changes which are predictive of the time of ovulation as opposed to oestrus. This would be more appropriate for the timing of inseminations. The manipulation of oestrus has been discussed elsewhere in this volume (Macfarlane, 1991) but it is this author's view that little improvement will be made to existing techniques in this area in the near future.

ESTABLISHMENT OF PREGNANCY

The ability to conceive is clearly vital in determining reproductive performance. A low pregnancy rate to first service is a major cause of poor reproductive performance. In the absence of specific infectious disease it has been shown that the major problem here, at least in cattle, is early embryonic death (Sreenan and Diskin, 1986), normally occurring before day 25 after service. The exact cause(s) of embryonic death is unknown but it is circumstantially related to premature regression of the corpus luteum. In other words the corpus luteum is normally maintained for the whole of gestation and early embryonic mortality is associated with its early loss. This results in a decrease in progesterone concentrations allowing the animal to return to oestrus, probably at the normal time.

Before examining methods of reducing embryo mortality it would be useful to provide a brief review of new findings in relation to the establishment of pregnancy. In the nonpregnant animal prostaglandin (PG) $F_{2}\alpha$ secreted by the endometrium causes regression of the corpus luteum. This is illustrated in Fig. 3. There is evidence that oestradiol-17β from developing ovarian follicles

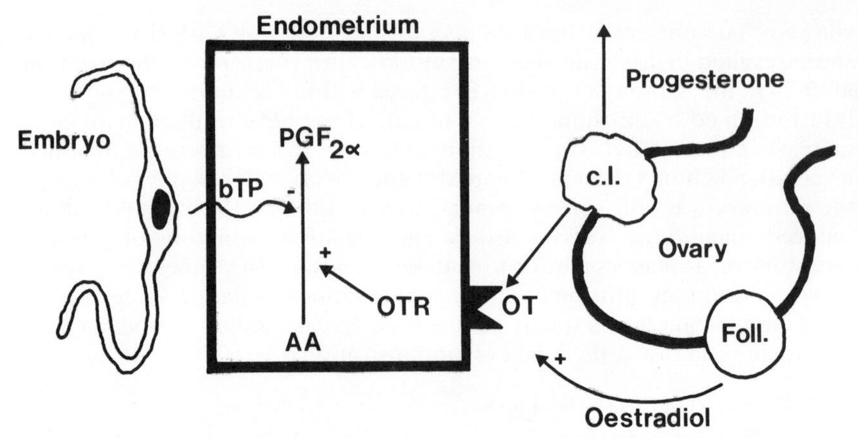

Fig. 3 *Relationship between the embryo, endometrium and ovary.*

stimulates the synthesis of receptors for oxytocin on endometrial cells. Oxytocin, now known to be of luteal origin (Wathes, 1984) binds to these receptors thereby stimulating the synthesis and secretion of $PGF_2\alpha$. In a normal ruminant early pregnancy a protein of molecular weight of approximately 18,000 daltons is secreted by the embryo which has an antiluteolytic effect. This has been termed ovine or bovine trophoblast protein 1 (e.g. oTP1). Stewart, Flint, Lamming, McCann and Parkinson (1989) recently showed that the amino acid sequence of oTP1 is 70.3% similar to bovine α2-interferon. Further studies have shown that oTP-1 and bTP-1 bind to receptors on the endometrium and intrauterine infusion of trophoblast proteins or recombinant interferon can extend the length of the luteal phase in nonpregnant animals (Stewart *et al*, 1989; Thatcher, MacMillan, Hansen and Drost, 1989). This work has led to the tentative conclusion that some embryo mortality may be caused by a failure of some embryos to produce sufficient trophoblast protein. These early results clearly offer the exciting possibility of using recombinant trophoblast protein to prevent or reduce embryo mortality in domestic animals.

Use of buserelin to reduce embryo mortality

A number of methods have been used in the field to improve pregnancy rates in cattle. Diskin and Sreenan (1986) reviewed literature on comparisons of progesterone concentrations in pregnant and nonconceiving cows before and after insemination and concluded that the data were conflicting and inconclusive in all respects. Similarly progesterone supplementation during early pregnancy has given equivocal results but does seem to be effective where control pregnancy rates are particularly low, i.e. 40% or below.

Also there have been numerous studies where either chorionic gonadotropin (LH-like) or GnRH have been administered on the day of service but again the overall results are equivocal.

A somewhat different approach was used by MacMillan, Taufa and Day (1986), to attempt to support the corpus luteum when it becomes susceptible to the luteolytic mechanism i.e. approaching day 16 after oestrus in the cow. Treated cows (approximately 225) received a single injection of 10 μg buserelin (synthetic analogue of GnRH) on day 11, 12 or 13 after AI. Treated and control cows were palpated at six to nine weeks to determine pregnancy status. Cows returning to service were reinseminated. Pregnancy rates at six to nine weeks were 72.4% and 60.9% for the treated and control cows respectively. Of those cows returning to service the pregnancy rates to second service were 85.1% and 69.5% for treated and control. The differences between groups were highly significant on both occasions. In further work Thatcher *et al* (1989) injected nonpregnant cows at three-day intervals from day 12 of the cycle to day 48 with 10 μg buserelin. The corpora lutea of these animals were maintained for the duration of treatment. Such findings if confirmed will indicate an additional application for a long-term controlled release formulation of GnRH or analogue. Thatcher *et al* (1989) have suggested that buserelin acts in these situations by disrupting normal waves of ovarian follicular growth and hence oestradiol secretion during this period, resulting in a failure of synthesis of the oxytocin receptor, a necessary step for the luteolytic mechanism (Fig. 3). It is also likely that accessory corpora lutea are formed which may boost progesterone production.

IMPROVING FECUNDITY

The increase in ovulation rate thereby resulting in increased litter size or fecundity has long been a goal of reproductive scientists. A number of approaches ahve been used including gonadotropin, particularly those with FSH-like activity. Thwe use of such gonadotropins has been an essential part of embryo transfer programmes. Other methods which will be briefly discussed here include immunization against steroids and inhibin.

Immunization against steroids

Ovarian steroids exert a negative feedback or suppressive influence on gonadotrophin secretion (Fig. 2). It has been found that immunization of sheep against a variety of steroids will increase ovulation rate and subsequent lambing percentage (Scaramuzzi and Hoskinson, 1984). Active immunization against androstenedione an oestrogen precursor was one of the most effective methods and is the basis of the product Fecundin (Pitman-Moore). Field trials on over 3,000 treated ewes in the U.K. showed a mean increase in lambs reared of about 25% (Stubbings and Maund, 1988). However there was considerable variation between farms in response of −2 to +49% suggesting interactions with breed, nutrition and other factors. Consequently the product has not been a commercial success in the U.K. A contributory factor may be the relative sophistication of such a technique and the very precise management required to obtain the maximum benefit. In this author's view such products will have to be extremely robust to perform consistently well in the field and this may present a major difficulty in utilizing such technology in developing countries. The consistent production of twin ovulations in cattle using steroid-immunization techniques has not yet proved possible.

Inhibin

Inhibin is a gonadal peptide produced in both the male and female which selectively suppresses FSH secretion (Fig. 2). In the female it is secreted by the follicular granulosa cells (Erickson and Hsueh, 1978) and accumulates in the follicular fluid (Tsonis, Quigg, Lee, Leversha, Trounson and Findlay, 1983).

Inhibin from sheep and cattle has a molecular weight of 58,000 daltons and consists of two subunits α and β of molecular weight 43,000 and 15,000 respectively (de Krester, 1986). However a lower molecular weight form also exists with a 20,000 processed form of the α subunit (Torney, Hodgson, Forage and de Kretser, 1989). Findlay, Tsonis, Staples and Cahill (1986) showed that the larger follicles (>0.5 mm) are the main source of inhibin in sheep. Administration of inhibin, usually in the form of charcoal-treated (to remove steroids) follicular fluid from various species results in a suppression of FSH in plasma usually after a delay of 2–3 hours (Findlay, Robertson and Clarke, 1987). In intact ewes the initial suppression of FSH secretion is followed by a rebound increase (McNeilly, 1985).

There are at least two ways in which the effects of inhibin might be exploited. One is to take advantage of the rebound effect, increasing FSH above control levels in order to increase ovulation rate (Wallace, McNeilly and Baird, 1985). Secondly, immunization against fractions of follicular fluid containing inhibin activity has been carried out (e.g. Cummins, O'Shea, Al-Obaidi, Bindon and Finlay, 1986). This resulted in a transient increase in mean ovulation rate from 1.2 to 2.3 in a small number of ewes which was restored in subsequent years following booster doses. Similarly transient increases in ovulation rate have been observed in preliminary experiments in cattle (Price, Morris, O'Shea and Webb, 1987). One of the problems of applying such findings in practice is the use of potent adjuvants to maximize immune responses in the experimental situation. Such adjuvants e.g. Freund's complete, are totally unacceptable for practical use. This can then often lead to great difficulties in finding a suitable adjuvant or vehicle with which to repeat the effect.

A further interesting feature related to inhibin is that the β-subunits from inhibin molecules can combine to form dimers with FSH-releasing activity (Ling *et al*, 1886). The physiological or practical significance of this protein is not yet known.

CONCLUSIONS

Selected areas of recent research into the physiology of reproduction of farm animals have been briefly reviewed. The application of biotechnology will bring exciting prospects for the manipulation and enhancement of animal fertility, particularly through the synthesis of peptides with hormonal activity and the development of novel immunogens. However, drug delivery and vaccine adjuvant systems should be developed in parallel as far as possible with physiological knowledge, so that new findings can be applied at the earliest opportunity.

Finally two notes of caution in view of past experiences. The introduction of sophisticated biotechnological treatments to improve fertility may not be appropriate unless certain minimal management, disease control and nutritional conditions can be met. Notwithstanding, very reliable and robust products will be required to be successful in the hostile field environment.

REFERENCES

Armstrong, J.D. and Britt, J.H. (1985). Pulsatile administration of gonadotropin-releasing hormone to anestrous sows: endocrine changes associated with GnRH-induced and spontaneous estrus. *Biology of Reproduction,* **33**, 375–380.

Britt, J.H., Armstrong, J.D., Cox, N.M. and Esbenshade, K.L. (1985). Control of follicular development during and after lactation in sows. *Journal of Reproduction and Fertility*, Supplement 33, 37–54.

Bulman, D.C. and Lamming, G.E. (1978). Milk progesterone levels in relation to conception, repeat breeding and factors influencing acyclicity in dairy cows. *Journal of Reproduction and Fertility*, **54**, 447–458.

Cox, N.M. and Britt, J.H. (1982). Pulsatile administration of GnRH to lactating sows: endocrine changes associated with induction of fertile estrus. *Biology of Reproduction*, **27**, 1126–1137.

Crowder, M.E., Herring, R.D. and Nett, T.M. (1986). Rapid recovery of gonadotroph function after down-regulation of receptors for GnRH in ewes. *Journal of Reproduction and Fertility*, **78**, 577–585.

Cummins, L.J., O'Shea, T., Al-Obaidi, S.A.R., Bindon, B.M. and Findlay, J.K. (1986). Increase in ovulation rate after immunization of Merino ewes with a fraction of bovine follicular fluid containing inhibin activity. *Journal of Reproduction and Fertility*, **77**, 365–372.

de Kretser, D.M. (1986). Inhibin becomes a reality. *Research in Reproduction*, **18**, 1–2.

Diskin, M.G. and Sreenan, J.M. (1986). Progesterone and embryo survival in the cow. In *Embryonic Mortality in Farm Animals* (eds. J.M. Sreenan and M.G. Diskin), pp. 142–158. Martinus Nijhoff, Dordrecht.

Dobson, H. and Kamonpatana, M. (1986). A review of female cattle reproduction with special reference to a comparison between buffaloes, cows and zebu. *Journal of Reproduction and Fertility*, **77**, 1–36.

Dodson, S.E., McLeod, B.J., Haresign, W., Peters, A.R. and Lamming, G.E. (1988). Endocrine changes from birth to puberty in the heifer. *Journal of Reproduction and Fertility*, **82**, 527–538.

Ellendorff, F. and Elsaesser, F. (1985). *Endocrine Causes of Seasonal and Lactational Anestrus in Farm Animals*. Martinus Nijhoff, Dordrecht.

Erickson, G.F. and Hsueh, A.J.W. (1978). Secretion of inhibin by rat granulosa cells *in vitro*. *Endocrinology*, **103**, 1960–1963.

Findlay, J.K., Tsonis, C.G., Staples, L.D. and Cahill, R.N.P. (1986). Inhibin secretion by the sheep ovary. *Journal of Reproduction and Fertility*, **76**, 751–761.

Findlay, J.K., Robertson, D.M. and Clarke, I.J. (1987). Influence of dose and route of administration of bovine follicular fluid and the suppressive effect of purified bovine inhibin (Mr31000) on plasma FSH concentrations in ovariectomized ewes. *Journal of Reproduction and Fertility*, **80**, 455–461.

Foster, D.L., Yellon, S.M. and Olster, D.H. (1985). Internal and external determinants of the timing of puberty in the female. *Journal of Reproduction and Fertility*, **75**, 327–344.

Hunter, G.L. (1968). Some factors affecting rebreeding during the post-partum period. *Animal Breeding Abstracts*, **36**, 347–377.

Jagger, J.P., Peters, A.R. and Lamming, G.E. (1987). Hormone responses to low-dose GnRH treatment in post-partum beef cows. *Journal of Reproduction and Fertility*, **80**, 263–269.

Jagger, J.P., Peters, A.R., McLeod, B.J. and Lamming, G.E. (1989). Pituitary and ovarian responses to prolonged administration of low doses of GnRH in prepubertal heifers. *Animal Reproduction Science*, **18**, 111–124.

Jainudeen, M.R. (1985). Reproduction in draught animals: does work affect female fertility? In *Draught Animal Power for Production* (ed. J.W. Copland), pp. 130–133. Australian Centre for International Agricultural Research Series No. 10, Canberra.

Johnsson, A.L. (1986). Induction of ovulation in anestrous mares with pulsatile administration of gonadotropin-releasing hormone. *American Journal of Veterinary Research*, **47**, 983–986.

Lamming, G.E. and McLeod, B.J. (1988). Continuous infusion of GnRH reduces the LH response to an intravenous GnRH injection but does not inhibit endogenous LH secretion in cows. *Journal of Reproduction and Fertility*, **82**, 237–246.

Ling, N., Ying, S.Y., Ueno, N., Shimasaki, S., Esch, F., Hotta, M. and Guillemin, R. (1886). Pituitary FSH is released by a heterodimer of the β-subunits from the two forms of inhibin. *Nature, London*, **321**, 779–782.

Macfarlane, J.S. (1991). The detection and manipulation of oestrus in farm animals. In *The Application of Biotechnology in Developing Countries* (ed. A.G. Hunter), pp. 70–90. Centre for Tropical Veterinary Medicine, University of Edinburgh.

McLeod, B.J., Peters, A.R. Haresign, W. and Lamming, G.E. (1985). Plasma LH and FSH responses and ovarian activity in prepubertal heifers treated with repeated injections of low doses of GnRH for 72h. *Journal of Reproduction and Fertility*, **74**, 589–596.

McLeod, B.J., Haresign, W., Peters, A.R., Humke, R. and Lamming, G.E. (1988). The development of subcutaneous delivery preparations of GnRH for the induction of ovulation in acyclic sheep and cattle. *Animal Reproduction Science*, **17**, 33–50.

MacMillan, K.L., Taufa, V.K. and Day, A.M. (1986). Effects of an agonist of gonadotrophin releasing hormone (Buserelin) in cattle. III. Pregnancy rates after a post-insemination injection during metoestrus or dioestrus. *Animal Reproduction Science*, **11**, 1–10.

McNeilly, A.S. (1985). Effect of changes in FSH induced by bovine follicular fluid and FSH infusion in the preovulatory phase on subsequent ovulation rate and corpus luteum function in the ewe. *Journal of Reproduction and Fertility*, **74**, 661–668.

Momongan, V.G. (1985). Reproduction in draught animals. In *Draught Animal Power for Production* (ed. J.W. Copland), pp. 123–128. Australian Centre for International Agricultural Research Series No. 10, Canberra.

Peters, A.R. and Riley, G.M. (1982). Milk progesterone profiles and factors affecting post partum ovarian activity in beef cows. *Animal Production*, **34**, 145–153.

Peters, A.R. and Lamming, G.E. (1990). Lactational anoestrus in farm animals. *Oxford Reviews in Reproductive Biology*,**12**, 245–288.

Price, C.A., Morris, B.A., O'Shea, T. and Webb, R. (1987). Active immunization of cattle against partly purified follicular fluid from sheep. *Journal of Reproduction and Fertility*, **81**, 161–168.

Riley, G.M., Peters, A.R. and Lamming, G.E. (1981). Induction of pulsatile LH release, FSH release and ovulation in post partum acyclic beef cows by repeated small doses of GnRH. *Journal of Reproduction and Fertility*, **63**, 559-565.

Scaramuzzi, R.J. and Hoskinson, R.M. (1984). Active immunization against steroid hormones for increasing fecundity. In *Immunological Aspects of Reproduction in Mammals* (ed. D.B. Crighton), pp. 445–474. Butterworths, London.

Sorenson, A.J., Hansel, W., Hough, W.H., Armstrong, D.T., McEntee, K. and Bratton, R.W. (1959). Causes and prevention of reproductive failures in dairy cattle. I. Influence of underfeeding and overfeeding on growth and development of Holstein heifers. *Bulletin of Cornell University Agricultural Experimental Station*, 936–951.

Sreenan, J.M. and Diskin, M.G. (1986). The extent and timing of embryonic mortality in the cow. In *Embryonic Mortality in Farm Animals* (eds. J.M. Sreenan and M.G. Diskin), pp. 1–11. Martinus Nijhoff, Dordrecht.

Stewart, H.J., Flint, A.P.F., Lamming, G.E., McCann, S.H.E. and Parkinson, T.J. (1989). Antiluteolytic effects of blastocyst-secreted interferon investigated *in vitro* and *in vivo* in the sheep. *Journal of Reproduction and Fertility*, Supplement 37, 127–138.

Stubbings, L.A. and Maund, B.A. (1988). Effects on the fecundity of sheep of immunization against androstenedione. *Veterinary Record*, **123**, 489–492.

Thatcher, W.W. (1974). Effects of season, climate and temperature on reproduction and lactation. *Journal of Dairy Science*, **57**, 360.

Thatcher, W.W., MacMillan, K.L., Hansen, P.J. and Drost, M. (1989). Concepts for regulation of corpus luteum function by the conceptus and ovarian follicles to improve fertility. *Theriogenology*, **31**, 149–164.

Torney, A.H., Hodgson, Y.M., Forage, R. and de Kretser, D.M. (1989). Cellular localization of inhibin mRNA in the bovine ovary by *in situ* hybridization. *Journal of Reproduction and Fertility*, **86**, 391–399.

Tsonis, C.G. Quigg, H., Lee, V.W.K., Leversha, L., Trounson, A.O. and Findlay, J.K. (1983). Inhibin in individual ovine follicles in relation to diameter and atresia. *Journal of Reproduction and Fertility*, **67**, 83–90.

Wallace, J.M., McNeilly, A.S. and Baird, D.T. (1985). Ovulation rate and embryo survival in Damline ewes after treatment with bovine follicular fluid in the luteal phase of the oestrous cycle. *Journal of Reproduction and Fertility*, **75**, 101–109.

Wathes, D.C. (1984). Possible actions of gonadal oxytocin and vasopressin. *Journal of Reproduction and Fertility*, **71**, 315–345.

Webb, R., Land, R.B., Pathiraja, N. and Morris, B.A. (1984). Passive immunization against steriod hormones in the female. In *Immunological Aspects of Reproduction in Mammals* (ed. D.B. Crighton), pp. 475–499. Butterworths, London.

Wright, P.J., Geytenbeek, P.E., Clarke, I.J. and Findlay, J.K. (1983). LH release and luteal function in post-partum acyclic ewes after the pulsatile administration of LH-RH. *Journal of Reproduction and Fertility*, **67**, 257–262.

Wright, P.J., Geytenbeek, P.E., Clarke, I.J. and Findlay, J.K. (1984). Induction of plasma LH surges and normal luteal function in acyclic post-partum ewes by the pulsatile administration of LH-RH. *Journal of Reproduction and Fertility*, **71**, 1–6.

3.8

The Implications for Education Training and Extension of Biotechnology

D. FIELDING
Edinburgh School of Agriculture, Edinburgh, Scotland

INTRODUCTION

From the perspective of the educationalist biotechnology is especially characterized by the speed and volume of production of new technological information that requires interpreting and processing for educational programmes. This is obviously a general requirement for all new knowledge and information but one that has become highlighted by the intensity of recent developments in biotechnology.

More specifically, the implications of biotechnology for education, training and extension can be said to arise from the anticipated impacts of biotechnology on all aspects of society; the potential negative impacts that it is wished to minimize or avoid and the potential positive impacts that it is wished to promote and if possible maximize. Thus, education, training and extension give society the means whereby it can hopefully optimize the exploitation of scientific developments such as biotechnology.

The objectives of this paper are therefore:

a) to review the nature of biotechnology with particular reference to education, training and extension,
b) to review some of the potential impacts of biotechnology with particular reference to livestock production in developing countries,
c) to identify the implications of biotechnology for education, training and extension arising out of a) and b),
d) to suggest policies and strategies in education, training and extension that can lead to the optimum exploitation of biotechnology.

THE NATURE OF BIOTECHNOLOGY

To help in understanding the nature of biotechnology it may be helpful to consider previous examples of sudden information increases in the technological field. At the scientific level one can take the example of microelectronics and the communication revolution and at the extension, farmer level, the so-called 'Green Revolution'. At the farm level and in livestock production there are also the examples of 'old biotechnology'; artificial insemination, including nitrogen storage of semen, oestrous control and alkali treatment of roughages.

All of these new applications of science were characterized by their technical rather than social emphasis, their fashion effect with many wanting to use them, their rejection component when their inappropriate aspects were identified and discarded and finally the identification of their sustainable aspects. The four aspects of technical, fashion, rejection, and sustainability would seem likely to apply to biotechnology.

Biotechnology is one of the fastest developing technologies we have ever known, as evidenced by the new journals and the increased number of conferences devoted to it. Lecturers in core biotechnology subjects point to the need to constantly revise courses (Levinthal, 1989), such is the speed of the subject's development. This speed of development implies a need to evaluate traditional educational methods and their applicability in the new circumstances prevailing.

As Anon (1988) pointed out "artificial insemination and embryo transfer facilitate natural processes, but biotechnology – in its purest form – allows the manipulation of actual cells and molecules and widens the gene pool beyond the limits of sexual compatibility". This is a daunting vision of what the future might hold. It is also a vision which seriously alarms many of the general public, at least in Britain, to such an extent that they are prepared to mount campaigns and carry out direct activities against institutions that are involved in biotechnology. However, it cannot be denied that there are real welfare and ethical issues associated with this type of work which need to be addressed by the workers concerned as well as educationalists charged with training the next generation of biotechnologists.

Many authors stress the inter-relationship of a wide range of scientific disciplines in biotechnology. Lanzavecchia and Mazzonis (1986) compare biotechnology to microelectronics in its discipline intersecting and interacting nature. Sastrapradja (1988) sees the interactive nature of biotechnology as a major challenge to public institutions which are so frequently orientated internally and externally on a discipline basis.

Biotechnology has attracted the involvement of industry and commerce in a way never previously experienced in applied biology. This is a new dimension for scientists in universities and public sector research institutes who have traditionally had little exposure to the commercial sector.

NEGATIVE AND POSITIVE IMPACTS

The speed of development of biotechnology is such that impact identification and analysis tends to be little more than 'imagineering'. Whilst scientists appear to be mastering the techniques of gene transfer it is doubtful if they are in actual control of the ultimate outcomes. Economic and social impact studies with reference to developing countries have been few and unavoidably speculative (Anon, 1988).

For livestock in developing countries the impact of biotechnology is much less clear than for crops. The following sections therefore represent a very tentative review of what the future might hold.

Negative impacts

Biotechnology focuses attention on technology, which may not be the limiting factor. Anon (1988), as a result of a major conference, concluded that the main reason for the decline in the share of developing country agricultural exports in world trade was northern subsidy of its agriculture and not a lack of technology in developing countries. Within country the fashion effect of embryo transfer, bovine somatotrophin etc. may attract financial and personnel resources away from more appropriate activities as has often occurred with artificial insemination and the use of liquid nitrogen for semen storage. The temptation to try to identify speculative 'breakthroughs' is strong and one often difficult to avoid.

A further negative aspect is the fact that most biotechnology is being carried out in the developed countries. There is a real danger that patenting of new methods and products, including animals, will make their use costly if not impossible in many developing countries. However, as Primrose (1987) points out, patenting is meant to be enabling in that patents are only granted when the product or process has been fully and publicly described. This is preferable to new information remaining a complete trade secret. Smith and Ashford (1989) suggest variations on patenting which may serve to reward the 'designers' of new livestock but still allow their widespread use.

The commercialization of biotechnology and the associated profits tend to encourage secrecy and competitiveness. Whittenbury (1984) commented that the grapevine rather than research journals may be the normal means of obtaining new information and that if you can't contribute to the grapevine you risk being excluded. There is thus a real danger that the flow of information about biotechnology to developing countries may be reduced or even stopped.

Biotechnology products will be costly, if only because of the investment that is going into their production. These costs may prevent their use in developing countries. Certainly it is the larger rather than the smaller farmer that is probably going to benefit from products such as bovine somatotrophin as a minimum infrastructure and level of husbandry are required before it can be exploited (Geisler and Dupois, 1989). Thus biotechnology is unlikely to help the truly poor.

In crop production there is the prospect that synthesized alternatives to tropical products such as coffee and cocoa may be commercially developed with consequent disastrous effects on these industries in developing countries (Bijman, Van der Doel and Junne, 1986). The equivalent issue in livestock production of meat substitutes or analogues is not clear. There is relatively little livestock trade between developed and developing countries as compared to that in crop products. However, if anything, biotechnology is likely to promote and facilitate the spread of vegetarianism as a result of amino acid enrichment of crop products through gene manipulation (Armstrong, 1985). It is doubtful if this prediction need immediately worry the pastoral peoples of the tropics. But, livestock production in the long-term is unlikely to be as secure as crop production or forestry. Forestry in particular has major potential as a source of biomass for biotechnology processes.

The 'monster effect' is a possible negative aspect of biotechnology that evokes a highly emotional response. The 'monster effect' is the situation where gene manipulation without proper controls results in catastrophic effects for society, possibly as a result of new virulent diseases or birth defects in animals and/or man. In the absence of any examples to support the monster theory it is a difficult topic to discuss although to some people it appears to be very real.

There is always the risk that livestock in developing countries may be prematurely used, even if inadvertently, to test drugs or vaccines arising from new biotechnology advances. Clearly this is a possibility which should be carefully guarded against.

Positive effects

Many authors, including those at this conference have written of the potential benefits of biotechnology to livestock. Armstrong (1988) pointed to the potential benefits of better disease prevention and control, increased efficiency through manipulation of reproduction and product composition, new food sources and improvements in food quality, and believed that they offered the possibility of proper nutrition for all the peoples of the developing countries.

The possibilities of food upgrading through the use of enzymes, the removal of anti-nutritional factors, improved additives for food conservation, are other attractive advances (Deymeyer, Dierick, Decuypere, Van Nevel, Spriet, Vervaeka and Henderickx, 1988). Nonruminants and dairying are the most technically responsive systems to technical change and it is in these systems that the first positive impacts are being seen.

Livestock will obviously benefit from advances in crop production as well as from advances in livestock technology as such. Nitrogen fixation by the bacteria associated with grasses is an exciting prospect.

Mahy (1989) pointed to the potential contribution of multiple ovulation embryo transfer, MOET, for accelerated cattle breeding, transgenics, monoclonal antibodies and DNA probes for improved disease diagnosis and genetically engineered and molecular vaccines for improved health care. Mahy (1989) further indicated that the possibility of introducing these new techniques depended upon education and the development of supporting skills.

Ultimately, and hopefully, biotechnology has the potential to contribute to the spread of true civilization by holding out the possibility of real leisure without poverty or starvation.

IMPLICATIONS FOR EDUCATION TRAINING AND EXTENSION

Implications arising from the above may be discussed at two levels:

- policy and approach
- practical implications

Policy and approach

Difficult as it may be to carry out there is a need to draw up national policies for biotechnology to which educationalists can contribute and interpret and communicate for all sectors of society. These policies might include:

- guidelines for the degree of access of international biotechnology companies to gene resources within the country and to the national market for any ensuing products
- methods for collecting, processing and communicating information on biotechnology advances from outside the country
- priorities for national research on biotechnology
- methods and guidelines for screening and monitoring biotechnology products
- methods and guidelines for measuring the impact of biotechnology
- procedures for regulation of biotechnology to be used as and when required
- guidelines for technological education.

The difficulties of implementing the above are not underestimated. Hamden and Elnawawy (1988) list the following constraints to the use of biotechnology in Arab Asian countries:

- no policy
- lack of appreciation of biotechnology by policy makers
- lack of clear plans
- brain drain
- high turnover rate of scientific staff
- lack of technical staff
- inadequate libraries
- lack of funds

This is a formidable list which will be applicable to a greater or lesser extent in many developing countries. Against such a background a discussion of the educational implications may seem rather fatuous. However, where the above situation applies it suggests that education in the form of awareness creation may have a role in stimulating the policies that education itself needs if it is to completely fulfil its role. Awareness creation might include the following points:

- that many of the gene resources upon which biotechnology will depend are to be found in the tropics
- that properly managed tropical forests are likely to be a major source of the biomass which biotechnology will need
- that the same biomass production will require energy, which from the sun is much more abundant in the tropics than temperate areas
- that on the evidence to-date the public fears associated with biotechnology are on balance probably exaggerated.

Overall there is reason to be confident about the long-term future benefits of biotechnology to the development of tropical countries provided that education is able to play its role as a catalyst.

Practical implications

The nature, characteristics and possible impacts of biotechnology have been reviewed above; they may be summarized as follows:

- technical emphasis, fashion effects, components to be rejected and retained
- a rapid increase in the production of new technological information
- welfare and ethical issues with reference to manipulation of animal genotypes
- fear of the unknown
- interdisciplinary
- commercial considerations and associations resulting in costly and patented products
- research and development isolation of developing country biotechnologists
- inappropriate diversion of resources
- uncertain long-term positive impacts but the possibility of real quality of life for world society.

This list points to the need for the highest possible quality of education and training. With the aim of achieving this quality possible practical initiatives include the following:

- an examination of existing courses to reduce their content of obsolete information
- an increase in the length of existing courses to enable coverage of the new material and concepts

- the design of new courses in biotechnology as, for example, taking place in one instance in Scotland (Scotvec, 1989)
- modularization of course material to enable students to learn at their own speeds, to design their own courses to meet their specific needs, to continue learning throughout life, to breakdown traditional approaches that partition science into artificial groupings; biology, chemistry etc.
- change working contracts and practices to enable staff to attend retraining and updating courses
- focus on developing the processes of learning rather than imparting content so that people can teach themselves new material throughout their lives
- encourage students to develop important skills such as reasoning, critical thinking, problem solving and working in teams

All of the above may have application according to the circumstances of the country in question. Some are short-term pragmatic strategies whilst others are fundamental and therefore more difficult to implement, but which are potentially far-reaching in their impact.

Changing the content of existing courses may appear to be relatively easy. However, researchers and lecturers are often dogmatic in their demands to retain their own particular subjects in course syllabi. This is a particular danger in colleges and universities where staff have more freedom to decide what is taught, rather than in schools where syllabi are handed down by national boards and committees.

One of the assumptions of this paper is that there is much new technical material in biotechnology which needs to be taught and discussed. Less obvious perhaps is the need for training in new subjects such as regulation methods and enforcement as suggested by Hatch and Kuchler (1989). Certainly specialized training in impact analysis would appear sensible. Yoxon (1986) argues that there is also a need for education to enable people to cope with technological change, although is not specific about how this should be done. If biotechnology is truly international its exploitation will depend on the ability of scientists to communicate in more than one language, another subject area that needs consideration.

In addition there is a need for course time to devote to discussions, possibly student led, on welfare and ethical issues. Welfare is concerned with avoiding what has traditionally been regarded as cruelty. Interestingly, as Remfrey (1987) points out, biotechnology may serve to reduce cruelty by working at the cell rather than whole animal level. Ethics may be defined as that part of philosophy that is concerned with human conduct, rules of behaviour, professional conduct (Anon, 1985). There is the fear that manipulation of animals will lead to a hardening in people's attitudes that will lead ultimately to the manipulation of human genotypes. Whether the latter is good or bad is an ethical topic obviously worthy of debate. Rollin (1983) argues strongly that value questions should be part of science and indeed that they are the very foundations of science and as such are currently often lacking in our education of scientists. At present scientists tend to be judged on their ability to publish pure science with little or no regard to its possible impact. This may be acceptable, but it can be questioned if a more holistic approach by scientists might not be more appropriate.

The commercial perspective in biotechnology is important. Perhaps for too long traditional science courses have ignored the study of business and commercial subjects. (*sic*) Persley (1989) suggested that it might be advantageous to involve commercial companies in actual education. This sometimes already takes place through sandwich courses and various forms of attachment, but could almost certainly be expanded with benefits for all concerned. Other possibilities include staff exchanges between teaching and commerce.

DeLoach (1989) stresses the need for scientists to become involved in the public debate on biotechnology and to be proactive rather than reactive, so as to counteract the fears of society and sometimes the allegations, often unfounded, of extreme groups. Communication is an area where scientists are not particularly successful, especially when they are asked to communicate with lay people in simple terms. Communication thus represents another important area for training.

Whilst appropriate in some instances, the setting up of new courses in biotechnology may also be misleading in that it suggests a discrete amount of knowledge that can be taught and learnt and which results presumably in a biotechnologist. However, biotechnology may be more a transient concept or method of approach, rather than a course subject in its own right. Modularization as a response of education and training to rapid developments in biotechnology is a far reaching initiative. The term simply means the division of knowledge and information into discrete units, modules, each with its own learning objectives and content. Units can be chosen to cover desired emphases and situations as required, and importantly, can be taken throughout a person's working life. Modularization thus allows maximum flexibility and puts the onus on the student to manage his/her own education and training. As can be anticipated, modularization demands a considerable commitment throughout a country's educational system and it is not without limitations if applied superficially (Watson, 1989).

A lack of resources commonly limits the scope for adult education and training. Yet in a situation where new information and techniques are appearing rapidly it would appear to be an option that cannot be ignored if personnel are not to become outdated and therefore of reduced value. Without retraining older staff may feel less confident and more insecure in comparison to newly trained staff. As a result a communication barrier often results which frustrates both groups and wastes national resources. Modest investment in the upgrading of older staff is thus likely to activate their own energies and at the same time enable them to better manage their junior but more technically advanced staff.

If resources prevent the application of some of the above initiatives then a conceptual change in education and training may be the only and in any case the best way of proceeding. Such a change is the introduction of training in learning skills. Two of the new skills required are those of reasoning and critical thinking, to equip people to identify what is appropriate and inappropriate in the context of solving real problems (Meyers, 1986).

Another new requirement arising out of the interactive nature of biotechnology is the ability of scientists to work in teams. If this is the case then education must be carried out in a way that fosters team skills such as the ability to listen to others and to know when to compromise. What is not required in real life is the ability to simply learn facts and information as an individual.

In practical terms the above skills will depend on the promotion of data handling and information skills which in turn imply increased computer literacy. Instead of lectures to groups of individuals the trend in education should perhaps be towards student centred learning that involves problems, projects, reports and essays that are solved and written by student teams rather than by individuals. And furthermore, the use of problems and case studies that are as close to reality as it is possible to make them. Holt (1982) caught the spirit of these increasingly accepted views in the statement "We don't have to make human beings smart all we have to do is stop doing the things that make them stupid".

Extension

At present the main and perhaps only implication of biotechnology for extension services is that of ensuring that inappropriate novel products and ideas do not divert attention from more appropriate solutions to the problems encountered. Even 'old biotechnology' such as artificial insemination is commonly inappropriate and reversion to methods based on natural mating are encountered (M.G. Ariyaratne, personal communication). This means that extension staff need training in asking the questions 'what is the real problem?', 'can farmers benefit from this new development?'

CONCLUSIONS

The main implication of biotechnology for education is general rather than specific and is simply the need for better quality education with increasing emphasis on process rather than content. More enlightened and positive approaches are also required to self-education and retraining throughout life. The educational content should also include training in effective communication with the general public about biotechnology and open discussions on welfare and ethical issues.

Biotechnology has not yet made any real impact on livestock production in developing countries. Extension training should prepare personnel for screening the new developments that are presently being developed.

Overall it is important for educationalists to help initiate and encourage a wider dialogue so that at least the first requirement of a national policy and approach to biotechnology is put in place.

REFERENCES

ANON (1985). *Chambers Concise 20th Century Dictionary.* W.R. Chambers, Edinburgh.

ANON (1988). *Agricultural Biotechnology and the Third World.* Briefing Paper. September, 1989. Overseas Development Institute, Regent's College, Inner Circle, Regent's Park, London.

Armstrong, D.G. (1985). The general implications of biotechnology in the agricultural industry. In *Biotechnology and its Application to Agriculture* (eds. L.G. Copping and P. Rodgers). Monograph No. 32. *Proceedings of a symposium held at Churchill College, Cambridge, 4th-6th September, 1985.* Organised by the Society of the Chemical Industry and the British Crop Protection Council. Lavenham Press Ltd.

Armstrong, D.G. (1988). The implication of biotechnology for livestock production. *Nutrition Abstracts and Reviews (Series B),* **58** (No. 8), 415–426.

Bijman, J., Van der Doel, K. and Junne, G. (1986). *The International Dimension of Biotechnology in Agriculture.* European Foundation for the Improvement of Living and Working Conditions. Loughlinstown House, Shankhill, Co. Dublin, Ireland.

DeLoach, J.R. (1989). Biotechnology: research in animal agriculture and regulatory policy. *Biotechnology and Applied Biochemistry*, **11**, 343–348.

Deymer, D., Dierick, N., Decuypere, J. Van Nevel, C., Spriet, S., Vervaeka, I. and Henderickx, H.K. (1988). Biotechnology for improvement of feed and feed digestion. In *Proceedings of the 8th International Biotechnology Symposium* (eds. G. Durand, L. Bobichon and J. Florent), vol. 2, pp. 884–898. Société Française de Microbiologie, Paris.

Geisler, C.C. and Dupois, E.M. (1989). From green revolution to gene revolution: common concerns about agricultural biotechnology in the first and third worlds. In *Biotechnology and the New Agricultural Revolution* (eds. J.J. Molnar and H. Kinnucan). American Association for the Advancement of Science. Selected Symposium 108. Westview, Colorado.

Hamden, L.Y. and Elnawawy, A.S. (1988). Current studies of biotechnology in Asian Arab countries. In *Proceedings of the 8th International Biotechnology Symposium* (eds. G. Durand, L. Bobichon and J. Florent), vol. 2, pp. 1362–1376. Société Française de Microbiologie, Paris.

Hatch, U. and Kuchler, F. (1989). Regulation of agricultural biotechnology. In *Biotechnology and the New Agricultural Revolution* (eds. J.J. Molnar and H. Kinnucan), pp. 51–71. American Association for the Advancement of Science. Selected Symposium 108. Westview, Colorado.

Holt, J. (1982). *How Children Fail* (rev. ed.), pp. 161. Dell, New York.

Lanzavecchia, G. and Mazzonis, D. (1986). *The Impact of Biotechnology on Working Conditions.* European Foundation for the Improvement of Living and Working Conditions. Loughlinstown House, Shankhill, Co. Dublin, Ireland.

Levinthal, C. (1989). Introductory lecture. In *Biotechnology for Livestock Production*, pp. 3–10. Animal Production and Health Division, Food and Agriculture Organisation, Rome.

Mahy, B. (1989). Recent advances in animal biotechnology for third world countries. In *Agricultural Biotechnology: Proposals for the Third World* (ed. J. Farrington). Overseas Development Institute, Regent's College, Inner Circle, Regent's Park, London.

Meyers, C. (1986). *Teaching Students to Think Critically.* Jessey-Bass Publications, London.

Persley, G. (1989). The application of biotechnology in developing countries. *AgBiotech News and Information* **1**, 23–26.

Primrose, S.B. (1987). *Modern Biotechnology.* Blackwell Scientific Publications, Edinburgh.

Remfrey, J. (1987). Ethical aspects of animal experimentation. In *Laboratory Animals: An Introduction for New Experiments* (ed. A.A. Tuffery), pp. 5–18. John Wiley and Sons Ltd., London.

Rollin, B.E. (1983). The teaching of responsibility. The Hume Memorial Lecture, 10th November, 1983. King's College, University of London. Universities Federation for Animal Welfare, Potter's Bar, England.

Sastrapradja, S. (1988). Biotechnology in developing countries. In *Proceedings of the 8th International Biotechnology Symposium* (eds. G. Durand, L. Bobichon and J. Florent), vol. 2, pp. 1294–1305. Société Française de Microbiologie, Paris.

Scotvec (1989). Scottish Vocational Educational Council, Hanover House, 24 Douglas Street, Glasgow.

Smith, A. and Ashford, T. (1989). Should life become private property? *Newsheet of Farmers' Third World Network,* **11** (1), 20–22.

Watson, D. (1989). *Managing the Modular Course: Perspectives from Oxford Polytechnic.* The Society for Research into Higher Education and the Open University Press.

Whittenbury, R. (1984). The Warwick experience. In *The Exploitation of Research in Biotechnology. Proceedings of a Conference at the University of Warwick, December 12th, 1984.* University of Warwick, Sussex and the Licensing Executive.

Yoxon, E. (1986). *The Impact of Biotechnology on Living and Working Conditions.* European Foundation for the Improvement of Living and Working Conditions. Loughlinstown House, Shankhill, Co. Dublin, Ireland.

3.9

Biotechnology and the World Bank

P. BRUMBY
The World Bank, Washington DC, U.S.A.

INTRODUCTION

The interest of the World Bank in biotechnology is largely based on trends in the world's food supply, particularly in much of Africa and Asia where progress in reducing poverty and hunger is modest and where food needs are increasing by over 4% a year. It is also provoked by some concern that the production increases of the older agricultural technologies of irrigation, fertilizer use, varietal improvement and area expansion have an end point that is perceptibly closer.

The particular issues in biotechnology which concern the Bank cover five main topics:

- The pattern of research financing;
- The role of Intellectual Property Rights;
- Risk assessment and environmental release;
- Changes in comparative advantage, farm structure and agricultural trade;
- The strategy of assistance.

RESEARCH FINANCING

The World Bank has now been in operation for about 43 years. In that time it has invested substantial sums of money in agricultural research. Currently there are in operation in developing countries 68 major agricultural research projects supported by the Bank; additionally, many production projects contain significant research components. The Bank is also a major supporter of the International Agricultural Research Centres. The first point I want to emphasize is the commitment of the Bank to helping advance agricultural technology, and to stress that this commitment is multiplied many-fold by the contributions that other funding sources make to these efforts.

You may ask why the Bank provides loans and credits rather than grants for national agricultural research. The answer is quite straightforward. The Bank raises the funds it lends by borrowing money at market rates from the private sector through the issuance of debt obligations, relends these resources at market rates and puts the earnings back into the Bank for further lending.

I mention this because it's important to understand that the financial support the Bank obtains in the world's money markets depends on the quality of Bank lending. The buyers of Bank obligations trust the Bank with their money. That trust must be maintained by careful and prudent lending. In short, the Bank cannot act as an important source of risk or venture capital.

Risk in lending for any form of agricultural research, and biotechnology in particular, depends on the competence of the staff entrusted to the use of the funds lent and this competence is based upon a solid training in the basic sciences. In our judgement a policy priority when thinking of biotechnology is to ensure a strong teaching and research capability in the basic biological sciences. This objective is one the Bank has sought to promote in the support it provides to national research and teaching institutions.

A second aspect of the financial picture is the changing pattern of research funding in agriculture.

Molecular biology had its origins in university laboratories, and academic research remains the home territory of biotechnology. Its practical use is, however, largely a commercial activity undertaken by the private sector. A new pattern of agricultural research funding is emerging from this linkage, with increased financing of basic research in the universities by private sources. Another change is that many public research institutions, particularly in developed countries, are now required to raise a substantial part of their research budget from nongovernment sources via contractual research, licensing agreements and royalties. The end result is a new pattern of agricultural research activities; one in which older methods of open interaction and communication in research are being rapidly altered, and one where intellectual property rights influence the extent of private investment.

Compared with traditional research, agricultural research using biotechnology is relatively expensive, especially in its demands for highly skilled manpower. Scientific research projects in biotechnology carry an appreciable risk of failure, but when successful, the application of the results obtained is likely to produce large profits. As a consequence we see the need for:

- greater administrative flexibility to enable publicly funded research operations to capture the profit from product or licence sales;
- an increased use of risk sharing mechanisms (such as joint ventures) in financing this research;
- a legal right to enter into joint venture and partnership arrangements with private companies.

For countries with a reasonable research infrastructure all of this is relatively straightforward. They can readily develop, adapt and transfer technology to location specific problems. But countries with a weak research structure have a much more difficult task in obtaining and using the products and processes of biotechnology. Strengthening their capability in the basic biological sciences is the first step. Encouraging stronger research and training facilities at the regional level is also appealing as are collaborative agreements that facilitate technology transfer between stronger and weaker groups.

INTELLECTUAL PROPERTY RIGHTS

The private sector, particularly in the Organization for European Cooperation and Development (OECD) countries, is now the repository of extensive practical skills in biotechnology and a new pattern of collaboration between private and public research groups is emerging. This collaboration is based on the recognition and protection of intellectual property rights; it is also based on the notion that, unless there is an adequate return to the costs in developing a new product, or variety, then no one will make the investment necessary to bring that product to the market place, be it the markets of developing countries or the markets of the industrialized countries. A corollary of this argument is that an important constraint to technology transfer is imposed by the absence of intellectual property rights.

On this issue there is cause for concern. National laws on biological patents and protection vary enormously. Among developing countries few governments enable patents to be granted on plants and animals and there is a growing nationalistic concern regarding the patenting of germplasm and genes originating in developing countries by companies in the developed world. The reality of biotechnology today is that unless protection of the type that patents provide is available, many products that could facilitate food production are simply not going to be developed, while research collaboration between high-tech laboratories in the private and public sector is going to be more difficult and more expensive than otherwise. A primary goal of the patent system in agriculture is to serve the public by promoting the progress of science, better international harmonization of patent protection seems essential for the large-scale diffusion of biotechnology.

I emphasize this point because the focal point of the growth in biotechnology in the industrialized countries is the development of partnership arrangements in biotechnology between private industry and the public sector. These collaborative ventures are increasing rapidly and are leading to substantial flows of new research money from the private sector to universities and public sector research. This money supports basic research in the biological sciences and is given in return for the rights to use the emerging results. In the absence of patent protection in developing countries this collaboration will be absent and the information flow resulting from the patenting process will be unavailable as industry seeks to protect its investment by resolving to secrecy and tight processing control.

ENVIRONMENTAL ISSUES

The public support biotechnology receives is largely based upon the perception of its utility and its safety. The first recombinant organism is now on the market in Australia, it is a biocontrol agent for crowngail in fruit trees. A number of other genetically engineered products are likely to follow quickly. The research which has led to their development has been the subject of well-publicized concerns, and these worries have centred on the possible ecological outcome of the use of genetic transformations.

Early research on genetic change was tightly controlled by the guidelines that grew out of the Asilomar Conference in the U.S.A. in 1975. But as experience has accumulated, more liberal regulatory policies have become feasible. In 1989 the Ecological Society of America made available a very detailed review of the problems inherent in the environmental release of modified organisms. It is useful to quote the conclusion of that study; "careful design of transgenic organisms, along with proper planning and regulatory oversight, will ensure that these new organisms will pose little or no ecological risk." At the World Bank we are encouraged by the pragmatic approach to environmental release and by the mechanisms for risk assessment now emerging.

Risk assessment is the key to quantifying the uncertainties associated with the release of modified organisms, and this assessment must be based on local research on the factors that influence the risk of that release. As generalizations from the increased use of genetic engineering become firmer, and as experience improves our knowledge of appropriate testing and regulatory techniques, the degree of uncertainty associated with environmental release will be diminished further and the ease of lending for genetic engineering thereby increased. Meanwhile, as a condition of any lending by the Bank for biotechnology, we believe each borrower should have in place:

- national review bodies and policies to regulate the release of genetically engineered organisms into the environment;
- a safety review procedure, using functioning guidelines, to govern the release of genetically engineered organisms;
- annually updated assessments on the experience and current policies of the biosafety review committees. By providing these assessments to international agencies other countries might benefit from the experience gained.

SOCIAL CHANGE

As biotechnology brings about technical change in the agriculture of developing countries there will be discussion on at least three aspects of that change: the social, the structural and the trade implications. We would like to think that wise policy planning by national governments might reduce the negative impacts that can result from the higher food production that results from better technology. Our main worry is that poorer farmers and poorer countries are disadvantaged by any rapid change as it is always harder for small farmers to adopt new technology. In the case of biotechnology there is going to be an increased premium on the value of knowledge in relation to the value of land, the comparative advantage of different areas of production will change, and new trade problems will arise because of the sensitivity of the new diagnostic tests for chemical residues and pathogens.

We face a dilemma. Without a change in technology the food needs of the next 25 to 30 years are less secure. With a change in technology the poorer farmers will have greater difficulty in adapting, and the export trade of the poorer countries is likely to be further jeopardized.

The time-scale of the changes likely to be associated with biotechnology is another important issue. As a pervasive generic technology, biotechnology and its diffusion is akin in many ways to computer technology; important changes in capital stock, skill profiles, industrial structure and social organization will be essential companions to its widespread use. These changes will require decades rather than years to accomplish. The Bank could play a useful role in emphasizing the relatively long time-scales involved and help thereby to avoid errors due to technological optimism as well as undue conservatism. Other ways in which the Bank might help include: strengthening national research capability, encouraging technology transfer, pushing for open trade and germplasm exchange policies, and recognizing the specific problems and needs of the poorer sectors of society. Can we usefully add to this list?

THE STRATEGY OF ASSISTANCE

The World Bank emphasizes the importance of increased production, savings, investment, exports and growth – we give great attention to incentives and priorities, and to poverty and living standards. The biotechnology policy of the Bank must fit into these considerations. We see it doing so primarily by concentrating on three objectives:

- the need to ensure the benefits of biotechnology are available to all developing countries;
- the need to encourage research which strengthens the productive capacity of smaller and poorer farmers;
- the need to avoid environmental harm in encouraging the use of biotechnology in these countries.

In essence, we seek to use the influence of the Bank to increase the flow of benefits from biotechnology in countries with a strong research capacity to those much weaker in this respect.

Further support for biotechnology development by the World Bank is likely to build upon the pattern of assistance to agricultural research already provided. This assistance also seems likely to embrace a greater proportion of equity funding to facilitate risk sharing, the encouragement of partnership arrangements between private industry and national organizations, an increased involvement in supporting biological education and training, particular attention to the assessment of research priorities, and a capability to provide sound advice on the policies needed to encourage local investment in agricultural biotechnology.

The translation of these objectives into an operational response hinges upon a knowledge of the technology available, of finding ways to transfer that information to target problems, of negotiating the licensing of technology and genetic constructs whose use is constrained by intellectual property rights, and of ensuring that adequate safeguards are in place to protect society from the unwise release of new biological materials.

These tasks go well-beyond the technical responsibilities in project preparation that international agencies have generally accepted, they are skills not yet available in the nonprofit foundations, the international research centres or in private consultant groups. Herein is the major gap limiting much greater support to agricultural biotechnology by the international agencies, this is the bottleneck we now need to address.

Footnote: The World Bank does not necessarily accept responsibility for the views expressed herein which are those of the author and should not be attributed to the World Bank or to its affiliated organization.

DISCUSSION OF SESSION 3

RANGNEKAR, INDIA *Our observations indicate two constraints to the use of fungi for bio-fermentation of straws:*

1. *A need for pre-treatment and controlled conditions.*
2. *Considerable loss of dry matter negating any benefit that may be there.*

Would you like to comment on this approach for improving straw quality?

BRODA Any biologically based process for upgrading lignocellulose is likely to be improved by physical or chemical treatment such as steam explosion to improve accessibility. It is also obvious that closer control of conditions will be important, as it has been with mushroom production. In our view a chemical engineering approach to the analysis of solid substrate fermentation could contribute much to making progress here. Where there is growth there will be loss in dry matter; here the question is whether that loss is equivalent as between the cellulose, hemicellulose and lignin components. If so, no benefit is obtained, but if for instance the cellulose is spared while hemicellulose degradation is coupled to that of lignin, an upgraded animal feed is obtained. This might be achieved either with cellulose deficient fungal strains, such as those described by K-E Eriksson and his colleagues, or with enzyme formulations lacking cellulases.

RANGNEKAR, INDIA *Farmers have been choosing paddy varieties producing better quality straw. We have confirmed this through degradability studies, and we feel strongly that attempts should be made to improve such varieties and include straw quality in the variety screening process.*

ØRSKOV I agree. I have emphasized this point in my paper and this meeting could recommend that these important crop characteristics should be selected for.

WANAPAT, THAILAND *The higher digestibility of rice stems as opposed to rice leaves could be due to their higher CP content when tested intact* in vitro. *We found in our* in vivo *investigations in cattle that the intake and digestibility of leaves were significantly higher than that of the stems.*

ØRSKOV This is an interesting observation which needs to be substantiated. The CP content of leaves and stems had no influence in our work as the N need of the rumen microbe was met at all times.

CAPPER, ETHIOPIA *I would like to modify slightly Dr. Orskov's statements regarding grain yield and straw degradability. In work on barley straw at ICARDA Syria, negative correlations were always found between these parameters. However they were usually numerically low and non-significant providing the possibility of selecting varieties combining favourable characteristics. Similar results were found with crops grown at Cambridge in England.*

ØRSKOV I wonder whether in systems in which forced ripening can occur such as is clearly the case in Syria, that you can get a correlation. If the sugars are not all transported to the grain, there will automatically be a negative correlation between grain yield and straw quality. This is conditioned by the environment, however, and is not really genetic in origin and further studies into this are required.

KABAIJA, KENYA *What is Dr. Ørskov's opinion on large-scale defaunation of the rumen?*

ØRSKOV I do not agree with wholesale elimination of rumenal protozoa. While protozoa will reduce protein availability/unit fermented the general consensus of opinion is that it will reduce intake of fibrous roughages. For poor quality and low N roughages, recycling of N within the rumen may be positive in so far that intake is increased due to recycling of N within.

MEPHAM *Early experiments with pST showed serious welfare problems for treated pigs. Even recent reports indicate disease of limb joints in some cases. What is Dr. Morgan's assessment of the scale of this welfare problem?*

MORGAN I am aware of this problem but have no information on its scale in practice. One laboratory has monitored the health of treated pigs very closely and found no problems with liver and kidney health. Certainly a limb joint defect would be a problem if the producer decided to keep a gilt for breeding purposes.

ØRSKOV *Can Dr. Morgan inform us of any progress in understanding protein nutrition in forage fed pigs?*

MORGAN Information is very limited. Workers in Belgium have shown that the ileal digestibility of essential amino acids is reduced with increasing fibre in the diet, particularly when the fibre is high in gel-forming polysaccharides. Thus the fibre component of the forage must be fully characterized before any assumptions can be made about effects on protein nutrition.

ØRSKOV *As sustained yield response to bST can only be achieved by higher levels of nutrition and intake, it is unlikely that the use of bST will be a useful biotechnology for most developing countries.*

HEAP I disagree with your generalization as there are a number of potential applications in developing countries such as buffalo in Thailand and dairy cows in East Africa.

RANGNEKAR, INDIA *Have the economics and residues in milk and meat of bST treatment been investigated?*

HEAP Yes, there are extensive studies on both these topics. IGF-1 increases in milk of cows treated with bST, but there is no increase in milk bST.

BUTTERWITH, U.K. *Has Dr. Heap carried out any carcass composition measurements in the transgenic animals described which exhibit pulsatile GH release?*

HEAP Not yet.

RUSSELL, TANZANIA *Dr. Topps described an experiment in which silage was made from defoliated maize. This sounds very labour intensive and may be a difficult idea to sell to farmers.*

TOPPS On smallholdings, farmers are likely to defoliate the maize daily and feed it fresh. For one or two cows this should be done relatively quickly and may not take any more time than harvesting and chopping of Napier fodder, which is an acceptable produce.

MACFARLANE, U.K. *Isn't it possible that the improvement of yields and nutritional value of straw for animal feeding will not be acceptable where cereals are the staple diet of the human population e.g. sorghum and millet in areas with poor rainfall?*

TOPPS I agree that grain yield must have first priority under such circumstances. However, for certain varieties and agronomic conditions it may be possible to combine better quality of straw and higher yield of grains in a plant breeding programme. This is being examined in some countries.

MACFARLANE, U.K. *As bST administered to cows causes a negative energy balance initially, until increased food intake balances the extra energy requirement of increased milk production, should its use be restricted to cows that have conceived, and implanted say at six weeks post-conception?*

MEPHAM That would seem to be sound advice.

RASTOGI, TRINIDAD AND TOBAGO *What effect does the sudden increase in milk production following bST administration have on the anatomy of the udder and gait?*

MEPHAM Transformation from low to high production is likely to be accompanied by problems associated with high milk yield e.g. reduced fertility and lameness. I am not aware of reports that bST significantly increases udder weight.

GUPTA, INDIA *In India, bST administered to lactating buffaloes every two weeks caused an increase in milk production but no increase in food intake or loss in body weight. What could be the reason for this?*

MEPHAM The response to bST is essentially one of nutrient repartitioning, so that in the longer term food intake has to increase to match the increased output of milk.

BOSTOCK, U.K. *What is the molecular basis of the heterogeneity of bGH isolated from pituitary?*

MEPHAM Lewis *et al* (1989) have shown that heterogeneity results from processes operating at several levels i.e. by pre-, co- and post-translational mechanisms, and following secretion. Although rbGH and pbGH appear to be galactopoietically equipotent, there are differences between these two preparations in terms of physiological and biochemical variables (Heap *et al*, 1989). These differences might be attributable to the fact that a singular molecular species is present in rbGH and/or to differences in molecular configuration between the pbGH and rbGH forms.

KNUDSEN, DUBAI *Is early embryonic death still considered to represent a 'safety valve' to dispose of individuals of inadequate genetic make-up?*

PETERS Cytogenetic evidence has not substantiated this theory of the 1960s, and the cause of embryonic death remains unknown.

COX, CHILE *Would Dr. Peters comment on the use of oTP1 for treatment of embryo mortality by preventing the regression of the corpus luteum? It would appear that depression in the production of an embryo derived protein may be due to a major embryo dysfunction which would not be corrected by maintaining corpus luteum function and that much more information is needed on the control of embryo growth and metabolism.*

PETERS I would agree that it is far too early to indicate whether oTP1 or bTP1 could be used as treatments for embryo mortality, and that much more research on embryonic activity is needed.

NYEKO, KENYA *Indigenous African cows which are normally grazed with bulls which would detect any silent heat, may take one to two years before conception, particularly in Uganda. What could be the reason for this?*

PETERS True anoestrus or complete inactivity of the ovaries, is the likely cause, particularly if the cows are suckling calves or are in a poor nutritional state.

MACFARLANE, U.K. Anoestrus in Zebus in Uganda and elsewhere is usually nutritional; lactational anoestrus tends to extend into the dry season and without supplementary feeding will last until the following rains resulting in a 24 month calving interval.

SMITH *It is far easier to carry out research and measure the results in intensive systems than to evaluate the productivity of animals in extensive systems. Should not the latter type of work be carried out by scientists in the developing world?*

PETERS I think that the main reason is financial and that the developed world has more funding to invest in research for the future. That is not to say that such research is irrelevant to developing countries as there will be inevitable 'spin-off'. Also some research is directly applicable e.g. the use of bST; India has recently licensed its use for a period of evaluation.

RANGNEKAR, INDIA *Would Dr. Fielding comment on the need to educate planners of research to identify critical problems requiring solutions rather than to develop technologies and then look for applications.*

FIELDING This is true; practising scientists have a responsibility to brief planning scientists and administrators who are often generalists. The danger of being technology driven rather than problem led is very real and should be guarded against, possibly through more peer interchange and review.

ASSELBERGS, MOZAMBIQUE *All speakers so far have expressed their sympathy with and interest in the problems of the poor and solving hunger in the world. Yet we see that almost all research reported is centred round problems of the intensive livestock systems of the North, and not applicable to the South. What in the opinion of the speakers are the main reasons for that, cultural, financial or political?*

MEPHAM The conventional view of scientific research is that it is pursued to obtain understanding of the natural world: the exploitation of that knowledge constitutes 'technology'. This 'neutrality' of science has always been questionable, but increasing commercial involvement in research, together with a blurring of the distinction between science and technology, poses new threats to scientific neutrality (Mepham, 1989b). In Britain most research is funded either by Western oriented industry or to support the UK's international competitiveness (AFRC Corporate Plan 1989–94, p6). In my paper, I argue that such priorities should be changed (on grounds of compassion, restitution *and* self interest: Mepham, 1987b), but they are unlikely to do so unless there is increased investment in appropriate technology for developing countries.

ANDERSON, MEXICO *Do we not need to see a shift in the generation and development of biotechnology from the North to the South so that appropriateness to the South is assured, and the 'dumping' on the South of inappropriate biotechnology from the North is avoided?*

JEGGO, AUSTRIA The role of international organizations is perhaps to assist in the transfer of 'appropriate' technology as well as biotechnology to the developing countries; thus investment by the developed countries in biotechnology is itself greatly assisting developing countries.

4.

ANIMAL HEALTH, DIAGNOSIS

Chairman: J.A. Hammond
CTVM
Edinburgh

4.1

Conventional Approaches to the Diagnosis of Infectious and Parasitic Diseases of Livestock – Their Limitations

A.G. HUNTER
Centre for Tropical Veterinary Medicine,
University of Edinburgh, Scotland

INTRODUCTION

Infectious and parasitic diseases of livestock are usually diagnosed by clinicians on the basis of clinical signs and disease history. The confirmation of diagnosis of such diseases, however, is based on demonstration, usually in the laboratory, of the presence of the pathogenic organisms in question in tissues or somewhat retrospectively, their antibodies in serum samples. The detection of serum antibodies cannot usually confirm active infection but merely that at some point infection has occurred and although the importance of serology in diagnosis is unquestionably considerable, this paper concentrates on the former approach i.e. demonstration of the presence of pathogenic organisms in tissues. Whether the pathogenic organism in question is a virus, rickettsia, bacterium, fungus, protozoan, helminth or ectoparasite, the approach to its demonstration in tissues is essentially similar and usually by one of the following methods:

- Visual detection e.g. certain helminths, arthropod larvae and ectoparasites.
- Detection under the microscope e.g. haemoprotozoal parasites in blood smears, anthrax in tissue necropsy smears, mange mites in skin biopsies, rotavirus in faeces by electron microscopy.
- Isolation by culture. Laboratory techniques are available and routinely used to isolate a wide range of pathogenic bacteria, viruses and fungi from tissues.
- Detection of the products of pathogenic organisms, e.g. helminth eggs,

coccidial oocysts in faeces samples, clostridial toxins in intestinal contents.

- Immunological detection. By treating appropriate samples with specific antiserum, the organism, if present, can be detected by use of a variety of techniques to 'visualize' the resultant antigen – antibody complex e.g. rinderpest virus by agar gel immunodiffusion, rabies and blackquarter by fluorescent antibody tests.

In many instances, the mere demonstration of an organism may be insufficient to confirm a diagnosis and further supportive tests may be required e.g. pathological, biochemical, toxicological and epidemiological.

Recent developments in biotechnology have already been incorporated into diagnostic methodology and will continue to do so, notably hybridoma technology and the production of monoclonal antibodies which are absolutely specific for individual epitopes of antigenic molecules. The specificity of monoclonal antibodies is such that they will largely replace conventional 'polyclonal' antisera in immunodiagnostic techniques. The incorporation of monoclonal antibodies into recently developed immunoenzyme assays, notably the enzyme-linked immunosorbent assay (ELISA) offers the promise of highly sensitive and specific diagnostic tests for antigen and serum antibody detection that can readily be applied without sophisticated laboratory facilities. Commercial ELISA kits are now available for detection of several antigens e.g. canine heartworm, feline leukaemia virus and rotavirus.

Recombinant DNA technology is still in its infancy but will increasingly be applied to disease diagnosis. By use of restriction endonuclease enzymes and hybridization assays, DNA probes can be used to detect matching DNA in cultures, tissues etc. Although still a research tool, DNA probes have been developed for the diagnosis of several organisms e.g. Marek's disease virus in feathers from infected chickens (Davidson, Moray, Alkinson and Becker, 1986).

The diagnosis of livestock diseases will continue to depend on the combination of clinical prowess with laboratory expertise and there will be no short cut to the correct execution of the 'conventional' approaches briefly outlined above. Nevertheless the incorporation of the use of monoclonal antibodies and eventually recombinant DNA technology into the diagnostician's armoury of techniques will undoubtedly bring great improvements, particularly where more traditional methods have been inadequate. In this paper, the author speculates on the limitations of conventional diagnostic methodology and whether these can be overcome by the use of biotechnology.

ECTOPARASITES

Ectoparasites can cause major disease problems in livestock e.g. mange in camels, tick worry in cattle. Fortunately the diagnosis of ectoparasitism is normally straightforward. Ticks, fleas and lice are visible to the naked eye although their identification by examination under the microscope requires a degree of skill and knowledge. Mange mites are not visible, but can usually be readily demonstrated by microscopic examination of scrapings of skin lesions.

Myiasis is the infestation of living animals with the larvae of diptera flies (Urquhart, Armour, Duncan, Dunn and Jennings, 1987). Blowfly myiasis and screw-worm myiasis can be major problems but are readily diagnosed clinically and by detection of the larvae (maggots). Other myiases have prolonged incubation periods during which the larvae develop and migrate through tissues; disease syndromes associated with the emergence of the final stages are readily diagnosed, but infections during the prepatent period are not e.g *Oestrus ovis* or nasal bots in sheep; *Dermatobia hominis* in South American cattle, or ura and *Hypoderma bovis* or warbles in cattle. *Oestrus ovis* and *Hypoderma bovis* can be controlled, if necessary, by strategic insecticide therapy and the serodiagnosis of warble fly infections in cattle by an ELISA test has been investigated as a possible aid to eradication schemes (Sinclair and Wassall, 1986). *Dermatobia hominis* can also be controlled, if necessary, but control is complicated by the wide host range of the fly.

HELMINTHS

Helminthiases of livestock in tropical countries are of major economic importance due to loss of productivity, mortality in serious cases and costs in control. Fortunately the diagnosis of most helminth caused diseases pose few technical problems. Enteric helminthiasis, lung worm infestation and liver fluke (fascioliasis) can be diagnosed in the live animals by microscopic examination of faeces for helminth eggs. Faecal helminth egg counts together with other information (epidemiological history, clinical findings etc.) are usually sufficient to provide a diagnosis. With the exception of *Nematodirus* spp., the common enteric trichostrongyle eggs (e.g. of *Haemonchus, Ostertagia, Trichostrongylus*) detected in faeces are indistinguishable and require further techniques (measuring and larvae culture) for differentiation. Due to the reliability of these commonly used coprological techniques, immunological tests have not been widely used (Tizard, 1987). Nevertheless, not all helminth diseases result in faecal shedding of eggs and these can be difficult to diagnose; in this category are included important zoonotic conditions in which domestic animals act as intermediate hosts and reservoirs of infection to man.

Cysticercosis

Cysticercus bovis in cattle and *C. cellulosae* in pigs are the larval stages of the human tapeworms, *T. saginata* and *T. solium* respectively, common infections throughout the developing world from ingestion of cysticercus infected beef and pork. The control of human taeniasis requires various measures including the detection of active cystercercus infections in cattle and pigs. Cysticercosis however, can only be diagnosed by detection of the cysticerci in muscle tissues by abattoir meat inspection and even then light infestations may be missed. A reliable sensitive test to detect active cysticercus infections in live cattle and pigs before slaughter would be beneficial to the control of human taeniasis. A monoclonal antibody based ELISA assay for this purpose is currently under development (Harrison, this volume).

Echinococcosis

Echinococcus granulosus is a small nonpathogenic tapeworm of dogs found worldwide; domestic and wild ruminants, camels, pigs and man act as the intermediate host in which the larval stage develops in hydatid cysts in either lungs or liver. Hydatidosis can be of pathogenic significance in man, and in some parts of the world where dogs have ready access to livestock offal and are in close contact with man, human hydatidosis is a major problem. Hydatid cysts are usually tolerated in domestic animals without clinical signs (Urquhart *et al*, 1987) and thus diagnosis is never required except in epidemiological studies. There are no tests to detect hydatid cysts in animals, and the diagnosis of infection in dogs is difficult as the small tapeworm segments are only shed intermittently in the faeces. The problem can be controlled by hygienic practices, but reliable tests to detect active infection in final and intermediate animal hosts would greatly benefit epidemiological studies.

Trichinosis

Trichinella spiralis can infect most mammals and is an important zoonotic helminth, raw or partially cooked pork being the usual source of infection to man. Trichinosis rarely causes clinical symptoms in animals and is usually diagnosed by microscopic examination of small samples of pig muscle. More recently, an ELISA test has been used to detect serum antibodies in infected pigs, although pigs with light infections may require more than five weeks to produce detectable antibody (Oliver, Singh, Abad and Vail, 1986).

Filariasis

Of the filarial helminths, *Dirofilaria immitis* which causes canine heartworm is probably of the greatest veterinary importance. Diagnosis of heartworm has traditionally been based on the combination of clinical signs and detection of larvae (microfilariae) in the blood. For various reasons, heartworm infested dogs are not consistently microfilaraemic, and various ELISA kits using monoclonal antibodies are now routinely used to detect antigen in suspect heartworm cases; sensitivity is related to the worm burden and the kits are 100% sensitive in detecting burdens of 20 worms or more (Whiteley, 1988). Other filarial worms include *Parafilaria bovicola* of cattle and buffalo, *Stephanofilaria assamensis* which causes 'hump sore' in cattle in the Indian subcontinent, and *Onchocerca* species; all cause cutaneous lesions which are diagnosed clinically and by demonstration of adult worms and microfilariae in the lesion.

PROTOZOA

Of the protozoal infections of livestock, the most important in tropical regions are haemoparasites transmitted by arthropod vectors i.e. *Trypanosoma, Babesia* and *Theileria* spp.

Trypanosomiasis

Trypanosomes pathogenic to livestock include species transmitted by tsetse flies in Africa (*T. congolense, T. vivax, T. brucei* and *T. simiae*) and species transmitted by haematophagous biting flies (*T. vivax* in South America and *T. evansi* worldwide). Tsetse fly transmitted trypanosomiasis is unquestionably a major constraint to livestock development in Africa and has been the subject of a great deal of research. Diagnosis is usually based on detection and identification under the microscope of the extracellular parasites in the blood by several methods varying in sensitivity. Difficulties arise when infections become chronic and parasitaemias fall to levels too low to be detected by conventional microscopy, a common situation with tsetse transmitted trypanosomiasis. Under these circumstances, blood from suspected cases can be subinoculated into laboratory rodents which are susceptible to *T. congolense, T. brucei* and *T. evansi* but resistant to most strains of *T. vivax*. This approach, however, is laborious and rarely practicable. More sensitive tests are therefore required, and ELISA tests to detect low levels of circulating trypanosomal antigens would appear to be the most promising.

T. equiperdum causes dourine, a venereally transmitted debilitating and usually fatal disease of equidae. Dourine is normally diagnosed clinically as it is rarely possible to detect the parasite in blood or tissues. It has been eradicated from Europe and North America and is a notifiable disease in some countries which permit only the importation of horses that are certified disease free by the complement fixation test (CFT). Unfortunately false positives to the CFT can result from infection with antigenically related trypanosomes i.e. *T. brucei* and *T. evansi*. Thus a specific and sensitive test would be of value for both clinical and statutory diagnostic work.

Babesiosis

Babesia infections of livestock transmitted by hard ticks are widespread throughout the tropics and bovine babesioses caused by *Babesia bovis* and *B. bigemina* are major constraints to upgrading cattle by introduction of exotic breeds. *Babesia* are intraerythrocytic parasites and cause anaemia and haemoglobinuria; confirmation of diagnosis is readily effected by detection and identification of the parasites in stained blood films examined under the microscope. In chronic cases, parasitaemias fall to low levels which may not be detectable by microscopy. Of greater epidemiological importance, however, is the carrier state that develops in recovered animals which are clinically normal. Infection in carrier animals cannot normally be detected by conventional microscopy, but requires laborious and expensive subinoculation of blood into susceptible animals. Knowledge of the prevalence of infection by indigenous carrier animals may be necessary if susceptible animals are to be introduced into an endemic area. This can be guaged by epidemiological surveys of serum antibodies for which various tests have been developed, but tests to detect carrier animals would be more meaningful.

Theileriosis

Theileria infections of livestock are also transmitted by hard ticks and their diagnoses are based on similar criteria to those of babesiosis. *Theileria* initially develop as schizonts in lymphocytes before merozoites are released and invade erythrocytes forming piroplasms; thus in diagnosis lymph node biopsy smears are examined for characteristic intra-lymphocytic schizonts as well as blood smears for piroplasms.

The two most important *Theileria* infections are *Theileria parva,* the cause of East Coast fever in cattle in east and central southern Africa, and *T. annulata,* the cause of tropical theileriosis in cattle in tropical and subtropical Asia, North Africa and the Mediterranean basin. Although the diseases are similar and the parasites are virtually indistinguishable in lymph node biopsy and blood smears, their distributions do not overlap and so their differential diagnosis poses no problem. Difficulties do arise, however, in differentiating *T. parva* and *T. annulata* from other less pathogenic or nonpathogenic *Theileria* infections, and the epidemiological history and clinical signs as well as the detection of schizonts and piroplasms must be taken into account (Losos, 1987). Tests to differentiate different species of *Theileria* would be of great value.

BACTERIA AND MYCOPLASMAS

In the confirmatory diagnosis of bacterial diseases, great care must be taken in handling samples, particularly in the tropics where autolysis of animal tissues can be very rapid. There is possibly more expertise and knowledge on the isolation and identification of bacterial pathogens than other organisms and providing correct samples taken from live clinical cases or recently dead animals are handled properly and subjected to appropriate laboratory procedures and tests, the prospects of diagnosing bacterial diseases are excellent.

Acute infections

Unfortunately some important bacterial infections of livestock in the tropics have a short course resulting in sudden or rapid death and competent veterinary staff rarely see clinical cases or recently dead animals. Anthrax is a notable example and although its diagnosis is straightforward in a newly dead animal, it may be difficult if autolysis has commenced as the causative organism, *Bacillus anthracis* is rapidly killed by putrefactive processes (Soltys, 1963). Other important bacterial infections that cause rapid deaths are *Pasteurella multocida* in buffaloes and cattle (haemorrhagic septicaemia) and *Clostridium chauvoei* in cattle (blackquarter).

Thus anthrax, haemorrhagic septicaemia and blackquarter are rarely confirmed, even though they are commonly regarded as important livestock diseases necessitating expensive national or regional vaccination campaigns for their control. It is the author's suspicion that many livestock deaths are 'conveniently' attributed to one of these diseases and this attitude would only change if diagnostic tests could be carried out on autolysed tissues to detect pathogenic bacteria. It has been suggested that DNA probes have a distinct advantage over culturing in this respect as they should be able to detect dead bacteria in autolysed tissues (Glasser and Gorham, 1989).

Chronic infections

Problems in diagnosis of bacterial infections can also arise in chronic diseases, notably tuberculosis of cattle and pigs caused by *Mycobacterium bovis.* The diagnosis and control of bovine tuberculosis has been universally based on the tuberculosis skin test which is prepared from cultures of *M. bovis* and *M. tuberculosis* (the cause of human tuberculosis) but the main limitation of the test is its poor specificity (Blood and Radostits, 1989). Infection with other *Mycobacterium* spp., namely *M. avium, M. tuberculosis* and *M. paratuberculosis* (the cause of Johne's disease in cattle) or vaccination against *M. paratuberculosis* or infection with *Nocardia farcinicus* (the cause of bovine farcy) can all cause false positives to the test. These false positives can be differentiated to a certain extent by use of a comparative skin test in which avian and mammalian tuberculin are injected simultaneously, but an improved, more specific test would be highly beneficial.

Pneumonia in goats can be a common problem in the tropics, but there is a great deal of confusion over differential diagnosis between pasteurellosis and contagious caprine pleuropneumonia (CCPP) which is caused by various strains of *Mycoplasma m. mycoides* over which there is some confusion (Losos, 1986). In outbreaks of acute CCPP diagnosis based on post mortem findings (pathology and culture), should be possible. Unfortunately pneumonia, including CCPP often occurs as a more chronic syndrome and the diagnosis may be based on clinical history and response to therapy which is very inaccurate. A reliable test to detect the presence of mycoplasma infection in goats with pneumonia would greatly alleviate the situation; the complement fixation test has been used to great effect for the diagnosis of the comparable disease in cattle (CBPP) caused by *M. m. mycoides* (Blood and Radostits, 1989).

RICKETTSIAS

Cowdriosis

Heartwarter is a disease of domestic ruminants caused by infection of endothelial cells with *Cowdria ruminantium* and which is transmitted by *Amblyomma* ticks. It is a major disease throughout most of sub-Saharan Africa and is also present in islands off Africa, Guadeloupe in the Caribbean and possibly the southern part of the Arabian peninsula where *Amblyomma variegatum* is established (Uilenberg, 1983). Acute cases of heartwater may be readily diagnosed by the clinical signs including characteristic nervous symptoms associated with invasion of capillary endothelial cells in the brain; and confirmation at autopsy is straightforward by detection of the organisms in cerebral or cerebellar cortex crush smears under the microscope. Unfortunately heartwater commonly presents itself as a febrile condition which unless treated promptly may result in death. Other than expensive and laborious subinoculation of blood into susceptible animals or microscopic examination of brain biopsy tissue, either of which is usually impracticable in the field, there is no method of demonstrating the organism and confirming a diagnoses in the live animal (Uilenberg, 1983). As infection can be transmitted mechanically by inoculation of blood a test to detect the organism in blood should be feasible.

Anaplasmosis

Bovine anaplasmosis is a tick-borne disease caused by *Anaplasma marginale* which invades erythrocytes causing fever, progressive anaemia and possiby death. The distribution and importance of this disease is similar to that of bovine babesiosis, and diagnosis in acute cases is confirmed by demonstration of the intraerythrocytic organisms microscopically in blood smears. Detection of the organism in chronic cases or asymptomatic carriers is difficult however requiring the same laborious and expensive approaches as for chronic babesiosis and a test to detect low levels of parasitaemia would be highly beneficial.

VIRUSES

Possibly the main limitation to diagnosing viral diseases is the care that must be taken over the collection and handling of samples, and the level of technology required to isolate and identify viruses. Thus confirmatory diagnosis is often beyond the means of veterinary diagnostic laboratories and is referred to specialist virology laboratories. In general, virus neutralization tests are the most specific and sensitive tests for either antibody or antigen detection, but they are costly and time consuming (Russell and Edington, 1985), and as such their execution is likely to be limited to specialist laboratories. Agar gel double immunodiffusion precipitation (AGDP) tests and their various modifications, however, are rapid, cheap, easy to perform and well within the capabilities of most routine veterinary diagnostic

TABLE 1 *General ranking order of viral diagnostic techniques using serology to detect antigen or antibody.*

Immunodiffusion (ID)
Complement fixation (CF)
Haemagglutinin inhibition (HI)
Indirect immunofluorescence (IIF)
Enzyme linked immunosorbent assay (ELISA)
Virus neutralization (VN)
Radioimmunoassay (RIA)

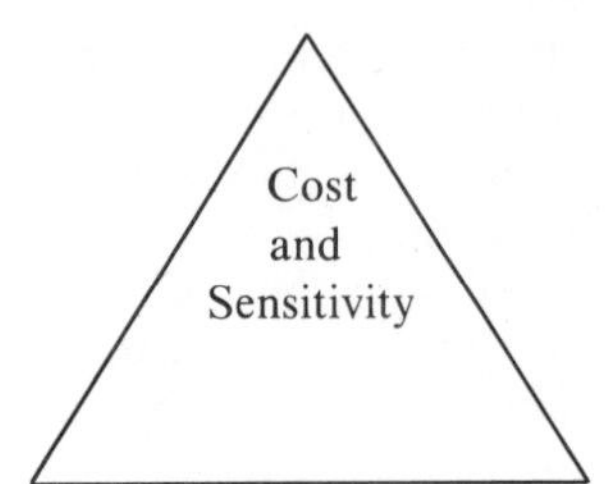

Adapted from: Edington and Russell (1988)

laboratories; examples of viral antigens detected in tissues by AGDP are swine fever, bovine viral diarrhoea and rinderpest. Unfortunately these tests are relatively insensitive and viral antigens may only be demonstrable early in disease before antibodies are developed (Russell and Edington, 1985).

Immunofluorescence (IF) tests are also carried out in diagnostic laboratories to detect viral antigens in tissues e.g. rabies and swine fever. IF tests to detect viral antigen may be direct in which the specific antiserum is conjugated to a fluorescent dye such as fluorescein isothiocyanate, or indirect in which a conjugated antiglobulin to the specific antiserum is used. The main disadvantage of IF tests is that an u.v. light source is required for irradiation when examining smears or films under the microscope. Also because of the subjective nature of the interpretation of IF tests, controls are essential (Tizard, 1987). Indirect IF tests are more sensitive than AGDP tests however (Russell and Edington, 1985).

Most of the problems of lack of sensitivity or ease of application can be solved by the use of ELISA tests which will be increasingly used in diagnosis of viral diseases. Confirmatory diagnosis, however, will continue to be a compromise between what can be achieved at diagnostic laboratory level and what must be referred to specialist reference laboratories. The general ranking order for cost and sensitivity of viral diagnostic tests is shown in Table 1.

Foot-and-mouth disease

One major limitation to diagnosis at present involves the laborious procedure to confirm a diagnosis of foot and mouth disease (FMD). Because of the importance of FMD, it is customary to forward vesicular samples from early cases to reference laboratories for isolation and identification of serotypes. The seven serotypes are distributed as shown in Table 2.

Within each serotype there are subtypes and because of antigenic drift in enzootic situations and the need for surveillance to ensure that appropriate vaccines are being used, it will continue to be necessary to send samples to reference laboratories (Russell and Edington, 1985). This can be time consuming, however, and in many circumstances when outbreaks occur all that is required is an immediate identification of the serotype. The author had the unfortunate experience of witnessing the first appearance of Asia I in North Yemen cattle in 1979; first cases occurred in local indigenous cattle in which it caused mild disease similar to the recognized enzootic serotypes but infection spread shortly afterwards to exotic Friesian cattle with serious consequences. Had there been a facility to identify the serotype of FMD at diagnostic laboratory level appropriate preventive measures could have been implemented. Fortunately an ELISA kit for this purpose is now under development (Jeggo, Richards and Dargie, this volume).

TABLE 2 *Regional distribution of FMD serotypes.*

Serotype	O	A	C	SAT 1	SAT 2	SAT 3	Asia 1
Africa	+	+	+	+	+	+	–
Asia	+	+	–	–	–	–	+
S. America	+	+	–	–	–	–	–
Europe	+	+	–	–	–	–	–

From: Russell and Edington (1985)

APPLICATION OF BIOTECHNOLOGY

This paper has briefly reviewed the current approaches to diagnosis of some important livestock diseases in developing countries and highlighted where conventional diagnostic techniques are inadequate.

With the recent parallel developments of monoclonal antibody technology and ELISA technology, prospects for diagnostic tests with high levels of specificity and sensitivity are now excellent. Moreover ELISA tests can be carried out without recourse to sophisticated laboratory facilities. Recombinant DNA technology and DNA probes also offer the prospect of techniques in which infectious agents can be detected and identified with great precision in a wide range of clinical material. The technology is already well-advanced in human medicine and will be increasingly applied in veterinary medicine. However, the development of monoclonal antibodies, DNA probes, and the standardization of diagnostic tests into which they are incorporated can only be considered in sophisticated laboratories. The advancement of these technologies will largely be in the hands of molecular biologists and immunologists, but it is imperative that developments are properly directed, namely:–

- to improve diagnostic tests that are currently inadequate
- to provide novel diagnostic tests where required.

Possible applications are summarized in Tables 3 and 4.

Hence it is essential that molecular biolgists, immunologists and veterinarians collaborate in future developments to ensure the appropriate channelling of resources.

TABLE 3 *Possible applications of biotechnology to improve existing diagnostic techniques.*

1. ELISA + Monoclonal antibodies for antigen detection

   e.g. Rinderpest in tissues
   FMD serotypes in tissues
   Low level parasitaemias
   (Trypanosomiasis)
   (Babesiosis)
   (Theileriosis)
   (Anaplasmosis)
   Heartwater (*C. ruminantium*) in blood

2. ELISA + Monoclonal antibodies for serum antibody detection in chronic disease

   e.g. Bovine tuberculosis
   Contagious caprine pleuropneumonia

TABLE 4 *Possible applications of biotechnology for novel diagnostic techniques.*

1. ELISA + Monoclonal antibodies for antigen detection in the live animal

   Bovine and porcine cysticercosis
   Hydatidosis
   Trichinosis

2. DNA probes to detect pathogenic organisms in autolysed tissues

   e.g. Anthrax (*B. anthracis*)
   Haemorrhagic septicaemia (*P. multocida*)
   Blackquarter (*C. chauvoei*)

REFERENCES

Blood, D.C. and Radostits, O.M. (1989). *Veterinary Medicine.* Seventh Edition. Baillière Tindall.

Davidson, T.M., Alkinson, M. and Becker, Y. (1986). Detection of Marek's disease virus antigens and DNA in feathers from infected chickens. *Journal of Virological Methods,* **13**, 231–244.

Glasser, J.W. and Gorham, J.R. (1989). An overview of the applications of biotechnology in veterinary medicine in the *57th session of the OIE, Paris, 22–26 May, 1989.*

Harrison, L.J.S. (1991). Monoclonal antibodies and DNA probes in diagnosis. In *The Application of Biotechnology in Developing Countries* (ed. A.G. Hunter), pp. 252–271. Centre for Tropical Veterinary Medicine, University of Edinburgh.

Jeggo, M.H., Richards, J.I. and Dargie, J.D. (1991). The use of immunoassay diagnostic kits in developing countries. In *The Application of Biotechnology in Developing Countries* (ed. A.G. Hunter), pp. 286–303. Centre for Tropical Veterinary Medicine, University of Edinburgh.

Losos, G.J. (1986). *Infectious Tropical Diseases of Domestic Animals.* Longman Scientific and Technical.

Oliver, D.G., Singh, P., Abad, M. and Vail, N. (1986). Development of a high volume testing system for certifying Trichina free park. In *IVth International Symposium of Veterinary Laboratory Diagnosticians*, Amsterdam, June 2–6, 1986. pp. 296–299. World Association of Veterinary Laboratory Diagnosticians.

Russell, P.H. and Edington, N. (1985). *Veterinary Viruses.* The Burlington Press, Cambridge.

Sinclair, I.J. and Wassall, D.A. (1986). Serodiagnosis of warble fly infections in cattle. In *IVth International Symposium of Veterinary Laboratory Diagnosticians, Amsterdam, June 1986, pp 304–306.* World Association of Veterinary Laboratory Diagnosticians.

Soltys, M.A. (1963). *Bacteria and Fungi Pathogenic to Man and Animals.* Baillière Tindall and Cox.

Tizard, I. (1987). *Veterinary Immunology – An Introduction.* Third Edition. W.B. Saunders Company.

Uilenberg, G. (1983). Heartwater: current status. *Advances in Veterinary Science and Comparative Medicine,* **27**, 427–480.

Urquhart, G.M., Armour, J., Duncan, J.L., Dunn, A.M. and Jennings, F.W. (1987). *Veterinary Parasitology.* Longman Scientific and Technical.

Whiteley, H. Ellen (1988). Your diagnostic protocol for *Dirofilaria immitis* infection in dogs. *Veterinary Medicine,* ?, 328–345.

4.2

Monoclonal Antibodies and DNA Probes in Diagnosis

L.J.S. HARRISON
Centre for Tropical Veterinary Medicine,
University of Edinburgh, Scotland

SUMMARY

Monoclonal antibodies and DNA probes are biological reagents which if used in appropriate situations could aid the diagnosis of diseases affecting domestic livestock in developing countries. The technology for preparing them is well-established and documented thus the approach is presently feasible. However, it is vital to identify those systems in which their use is justifiable. In addition the rationale behind their production must be thoroughly considered in order that suitable reagents are produced. A knowledge of the immunochemistry of the parasitic organism is a prerequisite to monoclonal antibody production. Similarly, DNA probes have many potential uses but these should be clearly defined with the aim of producing appropriate reagents for each parasite system. As some readers may wish some background information on these technologies, this paper first defines monoclonal antibodies and DNA probes, outlining the basis and rationale behind their preparation. Some of the preliminary analytical techniques involved will also be described. Illustrations will mainly be drawn from the author's own field since zoonotic cestodes and other helminths afford examples of the need, in defined circumstances, to take this approach. The illustrations include a description of the development of a monoclonal antibody based parasite antigen detection ELISA assay in a situation where infection with the live parasite cannot otherwise easily be detected, and the use of DNA probes in the differentiation of morphologically similar taeniid cestodes.

INTRODUCTION

This paper considers the diagnosis of disease by the identification of the disease causing organism or parasite either through analysis of its DNA, its metabolic products or the hosts immune response to infection. There are of course several methods of parasite identification and these could be divided into three distinct categories. The first is the use of morphological criteria. This requires clinical skills, often only available in a limited number of specialized laboratories. Naturally samples of the parasite or organism must be easily obtainable from the infected animal, preferably *ante-mortem* and they must be preserved so that they reach the diagnostic laboratory in good order. However, morphological criteria cannot be used to differentiate species or subspecies when such parameters overlap or are identical and it is often difficult to get the sample to the diagnostic laboratory in good enough condition for identification to take place. The second group of methods involves the identification and analysis of gene products either through the direct analysis of components such as proteins or enzymes or indirectly through immunological analysis or immunoassays which can include the use of monoclonal antibody reagents. Proteins and enzymes are labile and consequently difficult to transport. To some extent it is easier to handle fluids such as serum for immunoassays, however, again the components in the serum must be reasonably stable so that they are not accidentally destroyed before assay. The third group of methods is through the direct analysis of the parasite DNA and this includes the use of DNA probes. DNA is relatively stable and can be transported relatively easily since samples can be stored in ethyl alcohol.

A major contribution to the control of parasitic infections, whether by vaccination, vector control or diagnosis and drug treatment, is simply the precise establishment of prevalence and exposure levels within a population. The diagnostic tools used must be reliable, sensitive and specific. They should also be robust and operational under field conditions in the endemic areas of less developed countries. Immunoassays based on enzyme linked (ELISA) procedures (Tijssen, 1987) and monoclonal antibodies are often the only ones which are likely to meet these stringent requirements. The identification of parasite antigen-host antibody systems suitable for immunodiagnosis forms the basis for development of such assays. The objectives can be either the diagnosis of animals with viable infection i.e. antigen detection as opposed to antibody detection which indicates exposure but not necessarily current infection. In addition to serological techniques, the specificity and sensitivity of todays nucleic acid hybridization techniques will surely make a major impact in the area of parasite diagnosis, either through the production of cloned protein for immunoassay or through the use of DNA probes and hybridization techniques. This latter subject is covered in the second part of this paper.

Often the paucity of parasite material can itself dictate the use of the special approaches of monoclonal antibody production and molecular biology to supply materials on the scale necessary for any reasonably large-scale epidemiology surveys. For this reason, the emphasis must be on cloned protein antigens, rather than carbohydrate or lipid antigens, or the use of competition type monoclonal antibody based ELISA assays for antibody detection and trapping or competition type assays for parasite antigen detection. The general subject of diagnosis of internal parasitism was recently reviewed (Anderson, Facer and Rollinson, 1989; O.I.E., 1990).

The purpose of this paper is to give those readers who wish to familiarize themselves with the technologies of monoclonal antibody and DNA probe production a brief description of the necessary background studies and a general introduction into the methodologies used in their preparation. Zoonotic cestodes afford some examples of where it is appropriate to use this technology thus some of the examples are drawn from this field.

MONOCLONAL ANTIBODIES

Production

There are several critical factors which must be met for the preparation of monoclonal antibody producing hybridoma cell lines. Clonal selection theory (Burnet, 1959), that each mammalian B cell line has the potential to make a monospecific antibody, provides the basis for the production of monoclonal antibodies. However, plasma cells which secrete antibody are terminally differentiated, have a limited life time and cannot as a rule be grown in culture. Tumours of this type of cell can be found in most mammalian species. These tumour cell lines typically produce an antibody of their own and can be grown indefinitely in culture. Many different such cell lines are available and some have been developed which do not excrete any antibody at all. Therefore if a normal plasma cell producing antibody of a desired specificity can be fused with tumour cells such as these, the resultant cell line may combine the antibody producing capacity of the former cell with the growth potential of a tumour cell. A final essential is the inclusion of a step which ensures that only fused cells can survive in culture. This is often accomplished by using tumour cell lines which lack thymidine kinase or hypoxanthine phosphorylase transferase. These enzymes, of the nucleic acid salvage pathway, are essential if cells are to grow in the presence of aminopterin, which blocks the main nucleic acid synthesis pathway. Therefore, after the fusion the cells are grown in medium containing aminopterin so that only hybridoma cells which have inherited the ability to produce the salvage pathway enzymes from the plasma cell will be able to survive and grow. Usually the cells are grown in medium containing hypoxanthine, aminopterin and thymidine, this is commonly known as HAT medium.

The basic procedure followed in the actual fusion process can be summarized as follows. Cells, such as spleen or lymph node cells from an appropriately immunized or naturally infected animal are fused with cells from a chosen tumour cell line using a fusing agent such as polyethylene glycol. The cells are then divided amongst the pots of multiwell tissue culture plates, initially with HAT medium in order that only the fused cells will grow. Colonies of these hybridoma cells usually become apparent after 7 to 10 days and shortly after that samples of the medium in which the hybridoma cells were growing can be assayed for the presence of antibody using any number of available immunoassays. When colonies of hybridoma cells producing monoclonal antibody of interest are identified, the cells are cloned into the pots of further multiwell tissue culture and in due course assayed for the production of antibody. This process is repeated until the hybridoma cell line is pure. The cells can then be grown up in quantity either in tissue culture medium to collect the monoclonal antibodies or the cells can be placed back into animals and ascitic fluid containing the monoclonal antibody in high concentration can be collected. These monoclonal antibodies can then be purified and used as reagents. It is important that samples of the growing cells are removed for storage in liquid nitrogen at several points in the above procedure in order to provide stocks of cells and backup cells in case the cultures fail.

The available literature on the preparation of monoclonal antibodies is vast and obviously it is not possible to go into great detail in this short paper. Of the many publications available Harlow and Lane (1988) Kemeny and Challacombe (1988) and Campbell (1984) provide useful information. It is worth emphasizing at this point that monoclonal antibodies are reactive with a particular and definable epitope on an antigen molecule. Several different monoclonal antibodies could therefore be produced against different epitopes on the same antigen molecule.

General considerations

It is important that the monoclonal antibodies are prepared in a selective way so that the reagents perform the required task. This requires some preliminary analysis and consideration of the parasite itself and also a consideration of the design of the assay in which it is proposed to use the reagents. Immunodiagnosis of tropical diseases should ideally be specific, not only for the parasite species, but also for each stage or age of a given parasite. An assumption that we have made is that much of the problem of cross reactions between helminths and indeed many parasites, arises from the use of soluble extracts. These are frequently referred to as antigens in the literature, a practice which should be discouraged, since the mixture obtained by centrifugation of a homogenized entire organism is very far from being a defined antigen. An important point is that most helminths share common anabolic and catabolic activities, and the necessary biological components for these processes are likely to be conserved in evolution and thus cross-reacting. Soluble parasite extracts are quite likely to contain these 'housekeeping' components and hence their use results in unreliable (poor signal background ratios), or cross-reacting and thus nonspecific tests. Similarly, many structural proteins, for example cytoskeletal and mitotic spindle elements, as well as many carbohydrate prosthetic groups, are likely to be molecules which are conserved in nature and thus cross-reacting.

Unlike protective antigens, for which some degree of cross-reaction with a variety of different parasites might be acceptable, specificity is mandatory in diagnosis. The development of such parasite specific serological systems also involves and requires the acquisition of reliable reference serum banks from clinically defined cases of commonly occurring parasitic and other relevant diseases. Given these serum banks the suitability or otherwise, of a given reagent for specific diagnosis is easily assessed.

Thus as considered in a recent review (Parkhouse and Harrison, 1989) a better understanding of the host-parasite interphase in helminth and other parasite infections is required and, given the recent technical innovations in immunochemical analysis, molecular biology and monoclonal antibody production, is quite feasible. The new era of recombinant antigens, and anti-idiotypic reagents is ideally suited to the objective of reliable diagnosis. The following summary attempts to present a general overview of the field, emphasizing current principles and drawing upon systems with defined molecular correlates as the examples.

Relevant reviews, focusing on antigens described up to 1985 have been published for cestodes (Harrison and Parkhouse, 1985), nematodes (Almond and Parkhouse, 1985), schistosomes (Simpson and Smithers, 1985) and trematodes (Hughes, 1985). An excellent update on our current knowledge of defined helminth antigens is available (MacInnis, 1987). Also well-covered in the last two years are molecular aspects of recent studies on schistosomes (Capron and Capron, 1986; Rollinson and Simpson, 1987; Mahmoud, 1987), filarial nematodes (CIBA, 1987; Maizels and Selkirk, 1988) and intestinal helminths (Pawlowski, 1986).

Analysis of the immune response to helminths

Characterization of the immune responses of hosts to their parasites has relevance to diagnosis, control and understanding all aspects of parasitic diseases. In essence, this involves determining which parasite components are immunogenic and defining the range of immune responses and effector mechanisms called into play. The clinical status of the host, such as resistant versus susceptible, or degree of pathological damage, will depend on the interactions within this presumably complex network of immunological phenomena.

For convenience, the variety of different antigens presented to the host in helminth infections may be classified into four major levels: parasite stage, antigenic compartment within a stage (e.g. surface, secretions or somatic antigens), antigenic components within a compartment and antigenic epitopes of a single defined antigen. A further level of complexity in the serological response to a parasite is the variable immunoglobulin isotype profile elicited by each individual antigen or antigenic epitope.

The basic point to be emphasized is that each individual antigenic epitope of all the antigens, presented by a parasite to its host, elicits its own independent response, both in terms of quantity, isotype profile and antibody affinity (Almond and Parkhouse, 1986a,b; 1989; Almond, Worms, Harnett and Parkhouse, 1987; Gibbons, Harrison and Parkhouse, 1986; Hussain, Groge and Ottesen, 1987; Jassim, Hassan and Catty, 1987). The net result is an enormously complex array of antibody specificities, presenting the problem of elucidating which antibody specificities are relevant to diagnosis.

An important consideration is that many antigens, in particular surface and secreted components, may be stage (or age) specific. These provide a basis for stage specific diagnosis, protection and pathological reactions. A systematic study of parasite antigens is thus a prerequisite for a programme of investigation aimed at understanding the immunological dialogue between parasite and host.

The modern technological approach towards immunodiagnosis can be related to the three conveniently defined parasite antigen compartments: the surface, the secretions and the somatic antigens. In larval cestodes the cyst fluid can be considered as a fourth compartment. Thus surface antigens form an obvious focus for immunodiagnosis due to their frequent species and stage specificity. The approach of first defining, then cloning and testing of these surface antigens is essentially routine. Similarly, stage and species-specific antigens are found in the excretory-secretory (E/S) compartment of many helminths. These may well also contain possible vaccine targets (Lightowlers and Rickard, 1988; Lightowlers, 1990) and provide stimuli for pathological responses. From a diagnostic stand point they also form a logical focus as targets for parasite detection.

It is important to stress that only the surface and secretory compartments provide an interphase between the viable parasite and its host. It follows that all means of parasite evasion, and in turn host protective mechanisms, must act principally through the molecules of these compartments. The remaining somatic antigens are only recognized by the host when the parasite's surface has been breached by a potentially protective immune recognition process. Once this has occurred, however, parasite rejection may be favoured by immune responses to internal antigens, for example the enzyme glutathione transferase, which may play a role in schistosome membrane repair after granulocyte-mediated attack of the worm's surface (Smith, Da Verm, Board, Tiu, Garcia and Mitchell, 1986). On the death of the parasite by whatever means, the host is immediately presented with a multiplicity of somatic antigens, and so there is always the danger that some of these will provoke pathological reactions in addition to a multiplicity of potentially cross reactive antibody responses which can confound undefined diagnostic assay systems.

Many of the relevant parasite antigens will be proteins and thus their commercial production via recombinant nucleic acid technology is feasible. For nonprotein (i.e. nonclonable antigens) however, the preparation of anti-idiotype reagents to complementary monoclonal antibodies provides a possible mechanism for 'cloning the unclonable'. Such anti-idiotypic reagents find immediate application as diagnostic tools, substituting for antigen.

Other points to consider are possible heterogeneities not only in the parasite antigens but in the parasite population as well. This can be caused by factors such as antigenic changes in the parasite as it develops and also on a wider level heterogeneity in the general parasite population. For the reasons detailed above, the search for species-specific antigen/antibody systems is essential. However, specificity may also be improved by restricting antibody assays to one immunoglobulin isotype (Weiss, Hussain and Ottesen, 1982; Cabrera, Parkhouse, Forsyth, Gomez-Priego, Pabon and Yarzabal, 1988).

Detection of antibodies to the parasite

The current state of helminth diagnosis has recently been reviewed (Walls and Schantz, 1986) and indicates that most tests still focus on crude parasite extracts and there is little emphasis on working with defined systems. Over the next five years, however, we may expect dramatic changes in this area as cloned and expressed antigens and monoclonal antibody-based inhibition and anti-idiotypic assay systems enter routine use. Indeed the 1988 International Congress of Tropical Medicine and Malaria held in Amsterdam, contained abstracts on the use of cloned and expressed antigens in the diagnosis of schistosomiasis (Dell, Klinkert, Beck, Shi, Idris and Ruppel, 1988) and onchocerciasis (Lucius, Erondu, Kern, Donelson and Diesfield, 1988).

It should be emphasized that only assays which detect the living parasite firmly establish the presence of active parasite infections. Nevertheless detection of antibodies to the parasite, as evidence of previous exposure to the parasite, allow calculations to be made of exposure rates given population. The fact that the quantity and quality (Ig class) of antibodies synthesized to parasite antigens may vary, sometimes due to genetic differences between outbred hosts and often with time-dependent characteristics, has two important consequences for the construction of diagnostic tests based on the detection of anti-parasite antibodies. First, the probability of a given antigenic determinant being universally recognized by all sera from infected livestock at all times during and after infection must be low, and thus cloned antigen mixtures will probably be required for diagnostic tests with 100% sensitivity. Second, a thorough knowledge of the kinetics and classes of antibodies synthesized within a population will allow the construction of prognostic tests, or 'antibody windows' indicative, for example, of early versus late infections, susceptible versus resistant hosts or probability of pathological consequences in a particular host. Thus an immunochemical dissection of humoral anti-parasite responses may help in the understanding of protective versus pathological responses.

The first objective is to identify appropriately specific parasite antigen-host antibody systems. Following from this, routine testing can be envisaged using either a genetically engineered parasite antigen (or perhaps an anti-idiotypic antibody), or as an alternative, a monoclonal antibody to a specific parasite antigen. In the former case the parasite antigen forms the basis of a conventional antibody detection system and in the latter, binding of the parasite specific monoclonal antibody is inhibited by antibodies of similar specificity in the test sera (inhibition ELISA). In either case the procedure is ELISA based in order to achieve the necessary economy and simplicity for routine field use.

Detection of the parasite

In the absence of direct observation, only detection of circulating or urinary parasite products can unambiguously identify a current infection. Confirmation of a current infection would allow:

- recognition or asymptomatic cases for drug or other treatment
- recognition or re-establishment of the parasite following drug treatment or evaluation of control measures
- classification of areas with low, intermediate or high prevalence.

Paradoxically, parasite antigens, *per se*, are not ideal probes since by definition, they provoke antibody responses and thus are rapidly cleared from the circulation of the host. Nonantigenic or poorly antigenic, stage-specific secreted components, on the other hand, would form an ideal focus for the construction of serum or urine based immunochemical tests for parasites, since they are continuously released by live parasites and may not be rapidly cleared by the humoral immune system of the host (Parkhouse and Clark, 1983). Given an appropriately defined parasite product secreted by a viable parasite at a constant rate and a complementary monoclonal antibody, it would be possible to construct a dose-dependent (and thus quantitative) ELISA assay for the detection of parasites.

In general, the serological detection of viable parasites is far from routine. A recent example is detection of living cysticerci of *Taenia saginata* and *Taenia solium* using a monoclonal antibody recognizing a multiply-represented carbohydrate epitope present on a *T. saginata* metacestode surface and secreted glycoprotein (Harrison, Joshua, Wright and Parkhouse, 1989). This glycoprotein is found in the sera of infected hosts, and so the construction of a diagnostic parasite detection ELISA assay employing a single monoclonal antibody via a biotin-linked detection system was possible. The assay was suitably specific having an exceptionally low background with sera from cattle with a range of commonly occurring parasite infections. The detection level is approximately 100–200 live cysticerci per animal. The parasite product could be detected from about 5–6 weeks post infection onwards and detection was associated with current infection, as drug treatment of infected cattle to kill the cysticerci resulted in the disappearance of these components from the circulation, meanwhile the titre of anti-parasite antibody remained high. When tested using serum from herds of Kenyan cattle whose infection history was known through meat inspection results, the assay only detected herds with *T. saginata* infected animals while control herds with *Fasciola gigantica* and *Echinococcus granulosus* were negative unless there were also cattle infected with *T. saginata* cysticerci in the herd.

The parasite products detected in the assay were very robust and resistant to degradation making the assay very suitable for use in the field where serum samples may be subjected to less than optimal treatment. The same assay may be of value in the detection of *T. solium* cysticercosis in humans, as cerebrospinal fluid and serum from human cases of neurocysticercosis were positive in the assay. This latter finding was confirmed by further studies (Correa, Sandoval, Harrison, Parkhouse, Plancarte, Meza-Lucas and Flisser, 1989). Limited additional studies also suggest a use for this monoclonal antibody based capture assay in the diagnosis of *T. solium* cysticercosis in pigs (Rodrigues del Rosal, Correa and Flisser, 1989).

Possibly similar systems, based on the monoclonal antibody-based detection of circulating proteoglycan, have very recently been described for schistosomiasis (De Jonge and Deelder, 1988) and toxocariasis (Maizels, Kennedy, Meghji, Robertson and Smith, 1987). Double antibody capture assay for lymphatic filarial parasites, based on the use of a monoclonal antibody to phosphorylcholine, have been described (Forsyth, Spark, Kazura, Brown, Peters, Heywood, Dissanayake and Mitchell, 1985; Maizels, Burke and Deham, 1987), but has limitations imposed by the ubiquitous nature of the antigenic determinant, and also the neutralizing activity of corresponding host antibodies (Weiss, Van den Ende, Albiez, Barbiero, Forsyth and Prince, 1985).

RECOMBINANT DNA TECHNOLOGY AND DNA-PROBES

In the situation where a parasite can be obtained from an infected host, but morphological criteria are inadequate for identification or too labour intensive to be used routinely or the necessary skills are not available, DNA probes offer advantages. In fact recombinant DNA methods probably represent the definitive method of diagnosing many veterinary diseases since the DNA is the 'ultimate blue print' or plan of that parasite.

Available information suggests that there are no profound DNA rearrangements between the various life cycle stages of parasites. So that the same DNA is present in the parasite whether it is in its definitive, intermediate or vector hosts or indeed in its free-living stages. Thus race and species specific DNA probes cloned from more easily available stages of a parasite may be used to detect and/or define species, races and subspecies or rarer and less easily obtained stages of a parasite.

Many of the most recent advances in this technology have been made in the field of human medicine and these developments should be of advantage to the veterinary field. Although this paper concentrates on methods of diagnosing disease in animals through the detection of a particular parasite, disease causing organism and/or its products of metabolism or the detection of antibodies produced by the host as a result of infection, there are other equally important potential roles for recombinant DNA technology, some of which are explored elsewhere in this volume. The technology has potential uses in the determination of the genetic background of animals in order to identify inheritable defects in the genome of various breeds of animal and conversely in identifying animals with useful characteristics such as natural resistance to certain diseases. Finally the potential for the use of this technology to improve domestic animals by increasing yield or resistance to disease combined with the improvement of diagnostic procedures would appear to indicate a busy future for the field of veterinary biotechnology, which undoubtedly could be applied to the problems of the developing countries.

The purpose of this section of the paper is to attempt to give a very brief introduction to the concepts and techniques of recombinant DNA technology, which will act as an introduction to the following papers. The field may be considered by those unfamiliar with it to be very complicated. However, although some of the manipulations carried out, as outlined in the detailed manuals such as Maniatis, Fritsch and Sambrook (1982), Berger and Kimmel (1987) and Davies, Dibner and Battey (1986) are indeed complex, the general principals are relatively easily grasped.

Background

There have been several reviews produced in recent years which include brief summaries of the basis of recombinant DNA technology and gene manipulation as applied to diagnosis both of human and veterinary problems (Barker, 1989; Goldspink and Gerlach, 1990). These have covered the subject in greater detail than can be gone into here, particularly with reference to the overall structure and operation of DNA molecules in the cell.

As a general rule the more complex the organism, the more DNA required to produce it. Thus in vertebrate animals, including humans, the genetic information is present in upwards of 10^9 nucleotides or base pairs, decreasing by roughly a factor of 10 for each of helminths, protozoa, bacteria and viruses respectively. So that viruses have only 10^5 base pairs or even less in many cases (Simpson, Walker and Terry, 1988). There are four different nucleic acid bases which together form DNA (adenosine, thymidine, cytidine and guanosine). They join up in pairs, (adenosine with thymidine and cytosine with guanosine) by hydrogen bonding eventually forming a double helix. Thus within cells the genomic DNA consists of very long complexly twisted molecules.

The linear arrangement of the nucleotide in the DNA effectively dictates the arrangement of the amino acids in the proteins that are synthesized. Much of the DNA is not, however, translated into protein, but is involved in the regulation of gene expression and also some genes present in the genome which are not expressed are presumed to be redundant and simply left overs from evolution.

Each gene has promoters at each end which drives transcription from the 5' end of the DNA, thus forming RNA. In addition to the untranslated DNA at either end of the gene there are also sections of DNA within the gene that are not translated into protein. These sections are called interons. The process of transcription therefore results in the preparation of primary nuclear RNA from the genomic DNA. Further modifications occur to convert this RNA into messenger RNA or mRNA. The mRNA attaches to ribosomes as part of a process which eventually results in the production of protein. The mRNA can, however, act as a template which through the action of the enzyme, reverse transcriptase, can result in the formation of a complementary DNA or cDNA strand, which is free of interons. This cDNA can then act as a gene for cloning protein or can also be used as a probe for the identification of DNA fragments.

The discovery of restriction endonucleases, bacterial enzymes which digest DNA at very specific sites allowed the controlled manipulation of DNA. Each restriction enzyme recognizes a very precise nucleotide sequence. Bacteria may well have developed these enzymes as a kind of defence against their bacterial viruses, allowing the bacteria to digest sections of foreign virus DNA, thus destroying the virus DNA, while leaving their own bacterial DNA intact and functioning. Some restriction enzymes do not cut the DNA directly across but at points slightly offset from one another, thus leaving little single stranded tails sticking out at the end of the cut DNA sections. Since the restriction enzymes are so specific to particular DNA sequences, DNA from another source, if cut with the same enzyme will have similar and thus compatible tails sticking out from the ends of the cut pieces of DNA. If cut DNA pieces from different sources containing such compatible tails are mixed they can thus be joined up together using a ligase enzyme.

Vectors

Sections of DNA, whether prepared by restriction enzyme digestion of genomic DNA or pieces of cDNA have no capacity to propagate themelves. In order to do this they must be incorporated into an appropriate vector i.e. a piece of DNA which can, under the right conditions, replicate. Plasmids of bacteria such as *Escherichia coli* are small extra chromosomal pieces of DNA which propagate independently of the bacterial chromosomes. Pieces of foreign DNA can be inserted into plasmids and can hence be propagated along with the plasmid in the growing host bacteria. Plasmids are most suitable for propagation of pieces of DNA less than 10 k bases in length. Bacterial viruses such as lambda bacteriophage can also be used as vectors, the DNA pieces being inserted into the phage DNA. Phage vectors can be used for larger pieces of DNA than plasmids and can be used to clone DNA fragments of restriction enzyme cut genomic DNA fragments. The successful insertion of the DNA pieces into the phage vector DNA again allows the DNA to replicate along with the normal phage replication process in bacteria. This is the basis of 'gene cloning'. However, the problem remains of identifying which recombinant phage particles contain gene sequences of interest. It might be necessary to screen thousands of recombinant phage to find the ones containing the useful inserts.

Detection of useful DNA inserts

This can be done in basically two ways depending on whether or not the gene inserted into the phage is expressed or not. Host bacteria are infected with the recombinant phage at low density and then plated out onto an agar plate so that the phage particles will grow and form clear areas or plaques where the bacteria have lysed. Nitro-cellulose or other suitable types of membranes are overlaid onto the plate with the plaques. The filter picks up either the phage DNA or the expressed protein if an expression system is being used. After the DNA or protein is immobilized onto the membrane, it can be screened.

If the search is for particular DNA sequences this is usually conducted through DNA hybridization. Hybridization is a process in which conditions are created where single stranded DNA sequences can find and pair up with a complementary strand of DNA, which has previously been labelled in such a way that will allow its detection. This is typically done by radio-labelling the DNA using ^{32}P (Rigby, Dieckmann, Rhodes and Berg, 1977). Where there are complementary strands the DNA will hybridize with the radio-labelled DNA which can be detected by autoradiography (Southern, 1975).

Thus if the search is for a particular species-specific DNA sequence, replicate plaque lifts can be screened using labelled genomic DNA from the species or subspecies that are to be distinguished. Alternatively cDNA can be used or artificially created oligonucleotides. If the gene is expressed and protein is produced then this can be probed for by antibody in a procedure very similar to an antibody detection ELISA. In this case the substrate enzyme reaction results in an insoluble precipitate which forms usually as a purplish ring shape on the nitrocellulose. The position of the positive plaques on the nitro-cellulose paper can then be located visually and matched to a particular plaque on the agar plate. This plaque is removed from the plate and the phage recloned until pure. The DNA insert can be removed from the purified phage DNA and subjected to further characterization. Thus the above procedures result in a defined section of DNA and it may or may not be possible to use this DNA sequence to manufacture a particular protein defined by that particular DNA sequence.

Diagnostic assays based on cloned proteins

One use of cloned proteins prepared as described above is as antigens in immuno-assays designed to detect an antibody response to the parasite or infectious organism. Of course, a positive result in such an assay does not necessarily indicate current infection but rather indicates exposure to infection which may or may not be current. An alternative is to use the cloned antigens in competition assays to search for circulating antigen (Tijssen, 1987).

The critical point in developing assays of this nature is in the selection of the most suitable cloned protein or proteins to act as antigen in the assay. This is where the detailed analytical studies outlined in the first section make their input. Detailed sequential immunochemical analysis should be designed to reveal which protein molecules may be suitable for use as antigens in these assays. A complicating factor is that the protein antigens presented to the host by the parasite may alter as the parasite develops. Given the complexity of the host antibody response to a parasite and changes that may occur in that response throughout the course of an infection, it is perhaps unlikely that one single cloned antigen would be of use at all times. Probably in practice, a cocktail of various cloned proteins would give better results. Such a cocktail would nonetheless be composed of a limited number of highly defined proteins and would be fundamentally different from the ill-defined 'whole parasite somatic extracts' still used for some parasite diagnostic work.

One particularly useful analytical technique is the study of the antigenic composition of the biosynthetically radio-labelled components of the parasite following *in vitro* culture of the parasite at various stages in its development. If radio-labelled amino acid precursors are used in the culture, the methods allows the identification of those parasite proteins actually synthesized by the parasite at that point in time. Immune coprecipitation studies can then be used to identify the antigenic components and, if the serum is taken sequentially from infected animals, the time course of the antibody response of the host to any particular antigen produced by the parasite at any particular point in the parasites life cycle in that host can be monitored (Parkhouse and Clark 1983; Joshua, Harrison and Sewell, 1988, 1989, 1990).

Once suitable protein antigen molecules have been identified the question remains as to how to obtain antiserum to these antigens so that it can be used to screen the cDNA or genomic libraries. Several options present themselves:

- Polyclonal sera can be selected from naturally infected animals.
- The antigen can be semi-purified by conventional chromatographic techniques and used to prepare polyclonal sera in another or the same host species.
- Monoclonal antibodies can be prepared against the antigen and if they are suitable they can be used directly to screen the library.
- The monoclonal antibody can be attached to an immunoadsorbent matrix and then used to purify the complementary antigen by immunoadsorption.

This purified antigen can then be used to prepare a polyclonal serum against the chosen antigen, either in the same or in a different host. The exact choice of antiserum will depend on each particular system. However, this has illustrated another possible role for monoclonal antibody reagents. The various possible roles for monoclonal antibodies in diagnostic assays were outlined in reviews by Harlow and Lane (1988).

Diagnostic procedures based on DNA probes

The basis of diagnostic procedures involving DNA probes was outlined previously, it is hybridization of a known labelled DNA sequence to an unknown test sample. Most of the variations in the technique depend on how the sample and the DNA were treated prior to the hybridization taking place. The test sample can be prepared either whole or sectioned and the DNA examined directly from the organism using chosen labelled species or subspecies specific or cross reactive DNA probes i.e. *in situ* hybridization. Alternatively the DNA can be purified from the test sample and probed either as whole DNA fixed onto nitrocellulose membrane or first digested by either one or a combination of restriction enzymes, thus breaking it into variously sized small fragments which can be separated by electrophoresis on agarose or polyacrylamide gel, transferred to nitrocellulose and then probed by labelled DNA to pick out possible restriction enzyme polymorphisms. This procedure allows closely related strains to be identified.

If only tiny amounts of DNA can potentially be found, such as a single parasite egg, or where a parasite is present in a host at low concentration, the polymerase chain reaction (PCR) combined with the use of species or strain specific DNA probes and artificially manufactured oligonucleotide primers presently affords a possible means of identification. The potential uses of PCR in veterinary research and diagnosis was reviewed recently (Deacon and Lah, 1989).

The use of DNA probes for taxonomic studies such as the identification of subspecies and variations in species with geographical location is of genuine interest. However, from the veterinary view point interesting taxonomic minutiae are probably of less importance than making distinctions that are of specific zoonotic use or of use in specific veterinary or veterinary epidemiological situations i.e. tracing the sources of epidemics etc. Such situations would also include the differentiation of strains of a parasite having different infectivity for domestic animals and/or man and where the pathology resulting from infection may also vary from strain to strain, making it important to make such distinctions. In addition situations may be identified in which existing methodologies are inadequate or simply nonexistent and DNA technology either offers the only suitable alternative or a convenient short cut to the identification of parasites in vectors through the use of DNA probes developed against more easily obtained stages of a parasite (Harnett, Chambers, Renz and Parkhouse, 1989).

The zoonotic cestodes afford some good examples of the appropriate use of DNA technology. *Echinococcus granulosus* and *E. multilocularis* are responsible for the vast majority of human cases of hydatid disease. The adult tapeworms are found in dogs and cats who spread the hydatid disease, caused by the larval tapeworms to humans, via the eggs. The more usual intermediate hosts for *E. granulosus* are domestic ruminants while *E. multilocularis* usually develops in rodents. *E. granulosus* exists in biologically distinct strains which vary in their infectivity both to man and to domestic ruminants. It is important to identify which strain of a parasite is present in stock from certain areas so that the risk to man can be minimized. This would be of particular importance if stock was to be moved from one area to another. The strains of *E. granulosus* can be differentiated by other technologies such as enzyme electrophoresis (Le Riche and Sewell, 1978a,b). However, DNA technology offers clear advantages in the stability of the DNA versus the labile protein enzymes and the ease with which DNA preserved in ethyl alcohol can be transported. DNA technology has thus been used to carry out such differentiation (McMannus and Simpson, 1985; Rishi and McMannus 1987a, McMannus, 1990). In the latter cases the technology used involved digesting the extracted parasite genomic DNA digesting it with restriction enzymes, separating the fragments by electrophoresis and transferring them onto nitrocellulose so that the fragments could be probed by a labelled probe. Quite a complex procedure, however, differences were detected.

Similarly it is of clinical and epidemiological importance to be able to distinguish between the two common large intestinal tapeworms of man, *T. saginata* and *T. solium,* particularly because the latter in addition to infecting man as an adult intestinal tapeworm can also cause human *T. solium* cysticercosis, a sometimes fatal infection. Areas where accurate differentiation of the two parasites would be of advantage include the speciation of morphologically identical taeniid eggs from pasture for epidemiological studies and the identification of the cysticerci or cyst residues in bovine or porcine carcasses after slaughter or from human biopsy samples. It is particularly important to treat human cases of *T. solium* tapeworm infection because of the risk of spreading cysticercosis to other humans and to the tapeworm host itself.

As with *E. granulosus* strains, *T. solium* and *T. saginata* can be differentiated biochemically (Le Riche and Sewell, 1978a,b). However, current approaches are centred round the use of DNA probes. Consequently *T. saginata* specific and *T. saginata*/*T. solium* cross reactive probes were developed (Harrison, Delgado and Parkhouse, 1988, 1990) and also a *T. solium* specific probe (Rishi and McMannus, 1987b, 1988). The development of these three probes allows the unequivocal identification of these two parasite species. Whole genomic DNA can thus be extracted from the parasite, it can be fixed onto nitro-cellulose and probed with the labelled DNA probe. Identification can thus be effected relatively simply and quickly.

CONCLUSIONS

A thorough study of parasitic helminth antigens is a prerequisite for development of monoclonal antibody reagents for diagnosis. Studies should be directed at the identification of stage or age specific surface and secreted antigens which are the most likely to contain species-specific antigen epitopes and thus form a logical focus for the design of diagnostic assays. The complexity of these parasite systems and the host response to the parasite should not be underestimated. However, modern analytical techniques allow their detailed analysis in terms of the host's humoral antibody responses and afford the possibility of the future development of control and disease management procedures tailored to each individual host/parasite system. Many parasitic helminth antigens are defined both in terms of molecular weight and in their chemical nature. Serological responses to these are beginning to be dissected in terms of antigenic epitopes and the profile of Ig classes elicited. Monoclonal antibodies can also play a role in such analysis in addition to their diagnostic role. Properly designed monoclonal antibody based diagnostic assays should have the specificity, sensitivity and robustness necessary for general field use in the tropical environment and it should be possible to develop them for use in laboratories or in the field where there is limited technical facilities.

Parasites are now being analyzed in terms of their DNA composition, an approach which could lead to the development of cloned proteins of diagnostic potential in addition to species or strain specific DNA probes. The comparative robustness of DNA diagnosis and the potential sensitivity of modern diagnostic procedures including ELISA are a major advantage. Finally, detailed epidemiological data are required in order to assess the suitability of any particular diagnostic procedure as part of a general control programme or in the development of novel control, and/or disease management procedures.

REFERENCES

Almond, N.M. and Parkhouse, R.M.E. (1985). Nematode antigens. *Current Topics in Microbiology and Immunology,* **120**, 173–120.

Almond, N.M. and Parkhouse, R.M.E. (1986a). Immunoglobulin class specific responses to biochemically-defined antigens of *Trichinella spiralis. Parasite Immunology,* **8**, 391–406.

Almond, N.M. and Parkhouse, R.M.E. (1986b). The IgG class distribution of anti-phosphoryl choline responses in mice infected with parasitic nematodes. *Immunology,* **59**, 633–635,

Almond, N.M. and Parkhouse, R.M.E. (1989). The importance of antibody class in helminth infections. In *Progress in Vaccinology* (ed. G.P. Talwer), pp. 261–276. Springer-Verlag, Berlin.

Almond, N.M., Worms, M.J., Harnett, W. and Parkhouse, R.M.E. (1987). Variations in specific humoral immune responses of different mouse strains to microfilariae of *Dipetalonema viteae. Parasitology,* **95**, 559–568.

Anderson, R.M., Facer, C.A. and Rollinson, D. (1989). Research Developments in the study of parasitic infections. *Parasitology,* **99**, S1–S151.

Barker, D.C. (1989). Molecular approaches to DNA diagnosis. *Parasitology,* **99**, S125–S146.

Berger, S.L. and Kimmel, A.R. (1987). Guide to molecular cloning. *Methods in Enzymology,* Volume 152. Academic Press, London.

Burnet, F.M. (1959). *The Clonal Selection Theory of Acquired Immunity.* Cambridge University Press.

Caberra, Z., Parkhouse, R.M.E., Forsyth, K., Gomez-Priego, A., Pabon, R, and Yarzabal, L. (1989). Specific detection of human antibodies to *Onchocerca volvulus. Tropenmedizin und Parasitologie* (in press).

Campbell, A.M. (1984). Monoclonal antibody technology. *Laboratory Techniques in Biochemistry and Molecular Biology* (eds. R.H. Burdon and P.H. van Knippenberg). Elsevier, Amsterdam.

Capron, M. and Capron, A. (1986). Rats, mice and men – models for immune effector mechanisms against schistosomiasis. *Parasitology Today,* **2**, 69–75.

CIBA Foundation Symposium (1987). *Filariasis.* Vol. 127. John Wiley and Sons, London.

Correa, D., Sandoval, M.A., Harrison, L.J.S., Parkhouse, R.M.E., Plancarte, A., Meza-Lucas, A. and Flisser, A. (1989). Human neurocystercercosis: comparison of monoclonal and polyclonal EIA capture assays for the detection of parasite products in cerebrospinal fluid. *Transactions of the Royal Society of Tropical Medicine and Hygiene,* **83**, 814–816.

Davies, L.G., Dibner, M.D. and Battey, J.F. (1986). *Basic Methods in Molecular Biology.* Elsevier, London.

Deacon, N.J. and Lah, M. (1989). The potential of the polymerase chain reaction in verterinary research and diagnosis. *Australian Veterinary Journal,* **66**, 442–444

Dell, R., Klinkert, M.Q., Beck, E., Shi, Y., Idris, M.A. and Ruppel, A. (1988). Immunodiagnosis of schistosomiasis with defined antigens (Abstract). In *XIIth International Congress for Tropical Medicine and Malaria* (eds. P.A. Kager and A.M. Polderman) *Excerpta Medica International Congress Series* **810**, 58.

Forsyth, K.P., Spark, R., Kazura, J., Brown, G.V., Peters, P., Heywood, P., Dissanayake, S. and Mitchell, G.F. (1985). A monoclonal antibody-based immunoradiometric assay for detection of circulating antigen in bancroftian filariasis. *Journal of Immunology,* **134**, 1172–1177.

Gibbons, J.C., Harrison, L.J.S. and Parkhouse, R.M.E. (1986). Immunoglobulin class responses to *Taenia taeniaeformis* in susceptible and resistant mice. *Parasite Immunology,* **8**, 491–502.

Goldspink, G. and Gerlach, G.F. (1990). Prospective use of recombinant DNA methods in animal disease control. *Proceedings of the Society for Veterinary Epidemiology and Preventative Medicine.* Belfast 1990. Genetics and the application of new technologies, pp. 1–14.

Harlow, E. and Lane, D. (1988). *Antibodies – A Laboratory Manual.* Cold Spring Harbour Laboratory.

Harnett, W., Chambers, A.E., Renz, A. and Parkhouse, R.M.E. (1989). An oligonucleotide probe specific for *Onchocerca volvulus. Molecular and Biochemical Parasitology,* **35**, 119–126.

Harrison, L.J.S., Delgado, J. and Parkhouse, R.M.E. (1988). Differentiation of *Taenia saginata* and *Taenia solium* by use of cloned DNA fragments. *Transactions of Tropical Medicine and Hygiene,* **82**, 939.

Harrison, L.J.S., Delgado, J. and Parkhouse, R.M.E. (1990). Differential diagnosis of *Taenia saginata* and *Taenia solium* with DNA probes. *Parasitology,* **100**, 459-461.

Harrison, L.J.S., Joshua, G.W.P,, Wright, S.H. and Parkhouse, R.M.E. (1989). Specific detection of circulating surface/secreted glycoproteins of viable cysticerci in *Taenia saginata* cysticercosis. *Parasite Immunology,* **11**, 351-370.

Harrison, L.J.S. and Parkhouse, R.M.E. (1985). Antigens of taeniid cestodes in protection, diagnosis and escape. *Current Topics in Microbiology and Immunology,* **120**, 159-172.

Hughes, D.L. (1985). Trematodes, excluding schistosomes with special emphasis on *Fasciola. Current Topics in Microbiology and Immunology,* **120**, 241-260.

Hussain, R., Groge, M. and Ottesen, E. (1987). IgG antibody subclasses in human filariasis. Differential subclass recognition of parasite antigens correlates with different clinical manifestations of infection. *Journal of Immunology,* **139**, 2794-2798.

Jassim, A., Hassam, K. and Catty, D. (1987). Antibody isotypes in human *Schistosomiasis mansoni. Parasite Immunology,* **9**, 627-650.

De Jonge, N. and Deelder, A.M. (1988). Immunodiagnosis of schistosomiasis by ELISA for the detection of circulating anodic antigen using monoclonal antibodies (Abstract). In *XIIth International Congress for Tropical Medicine and Malaria* (eds. P.A. Kager and A.M. Polderman). *Excerpta Medica International Congress Series,* **810**, 93.

Joshua, G.W.P., Harrison, L.J.S. and Sewell, M.M.H. (1988). Excreted/secreted products of developing *Taenia saginata* metacestodes. *Parasitology,* **97**, 477-487.

Joshua, G.W.P., Harrison, L.J.S. and Sewell, M.M.H. (1989). Developmental changes in proteins and glycoproteins revealed by direct radio-iodination of viable *Taenia saginata* larvae. *Parasitology,* **99**, 265-274.

Joshua, G.W.P., Harrison, L.J.S. and Sewell, M.M.H. (1990). Protein antigens in cyst fluid of *Taenia saginata* cysticerci. *Parasitology,* **100**, 463-467.

Kemeny, D.M. and Challacombe, S.J. (1988). *ELISA and Other Solid Phase Immunoassays: Theoretical and Practical Aspects.* Wiley Chichester.

Lightowlers, M.W. (1990). Cestode infections in animals: immunological diagnosis and vaccination. *Reviews Scientifique et Technical Office International des Epizooties,* **9**, 463-477.

Lightowlers, M.W. and Rickard, M.D. (1988). Excretory-secretory products of helminth parasites: effects on host immune responses. *Parasitology,* **96**, S123-S166.

Lucius, R., Erondu, N., Kern, A., Donelson, J.D. and Diesfeld, H.J. (1988). An *Onchocerca*-specific cloned polypeptide for immunodiagnosis of onchocerciasis (abstract). In *XIIth International Congress for Tropical*

Medicine and Malaria (eds. P.A. Kager and A.M. Polderman). *Excerpta Medica International Congress Series*, **810**, 63.

MacInnis, A.J. (1987). Molecular paradigms for eradicating helminthic parasites. *UCLA Symposia on Molecular and Cellular Biology. New Series 60.* Alan R. Liss, New York.

McMannus, D.P. (1990). Characterisation of taeniid cestodes by DNA analysis. *Reviews Scientifique et Technical de l'Office International des Epizooties,* **9**, 489–507.

McMannus, D.P. and Simpson, A.J.G. (1985). Identification of the *Echinococcus* (hydatid disease) organisms using cloned DNA markers. *Molecular and Biochemical Parasitology,* **17**, 171–178.

Mahmoud, A.A.F. (1987). *Schistosomiasis.* Baillière's Clinical and Tropical Medicine and Communicable Diseases 2, No. 2.

Maizels, R.M., Burke, J. and Denham, D.A. (1987). Phosphorylcholine bearing antigens in filarial nematode parasites: analysis of somatic extracts, *in vitro* secretions and infection sera from *Brugia malayi* and *B. pahangi. Parasite Immunology,* **9**, 49–66.

Maizels, R.M. and Kennedy, M.W., Meghji, M., Robertson, B.D. and Smith, H.V. (1987). Shared carbohydrate epitopes on distinct surface and secreted antigens of the parasitic nematode *Toxocara canis. Journal of Immunology,* **139**, 207–214.

Maizels, R.M., Selkirk, M.E. (1988). Antigens of filarial parasites. *ISI Atlas of Science,* 1–5.

Maniatis, T., Fritsch, E.F. and Sambrook, J. (1982). *Molecular Cloning.* Cold Spring Harbour Publications, New York.

OIE (1990). Immunity to and diagnosis of internal parasitism. *Revue Scientifique et Technique, Office International des Epizooties*, **9** (2), June.

Parkhouse, R.M.E. and Clark, N.W.T. (1983). Stage specific secreted and somatic antigens of *Trichinella spiralis. Molecular and Biochemical Parasitology,* **9**, 319–327.

Parkhouse, R.M.E. and Harrison, L.J.S. (1989). Antigens of parasitic helminths in diagnosis, protection and pathology. *Parasitology,* **99**, S5–S19.

Pawlowski, Z.S. (1986). Intestinal helminthiasis and human health: recent advances and future needs. Parasitology – *Quo Vadit*? *Proceedings of the Sixth International Congress of Parasitology* (ed. M.J. Howell), pp. 159–167. Australian Academy of Science.

Le Riche, P.D. and Sewell, M.M.H. (1978). Differentiation of *Taenia saginata* and *Taenia solium* by enzyme electrophoresis. *Transactions of the Royal Society of Tropical Medicine and Hygiene,* **71**, 237–238.

Le Riche, P.D. and Sewell, M.M.H. (1978). Differentiation of taeniid cestodes by enzyme electrophoresis. *International Journal for Parasitology,* **7**, 476–483.

Rigby, P.W.J., Dieckmann, M., Rhodes, C. and Berg, P. (1977). Labelling deoxyribonucleic acid to high specific activity *in vitro* by nick translation with DNA polymerase I. *Journal of Molecular Biology,* **113**, 237–251.

Rishi, A.K. and McMannus, D.P. (1987a). Genomic cloning of human *Echinococcus granulosus* DNA: isolation of recombinant plasmids and their use as genetic markers in strain characterisation. *Parasitology*, **94**, 369–383.

Rishi, A.K. and McMannus, D.P. (1987b). DNA probes which uambiguously distinguish *Taenia solium* from *Taenia saginata*. *The Lancet*, 1275–1276.

Rishi, A.K. and McMannus, D.P. (1988). Molecular cloning of *T. solium* genomic DNA and characterization of taeniid cestodes by DNA analysis. *Parasitology*, **97**, 161–176.

Rodriguez del Rosal, E., Correa, D. and Flisser, A., (1989). Swine cysticercosis: detection of parasite products in serum. *Veterinary Record*, **124**, 488.

Rollinson, D. and Simpson, A.J.G. (1987). *The Biology of Schistosomes. From Gene to Latrine.* Academic Press, London.

Simpson, A.J.G. and Smithers, S.R. (1985). Schistosomes: surface, egg and circulating antigens. *Current Topics in Microbiology and Immunology*, **120**, 205–239.

Simpson, A.J.G., Walker, T. and Terry, R. (1986). An introduction to DNA technology. *Parasitology*, **91**, S7–S14.

Smith, D.B., Da Verm, K.M. Board, P.G., Tiu, W., Garcia, E.G. and Mitchell, G.F. (1986). Mr 26 000 antigen of *Schistosoma japonicum* recognized by resistant WEHI 129/J mice is a parasite glutathione-S-transferase. *Proceedings of the National Academy of Sciences, USA*, **83**, 8703–8707.

Southern, E. (1975). Detection of specific sequences among DNA fragments separated by gel electrophoresis. *Journal of Molecular Biology*, **98**, 503–517.

Tijssen, P. (1987). Practice and theory of enzyme immunoassays. *Laboratory Techniques in Biochemistry and Molecular Biology* (eds. R.H. Burdon and P.H. van Knippenberg). Elsevier.

Walls, K.W. and Schantz, P.M. (1986). Helminthic diseases. In *Immunodiagnosis of Parasitic Diseases*, vol. 1. Harcourt Brace Javonovich, Academic Press, London and New York.

Weiss, N., Hussain, R. and Ottesen, E.A. (1982). IgE antibodies are more specific than IgG antibodies in human onchocerciasis and lymphatic filariasis. *Immunology*, **45**, 129–137.

Weiss, N., Van den Ende, M.C., Albiez, E.J., Barbiero, V.K., Forsyth, D.P. and Prince, A.M. (1985). Detection of serum antibodies and circulating antigens in a chimpanzee experimentally infected with *Onchocerca volvulus*. *Transactions of the Royal Society of Tropical Medicine and Hygiene*, **80**, 587–591.

4.3

Biotechnologies Applied to the Diagnosis of Disease, with Special Reference to Trypanosomiasis and Theileriosis of Livestock

A.J. TEALE
International Laboratory for Research on Animal Diseases, Nairobi, Kenya

INTRODUCTION

For the purposes of this paper, 'diagnosis' is considered as parasite detection and characterization in artificial (laboratory) and natural (field) infections. It is intended that it should encompass infections of arthropod vector species as well as mammalian hosts. The biotechnologies which will be considered are those involving DNA/RNA manipulations and the development and application of monoclonal antibodies (MAb).

Diagnosis is an essential prerequisite of any planned disease control programme, whether based on individual or herd treatment, prevention (through herd management strategies, vaccination, movement control, etc.), or disease eradication. Ideally, a diagnostic procedure should maximize the information on the parasite involved, be easy to apply, rapid enough for mass screening, robust enough for field use and not prohibitively expensive in those situations where it will be most needed. It is a challenge to those involved in developing newer biotechnologies for livestock disease control to meet these requirements. There is little doubt, however, that such requirements can be met given the continuing pace of technological advance, particularly in the recombinant DNA technologies. In the area of MAb development and application, these requirements are already close to being met.

In this paper, I will review the development and application of MAb and recombinant DNA approaches specifically in the context of diagnosis of theileriosis and trypanosomiasis of livestock. The purpose is to provide an indication of progress to date and of what may still be to come.

DIAGNOSIS OF THEILERIOSIS AND TRYPANOSOMIASIS

Established methods of diagnosis rely on direct observation of parasites, detection of serological responses, inoculation of potentially infective material into naive reporter animals, and in some cases on rather tedious immunological methods for antigen detection. None of these methodologies is ideal. Direct observation of parasites is not always possible, detection of serological responses does not necessarily indicate a parasitized state and subinoculation into reporter animals is time-consuming, expensive and, in some circumstances, questionable on ethical grounds.

Whatever method is employed, definitive diagnosis of infection inevitably relies initially on detection of parasites. The second stage in diagnosis involves obtaining sufficient information to precisely identify the pathogen, that is, to identify the isolate and its relationship to existing isolates, stocks and strains. With all methods of detection of parasites in potentially-infected samples, success inevitably depends in part on the relative abundance of parasite material. This is a major factor limiting the success of methods based on microscopical visualization of whole organisms, for example.

In the case of theileriosis, parasite detection *per se* is not particularly problematical except where a carrier state is involved. The major diagnostic problem is one of parasite characterization, that is definition of the relationship of a parasite isolate with known stocks and strains. This requirement is especially important in laboratory studies with the objectives of understanding immune responsiveness and improving vaccination strategies. Characterization of breakthrough stocks is also of obvious relevance for assessment of field vaccination programmes.

The major difficulties concern discrimination between isolates and stocks which are immunologically distinct, especially in the case of the *Theileria parva* group of parasites causing the East Coast fever (ECF) disease complex. Even distinguishing between the commonly accepted three subspecies *T.p. parva, T.p. bovis* and *T.p. lawrencei*, is not straightforward with existing methodologies. They are morphologically and serologically indistinguishable and are only differentiated on epidemiological and behavioural grounds. There is therefore a pressing need for a simple, rapid and reliable means of parasite characterization, which will be informative and applicable in the design of control strategies and which therefore, by implication, is informative with regard to immunogenic differences between stocks.

Diagnosis of trypanosomiasis has hitherto relied largely on various light microscope methods to reveal parasites in peripheral blood of mammalian hosts. The clinical signs of trypanosomiasis, that is cachexia, lymphadenopathy, anaemia and infertility, are not restricted to trypanosome infections. As discussed previously, detection of circulating antibodies does not necessarily indicate current infection. With respect to direct observation of parasites, this cannot be expected to invariably reveal parasitosis in an infected animal, especially as levels of parasitaemia fluctuate quite markedly during the course of an infection. Moreover, those methods with the greatest sensitivity are not optimal for precise identification of the parasite species/subspecies. Detection of parasites in vector species is further complicated by the necessity for careful dissection and examination, and although the site of infection in tsetse flies indicates the major group of infecting organism, it is not possible to distinguish the species by this approach.

In the case of trypanosomiasis therefore, the initial problem is one of straightforward detection of parasites when they may be present in very low numbers in any given sample. Once this is achieved, the need to differentiate the species and subspecies arises. Moreover, there is a requirement for a sensitive and reliable means of detecting infection in vector species, particularly in order to assess challenge levels in epidemiological surveys and to monitor the status of control programmes.

DIAGNOSIS BASED ON DNA CHARACTERIZATION

DNA methodologies (and serological approaches, *infra red*) can incorporate amplification steps which will increase the sensitivity of initial detection in materials taken directly from a suspected case animal. With methods applicable to the genome of the parasites, amplification can be achieved in two ways. First, parts of the genome which are present in each individual organism in high copy number can be searched for. Second, target sequences can be enzymatically amplified utilizing the polymerase chain reaction (PCR) (reviewed by White, Arnheim and Erlich, 1989) before attempted detection.

Whatever method is employed, subsequent characterization of the parasite based on its genotype, eventually depend on determination of actual sequences of parasite DNA or RNA and searches for homologies or disparities with existing sequence data. Ultimately, determination of base sequences using conventional sequencing strategies, which at the present stage of technological development are still relatively tedious, provides definitive information. However, sequence comparisons can also be achieved in other more convenient ways. These include:

- Determination of restriction fragment length polymorphism (RFLP). RFLPs can be determined by direct visualization of DNA bands in agarose gels which provides a 'fragment print' of the whole genome. Alternatively, the lengths of only those fragments containing sequences homologous with a DNA probe of known specificity can be visualized after 'Southern blotting' of the electrophoresed DNA onto a membrane and hybridization with a probe appropriately labelled so that it can subsequently be visualized.

- Determination of homology of target DNA and an informative probe on the basis of quantitative hybridization differences under carefully controlled conditions. For this purpose, relatively short (oligonucleotide) probes are most sensitive to small sequence differences. The power of this 'allele-specific oligonucleotide' (ASO) approach may be increased by amplification or enrichment for parasite DNA.

- Assay of ligation of two chosen oligonucleotides following their hybridization to homologous target DNA sequences 'oligonucleotide ligation assay' (Landegren, Kaiser, Sanders and Hood, 1988).
- Application of 'scanning techniques' such as those using RNA digestion in regions of disparity with target DNA, denaturing gradient gel electrophoresis and chemical cleavage of mismatched base pairs.

It may be anticipated however, that automation will make rapid determination of sequence of long stretches of target DNA simple, rapid and reliable in the relatively near future, though the process will remain expensive.

Theileriosis

Whilst it has been shown to be possible to discriminate between stocks of *Theileria* parasites on the basis of band patterns produced by restriction enzyme digestion and subsequent electrophoresis, especially when rare-cutter enzymes are used (Conrad, Iams, Brown, Sohanpal and ole-MoiYoi, 1987a; S.P. Morzaria, personal communication), efforts have so far concentrated on the isolation of clones of parasite DNA and their application as probes. From the point of view of generally applicable diagnostic procedures this is a realistic direction in which to proceed because fragment prints require purified DNA, whereas probing of parasite DNA is applicable to relatively crude sources, especially following amplification of target sequences.

A dominant genetic repeat (DGR) has been cloned independently by two groups working on the molecular biology of *T. parva* parasites. The DGR appears to be present in high copy number (100 copies in the genome of the *T.p. parva* group) and to have an average size of about 1.5 kb. Probes for this region do not hybridize with stocks of *T. annulata, T. mutans* and *T. taurotragi* (Conrad *et al*, 1987a) and so are potentially useful species-specific diagnostic tools. Moreover, on the basis of RFLPs, such probes are capable of discriminating between populations of *T. parva* parasites (Conrad *et al*, 1987a; Allsopp and Allsopp, 1988; Allsopp, Carrington, Baylie, Sohal, Dolan and Iams, 1989). However, and somewhat disappointingly, the probes so far tested have not revealed correlation between genotype and serologically-determined phenotype. Further, the polymorphisms that they reveal do not correlate with immunological and parasitological distinctions between stocks within the problematical *T. parva* group (*T.p. parva, T.p. bovis* and *T.p. lawrencei*). This was also clearly evident in a recent study, in which it was found that there was no correlation between the genotypes revealed by DGR probes and the specificity of immune cytotoxic T cells (CTL) generated *in vitro* (B.M Goddeeris, W.I. Morrison, P.G. Toye and R. Bishop, personal communication). However, Conrad and coworkers (Conrad *et al,* 1987a) reported weaker hybridization with probe IgTpm-23· to DNA of the Marikebuni stock of *T. parva* than with some other *T.p. parva* stocks.

Allsopp and co-workers (Allsopp *et al*, 1989) also reported quantitative hybridization differences, which they suggested may be due to copy number differences in target DNA, when they probed various different stocks. They observed much stronger hybridization signals with target DNA derived from parasite populations which they considered as 'typical ECF-causing' (*T.p. parva* Muguga, Mariakani and Kilifi) than with DNA from other stocks (*T.p. parva* Marikebuni, *T.p. parva* Uganda, *T.p. bovis* Boleni and *T.p. lawrencei* 3081). Such differences are however rather subjective and cannot be considered to represent a significant diagnostic advance.

Allsopp and coworkers (Allsopp *et al*, 1989) carried their study to the level of the sequences of target parasite DNA fragments hybridizing with some of the genomic clones available. They found considerable homology between sequences of different stocks. Differences between 'typical ECF-causing' stocks were found to be as great as those between members of the group and the sequence of a *T.p. lawrencei* stock.

In many ways however, the probes which have so far been reported have been very informative. They are able to discriminate between all of the stocks of *T. parva* parasites examined to date, whether DNA is derived from purified schizont material or from lymphoblastoid cell lines. Importantly, they have revealed differences between isolates of *T.p. parva* Muguga (Allsopp and Allsopp, 1988), between isolates taken from a single carrier buffalo (*Syncerus caffer*) at different times and even between subclones of a single lymphoblastoid cell line isolate taken from a buffalo (Conrad, ole-MoiYoi, Baldwin, Dolan, O'Callaghan, Njamunggeh, Grootenhuis, Stagg, Leitch and Young, 1989). They have therefore revealed very great genetic diversity within the *T. parva* group of parasites and the probable high frequency of multiple infections. Consequently, they have highlighted the need for researchers to obtain cloned parasites, especially for studies of immune response in theileriosis. Certainly, existing probes and others which will follow will constitute valuable tools for genetic dissection of *Theileria* parasites, and for studies of their life cycle, irrespective of their diagnostic applications.

In addition, and of potential practical use, is the finding that the DGR probes can detect parasite DNA derived from a single infected acinus in blots of squash preparations of tick salivary glands (P.A. Conrad and R. Bishop, personal communication).

A significant development has been the use of PCR technology together with oligonucleotide probes in order to discriminate between stocks of *T.p. parva* (Allsopp *et al*, 1989). This technology is potentially very powerful. Sequence data for the DGR revealed relatively monomorphic regions of potential primer sequences, although primers are not yet available for all stocks. Parasites derived from buffaloes are the most problematical in this regard, a situation which may be alleviated by the discovery of a *T.p. lawrencei* DGR. Probes based on the sequences of the variable regions of the *T.p. parva* DGR have been shown to give differential hybridization with PCR-amplified DNA of a number of different stocks, including at least some de-

TABLE 1 *Hybridization of oligonucleotide probes with PCR-amplified* Theileria parva *DNA's.*

	PROBE			
DNA	**Muguga**	**Tp3081**	**Pugu1**	**994/KB2**
T.p. parva				
Muguga	+	–	–	–
Pugu1	f	–	+	–
Kiambu4	+	–	f	–
Mbita6	–	+	+	–
Kilae1	+	–	f	–
Uganda/G6	f	–	–	–
Marikebuni/D211	–	–	–	–
Mariakani/G6	+	–	+	–
T.p. lawrencei				
3081/G6	–	+	+	–
803/KB2	f	–	–	–
994/KB2	–	–	–	+
994/6147	–	–	–	–
6252/KB2	f	–	–	–
3081/D788	f	–	f	f
* 3081/F132	–	–	f	f
3081/E231	–	–	–	–
T.p. bovis				
Boleni/D773	–	–	–	–
Boleni/D769	–	–	–	–
* Boleni/1/1	–	–	–	–

* – cloned parasites
f – faint hybridization

This table was compiled with data provided by Dr. B.A. Allsopp of the Department of Biochemistry, University of Cambridge and Dr. R. Bishop of the International Laboratory for Research on Animal Diseases, Nairobi.

rived from buffaloes. However, once again, differences do not correlate with immunological distinctions. Nevertheless, it is conceivable that it will ultimately be possible to design ASOs and primers specific for those genes encoding molecules of importance in eliciting protective immunity in livestock. For the purposes of developing disease control strategies, these will be invaluable, and given that the technology already exists for their application, they will be immediately applicable. The specificity of four characterization probes applied to PCR-amplified material is shown in Table 1.

Trypanosomiasis

Quite a large proportion of the genome of trypanosomes comprises repetitive sequences which can be present in copy numbers of several thousands. In the case of *T. brucei* for example, it has been estimated that repetitive elements account for approximately 12% of total nuclear DNA (Sloof, Bos, Konings, Menke, Borst, Gutteridge and Leon, 1983). This phenomenon was exploited from the outset in the search for DNA diagnostic tools applicable to trypanosomiasis which would be capable of reliable species differentiation (reviewed by ole-MoiYoi, 1987). It is now apparent that the sequences are very different in the different species and even between apparent subspecies, which is probably a reflection of the rather loose evolutionary constraints on DNA of this type. The high copy number in target DNA and polymorphism in the repetitive elements themselves, provide sensitivity and specificity, respectively, and thus make DNA characterization of trypanosomes a realistic approach to diagnosis.

Probes are of two basic types. The first, represented by pgDR1 (Ingi) (Kukla, Majiwa, Young, Moloo and ole-MoiYoi, 1987; Kimmel, ole-MoiYoi and Young, 1987) detects a dispersed repetitive element in the genome of the *Trypanozoon* subgenus. The cloned DR1 sequence is 1,600 base pairs (bp) long and the complete repeat in which the cloned sequence occurs is now known to be 5,280 bp long. There are of the order of 200 copies of this repeat in the genomes of *T. brucei brucei, T.b. gambiense, T.b. rhodesiense,* and *T. evansi*. This, together with radioactive labelling of the probe to high specific activities makes it possible to detect as few as 100 parasites in a sample of blood of mammalian hosts and to detect infection in single tsetse flies.

The second type of probe is represented by a 177 bp sequence which is present in very high copy number in the *T. brucei* genome (Borst, Fase-Fowler, Frasch, Hoeijmakers and Weijers, 1980; Sloof *et al*, 1983). The repetitive elements in this case are arranged in tandem arrays typical of so-called ‘satellite DNA’.

Probes are now available which are specific for all of the important species of trypanosomes. It is also possible to differentiate populations of *T. congolense* which are known to differ with respect to chromosome profiles revealed by orthogonal field alternation electrophoresis (Majiwa, Masake, Nantulya, Hamers and Matthyssens, 1985) and on the basis of isoenzyme characterization (Gibson, Dukes and Gashumba, 1988). Importantly, probes also exist which enable *T. simiae* to be distinguished from *T. congolense* parasites (Majiwa and Webster, 1987; Gibson *et al*, 1988). A list of published probes is given in Table 2.

With respect to application of the probes, as already intimated, they may be used to detect parasites in the blood of mammalian hosts and in tissue preparations from arthropod vectors. Specificity is revealed at the level of hybridization rather than in the diversity of the genomic environment of hybridizing target sequences. This simplifies application because it avoids complex DNA preparative procedures, enzyme digestion, electrophoresis

TABLE 2 *Potential diagnostic probes for trypanosome DNA.*

Probe	Repeat unit (bp)	Type	Copy number	Species specificity	References
pgDR1	5280	DR	200	*T. brucei* group	Kukla *et al*, 1987 Kimmel *et al*, 1987
177	177	TR	NK	*T. brucei* group	Borst *et al*, 1980 Sloof *et al*, 1983
pgNRE-372	372	TR	3000	*T. congolense*	Majiwa *et al*, 1985, 1987
pgNIK-450	450	TR	4000	*T. congolense*	"
	369	TR	NK	*T. congolense*	Gibson *et al*, 1988
	350	TR	NK	*T. congolense*	"
	400	TR	NK	*T. congolense*	"
pgNS-600	550	TR	1000	*T. simiae*	Majiwa *et al*, 1987
	200	TR	NK	*T. simiae*	Gibson *et al*, 1988
lgDIL-10	NK	NK	NK	*T. vivax*	Kukla *et al*, 1987
	177	TR	NK	*T. vivax*	Dickin and Gibson, 1989

TR – tandem repeat DR – dispersed repeat NK – not known

and Southern blotting. DNA can be prepared relatively crudely and quite rapidly from blood samples before 'spotting' onto a suitable membrane prior to probing. In the case of the vector, it has been found that it is sufficient to spot the abdominal contents of a single fly in order to detect *T. brucei* or *T. congolense* infection (Kukla *et al*, 1987). Preparations of proboscides may also be examined in this way (Kukla *et al*, 1987; Gibson *et al*, 1988).

Before such probes as those described may be considered for widespread field use, it will be necessary to avoid the requirement for radioactive labelling. There are a number of possibilities in this regard, such as the use of biotin-avidin-enzyme complexes which depend on biotinylated nucleotide incorporation into probe DNA. Identification of means of chemical derivitization of probe DNA which would maintain probe sensitivity while minimizing false positives, is in progress.

DIAGNOSIS WITH MONOCLONAL ANTIBODIES

Theileriosis

MAb have found wide application in the diagnosis of numerous infectious diseases because of the improvements they have made possible in the sensitivity and specificity of antigen detection systems. The case of theileriosis is no exception. MAb are used frequently in indirect fluorescence antibody tests (IFAT) for *Theileria* antigens, especially when the antigen may be present in relatively small amounts, such as in early infected lymph node material.

Since Pearson and coworkers (Pearson, Pinder, Roelants, Kar, Lundin, Mayer-Withey and Hewett, 1980) reported the production of MAb recognizing antigens present within and on the surface of cells of an infected lymphoblastoid cell line, a number of antibodies have been cloned which recognize monomorphic and polymorphic antigens present in the schizont stage of *T. parva.* Pinder and Hewett (1980) first demonstrated with MAb that there are antigenic differences in schizont-infected lymphoblastoid cells of cell lines derived from transformation with different stocks of *T. parva.* Minami and coworkers (Minami, Spooner, Irvin, Ocama, Dobbelaere and Fujinaga, 1983) extended this study with an increased number of antibodies and were able to place the different stocks of *T.p. parva* which they examined into one of three groups based on their reactivities with the MAb panel. (The panel included the original seven MAb reported by Pinder and Hewett.) The possible significance of this classification, from an immunological standpoint, was revealed by cross-immunity studies reported by Irvin and co-workers (Irvin, Dobbelaere, Mwamachi, Minami, Spooner and Ocama, 1983) and subsequently supported by extensive field challenge studies of immunized cattle (Morzaria, Irvin, Taracha, Spooner, Voight, Fujinaga and Katende, 1987). Interestingly, there appears to be no relationship between the geographical origin of parasites of the *T.p. parva* group and their MAb profile, that is, parasite isolates from the same area may differ markedly in their profiles whereas parasites obtained from sites many hundreds of miles apart, may be indistinguishable.

The study undertaken by Minami and colleagues (Minami *et al,* 1983) also revealed that a given stock of *T.p. parva* may contain more than one parasite population. Since that time, evidence of heterogeneity within stocks has been obtained in DNA studies (Allsopp and Allsopp, 1988; Allsopp *et al,* 1989). These findings introduce a serious caveat into the design of experiments and interpretation of immunogenic relationships within this parasite grouping.

Conrad and colleagues (Conrad *et al,* 1987b; 1989) used a further-extended panel of MAb to examine the profiles of buffalo-derived parasites. Considerable antigenic diversity was revealed in these parasite populations and it did not prove possible to find profiles typical of *T.p. lawrencei* parasites as distinct from *T.p. parva* and *T.p. bovis* parasites. This was despite the fact that in the later study the panel of antibodies included some raised against parasites of buffalo origin. An important observation however, supported by 'DNA profiles' (Conrad *et al,* 1989), was that a single infected animal could be the source of more than one parasite population at any given time and, perhaps not unexpectedly therefore, that isolates from an individual could differ when obtained over a time course.

A discussion of MAb detecting polymorphic *Theileria* antigens cannot ignore their role in studies with the objective of isolating parasite molecules carrying immunogenic determinants associated with protection against challenge. An intriguing observation in this regard was that the molecule reactive with some of the MAb in the panel applied by Minami and co-workers (Minami *et al*, 1983) shows size polymorphism between stocks (Shapiro, Fujisaki, Morzaria, Webster, Fujinaga, Spooner and Irvin, 1987). However, this size polymorphism does not appear to bear any relationship to the results of cross-immunity trials (Irvin *et al*, 1983). In view of the fact that it appears that cell-mediated immune responses, of which the cytotoxic T cell response is clearly an important component, are responsible for immune responses to the intracellular stages of the parasite in the mammalian host (Morrison, Goddeeris, Teale, Baldwin, Bensaid and Ellis, 1986) the question arises as to the ultimate significance of antibody-detected polymorphism for vaccine research. At this point, it is impossible to answer this question. However, in view of the fact that there is polymorphism in the immunogenicity of *Theileria* parasites, any system which likewise reveals polymorphism must be of continuing interest. Moreover, whether or not antibody-detected polymorphism has any relevance to cross-immunity, it does provide a simple and practical means of phenotyping and therefore constitutes a useful tool for the parasitologist and epidemiologist.

Trypanosomiasis

It is perhaps in the area of detection of parasite antigen with specific MAb that the newer biotechnologies are closest to meeting the requirements of a successful, field applicable diagnostic system for trypanosomiasis, whether of livestock or man. Efforts in this area have been concentrated on antigen detection systems because of the inherent difficulties and uncertainties, which have been outlined, associated with other approaches.

The foundations for the development of MAb-based antigen detection in the case of trypanosomiasis were laid by Pearson and colleagues (Pearson *et al*, 1980), who demonstrated the feasibility of raising MAb to polymorphic trypanosome antigens and by Rae and Luckins (1984) who developed an enzyme-linked immunosorbent assay (ELISA) for detection of *T. evansi* antigens with a guinea pig antiserum as the source of both capturing and enzyme-conjugated antibodies.

Further development came with the report (Liu and Pearson, 1987) of an ELISA system based on the use of rabbit antisera to procyclic culture form trypanosomes as capture antibodies and a mixture of selected, biotinylated anti-trypanosome MAb as the second step reagent. The use of a biotin-streptavidin-peroxidase detection system lent great sensitivity to this assay for *T. brucei* group antigens, with as few as 5,000 organisms per millilitre of sample being detectable (500 per assay microwell). This sensitivity is much greater than that obtainable with microscopical methods (Paris, Murray and McOdimba, 1982) or with the ELISA method reported by Rae and Luckins (1984).

In a further development, a comprehensive panel of MAb raised against *in vitro*-cultivated procyclic forms of *T. congolense, T. vivax, T. brucei brucei* and *T. brucei rhodesiense* was reported (Nantulya, Musoke, Rurangirwa, Saigar and Minja, 1987) together with successful application in both IFAT and ELISA. Antibodies were obtained which were specific for the plasma membrane antigens of the different species, that is, antibodies were either specific for the *brucei* group, specific for *T. vivax*, or specific for *T. congolense* and *T. simiae*. The ELISA system used MAb both for antigen capture and detection and the detecting MAb were directly conjugated to peroxidase for the assay. With this system, detection of down to 10^5 procyclic forms as lysate was shown to be possible. Also, as in the case of the ELISA reported by Liu and Pearson (1987), parasite species specificity was clearly demonstrated.

An examination of the performance of some of the antibodies described by Nantulya and colleagues (1987), when used in the ELISA system for the diagnosis of experimental infections with *T. brucei, T. congolense* and *T. vivax* in cattle, was subsequently reported (Nantulya and Lindqvist, 1990). An important observation was that it was possible to detect antigen with the MAb even when parasites were not observed by microscopical examination of buffy coat. Antigen was detectable for several weeks following Berenil treatment of the cattle.

In another study (Nantulya, Bajyana Songa and Hamers, 1990), the performance of one of the antibodies raised against antigens of the *T. brucei* group, in the diagnosis of experimental and natural infections of a number of different species with *T. evansi,* was examined. Antigen was found to be detectable as early as six days after experimental infection and to persist throughout the 60 day observation period. Significantly, when sera from a large herd of Asian water buffaloes (*Bubalus bubalis*) were examined, all those from animals diagnosed as infected by conventional techniques were found to be antigen-positive, as were some sera from animals which were not detectably infected by microscopical examination.

When the same system was applied to the examination of sera of camels from locations in Kenya and Mali (Nantulya, Lindqvist, Diall and Olaho-Mukani, 1990), antigen was also detected in cases where microscopical examination yielded negative results. No antigen was found in camels held in a nonendemic area. In this study, the assay was also adapted successfully to a tube system rather than a microplate system. The tube assay has obvious potential for direct use in the field as it is easily performed and easily interpreted visually.

CONCLUDING REMARKS

There is little doubt that in some areas the biotechnologies are bringing improvements in diagnostics. At the present time, however, this is largely restricted to circumstances where relatively sophisticated laboratory equipment and expertise are available. An example is the application of DNA probes. Except for techniques based on MAb for the diagnosis of trypanosomiasis, there is a considerable way to go before successful diagnostic kits for 'field' use become available for the diseases discussed in this review.

The problem of identifying the different *Theileria* parasites (especially those of the *T. parva* group) as they are distinguished by the immune system of cattle, remains. Developing diagnostic systems for field use for trypanosomiasis based on DNA probes awaits the development of new means of labelling which do not rely on radioisotopes. In this particular case, moreover, it is probable that the MAb systems will always have greater application because, inevitably, the DNA techniques will be a little more complex and unwieldy.

It is likely that it will be in the area of diagnosis of trypanosomiasis at the level of the vector that the DNA technologies will make the greatest contribution. It is easy to see that large fly surveys could be carried out in the field and samples prepared on site for subsequent analysis in the laboratory. Moreover, this is possible with existing methods based on DNA analysis. Where sample storage and longevity are a concern, DNA certainly offers considerable advantages over other types of material on which to base diagnostic procedures.

In the case of theileriosis, it is also possible that DNA probe detection of infection at the level of the vector will develop. Potential applications of ASOs include field monitoring of the spread, or otherwise, of vaccine strains as well as general survey work. The development of a probe specific for *T. taurotragi* would also be of great use in assessing field challenge through examination of tick material. In this instance there is a clear need for the capability to distinguish *T. taurtotragi* from *T. parva* parasites.

The brightest hopes at the present, therefore, are the MAb technologies for diagnosis of trypanosomiasis in the mammalian host and DNA-based methods for detection of trypanosome and *Theileria* parasite material in vector species. The future for the biotechnologies in diagnosis of theileriosis in mammalian hosts is less easy to predict.

ACKNOWLEDGEMENTS

I would like to thank my colleagues at ILRAD for their help and constructive criticism in the compilation of the manuscript. These included Dr. R. Bishop, Dr. K. Iams, Dr. O.K. ole-MoiYoi, Dr. S.P. Morzaria, Dr. V. Nantulya and Dr. J.R. Young. My thanks are also due to Dr. B.A. Allsopp of the Department of Biochemistry, University of Cambridge, for his advice.

REFERENCES

Allsopp, B. and Allsopp, M.T.E.P. (1988). *Theileria parva*: genomic studies reveal intra-specific sequence diversity. *Molecular and Biochemical Parasitology*, **28**, 77–84.

Allsopp, B., Carrington, M., Baylis, H., Sohal, S., Dolan, T. and Iams, K. (1989). Improved characterization of *Theileria parva* isolates using the polymerase chain reaction and oligonucleotide probes. *Molecular and Biochemical Parasitology*, **35**, 137–148.

Borst, P., Fase-Fowler, F., Frasch, A.C.C., Hoeijmakers, J.H.J. and Weijers, P.J. (1980). Characterization of DNA from *Trypanosoma brucei* and related trypanosomes by restriction endonuclease digestion. *Molecular and Biochemical Parasitololgy,* **1**, 221–246.

Conrad, P.A., Iams, K., Brown, W.C., Sohanpal, B. and ole-MoiYoi, O.K. (1987a). DNA probes detect genomic diversity in *Theileria parva* stocks. *Molecular and Biochemical Parasitology,* **25**, 213–226.

Conrad, P.A., Stagg, D.A., Grootenhuis, J.G., Irvin, A.D., Newson, J., Njamunggeh, R.E.G., Rossiter, P.B. and Young, A.S. (1987b). Isolation of *Theileria* parasites from African buffalo (*Syncerus caffer*) and characterisation with anti-schizont monoclonal antibodies. *Parasitology,* **94**, 413–423.

Conrad, P.A., ole-MoiYoi, O.K., Baldwin, C.L., Dolan, T.T., O'Callaghan, C.J., Njamunggeh, R.E.G., Grootenhuis, J.G., Stagg, D.A., Leitch, B.L. and Young, A.S. (1989). Characterization of buffalo-derived theilerial parasites with monoclonal antibodies and DNA probes. *Parasitology,* **98**, 179–188.

Dickin, S.K. and Gibson, W.C. (1989). Hybridisation a repetitive DNA probe reveals the presence of small chromosomes in *Trypanosoma vivax. Molecular and Biochemical Parasitology,* **33**, 135–142.

Gibson, W.C., Dukes, P. and Gashumba, J.K. (1988). Species-specific DNA probes for the identification of African trypanosomes in tsetse flies. *Parasitology,* **97**, 63–73.

Irvin, A.D., Dobbelaere, D.A.E., Mwamachi, D.M., Minami, T., Spooner, P.R. and Ocama, J.G.R. (1983). Immunisation against East Coast fever: correlation between monoclonal antibody profiles of *Theileria parva* stocks and cross immunity *in vivo. Research in Veterinary Science,* **35**, 341–346.

Kimmel, B.E., ole-MoiYoi, O.K. and Young, J.R. (1987). Ingi, a 5.2-kb dispersed sequence element from *Trypanosoma brucei* that carries half of a smaller mobile element at either end and has homology with mammalian LINEs. *Molecular and Cellular Biology,* **7**, 1465–1475.

Kukla, B.A., Majiwa, P.A.O., Young, J.R., Moloo, S.K. and ole-MoiYoi, O.K. (1987). Use of species-specific DNA probes for detection and identification of trypanosome infection in tsetse flies. *Parasitology,* **95**, 1–16.

Landegren, U., Kaiser, R., Sanders, J. and Hood, L. (1988). A ligase-mediated gene detection technique. *Science,* **241**, 1077–1080.

Liu, M.K. and Pearson, T.W. (1987). Detection of circulating trypanosomal antigens by double antibody ELISA using antibodies to procyclic trypanosomes. *Parasitology,* **95**, 277–290.

Majiwa, P.A.O., Masake, R.A., Nantulya, V.M., Hamers, R. and Matthyssens, G. (1985). *Trypanosoma* (*Nannomonas*) *congolense*: identification of two karyotypic groups. *The EMBO Journal,* **4**, 3307–3313.

Majiwa, P.A.O. and Webster, P. (1987). A repetitive deoxyribonucleic acid sequence distinguishes *Trypanosoma simiae* from *T. congolense. Parasitology,* **95**, 543–598.

Minami, T., Spooner, P.R., Irvin, A.D., Ocama, J.G.R., Dobbelaere, D.A.E. and Fujinaga, T. (1983). Characteristion of stocks of *Theileria parva* by monoclonal antibody profiles. *Research in Veterinary Science,* **35**, 334–340.

Morrison, W.I., Goddeeris, B.M., Teale, A.J., Baldwin, C.L., Bensaid, A. and Ellis, J. (1986). Cell-mediated immune responses of cattle to *Theileria parva. Immunology Today,* **7**, 211–216.

Morzaria, S.P., Irvin, A.D., Taracha, E., Spooner, P.R., Voight, W.P., Fujinaga, T. and Katende, J. (1987). Immunization against East Coast fever: the use of selected stocks of *Theileria parva* for immunization of cattle exposed to field challenge. *Veterinary Parasitology,* **23**, 23–41.

Nantulya, V.M., Musoke, A.J., Rurangirwa, F.R., Saigar, N. and Minja, S.H. (1987). Monoclonal antibodies that distinguish *Trypanosoma congolense, T. vivax* and *T. brucei. Parasite Immunology,* **9**, 421–431.

Nantulya, V.M., Lindqvist, K.J., Diall, O. and Olaho-Mukani, W. (1990). Two simple antigen-detection enzyme immunoassays for the diagnosis of *Trypanosoma evansi* infections in the dromedary camel (*Camelus dromedarius*). *Tropical Medicine and Parasitology,* 40, 415–418.

Nantulya, V.M. and Lindqvist, K.J. (1990). Antigen-detection enzyme immunoassays for the diagnosis of *Trypanosoma vivax, T. congolense* and *T. brucei* infections in cattle. *Tropical Medicine and Parasitology,* **40**, 267–272.

Nantulya, V.M., Bajyana Songa, E. and Hamers, R. (1990). Detection of circulating trypanosomal antigens in *Trypanosoma evansi*-infected animals using a *T. brucei* group-specific monoclonal antibody. *Tropical Medicine and Parasitology,* **40**, 263–266.

ole-MoiYoi, O.K. (1987). Trypanosome species-specific DNA probes to detect infection in tsetse flies. *Parasitology Today,* **3**, 371–374.

Paris, J., Murray, M. and McOdimba, F. (1982). A comparative evaluation of the parasitological techniques currently available for the diagnosis of African trypanosomiasis in cattle. *Acta Tropica,* **39**, 307–316.

Pearson, T.W., Pinder, M., Roelants, G.E., Kar, S.A., Lundin, L.B., Mayor-Withey, K.S. and Hewett, R.S. (1980). Methods for derivation and detection of anti-parasite monoclonal antibodies. *Journal of Immunological Methods,* **34**, 141–154.

Pinder, M. and Hewett, R.S. (1980). Monoclonal antibodies detect antigenic diversity in *Theileria parva* parasites. *Journal of Immunology,* **124**, 1000–1001.

Rae, P.F. and Luckins, A.G. (1984). Detection of circulating trypanosomal antigens by enzyme immunoassay. *Annals of Tropical Medicine and Parasitology,* **78**, 587–596.

Shapiro, S.Z., Fujisaki, K., Morzaria, S.P., Webster, P., Fujinaga, T., Spooner, P.R. and Irvin, A.D. (1987). A life cycle stage-specific antigen of *Theileria parva* recognized by anti-macroschizont monoclonal antibodies. *Parasitology,* **94**, 29–37.

Sloof, P., Bos, J.L., Konings, Ad, F.J.M., Menke, H.M., Borst, P., Gutteridge, W.E. and Leon, W. (1983). Characterization of satellite DNA in *Trypanosoma brucei* and *Trypanosoma cruzi. Journal of Molecular Biology,* **167**, 1–21.

White, T.J., Arnheim, N. and Erlich, H.A. (1989). The polymerase chain reaction. *Trends in Genetics,* **5**, 185–189.

4.4

The Use of Immunoassay Diagnostic Kits in Developing Countries

M.H. JEGGO, J.I. RICHARDS and J.D. DARGIE
Joint FAO/IAEA Division of Nuclear Techniques in Food and Agriculture, IAEA, Vienna, Austria

INTRODUCTION

The Animal Production and Health Section of the Joint Food and Agriculture Organisation/International Atomic Energy Agency (FAO/IAEA) Division in Vienna provides institutes and individual or groups of scientists in developing countries with support to conduct research in animal nutrition, reproduction and disease diagnosis. The requirements of these institutes and scientists are often very different to those in the more developed parts of the world and to be of real benefit, any support they receive requires a clear understanding of the particular situation in the countries and laboratories concerned.

The type of research supported by FAO/IAEA aims both to define and to provide answers to problems affecting animal productivity in developing countries, be they of a basic or applied nature. This in turn necessitates the development and application of suitable field and laboratory techniques and the interpretation of the results obtained using these methods. Consequently, scientists tackling any particular problem may be involved solely in method development, in problem identification, in problem solving or in a combination of all three. To support research, provision must be made to train adequate numbers of local staff, to supply equipment and a system of equipment maintenance; consumables on a routine basis; access to current literature; administrative support and not least, a means of informing others of the results. In developed countries these requirements are usually met and where extra funding is required, well-established systems for obtaining this already exists.

This type of support base, or at least significant parts of it, is not usually available in less developed countries. Given this situation, it is important that the assistance available through international and other organizations to improve the capacity of veterinary and agricultural institutions in these countries to study and solve the problems of low animal productivity is directed in the most appropriate and cost-effective manner.

The FAO and IAEA receive many requests for assistance from developing countries to train staff and to provide equipment and other support for research in animal production. Invariably such requests involve the establishment of a capability to use immunoassay technology (radio-immunoassay, RIA and/or enzyme-linked immunosorbent assay, ELISA) within the context of studies on reproductive efficiency and the diagnosis or surveillance of animal diseases. Often, a significant component of the work plan (and of the costs involved!), is to develop the technology from scratch - something which can involve years of painstaking research and may cost upwards of U.S. $100,000 using highly sophisticated equipment and methodology.

However, the introduction and use of immunoassay technology into countries with limited infrastructure and financial resources can be easily established with U.S. $5,000 worth of equipment requiring no mains electrical power supply and only one month of training to a technician - provided that the assay system selected is simple, reliable and cheap. Such assay kits are available commercially, but these are not cheap - in fact they cost upwards of U.S. $300 for 100 analyses and they are often unreliable. Moreover, few commercial companies market kits for the animal or veterinary market (95% of immunological kits are for medical use) and hardly any provide technical or other support for the use of their products in developing countries; this, combined with the variety of products available on the market, means that results are difficult to interpret and impossible to compare.

However, as will be described later, systems which are both reliable and cheap have been developed by the FAO/IAEA through collaboration with national and international research institutes and are being provided in a fully standardized format complete with training and simple instructions on how to use them. This way, even the very 'highest tech' can be packaged into a format which will work reliably under the most basic laboratory conditions. Such an approach is more appropriate for the conditions which are usually faced by livestock specialists in developing countries, offering the opportunity of using immunoassay technology to study and resolve the more immediate problems of low livestock productivity (Dargie, 1989).

IMMUNOASSAY KITS FOR REPRODUCTION

Concepts

Central to livestock production is the ability of animals to reproduce. Constraints on this can be considered in terms of the disorder (i.e. anoestrus, repeat breeding, early embryonic death and abortion, retained placenta) or the causative factor (i.e. poor management, inadequate or unbalanced nutrition, intercurrent disease). Either way, the measurement of reproductive efficiency is the key to understanding and improving animal reproduction and thus ultimately livestock productivity. An efficient and reliable method for such measurement is clearly essential.

Reproductive performance in cattle can be measured using a variety of indices such as age at puberty, number of calves produced per year and per lifetime, intercalving interval, period to resumption of heat after calving and services per conception (Hawk, 1979). Most of these parameters concern the ovarian activity of the animal which can be assessed in several ways. On the one hand in cattle, simple observation and breeding records combined with rectal palpation can provide information at the farm level on the reproductive status. But this is highly subjective, difficult to quantify, time-consuming and often unreliable. On the other hand physiological parameters such as the electrical conductivity of the vaginal wall and biochemical parameters such as follicle stimulating hormone, luteinizing hormone and progesterone can be determined (Veterinary Endocrinology and Reproduction, 1980).

The objective, however, is to measure reproductive performance accurately and as simply as possible in a group of animals in a particular location (farm, region, country) under defined conditions and to monitor the effect of management changes introduced to improve reproductive efficiency.

What is ideally required is a single parameter that can be measured accurately and quantitatively, in an objective manner and on a routine basis; the key to this is the hormone progesterone (Christensen, Hapwood and Wiltbank, 1974). Levels of this hormone in blood and milk rise and fall during the oestrous cycle. They are at a low level when the animal is in anoestrus and at high levels during pregnancy (Fig. 1). Thus measurement of progesterone concentration in milk or blood on a routine and quantitative basis can provide an accurate insight into the animal's reproductive status. But how to make this determination?

Progesterone is found, even when levels are at their peak, in minute amounts (0–30 nmol/l) in blood plasma and skimmed milk and thus direct measurement is difficult. Progesterone itself is not immunogenic but when coupled to a suitable carrier it induces an immune response and thus immunoassays can be used to determine its presence. Both RIA and enzyme immunoassay (EIA) techniques have been developed for the measurement of progesterone and for some time commercial kits have been available for use in the laboratory and on the farm (Van de Wiel, Koops and Vos, 1986). However most of these techniques have a number of factors precluding their use in developing countries. First and foremost they are expensive to purchase commercially. They may also have critical storage requirements (+4° C), require expensive equipment, demand high technical competence and may only be qualitative.

The solution adopted by the Joint FAO/IAEA Division to support research in animal reproduction in developing countries has been to develop

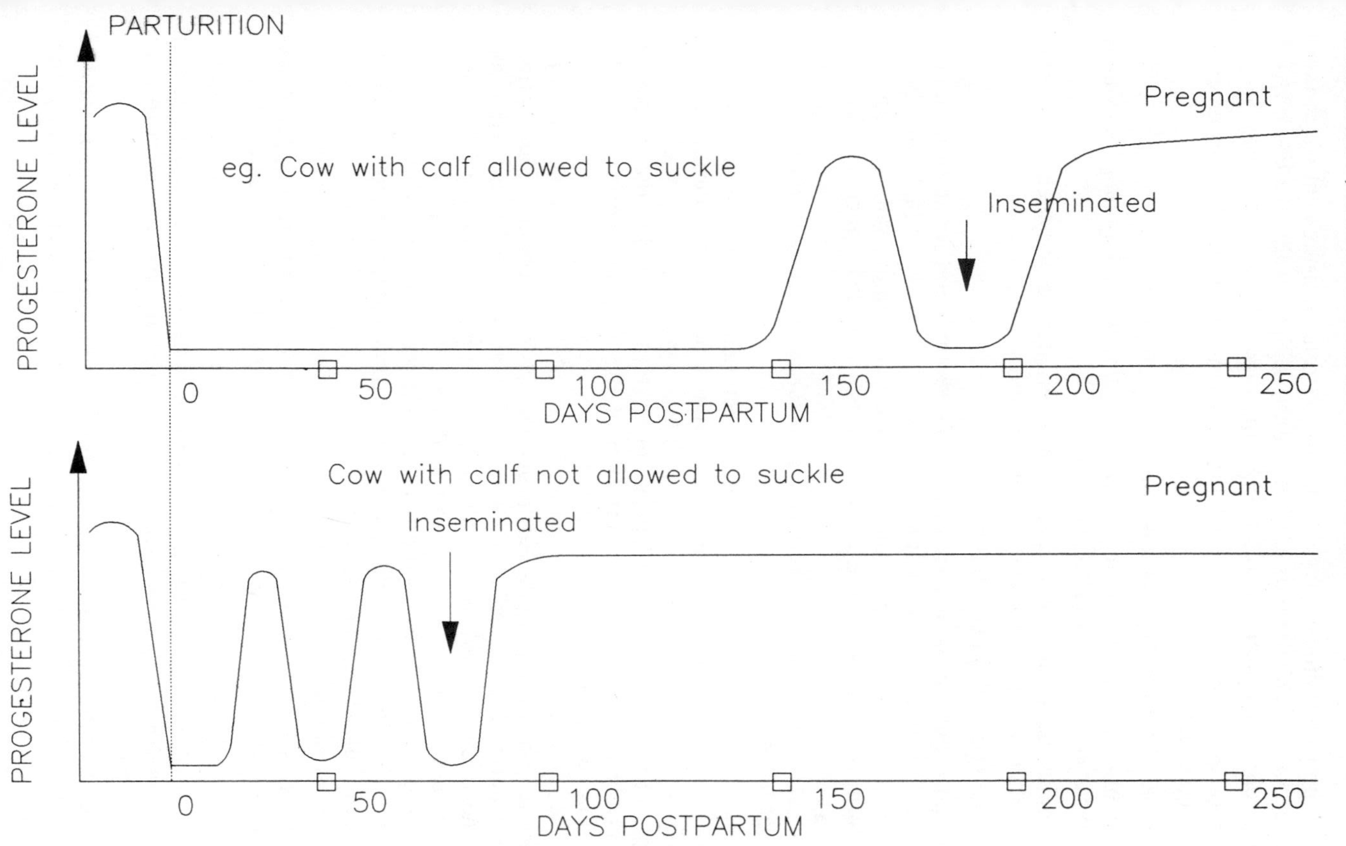

Fig. 1 *Progesterone levels in pregnant and nonpregnant cattle.*

and supply an immunoassay kit for progesterone measurement which takes into account the constraints in these countries. Specifically, the FAO/IAEA progesterone kit meets the following requirements:-

- good performance and reliability under many different environmental conditions
- rapid, sensitive and quantitative
- employed with a minimum amount of equipment and training for average experienced laboratory technician
- applicable to different species of domesticated livestock (i.e. cattle, buffalo, sheep, goats, camelids, swine and yak)
- cheap (U.S. $35 per 100 tubes)

This kit enables progesterone to be measured in blood serum or plasma as well as in skimmed (defatted) milk. Low (0.5 nmol/l) and high (80 nmol/l) concentrations of progesterone are measured equally well. The assay is performed simply without extraction - it is a so-called 'direct' assay.

The FAO/IAEA radio-immunoassay kit for the measurement of progesterone

The assay depends on the competition between progesterone in the sample and ^{125}I-labelled progesterone for a limited number of binding sites on progesterone-specific antibody immobilized on the internal wall of a test tube. The proportion of ^{125}I-labelled progesterone bound to the antibody is inversely related to the concentration of the progesterone present in the plasma/serum or skimmed milk sample.

The solid-phase technique (antibody immobilized on the tube surface) in conjunction with ^{125}I-labelled progesterone as a tracer is an optimal combination meeting all requirements. Since the separation of free and bound fractions involves only a simple decanting step, no centrifugation is required. The use of gamma-ray emitting ^{125}I avoids liquid scintillation counting with all its disadvantages. After separation it is possible to read the blood or milk progesterone concentration from a standard curve using the level of radioactivity bound to the antibody.

The kit comprises:-

- Progesterone antibody-coated tubes. These are provided in zippered bags of 100 tubes and are stable for at least one year when stored at +4° C.
- Buffered ^{125}I-progesterone (105 ml/bottle); stable at room temperature.
- Progesterone standards (for plasma or skimmed milk). Seven vials of freeze-dried standards cover the physiological range prevalent in most domestic livestock.
- Quality control samples. Freeze-dried samples containing high and low concentrations of progesterone are included as internal quality controls.

All components of the kit are able to withstand the rigours of travel in tropical conditions but should be held between 2 and 8° C on arrival at the testing laboratory.

An external quality control service is now in operation and samples for testing are sent out four times a year; results this year indicated less than a 4% coefficient of variation in results obtained between the various laboratories.

This coated-tube methodology offers significant advantages over other techniques presently available:-

- There are only two reagents to dispense into the antibody-coated tubes.
- The sample (or standard and/or quality control) and the tracer, and these can be handled simultaneously using a hand-held reservoir pipette.
- No centrifuge is required.
- Neither extraction nor predilution is required.
- Incubation time is only four hours at room temperature (15° C–35° C); alternatively, overnight incubation is equally effective.
- No washing steps; the tubes can be vigorously decanted without loss of antibody-bound material. This results in a clear separation of bound from free progesterone, with negligible nonspecific binding.
- Coefficients of variation are low (inter-assay cv of 12%; intra-assay cv of 8%).
- The antiserum is highly specific for progesterone, with low cross-reactivity with other steroids.
- The sensitivity of the assay is 0.2 nmol/l.

This kit has been validated for use with cattle, buffalo, sheep, goats, camelids and pigs.

RIA progesterone kit distribution and usage

Many scientists in developing countries now use these kits and in the past few years there has been a steady increase in the number of kits dispatched (Fig. 2). In 1988 over 4,000 kits were sent to 70 institutes in 50 countries (Fig. 3) from the IAEA Laboratories, Seibersdorf. At present the kits are sent out every two months as frequent distribution of the labelled progesterone is needed due to the short half-life of ^{125}I (60 days). However, 'jumbo kits' containing greater quantities of the other kit components can also be sent, with only the labelled iodine being distributed on a routine basis.

The kits are used for studies on the reproductive performance of many different types of livestock in developing countries ranging from alpacas in the High Andes to buffaloes in Asia (Dargie, 1989). Much of this work is conducted within the framework of FAO/IAEA Coordinated Research Programmes and IAEA Technical Cooperation Projects, the results of which are published by the IAEA and as individual papers in a variety of

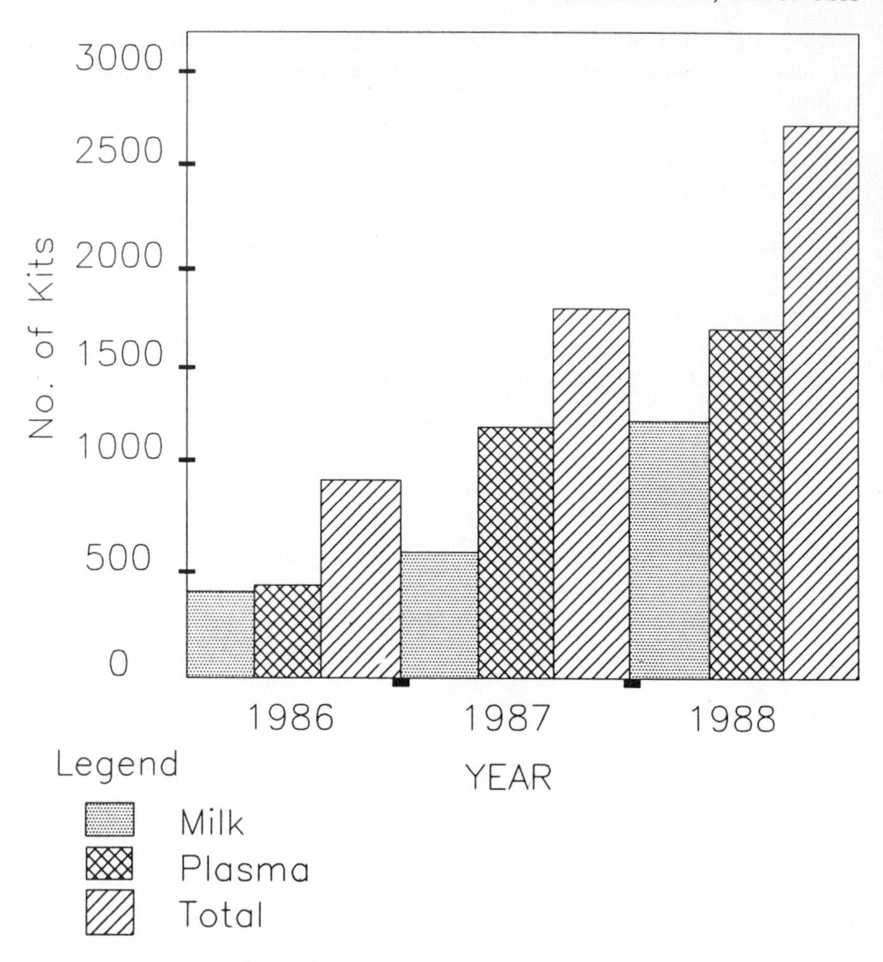

Fig. 2 *RIA kit production 1986, 1987, 1988.*

international journals. In essence the aim is to help in the collection of baseline data on the performance of animals in tropical environments in terms of onset of puberty, cyclicity, return to service after calving and anoestrus as well as for the assessment of management changes introduced to improve productivity. Linking measurement of progesterone with other clinical, behavioural and on-farm data provides a detailed evaluation of the productivity of a particular livestock group. The simple assay system described has enabled a wide spectrum of improvement regimes to be evaluated in a quantitative manner thereby providing a real insight into what changes are appropriate to different developing country situations.

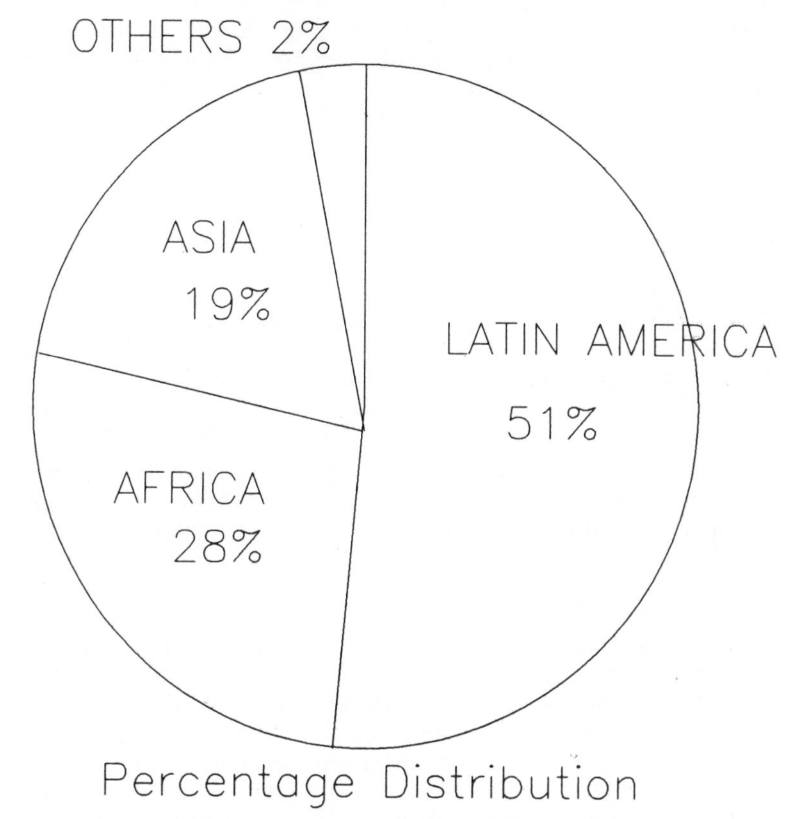

Fig. 3 *RIA kit distribution (blood and milk) 1985-1988.*

Problems encountered with radio-immunoassay

RIA methods have high sensitivity because they provide a clear and distinct signal for detection, with a very high signal-to-noise ratio. The use of radioactive isotopes can, however, also have some distinct disadvantages:-

- limited shelf-life and stability of radio-labelled compounds
- need for expensive counting equipment and for regular servicing
- need for well-trained personnel and a specialized isotope laboratory
- disposal of radioactive waste
- increasing legislative restrictions on the use of radioactive materials

The use of ^{125}I as the label and the manner in which the FAO/IAEA kit is supplied, overcomes most of these disadvantages. However public resistance to the use of isotopes has resulted in many attempts to develop nonisotopic labels such as enzymes. So far none of these has proved reliable or workable under the conditions which exist in developing countries. Considerable effort has been directed at developing an EIA for progesterone determination at the IAEA's laboratory in Austria but comparisons carried out in developing country laboratories, even with experienced staff, demonstrated that RIA is presently the test of choice for measuring hormone levels even in those countries with experienced staff.

IMMUNOASSAY KITS FOR DISEASE DIAGNOSIS

Concepts

For many years laboratories in developing countries have been faced with the problem of diagnosing and assisting in the control of a whole range of diseases. To do so necessitates the use of a variety of tests each requiring its own set of reagents, equipment and specialized training. In fact a whole plethora of tests can be employed both for antibody and/or antigen detection of any one disease (Tables 1 and 2).

In the most advanced laboratories in the world maintaining this range of tests is not easy, but for the developing countries it has proved impossible, and many laboratories, particularly in Africa, have to limit themselves to the diagnosis of only a few diseases. In considering infectious diseases, the smaller the causative agent the harder the task becomes. In the case of parasitic diseases therefore, diagnosis is relatively simple and can be carried out by most laboratories in the tropics. On the other hand virus isolation or identification lies outside the scope of a large number of these laboratories. In Africa, for example, the routine conduct of virus neutralization tests and the accompanying requirement for tissue culture are beyond the ability of 80% of the national laboratories. Yet the diagnosis and study of virus diseases in the region is of the utmost importance.

What constraints affect the ability of these laboratories to operate?

- *Finance*: insufficient hard currency to purchase equipment and reagents. Insufficient local currency for salaries, vehicles, petrol, equipment maintenance.
- *Equipment*: not available locally and difficult to maintain due to high humidity and/or frequent power fluctuations.
- *Reagents*: expensive and not available locally, thus maintenance of routine supply difficult.
- *Laboratory*: Power and water supply inadequate. Insufficient air conditioners and hot, dusty working conditions.
- *Staff*: insufficient training of local staff; those sufficiently trained are attracted by higher salaries elsewhere.
- *Transport*: inadequate to allow routine sample collection and field investigations.

Given the present financial climate in these countries, many of the aforementioned constraints cannot be overcome. Thus, if any improvement

TABLE 1 *Diagnostic tests for detecting antibodies against African swine fever.*

Property	Enzyme immunoassay	Immuno electro-osmophoresis	Indirect immuno-fluorescence	Radio immunoassay	Complement fixation
Sensitivity	high	low	high	high	low
Specificity	high	low	high	high	low
Reproducibility	high	high	high	high	high
Ease	easy	easy	easy	hard	hard
Cost	low	low	low	high	low
Use in field	yes	yes	no	no	yes
Stability of reagents	good	good	good	poor	good
Training required	low	moderate	moderate	high	moderate
Interpretation of results	easy	moderate	easy	easy	moderate
Automation	yes	moderate	now	yes	yes
Safety	some hazard	safe	safe	some hazard	safe

TABLE 2 *Diagnostic tests for detecting African swine fever antigens.*

Property	Enzyme immunoassay	Haemad-sorption	Direct fluoro-escence	Radio immunoassay	Complement fixation	Immuno peroxidase	Electron microscopy
Sensitivity	high	high	moderate	high	low	moderate	low
Specificity	high	high	high	high	low	high	low
Reproducibility	high	high	low	high	low	moderate	low
Ease	easy	easy	moderate/easy	hard	hard	moderate/easy	hard
Cost	low	moderate	low	high	low	low	high
Use in field	yes	no	no	no	yes	no	no
Stability of reagents	good	poor	good	poor	poor	good	–
Training required	low	moderate	low	high	moderate	moderate	high
Interpretation of results	easy	hard	hard	easy	easy	easy	hard
Automation	yes	no	no	yes	yes	no	no
Safety	some hazard	safe	safe	hazard	safe	safe	safe

in the diagnostic capability of these laboratories is to occur these constraints have to be taken into account. In the case of infectious diseases a possible solution would be a single test, requiring the minimum of equipment and training, applicable to a wide range of diseases and diagnoses and which detects both the causative agent and the antibody response to it.

The enzyme-linked immunosorbent assay (ELISA) meets these requirements. Since its introduction in 1972 (Engvall and Perlmann, 1972), the mass of published work employing this technique clearly indicates its many advantages for the diagnostician, epidemiologist and research worker in the biological field. In the area of diagnostic virology, both for antigen and antibody determination, its use is widespread (Jeggo, 1986), although the reasons for its preferential selection are many and varied (Table 3). In animal disease diagnosis, laboratory confirmation using ELISA is now available for a wide range of infections and in many cases the ELISA compares favourably with alternative diagnostic procedures (Tables 1 and 2).

In the mid-70s the high sensitivity and relative novelty of the ELISA were considered a handicap to the diagnostician and the test was mainly used in research. However in the last 15 years, with ever increasing use of the test and the advent of new technologies (e.g. monoclonal antibodies), ELISA offers the diagnostician a rapid and simple means of providing information hitherto unobtainable using other methods. Thus it is now possible to obtain details of virus subtypes and antibody subclasses using well-characterized reagents. ELISA now forms the basic tool for monitoring the efficacy of many national eradication and control programmes (e.g. Aujeszky's disease and Visna-Maedi in the U.K.) and with the international use of this assay system for verifying freedom from disease it is central to several international projects such as the AIDS programme in Africa. Finally, although the ELISA offers

TABLE 3 *Advantages of ELISA over other antigen/antibody detection systems.*

Sensitivity	–	Concentrations as low as 1 to 10 ng/ml detected
Speed	–	Results in 1 to 24 hours
Scale	–	Many hundreds of samples can be easily processed. Ideal for national campaigns
Specificity	–	Can easily differentiate subtypes of immunoglobulin subclasses
Easily quantifiable		
Easily standardized		
Low cost	–	Efficient use and long shelf-life of reagents
Simple		
Does not need live antigen	–	Important for exotic disease diagnosis

TABLE 4 *Advantages of using ELISA in developing countries.*

Simple	–	Simple step-by-step procedures required in execution of the test
Inexpensive	–	High dilution of reagents and microplate usage drastically reduce need for hard currency
Nonsterile	–	Problems related to laboratory and reagent sterility avoided
Easily standardized	–	Enables comparisons and therefore checks to be made between laboratories
Low equipment needs	–	Little expensive equipment required and continual power supply not essential
Exportability	–	Tests can be developed in high technological laboratories and then sent with reagents in small highly concentrated amounts to less advanced laboratories

unique advantages to all diagnosticians its use in developing countries is even more compelling (Table 4).

The Animal Production and Health Section of the Joint FAO/IAEA Division in Vienna through links established between its own laboratories in Austria and internationally renowned institutes (e.g. Pirbright Laboratories, U.K.; Biomedicum Centre, Sweden; International Laboratory for Research on Animal Diseases (ILRAD), Kenya and the Commonwealth Scientific and Industrial Research Organization (CSIRO), Long Pocket Laboratories, Indooroopilly, Australia) has refined the ELISA to produce standardized ELISA kits specifically designed for use in developing countries and covering a range of diseases of importance in these areas. Adopting similar methodology and reagents throughout means that, once the kit has been implemented for the investigation of one disease, a change of the detecting antigen or antibody suffices to investigate another disease. The training equipment, most of the reagents and often even the samples (i.e. serum) remain the same. To a large extent this meets the ideal of one test for all disease diagnosis or surveillance.

FAO/IAEA ELISA kits for disease diagnosis and surveillance

Within the general context of an ELISA many approaches can be adopted and that chosen for the FAO/IAEA kits takes into account the situation in developing countries and the need for consistency in the diagnosis of various diseases. The kits developed to date (Table 5) concentrate on antibody detection and in principle employ a simple indirect assay in which the detecting antigen is bound to the plate and the test serum added to this. Any specific binding is then detected using a specific antispecies horseradish per-

TABLE 5 *Joint FAO/IAEA Division: ELISA kits for disease diagnosis.*

Disease	Collaborating laboratories
In field use	
Rinderpest	Pirbright Laboratories, U.K.
Brucella	Central Veterinary Laboratory (CVL), Weybridge, U.K.; Agriculture, Canada
Trypanosomiasis	ILRAD, Kenya; CTVM, Scotland
Aujeszky's disease	Biomedicum Centre, Uppsalla and CVL, Sweden
Bovine leucosis	Biomedicum Centre and CVL, Sweden
Babesiosis	CSIRO, Australia
General antibovine kit	
Under development	
Foot-and-mouth disease	Pirbright Laboratories, U.K.
Bluetongue	Pirbright Laboratories, U.K.
Rota/corona virus	Moredun Research Institute, Scotland
Anaplasmosis	CSIRO, Australia
Rift Valley fever	WHO, Geneva
Infectious bovine rhinotracheitis	Cornell University, U.S.A.

oxidase conjugate and O-phenylenediamine (OPD)/ H_2O_2 as the chromogen/ substrate. Fundamental to the kit is a self-coating system with the plates being supplied separately. The reagents presently provided in each kit, by the IAEA's Laboratory, Seibersdorf are sufficient for testing 20,000 sera.

Bulk purchase of all the reagents and the plates through the FAO/IAEA ensures standardization and facilitates troubleshooting. The detailed protocol manuals which accompany the kits describe not only the method but also the equipment needed, interpretation of results, serum sampling procedures and solutions and to possible problems encountered.

Through its various Coordinated Research Programmes and individual country Technical Cooperation Projects, the Joint FAO/IAEA Division provides training, equipment and technical back stopping in the use of the kits thus helping to promote an international level of standardization and acceptance.

Kit distribution and usage

All reagents in the kits are designed to withstand the rigours of travel in the tropics and indeed the kits can sit at international airports for many weeks without any deleterious effects. The boxes used for transporting the kits are small and robust and are sent out to the laboratories concerned via local United Nations Development Programme offices. To date, some 50 kits have been distributed to over 40 countries permitting the testing of over 1 million samples.

Two examples are given below of the use of these kits – one using an antibody detection system (rinderpest), and the other, an antigen detection system (trypanosomiasis). However kits are now produced for a range of diseases including brucellosis, babesiosis, infectious bovine rhinotracheitis, Aujeszky's disease, bovine leucosis and a general antibovine kit for use by laboratories providing their own antigen (Table 5). Kits for several other diseases will be available shortly (foot-and-mouth disease, bluetongue, anaplasmosis). Linked with many of them is both an internal and external quality control service.

ELISA kit for the detection of antibodies to rinderpest virus

Throughout Africa, attempts are being made to control and eventually eradicate rinderpest from the continent through mass vaccination. This Pan African Rinderpest Campaign (PARC) is coordinated by the Organisation for African Unity (OAU) and funded primarily by the EEC.

To help ensure the success of this campaign a sero-monitoring programme is being implemented in each participating country to assess the level of vaccination achieved on an annual basis. Of paramount importance to this sero-monitoring network is the use of the FAO/IAEA ELISA kit for the detection of antibodies to rinderpest virus. This kit is recognized by OAU/IBAR (Inter-African Bureau for Animal Resources) as the official test for PARC and was developed by the FAO/IAEA through a collaborative programme with the Pirbright Laboratories of the Institute for Animal Health, U.K. and funded by the Swedish International Development Authority (SIDA).

The kit is at present being used for sero-monitoring purposes in the central veterinary laboratories of 19 African countries and it is envisaged that over ¼ million cattle sera will be tested annually as part of PARC. The test has been fully validated against the virus neutralization test – the only other detection system available for rinderpest virus antibodies but which is entirely unsuitable for this task of large-scale testing, given the situation in most African laboratories.

In each participating national laboratory one scientist has been awarded a Research Contract under an FAO/IAEA/SIDA funded Coordinated Research Programme entitled 'Sero-surveillance of Rinderpest Throughout Africa'. This programme, coordinated from IAEA headquarters in Vienna covers not only the supply of rinderpest ELISA kits, but also the provision of much of the necessary laboratory equipment; the running of specialized training courses in ELISA, serum sampling procedures and the use of computers to assist the programme; the running of annual research coordination meetings; and the provision of technical back stopping in national laboratories using FAO/IAEA experts. The field collection of the sera is, however, the responsibility of the rinderpest national coordinators in each country and much of the equipment for this is provided by EEC funding with technical back stopping by FAO. The effectiveness of this joint national and international sero-monitoring effort throughout a continent is considerably enhanced by the use of a single standardized assay that is provided and supported on a regional basis by the Joint FAO/IAEA Division.

ELISA kit for the detection of trypanosome antigens

ELISA tests have been developed by ILRAD, Kenya and the Centre for Tropical Veterinary Medicine (CTVM), Scotland, to detect trypanosomes in the blood of cattle and camels in Africa. The initial objective is to compare existing methods such as thick/thin blood smears and the buffy coat phase contrast method with the ELISA, and thereafter to use the ELISA to enable a more rapid and accurate appraisal of trypanosomiasis control programmes.

The kits themselves are designed to detect circulating antigens of the four different species of trypanosomes which affect cattle or camels in Africa - *T. brucei, T. congolense, T. vivax* and *T. evansi.* Use is made of monoclonal antibodies to provide the required degrees of specificity and sensitivity and the system used involves a sandwich ELISA. Mouse monoclonal antibody against the particular trypanosome is bound to a microtitre plate prior to addition of the test sera. The same monoclonal antibody, this time conjugated to horseradish peroxidase, is then added to detect the bound antigen with Azio-ethyl-benz-thiazoline-6-sulfuric acid (ABTS)/H_2O_2 being used as the chromogen/substrate mixture.

These kits are being supplied to scientists in 14 African laboratories who have been awarded Research Contracts under an FAO/IAEA Coordinated Research Programme funded by the Government of the Netherlands.

Problems encountered

Initially it was envisaged that one methodology and set of reagents would provide a universal ELISA for the whole range of relevant diseases. In reality it has proved necessary to adapt the standard ELISA to each disease covered, the modifications usually being associated with changes in buffer composition and occasionally the substrate used.

The basic philosophy, however, remains the same i.e. introducing ELISA technology to a laboratory initially through one disease, and then once this has been mastered, to introduce other ELISA kits with no further training, equipment or major reagents being required.

On occasions difficulties have been encountered in validating these kits at the local level. Often the results obtained from tests previously used were not reliable, and therefore, not suitable as positive or negative controls to validate the ELISA. Verification of animals positive to a particular infection was often not possible nor could a negative population of animals be guaranteed. Surprisingly local values for negative animals - in terms of optical density readings, were lower than the control samples provided with the kits and varied from country to country. For all the kits, therefore, it has been necessary to determine a local negative value and, if this differed significantly from the controls provided with the kits, to include this local negative as the control.

When introducing ELISA kits, it was always envisaged that it would be necessary to provide technical back stopping, particularly in the early stages. This has indeed proved vital to the successful introduction of the tests and to overcoming problems encountered locally.

One question frequently asked is that of the long-term supply of FAO/IAEA immunoassay kits - it is argued by some that because of this supply no local expertise exists in technique development and that the work presently being conducted would cease if kits were not supplied. In this respect the FAO/IAEA Animal Production and Health Section views the supply of these kits as a long-term commitment, and the need to develop local expertise in immunoassay reagent production of substantially lower priority for developing countries than the need to use these tests in a reliable and standardized way to assist in disease diagnosis, surveillance and control (Dargie, 1989).

CONCLUSIONS

Livestock production is a major contributor to the national economies of the developing countries and optimizing animal reproduction and disease diagnosis and control is vital to the success of this sector of the economy. However scientists in these countries work under tremendous difficulties in trying to study and solve problems, and although advances in developed countries can greatly assist this process they are only relevant if provided in an appropriate form and when comprehensively supported. In this context the FAO/IAEA programme of support for the use of immunoassays in developing countries aims to assist the transfer of this technology through the provision of tailor-made kits combined with training and other associated forms of assistance. In this way scientists in these areas can concentrate on solving the many problems facing their livestock industry without having to embark on technique development.

REFERENCES

Dargie, J.D. (1989). Helping small farmers to improve their livestock. AEA Yearbook, 1989, pp. B35–B55. IAEA, Vienna.

Christensen, M., Hapwood, L. and Wiltbank, J.N. (1974). Levels of hormones in the serum of cycling beef cows. *Journal of Animal Science,* **38**, 577–580.

Engvall, E. and Perlmann, P. (1972). Enzyme-linked immunosorbent assay ELISA III. Quantitation of specific antibodies by enzyme-labelled anti-immunoglobulin in antigen coated tubes. *Journal of Immunology,* **109**, 172–180.

Hawk, H.W. (1979). Infertility in dairy cattle. In *Animal Reproduction.* Proceedings of the 3rd Beltsville Symposium on Agricultural Research. Allenheld, New Jersey, 1979.

Jeggo, M.H. (1986). Diagnosis of viral disease using ELISA techniques – current status and future prospects. In *Nuclear and Related Techniques in Animal Production and Health.* Proceedings of a Symposium, IAEA, Vienna, Austria, 1986. pp. 289–303.

Veterinary Endocrinology and Reproduction (1980). (ed. L.E. McDonald) 3rd edition, pp. 274–330. Lea and Febiger, Philadelphia.

Van de Wiel, D.F.M., Koops, W. and Vos, E. (1986). Enzyme and radioimmunoassay techniques for hormone determination in livestock. In *Nuclear and Related Techniques in Animal Production and Health.* Proceedings of a Symposium, IAEA, Vienna, Austria, 1986, pp. 243–253.

4.5

The Development of the Commercially Produced Veterinary Immunodiagnostic Kit

J. CHESHAM
Cambridge Life Sciences plc, U.K.

CLINICAL STAGES IN THE DEVELOPMENT OF THE COMMERCIALLY PRODUCED IMMUNODIAGNOSTIC

The key stages involved in the production of the immunodiagnostic kit are shown below.

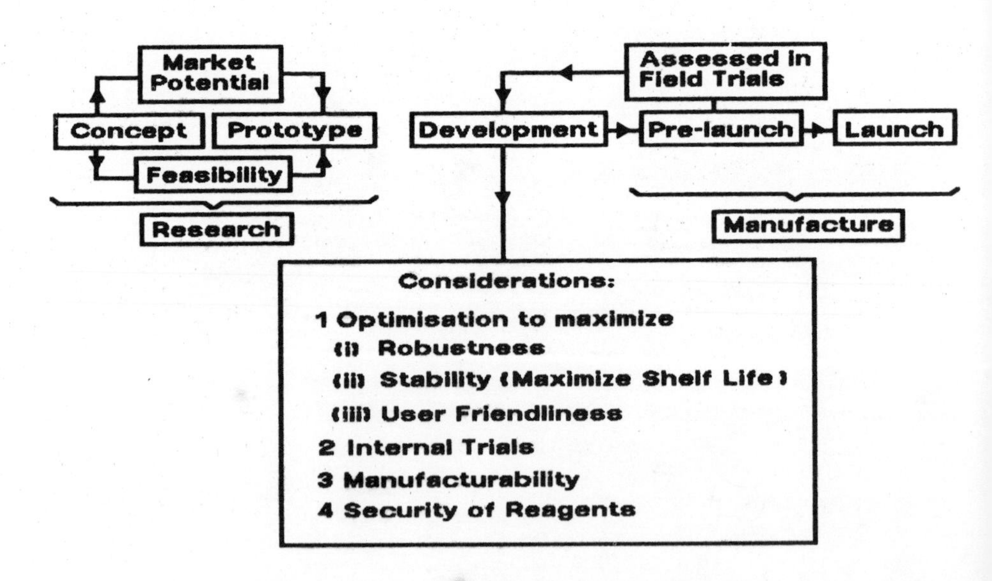

Clearly, the activities of several departments have to be coordinated to arrive at a finished product ready for sale. There is no guarantee of course that once in the system the original concept will make product status. Indeed, a good many concepts with tremendous commercial potential fall at the first hurdle. Obviously the further along the flow chart above, from left to right, a project is, the more chance it will have of ultimately making the market place. Once out there, it's success depends largely on the marketing and sales prowess of the company concerned. However, a well-developed, high quality product will always make the selling job considerably easier.

The use of an example to detail the major considerations involved at each of the stages of a kit's development is, I feel, appropriate. The example I will use is an immunodiagnostic kit for the on-farm monitoring of the fertility status of cows (Ovucheck Cowside, Cambridge Veterinary Sciences, Cambridge, U.K.).

THE CONCEPT

"The on-farm measurement of progesterone in cow's milk as an indicator of the animal's fertility status."

Considerable experience had already been gained in the measurement of progesterone in milk and several laboratory based immunodiagnostic tests have been successfully launched and marketed. Market research, however, identified a need on the part of the farmer for a rapid, but simple 'Cowside test' that would improve herd management. The financial benefits of fertility testing have been well-established (Eddy and Clark, 1987). Having identified a market requirement for such testing a feasibility study was embarked upon that would ultimately yield a prototype. Concurrently market research was conducted which allowed for a specific set of criteria to be drawn up relevant to an on-farm progesterone test. The most important criteria were that the test would yield a result within 15 minutes, would not use precision pipettes and that the end point was visually interpretable (instrumentation of any type was unacceptable).

THE PROTOTYPE

A prototype was produced based on an antibody coated plastic tube format. Milk samples to be analysed were added to the tube via a plastic disposable pipette. A chemically synthesized conjugate of progesterone and horseradish peroxidase (HRP) was added to the tube and the contents allowed to incubate for three minutes. The tubes were then thoroughly washed out using tap water and a substrate added by dropper bottle and incubated for a further three minutes.

This type of assay is termed 'competitive' because there is competition for specific antibody binding sites (on to the plastic tube in this case) between the progesterone in the sample and the progesterone associated with the HRP conjugate. Therefore, the more progesterone there is in the sample the less conjugate will bind to antibody hence less substrate will be turned over and, consequently, less colour produced. That is to say, the colour formed is inversely proportional to the concentration of the progesterone in the milk. Even at the prototype stage the assay would quite clearly differentiate between levels of progesterone associated with an animal in oestrus (<1ng/ml) and those levels associated with the pregnant or midcycle cow (≈10ng/ml and greater). We were therefore ready to enter the developmenmt phase having satisfied the principal criteria laid down at the start of the feasibility study.

KIT DEVELOPMENT

The first task is to optimize what may be, in some cases, a crude prototype. With the immunodiagnostic this normally means finding the right combination of antibody and conjugate and applying them at optimum concentrations to give, in the case of a visual test, maximum resolution over the critical analyte range. There may, however, be a need to compromise the resolution in order to speed up the test, immunochemistry often turns out to be a fine balancing act. This is a characteristic of the immunodiagnostic that can and frequently does lead to frustration in manufacturing. If we again consider the on-farm progesterone test the immunochemistry had to be delicately manipulated to give maximum visual resolution over the range 1 to 10 ng/mL progesterone. The standard curve depicted in Fig. 1 was achieved on fine tuning of the antibody coating concentration and conjugate concentration. An optical density drop of 0.165 (E_{620}) was achieved between 1 and 10 ng/mL after a three minute substrate incubation. The choice of substrate is most important when the end point is to be read visually. Historically, ortho-phenylene-diamine (OPD) has been used in conjunction with horseradish peroxidase. Recently, however, 3.3 5'5' – tetramethyl benzidine (TMB) has been favoured principally because of improved safety. It is also an ideal substrate from the point of view of end point visualization since a blue dye is produced; the eye being more sensitive to blue in the visual spectrum than the yellow product of OPD's oxidation by HRP. A second combination of enzyme and substrate which has received much attention in the world of the commercially-produced, instrument-independent immunodiagnostic is alkaline phosphatase and bromo chloro indolyl phosphate (BCIP). (Table 1 lists the characteristics of commonly used enzymes and gives examples of their substrates which have been used in the commercially-produced immunodiagnostic.) With respect to the progesterone example above, the 1 ng/mL standard gave an intense blue colour whilst the 10 ng/mL standard gave an easily discernible paler blue colour.

The visually-interpretable field test must be robust. If we again consider the progesterone on-farm tube kit, the farmer is expected to add his milk samples to the tubes via a plastic disposable pipette. Subsequent reagents (conjugate and substrate) are added via plastic dropper bottles. Dispensed volume errors in the region of + or −20% can be expected at each stage. Couple this with errors in timing of the two three minute incubations (few farmers carry on

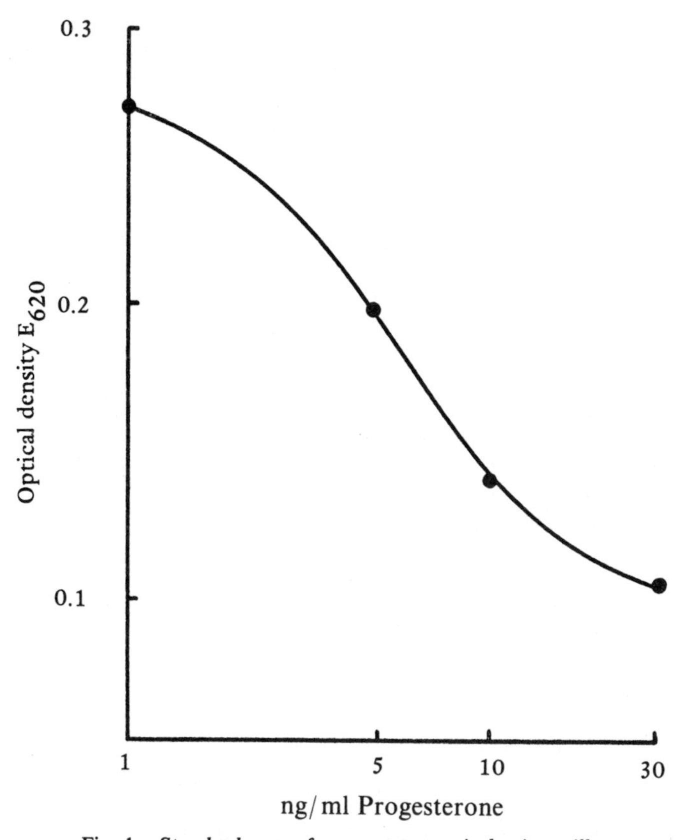

Fig. 1 *Standard curve for progesterone in bovine milk.*

their person a precision timer). These problems are further compounded by the need for this kit to perform well over a wide temperature range. The kit had to be developed to tolerate these potential problems, thus avoiding a catastrophic error (e.g. insemination of a pregnant cow). Clearly the antibody loading and conjugate concentration play a critical role as indeed does the sample to conjugate volume ratio. Milk is one of the more complicated matrixes in which to measure an analyte. It's composition (principally lipid) can change dramatically between animals. It is important, therefore, that the sample volume to conjugate volume ratio is in the favour of the conjugate (1:2 in the case of the progesterone kit) to effectively dilute out some of the matrix problems.

If one was to ask the development technician what was the bane of his working life he would probably reply 'stability study'. Our marketing colleagues rightly demand products with extensive shelf lives. For practical reasons a shelf life of six months is generally regarded as the lower limit

TABLE 1 *Characteristics of the three most commonly used enzymes in the commercially produced immunodiagnostic.*

Enzyme	Molecular weight	Turn-over number	Optimum temperature	Substrates producing a soluble product	O.D.* MAX	Substrates producing an insoluble product
HRP	40,000	216,000	25°C	Ortho-phenylenediamine	450/492 nm	Diamino benzidine
				Tetra methylbenzidine	650/450 nm	
				2-2 Azino-Di(3 ethyl-benzthiazoline sulphonic acid – 6) ammonium salt	405 nm	4 Chloro-1-napthol
β-Galactosidase	540,000	486,000	37°C	Ortho nitrophenyl – β – D – galactosidase	410 nm	–
Alkaline phosphatase	100,000	100,000	37°C	Para nitrophenyl phosphate	405 nm	Bromochloroindolyl phosphate (BCIP)

*Where two figures are quoted the first is the O.D. Max of the unstopped reaction, the second that of the acid-stopped product.

(although many kits have been launched successfully on substantially less). Studies are put into place at a very early stage of a kits development to examine shelf life. Whilst information on the stability of individual components is valuable it is important to monitor whole kit stability at the earliest opportunity and preferably on manufactured pre-launch reagents. Methods of enhancing the stability of antibodies and enzyme-analyte conjugates are well-known to people within the trade. The use of the preservatives sodium azide and thiomersal and proteins such as bovine serum albumin have been long-established. Gelatin at 0.1–0.2% has long been favoured for its ability to block plastic solid phases and reduce nonspecific binding of enzyme conjugates to an absolute minimum. Many other reagents and methods are being used. The nature of these being closely guarded commercial secrets, many being the subject of the numerous patents which proliferate in this area.

Many companies cannot afford the luxury of launching a kit on 'real time' stability data. The area of immunodiagnosis is fearfully competitive and often being the first in the market place can prove essential. For this reason many companies will launch an immunodiagnostic with a shelf life based on accelerated stability data (this should be conservative). For example a kit that performs to specification after six and a half weeks at 22° C should, if one assumes Arrhenius' equation applies, hold up for six months at +4° C.

Many companies also study kit stability at 37° C. Such studies can give a relatively speedy insight into whether a kit will stay the course for a designated shelf life. However, in my opinion 37° C stability data should be treated with a degree of scepticism. I have worked on many kits where their 37° C stability characteristics have been found wanting, only to find that at +4° C the kit manages to attain a healthy shelf life. It is important when designing a stability study to include an up-front stressing of the kit to simulate what might be expected to happen to it when in transit between the manufacture and customer. For example, I would have tremendous confidence in assigning a kit a six month shelf life at +4° C if it easily tolerated 72 hours at 28–30° C followed by six and a half weeks at 22° C.

In terms of user-friendliness the progesterone kit represented a major step forward compared to what was available prior to its launch (45–60 minute instrument-dependent laboratory tests). This kit however still requires the user to measure volumes (via pipettes and dropper bottles) and to time two incubations which are interspersed by a tube washing stage to remove the unbound enzyme-progesterone conjugate. Technology is now available, the so-called 'self performing assay' technology, which effectively removes these constraints. One such five minute test employing this technology is the Clearview HCG test for human chorionic gonadotropin (HCG) (Unipath/Oxoid, Bedford, U.K.). A brief insight into how this test works is, I feel, appropriate. A urine sample is first applied to a sample window where upon it travels via horizontal wicking through a filter bed. As it travels through the filter bed a layer of blue coloured latex to which antibodies to HCG have been linked is mobilized. The antibodies duly bind any HCG present in the urine. This complex continues to travel through the filter bed until it encounters a layer of irreversibly bound monoclonal antibodies to HCG whereupon the HCG and associated blue latex is 'captured' and consequently concentrated. A discrete blue line in the result viewing window is confirmation of pregnancy, the absence of a blue line in this window indicating non-pregnancy. The presence of a blue line in a second window tells the customer the test has worked. This is the test's 'internal control' which is formed by again laying down a discrete layer of antibody, but this time of anti-immunoglobulin specificity. This captures the blue latex-antibody conjugate which has not complexed with HCG and is, therefore, not immobilized by the first layer of irreversibly bound anti-HCG antibodies.

Whether this methodology will ultimately transcend to the area of veterinary diagnosis is not in question. Technically there is no reason why it should not. What will determine its success will be how reliable and, indeed, how economically it can be produced for sale into the veterinary market sector.

MANUFACTURE

Having successfully optimized the kit to satisfy both the practical and marketing criteria set down at the onset of the kit's development the kit is ready to enter the launch phase. This involves, first and foremost, demonstrating that the kit can be reproducibly manufactured. Several batches of pre-launch kits are manufactured according to very strict standard operating procedures. These kits will be put immediately into stability studies at their designated shelf life temperature. Kit stability will also, as already mentioned, be monitored at elevated temperature (22° C and 37° C). This data is likely to be used in setting the kits shelf life at launch (this shelf life may be extended as real time +4° C stability data is accrued). Internal trials are conducted on both spiked and field samples to determine the accuracy, precision and reproducibility of the test. It is important at this stage to establish whether the kit, designed for in-field use, delivers a satisfactory result in the hands of the 'novice'. This is the week when nonscientific colleagues get to sample life at the bench (they usually manage to do better than their scientific counterparts).

Provided there are no apparent problems at this stage the kit will go out to clinical trials. Subject to satisfactory results being achieved in the clinical trial the kit will proceed to launch.

Taking a concept and moulding it into a marketable product can take up to three years for the immunodiagnostic; the norm being one and a half to two years. The resource required will vary from project to project, but a typical development team will consist of a project leader (typically a PhD or experienced graduate), a development scientist and one or two technicians. There will be inputs, on a regular basis, from Quality Assurance, Manufacturing and Marketing. Clearly the manpower resource required to see a

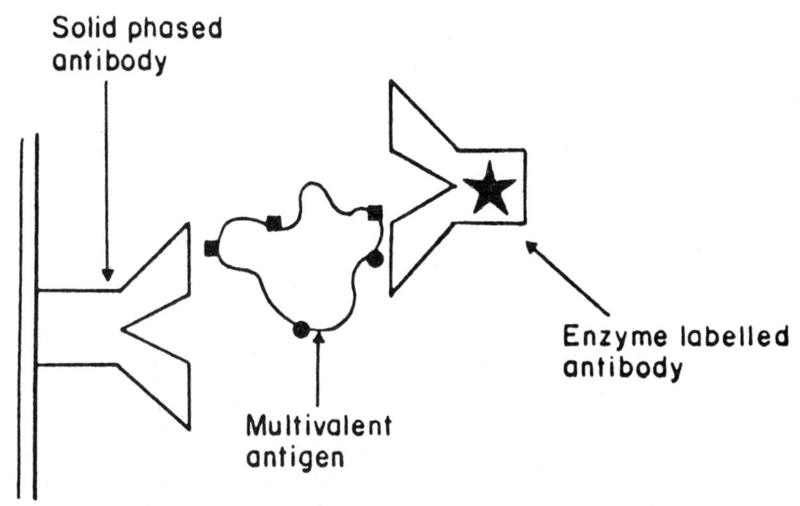

Fig. 2 *Schematical representation of the sandwich ELISA.*

product through to launch is considerable. A well-marketed, quality product, will however, repay this initial investment with interest.

Two innovative tests will enter the veterinary diagnostics market place early in 1990. Both are disease diagnostics. The first, is an enzyme-linked immunosorbent assay (ELISA) for the diagnosis of calf enteritis (Cambridge Veterinary Sciences, Cambridge, U.K.). This kit will generate considerable interest, not necessarily through the technology employed, but the underlying philosophy. The kit is of the differential diagnosis type. It will tell the veterinary practitioner whether a scouring animal has either rotavirus Group A, bovine coronavirus or *E. coli* (K99) infections or indeed a combination of these. Depending on the outcome of the test the veterinary practitioner can administer the appropriate therapy and recommend suitable herd management. This link between diagnosis and therapeutics is a crucial one which will be exploited to the full in the coming years. The kit itself is, as mentioned, an ELISA, of the sandwich type (Fig. 2 shows a schematic representation of a sandwich ELISA). It employs three monoclonal antibodies to rotavirus Group A, bovine coronavirus and *E. coli* (K99). A cocktail of these antibodies is coated onto microtitre wells. These then function to capture the infectious agent within the samples applied. The same antibodies, but this time labelled with horseradish peroxidase are used to specifically detect the infectious agent. The test will deliver a result on a faecal sample inside of one and a half hours, which is a significant improvement over conventional methodology.

A second test which should make its debut in 1990 is the Abbott *Chlamydia psittaci* Test Pack (Abbott International, Chicago, U.S.A.). This is of interest for two reasons. Firstly, because it will be the first rapid disease diagnostic for

Chlamydia to be developed specifically for the veterinary market (genus specific *Chlamydia* tests developed for clinical market have been used in the veterinary diagnostics area). Marketing is being targeted at the testing of exotic birds, however, it may have applications in the ovine species. The second point of interest is the technology this kit used. This, the now famous Abbott Test Pack technology, was inherited from Abbott Clinical diagnostics effort. These tests are easy to perform and instrument independent. The result is of the simple yes/no type but how this is derived is extremely clever and worthy of note.

Antibodies specific for *C. psittaci* are coated on to latex particles. These latex particles are then printed as a vertical bar on to a membrane that sits on top of a filter bed. A second antibody which will bind the detection conjugate (goat anti-mouse IgG-B-galactosidase) is again immobilized on to latex and printed as a horizontal bar on the membrane. The operator first filters the faeces sample using a simple device supplied with the kit. The sample is then applied to the Test Pack via a plastic disposable pipette. Any *C. psittaci* in the sample will be captured by the antibody laid down in the vertical bar. After a washing stage a mouse monoclonal antibody to *C. psittaci* is applied via a dropper bottle. This will bind to the antigen captured by antibodies in the vertical bar. A second antibody, goat anti-mouse IgG labelled with B-galactosidase, is immediately added. This binds specifically to any mouse monoclonal in the vertical bar. The enzyme conjugate will also be captured by antibodies in the horizontal bar. After a further washing step a chromogen is added. In the absence of *C. psittaci* in the sample the test will show a yellow '–' sign, in the presence of antigen a yellow '+' sign will be displayed – immunodiagnostic artistry at its best!

CONCLUSIONS

I have attempted to give a broad overview of the major steps that contribute to the successful development of the commercially produced immunodiagnostic. I have discussed several veterinary diagnostics some of which are already succeeding in the market place and some which the market place eagerly awaits. So, what does the future hold for the veterinary diagnostic? I think we will continue to see a transfer of technology from the human diagnostic area. The emphasis must be, however, on cost-effective testing. Further strong links must be established between diagnosis and therapeutics and/or animal management.

REFERENCES

Eddy, R.G. and Clark, P.J. (1987). Oestrus prediction in dairy cows using an ELISA progesterone test. *Veterinary Record,* **120**, 31–34.

Lattuada, C.P., Winslow, C.J. and Kelton, A.A. (1986). *Commercial Markets for Veterinary Infectious Disease Diagnostics.* Presented at the Robert, S. First Inc. Conference, Chicago, U.S.A.

DISCUSSION SESSION 4

ASSOKU, GHANA *With the advances of biotechnology and the development of diagnostic kits for many livestock diseases, are there any coventional diagnostic methods that would still be preferred to the former in respect of efficacy, suitability and sensitivity?*

HUNTER This is a very good question as we must avoid getting carried away with the idea that biotechnology will provide all the answers to our diagnostic problems. I would argue that the development of improved diagnostic tests using biotechnology will be so expensive in resources that in the first instance, such development should be channelled towards the greatest need i.e. to improve diagnostic tests that are inadequate or develop novel tests where required. Thus for the foreseeable future those 'conventional' tests that are proven and reliable shall continue to be used.

MAJOK, U.S.A. *Do you see any clear role for epidemiology in the application of biotechnology at the moment?*

HUNTER Yes. With the promise of diagnostic tests of improved specificity and sensitivity, I foresee problems in comparing the results of epidemiological studies using different assays. Perhaps the epidemiologists will have to introduce correction factors into their analyses to allow for tests with different levels of sensitivity and specificity.

MASAKE, KENYA *Would Dr. Harrison like to comment on the specificity of DNA probes for* Taenia saginata? *Does this probe detect* T. saginata *from various parts of the world.*

HARRISON

- The DNA probes mentioned in the talk were tested against a panel of cestode DNA including *T. saginata, T. solium, T. taeniaeformis, T. crasiceps, Echinococcus granulosus* and DNAs of bovine, porcine and human origin. On this basis, one of the DNA probes described was specific for *T. saginata* while the other reacted with DNA from both *T. saginata* and *T. solium* but not the other DNAs tested.
- The DNA probes were developed from *T. saginata* material of East African origin. Collections of *T. saginata* DNA from various locations throughout the world are being made to determine if there are any variations in the parasite DNA from different geographic locations. The

main question is whether a parasite is *T. saginata* or *T. solium*; genetic variations in parasites due to geographic location are of more interest to taxonomists unless of course the differences are related to, for example, variations in pathogenicity.

NYEKO, KENYA *For field application of DNA probes, the specimen should be preserved to prevent lysis or degradation of the parasite DNA. Are there simple methods to overcome this problem in the field?*

HARRISON Samples can be stored in 70% ethyl alcohol for transportation. One of the advantages of using DNA analysis is the stability of DNA and the ease with which samples can be transported.

SUDI, TANZANIA *Diagnostic kits will always cost money to develop, so the idea of free diagnosis should not arise. When you talk of cheap diagnostic methods, are you thinking of the farmer who will always decide whether to invest his money or not, or government services?*

HUNTER Government services in developing countries usually operate on limited budgets and costs are always relevant. Farmers may be reluctant to pay for a diagnostic assay, even a cheap one, as such work is usually carried out free of charge to the farmer. I would say that as a general rule in developing countries, costs of diagnostic tests are of most relevance to government services.

JEGGO In the case of FAO/IAEA ELISA kits, these are supplied to government funded institutes or individuals and not to the farmer. These kits are relatively cheap to produce but are provided without direct charge to research contract holders or technical cooperation projects as part of the support package offered to scientists in developing countries. The aim of this exercise is to effect appropriate technology transfer and no attempt is made to put it on a commercial footing.

CHESHAM Whether you are selling a commercially developed diagnostic into a government service laboratory, a private laboratory or indeed the farmer, the same basic rule applies, i.e. a test will only be conducted if it can be seen to be cost-effective. Therefore, the test has to be competitively priced. Fertility testing is a prime example of where the immunodiagnostic can in the medium to long-term significantly improve the economics of the herd.

RANGNEKAR, INDIA *Is the work described by Dr. Teale being extended to* Theileria *and* Trypanosoma *species prevalent in Asia and is the technique being used commonly in Kenya and other African countries? What is the cost of testing one sample?*

TEALE The MAb/ELISA diagnostic tests have been applied at experimental level in the diagnosis of *T. evansi* infections in Asian buffaloes and show promise.

The technique is now beginning the field testing stage in various African countries but what the costs will be are not clear at present.

ASSOKU, GHANA *Would Dr. Teale comment on the stability of the trypanosome monoclonal antibodies and their long-term use in field tests?*

TEALE The monoclonals have good stability at 4°C in the presence of sodium azide and when frozen. The system is currently being field validated in a joint FAO/IAEA/ILRAD project. Results so far are promising.

SINGH, INDIA *Is there any cross protection between trypanosomes in Africa?*

TEALE There is no apparent cross protection between trypanosome species in Africa.

SSENYONGA, UGANDA *Would Dr. Teale please elaborate on whether the developed DNA probe against* Theileria parva *will hybridize on different development stages of the organism, i.e. the schizonts in lymphocytes, erythrocyte piroplasms and sporozoites in tick salivary glands?*

TEALE Probes are effective with DNA-derived from infected cell lines and piroplasms.

OZAWA, FRANCE *Is ILRAD considering to develop a simple pen-side diagnostic technique for diagnosis of trypanosomiasis using colour changes on paper or similar methods?*

TEALE Not at present. There would appear to be no obvious technical reason why this should not be achieved but perhaps this will be for other institutes/companies/organizations to develop, now that the basic principles have been established.

BARZILAI, ISRAEL *Isn't there a risk that monoclonal antibodies used in diagnosis will give negative results compared to polyclonal antibodies? Aren't polyclonal antibodies more reliable for routine diagnoses?*

TEALE The monoclonals in use for trypanosomiasis diagnosis detect species-specific epitopes in the plasma membrane. It is not likely that these will alter especially as they are not the target of the majority of antibodies generated during the immune response. If they were to disappear, and thus give false negatives, this would soon be apparent, and indeed would be an interesting and potentially important observation, which arguably would be missed with polyclonal antibodies.

ASSELBERGS, MOZAMBIQUE *For Dr. Jeggo. What is the smallest quantity of serum that you can use in your diagnostic kits because often it is easier to collect just small quantities of blood from the tail tip instead of larger quantities from the jugular vein?*

JEGGO One can use the blood drop method (i.e. dried blood on filter paper) but FAO/IAEA recommends and encourages the sampling and storage of larger quantities of serum for use in more than one diagnostic kit, since the practice of blood sampling is in itself a costly procedure.

GIBBENS, U.K. *Please could Dr. Jeggo tell us how laboratories can get on the distributions lists for the RIA kits?*

JEGGO Individual scientists or technical cooperation projects must apply to FAO for inclusion in the programme. We do not 'sell' kits but provide them as part of a support package to scientists in developing countries and thus to receive kits, whether ELISA or RIA, the individual would need to be either a research contract recipient or a member of staff of an institute supported through a technical cooperation project.

RANGNEKAR, INDIA *I hope the FAO would support making the kits in developing countries for sustainability of the diagnostic approach?*

JEGGO We feel it more appropriate with the limited funds available to concentrate on supporting problem solving rather than method development and the FAO/IAEA is committed, within budgetary constraints, to continue the supply of immunoassay kits for the foreseeable future.

SHAMBWANA, TANZANIA *What is the FAO/IAEA programme to cover countries in Asia and Latin America?*

JEGGO Time did not permit the decription of our programmes of support in these areas but they are similar to those in Africa and indeed we see a considerable expansion of our support in Latin America.

SINGH, INDIA *What are the costs of the diagnostic and pregnancy test kits?*

JEGGO The kits are supplied free to those scientists and institutions supported by IAEA through our coordinated research programme or individual technical cooperation projects.

SSENYONGA, UGANDA *With regard to the use of RIA progesterone assay, would Dr. Jeggo please elaborate on the safety to personnel, disposal of radioactive materials and legislation?*

JEGGO I^{125}, the isotope used in our RIA progesterone kit is relatively safe and the handling of this isotope is within the legislative requirements and scope of most laboratories in most developing countries.

SSENYONGA, UGANDA *Is FAO/IAEA planning to develop a hormone detection kit based on EIA?*

JEGGO To date EIA has not proved reliable or reproducible enough for a progesterone detection system suitable for conditions in developing countries. We feel that the RIA/IAEA progesterone kit is the method of choice in these situations.

MAJOK, U.S.A. *How is the performance of the IAEA kits evaluated in the field?*

JEGGO There are two distinct ways. Firstly at annual research coordination meetings, individual research contract holders present details of their work conducted in the previous 12 months which will include full details of the use of the RIA progesterone kits. Secondly we now operate an external quality control service involving sending out samples four times a year for testing. This year a 96% correlation was obtained from the various laboratories receiving the kit.

GALINA, MEXICO *Would Dr. Chesham comment on the sensitivity of the progesterone kit in cows not in dioestrus or oestrus?*

CHESHAM The test will deem a sample to be from an animal in oestrus if the progesterone levels are less than 1 ng/ml and to be in mid cycle or possibly pregnant if greater than 8 ng/ml. The vast majority of samples tested fall into these categories (i.e. >90%). However, where a sample falls in the 'grey zone', the results of the test would be inconclusive and the farmer would be asked to retest the following day.

RANGNEKAR, INDIA *What is the cost of the progesterone kit, and of testing a sample?*

CHESHAM The on-farm Progesterone Rapid Tube Kit costs £30.00. The kit will allow a maximum of 20 samples to be tested making a cost of £1.50 per test.

NYEKO, KENYA *Marketing managers operating in developing countries usually sell their equipment and reagents through heads of government departments. In most cases there are not scientists capable of using the equipment and reagents which are then discarded. Marketing managers should try to locate local scientists first who can use such items before accepting orders from administrators.*

CHESHAM This is extremely good advice. It is crucial that the intended user is involved at all levels of the decision making process when it comes to the purchase of new diagnostic systems.

OZAWA, FRANCE In the animal health field there may be a risk of putting more emphasis on vaccine research and giving a low priority to diagnostic methods which are fundamental to veterinary services. Demand by farmers for diagnostic services is limited at present because reliable diagnostic techniques are not reaching farmer level. There is a need to develop new pen-side diagnostic methods to creat a new demand for diagnostic services in developing countries, and to find the means of commercialization the production and delivery of diagnostic kits.

5.

ANIMAL HEALTH, VACCINES

Chairmen: H.W. Reid,
Moredun Research Institute,
Edinburgh

and

A.G. Hunter,
CTVM,
Edinburgh

5.1

Conventional Vaccines against Viral Diseases – their Efficacy and Safety

R. BARZILAI
Israel Institute for Biological Research, Ness Ziona, Israel

ABSTRACT

Currently used viral vaccines fall generally into two major categories: live and inactivated. Both approaches have proved (with some exceptions) to be highly effective in limiting the spread of major diseases in humans and their livestock. Both approaches, however, suffer from some disadvantages. The major disadvantage seems to be that some compromise has to be reached between safety and efficacy.

Live vaccines present the constant hazard of revertants; inactivated vaccines are afflicted by incomplete inactivation. Improved live vaccines may be over-attenuated; improved inactivated vaccines may be poor immunogens.

Modern views as to future vaccines indicate two major avenues of development:

- Isolated peptides or polypeptides, absolutely free of viral genome
- Vectored segments of viral genomes, which are unable to replicate by themselves.

(These two avenues are not fundamentally different from the two classical categories).

This review will present some circumstantial evidence pointing to a possible new hazard associated with these future vaccines. They may be risk-free for the individual, but may present a potential risk for whole populations.

Second generation vaccines will in effect immortalize some selected epitopes, with no possible change in the amino acid's order or composition. The great ease of obtaining 'runaway' or 'escape' viral mutants by selection with monoclonal antibodies may be an illustration of what may happen when whole populations are immunized by selected, immutable epitopes.

5.2

Prospects for Novel Vaccines against Foot-and-Mouth Disease

T.R. DOEL
Institute for Animal Health, Pirbright Laboratory, England

INTRODUCTION

Foot-and-mouth disease is a highly contagious disease of cloven-hoofed animals, and, as such, is of great concern to the agricultural economies of the world. Its importance relates not only to reduced productivity of livestock but also to the embargoes and restrictions on exports from the unfortunate country to nations which have no foot-and-mouth disease (FMD).

Vaccines based on chemically inactivated 146S particles of foot-and-mouth virus (FMDV) are used extensively throughout the world to control the disease. High levels of protection may be achieved given optimum conditions of production and regular application of the vaccine to a high percentage of susceptible animals. Whereas this is the case with most parts of Western Europe, many less developed countries are unable to achieve comprehensive protection for a number of reasons which include inherent limitations with conventional FMD vaccines.

Because of the antigenic variability of FMDV, it is necessary to match closely the vaccine strain to the field strain otherwise the level of protection achieved will be compromised. In theory this means that it is necessary to have a vaccine for each of the eight major types of FMD. In practice, it is common to prepare vaccines from local field strains to minimize antigenic differences.

In contrast to other picornaviruses such as polio, FMDV is extremely acid and heat labile (Doel and Baccarini, 1981) and there is some evidence for degradation on adsorption to Al $(OH)_3$ gel (Doel and Staple, 1982). This raises cold chain problems and may contribute to the relatively short duration of immunity in cattle. It also inhibits possible uses of the virus in novel vaccines such as controlled slow release preparations.

One of the most publicized drawbacks to conventional FMD vaccines is that of residual infectivity because of incomplete inactivation. A number of outbreaks attributable to this problem have been documented in Europe where the low incidence of 'natural' disease focuses attention on the hazards associated with the production and use of vaccine.

For the above reasons, there has been considerable effort to develop synthetic alternatives to conventional FMD vaccines. The early studies concentrated on the expression of the immunogenic VP1 protein of the virus in bacterial systems (Kleid, Yansura, Small, Dowbenko, Moore, Grubman, McKercher, Morgan, Robertson and Bachrach, 1981). However, the VP1 vaccines were relatively ineffective and, following the work of Strohmaier, Franze and Adam (1982), led to the next generation of synthetic FMD vaccines. These were oligopeptides equivalent to the most immunogenic sequences within the VP1 protein and our experimental results with these materials form the basis of this paper.

STRUCTURE OF FMDV ANTIGENS

FMDV is an icosahedral virus composed of 60 copies of each of four proteins, VP1, VP2, VP3 and VP4, surrounding a single strand of positive sense RNA. Peptides used in the present work were based on sequences of the VP1 proteins of either the O1 Kaufbeuren, the A24 Cruzeiro or the C3 Indaial strains of FMDV. Fig. 1 indicates that a typical peptide, in this case O1 Kaufbeuren, is composed of two different regions of the VP1 connected and terminated with short 'non-VP1' sequences. The P-P-S sequence was introduced to create a bend in the peptide bringing the two sites closer together to facilitate disulphide bridging between the cysteines of the terminal C-C and P-C-G sequences.

PROTECTIVE CAPACITY OF SYNTHETIC PEPTIDE VACCINES

Guinea pigs

The O1 peptide (O40) in Freund's Complete Adjuvant was used to immunize guinea pigs. Other peptides in this experiment were 141–158-P-C-G (O21), the same sequence but coupled to keyhole limpet haemocyanin (KLH), and a version of O40 but lacking C-C at the amino terminus (O38). The results given in Table 1 are the serum neutralizing antibody titres at 27 days post vaccination (d.p.v.) and resistance to challenge with virulent O1 Kaufbeuren virus at 28 d.p.v.

It can be seen that both O38 and O40 peptides were highly effective in this animal model. Use of just the 141–158 sequence gave significantly less protection and it's covalent attachment to a large carrier protein rendered this peptide ineffective. We have observed similar results with O40 coupled to various carrier molecules and conclude that it is essential that the sequence is

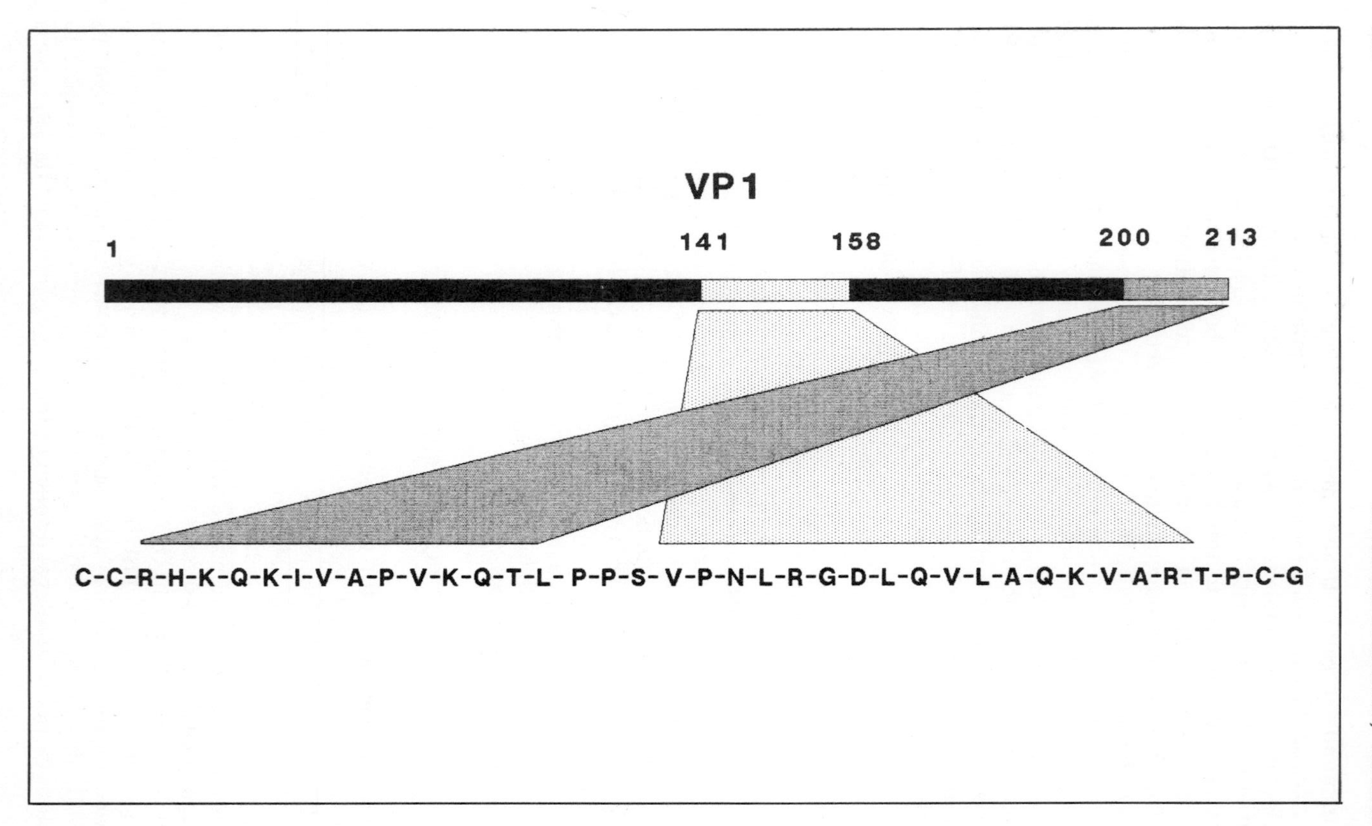

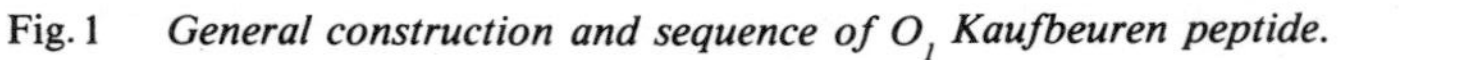
Fig. 1 *General construction and sequence of* O_1 *Kaufbeuren peptide.*

TABLE 1 *Protection of guinea pigs against FMD with synthetic peptides.*

Peptide dose (nmol)	Protection (neutralizing antibody titre) O21	O21 + KLH	O38	O40
150	5/5* (2.3)	0/5 (0.8)	5/5 (2.9)	5/5 (3.6)
50	1/5 (0.8)	"	5/5 (3.1)	5/5 (3.1)
17	2/5 "	"	5/5 (3.0)	5/5 (3.1)
6	0/5 "	"	4/4 (2.9)	5/5 (2.1)
2	"	"	3/4 (2.1)	4/5 (2.3)
0.6	"	"	5/5 (1.0)	3/5 (2.1)
0.2	"	"	1/5 (1.2)	1/5 (1.8)

* Indicates number protected/number vaccinated
Protection = resistance to challenge with O1 Kaufbeuren at 28 d.p.v.
Neutralizing antibodies at 27 d.p.v.

TABLE 2 *Protection of guinea pigs against FMD with synthetic peptides.*

VP1 sequence of peptide	Dose of peptide (n mol) 125	25	5	1
200–213	0/4	0/4	0/4	0/4
134–160	3/4	0/4	0/4	0/4
CC(200–213)PPS(141–158)PCG	4/4	3/4	0/3	0/4
(134–160)(196–213)	4/4	3/4	0/3	0/4
161–213	0/4	0/4	0/3	0/4
134–213	1/4	0/4	0/4	0/4

Protection indicated as Table 1.

not compromised by close association with other structures (Doel, DiMarchi and Brooke, unpublished observations).

We have also examined the role of the 200-213 sequence using a number of peptides and Table 2 summarizes the results of the guinea pig challenge studies.

These results confirm the superiority of the O40 peptide over the shorter sequence equivalent to the 141–158 region of VP1. It is also apparent that the peptide (134–160) (196–213), which contains both sites in their 'natural' order, was as effective as O40. The 200–213 sequence was ineffective in isolation and as a component of the larger peptide 161–213. Surprisingly, the

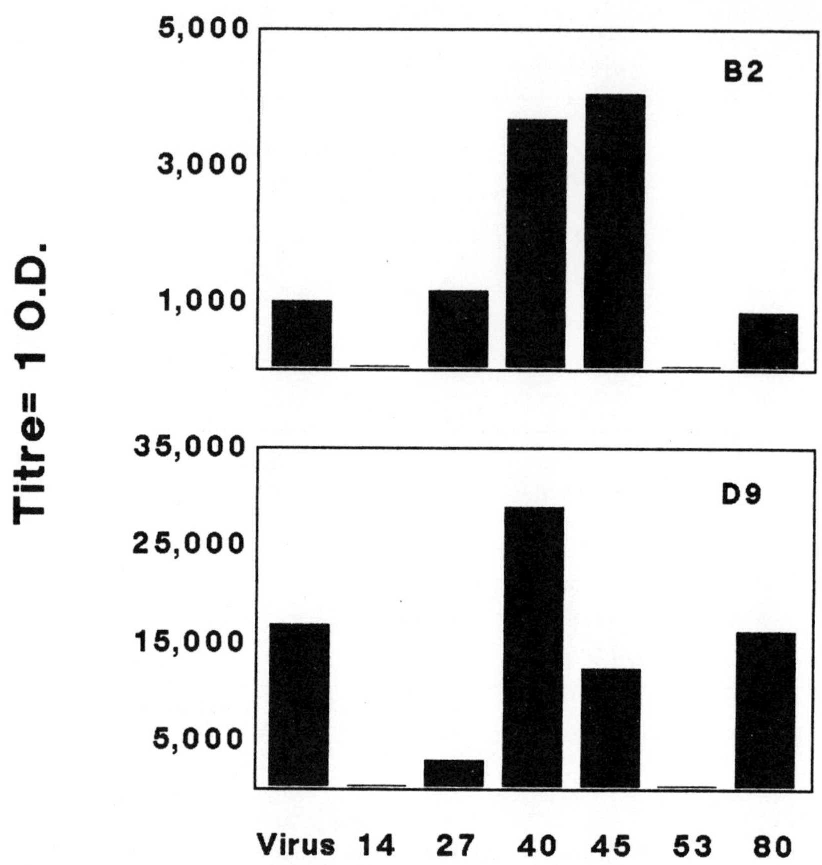

Fig. 2 *ELISA of two virus neutralizing monoclonal antibodies (B2, D9) against virus and a number of FMD synthetic peptides.*

V = Virus	*40 = CC(200—23)PPS(141—158)PCG*
14 = 200—213	*45 = (134—160)(200—213)*
27 = 134—160	*53 = 161—213*
	80 = 134—213

largest peptide, 134–213, which contained both sites and many more amino acids between them gave very little protection. In conjunction with serology not shown here (Doel, Gale, Brooke and DiMarchi, 1988), we concluded that the 141–158 sequence was obscured for immune recognition. The role of the 200–213 sequence which is neither immunogenic nor antigenic in isolation (results not shown) remains a mystery. Certainly, it fails to be recognized by two neutralizing monoclonal antibodies (Fig. 2), whereas the most potent peptides in Table 2 [O40 and (134–160) (200–213)] bind these antibodies more effectively than virus.

Cattle

Similar studies to those conducted in guinea pigs have been done in cattle. Peptide O40 and the A24 Cruzeiro equivalent (A40) were formulated respectively in Freund's Complete Adjuvant and an incomplete oil adjuvant and administered to 6–9 month old Friesian heifers by the subcutaneous route. All animals were challenged by intradermolingual challenge with 10^5 ID_{50} per ml of the homologous challenge virus at 28 d.p.v. Selected results from several larger experiments are shown in Table 3.

TABLE 3 *Protection of nine cattle against FMD with synthetic peptides.*

Treatment	Neutralizing antibody v. homologous virus*	Protection
0.2 mg O40	1400	No
0.2 mg O40	1400	No
0.2 mg O40	1000	No
5.0 mg O40	1400	Yes
5.0 mg O40	1400	Yes
5.0 mg O40	1000	No
5.0 mg A40	32	No
5.0 mg A40	178	Yes
5.0 mg A40	1400	No

* Titre of serum taken on challenge day expressed as reciprocal of dilution required to neutralize 50% of virus in IB-RS2 cell monolayers.

Challenge = 10^5 ID_{50} of homologous virus at 28 d.p.v.

Table 3 indicates protection of cattle in the face of virulent virus challenge. It should be noted that all control animals showed generalization of disease within 48 hrs post challenge. An important point to draw from these experiments is that protection did not appear to correlate with neutralizing antibody titre. Several unprotected animals had titres of 1,000 or more, which are considerably higher than seen with conventional FMD vaccines. On the basis of experience with the latter, titres of 100 or greater will usually confer protection. The explanation for this discrepancy is, as yet, unresolved but will be considered further after the next section. Finally, almost all animals which have received two doses of peptide vaccine in our experiments have been protected (DiMarchi, Brooke, Gale, Cracknell, Doel and Mowat,1986; Doel, Gale, Do Amaral, Brooke, Mulcahy and DiMarchi, 1990).

CROSS-REACTIVITY OF SYNTHETIC PEPTIDE VACCINES

It is a reasonable assumption that synthetic peptide vaccines in general and FMD vaccines particularly will be too specific compared to their whole virus counterparts and bearing in mind the basic requirement for a range of conventional FMD vaccines to cover field strains and variants. To examine this possible limitation, we prepared synthetic peptide vaccines corresponding to the VP1 sequences of the C3 Indaial, A24 Cruzeiro and O1 Kaufbeuren strains of FMD using the general construction shown in Fig. 1. These vaccines were used to immunize groups of guinea pigs and subgroups subsequently challenged at 28 d.p.v. with one of the three challenge viruses.

The results in Table 4 clearly indicate high levels of heterotypic as well as homotypic protection. This is in direct contrast with conventional FMD vaccines where heterotypic challenge cannot be achieved even with multiple immunizations (Black, Nicholls, Rweyemamu, Ferrari and Zunino, 1986). Lower levels of protection consistent with the above results were also seen with a dose level of 0.2 mg peptide (Doel *et al*, 1990).

When sera from the above experiment were assayed for neutralizing antibody, the titres obtained were type specific and bore no relationship to cross-protection (results not shown). The only *in vitro* test which related to cross-protection was that of anti-peptide titres by ELISA (Table 5).

For the most part, these results agree with the protection data given in Table 4 and are interesting in view of the lack of sequence conservation among the three peptides. Indeed, the 141–160 region of the VP1 protein was originally suspected of being involved in a major antigenic site because of the considerable sequence diversity between different strains of the virus.

In the case of amino acids 141–158, the sequence conservation with a given pair of viruses ranges from 33 to 44% whereas values from 64 to 86% are apparent with amino acids 200–213. Although this data would suggest that the 200–213 sequence is responsible for the induction of heterotypic antibody, two pieces of evidence suggest that the sequence R-G-D within 141–158 is more likely. Firstly, isolated 200–213 does not protect guinea pigs or induce anti-viral antibody unless combined with 141–158. Secondly, Fox, Parry, Barnett, McGinn, Rowlands and Brown (1989) have demonstrated that this highly conserved tripeptide is intimately involved in the cell attachment site on FMDV and antibody to it may be effective by preventing virus from binding to cell receptors.

NEUTRALIZING ANTIBODY AND PROTECTION

There is a clear dilemma with the ability of synthetic peptide vaccines to induce very high levels of neutralizing antibody and achieve, at least in cattle, only moderate levels of protection. As has been stated above, conventional FMD vaccines commonly induce much lower titres but protect more effectively. One explanation would be to invoke cell mediated immune mechanisms and there is some evidence for their existence in FMD infected

TABLE 4 *Protection of guinea pigs to homotypic and heterotypic FMD challenge.*

Peptide	Dose (mg)	Challenge virus A	C	O
A40	5.0	5/5	1/5	3/5
C40	5.0	1/5	5/5	3/5
O40	5.0	4/5	1/5	5/5

TABLE 5 *Anti-peptide titres of guinea pig sera (27 d.p.v.).*

Peptide serum*	Peptide in ELISA	ELISA titre equivalent to 1 O.D. at 492 nm
A40	A40	3262
A40	C40	339
A40	O40	1123
C40	A40	708
C40	C40	3877
C40	O40	108
O40	A40	1639
O40	C40	92
O40	O40	2908

* Each serum was a pool corresponding to a group of five guinea pigs.

animals. Knudsen, Groocock and Andersen (1970) demonstrated delayed-type hypersensitivity responses in guinea pigs but concluded that there was no correlation with protection to challenge. Unpublished results from our laboratory (Collen and Doel) have indicated cytoxic-T-lymphocytes-like activity in guinea pigs previously infected with FMDV.

Initially, however, we have directed our attention to identifying qualitative differences between virus and peptide induced sera. A range of sera from cattle immunized with peptide or FMDV or infected with FMDV have been examined in antibody isotype assays (Mulcahy, Gale, Robertson, Iyisan, DiMarchi and Doel, 1990) and a mouse protection test. Using monoclonal

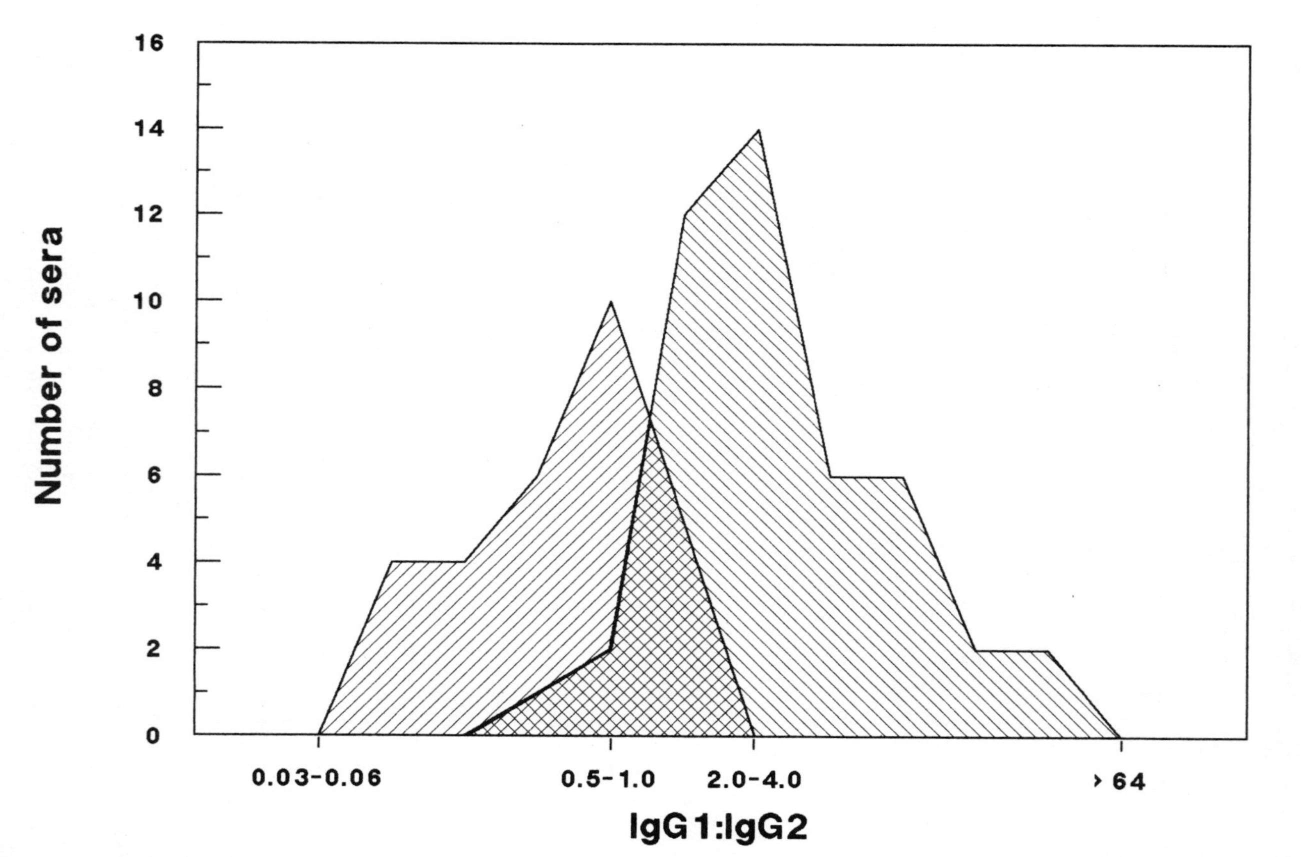

Fig. 3 *Frequency distribution of IgG1:IgG2 ratios in cattle sera following vaccination with either synthetic peptides ( ) or FMDV ( ).*

anti-bovine IgG1, IgG2, IgA and IgM, a clear pattern emerged on the basis of the IgG1/IgG2 ratios. Cattle vaccinated with synthetic peptide tended to produce more IgG2 than IgG1 whereas virus infection or vaccination gave more IgG1 than IgG2. This is best shown by a frequency distribution (Fig. 3) where two clear populations can be seen. A particularly interesting result was obtained with an animal given 5.0 mg of the A40 peptide which developed a high level of neutralizing antibody (1400, Table 3) but was not protected. Almost all of the antibody detected was IgG2 with only minimal levels of the other isotypes (results not shown). In general, the IgA and IgM responses of all cattle were low relative to the IgG1 and IgG2 responses.

On the basis of these observations, we would suggest that the IgG1 isotype is more relevant to clearance of infectious virus *in vivo* and that the presence of significant levels of IgG2 may be counterproductive by blocking the binding of the more effective IgG1 isotype.

The conclusions from the isotype assays are also consistent with the results from a mouse protection test. With this experimental approach, in which mice were passively immunized prior to challenge with a suitably adapted virus strain, anti-viral sera were significantly superior to antipeptide serum (Mulcahy, Pullen and Doel, in preparation). We are currently examining anti-peptide and anti-viral sera in the context of their opsonizing activity.

DISCUSSION

In the studies reported here, we have achieved some of the objectives of a successful synthetic alternative to conventional FMD vaccines.

Clearly, synthetic peptides will not suffer from the documented problems of residual infectivity of conventional FMD vaccines and escape of virus from production plants. Although we have not conducted a specific experiment, there has been no evidence of instability of the FMD peptides reported here either in solution or as lyophilized preparations.

One of the perceived disadvantages of synthetic peptide vaccines is that of specificity. Experiments reported here have shown that, on the contrary, peptides A40, C40 and O40 can confer significant levels of heterotypic as well as homotypic protection. This represents a major advantage over conventional FMD vaccines. The sequences responsible for inducing heterotypic protection are unknown at this stage although the R-G-D sequence within the 141–158 region of VP1 has been implicated. There are both positive and negative aspects to this observation. On the one hand, the consequences of inducing antibody to a sequence which binds to a protein on the surface of a cell need to be considered. It is possible that we are inadvertently inducing antibody which will inhibit the natural role of the FMDV receptor protein on susceptible cells. On the other hand, it is intriguing that it is possible to provoke antibody to a heterotypic determinant in the virus which is otherwise silent even with repetitive doses of conventional FMD vaccine. This suggests that the use of carefully tailored synthetic antigens could allow the stimulation of useful immune responses where either antigenic variability or lack of immunogenicity of a whole pathogen makes the induction of a protective immune response difficult or impossible.

The outstanding disadvantage of our synthetic FMD vaccines is the failure to induce high levels of protection in cattle following a single dose of peptide vaccine despite the presence of very high titres of neutralizing antibody. This observation is strongly indicative of qualitative differences between antibodies induced by virus and synthetic peptide vaccines.

Nevertheless, the titres obtained with our peptide vaccines allow some optimism for their future as commercially viable alternatives to conventional preparations. A number of approaches can be considered to induce qualitatively superior immune responses. For example, the route of administration and the structure of these peptides in relation to T-cell epitopes could influence greatly the immune response of the target species. With regard to T-cell epitopes, the incorporation of potent sequences may effect more relevant isotype switching and memory induction and work is in progress to examine these questions. In the case of route and mode of administration, there is the possibility of targeting the peptides towards more appropriate antigen presenting cells and stimulating more effective immune responses by means of novel adjuvants. Perhaps the most attractive, and in the case of developing countries, the most economic and practical approach, is to deliver peptides by means of an attenuated viral vector acceptable for use in farm animals. Given these options, the prospects for commercial synthetic FMD vaccines remain good.

REFERENCES

Black, L., Nicholls, M.J., Rweyemamu, M.M., Ferrari, R. and Zunino, M.A. (1986). Foot-and-mouth disease vaccination: a multifactorial study of the influence of antigen dose and potentially competitive immunogens on the response of cattle of different ages. *Research in Veterinary Science,* **40**, 303–307.

DiMarchi, R., Brooke, G., Gale, C., Cracknell, V., Doel, T. and Mowat, N. (1986). Protection of cattle against FMD by a synthetic peptide. *Science,* **232**, 639–641.

Doel, T.R. and Baccarini, P.J. (1981). Thermal stability of foot-and-mouth disease virus. *Archives of Virology,* **70**, 21–32.

Doel, T.R., Gale, C., Brooke, G. and DiMarchi, R. (1988). Immunization against foot-and-mouth disease with synthetic peptides representing the C-terminal region of VP1. *Journal of General Virology,* **69**, 2403–2406.

Doel, T.R., Gale, C., Do Amaral, C.M.C.F., Brooke, G., Mulcahy, G. and DiMarchi, R. (1990). Heterotypic protection induced by synthetic peptides corresponding to three serotypes of foot-and-mouth disease virus. *Journal of Virology,* **64**, 2260–2264.

Doel, T.R. and Staple, R.F. (1982). The elution of foot-and-mouth disease virus from vaccines adjuvanted with aluminium hydroxide and with saponin. *Journal of Biological Standards,* **10**, 182–195.

Fox, G., Parry, N., Barnett, P., McGinn, B., Rowlands, D. and Brown, F. (1989). The cell attachment site on foot-and-mouth disease virus includes the amino acid sequence RGD (Arginine-Glycine-Aspartic Acid). *Journal of General Virology*, **70**, 625–637.

Kleid, D.G., Yansura, D., Small, B., Dowbenko, D., Moore, D.M., Grubman, M.J., McKercher, P.D., Morgan, D.O., Robertson, B.H. and Bachrach, H.L. (1981). Cloned viral protein vaccine for foot-and-mouth disease: responses in cattle and swine. *Science*, **214**, 1125–1129.

Knudsen, R.C., Groocock, C.M. and Andersen, A.A. (1979). Immunity to foot-and-mouth disease virus in guinea pigs: clinical and immune responses. *Infection and Immunity*, **24**, 787–792.

Mulcahy, G., Gale, C., Robertson, P., Iyisan, S., DiMarchi, R. and Doel, T.R. (1990). Isotype responses of infected, vaccinated and peptide-vaccinated cattle to FMDV. *Vaccine*, **8**, 249–256.

Strohmaier, K., Franze, R. and Adam, K.H. (1982). Location and characterization of the antigenic portion of the FMDV immunizing protein. *Journal of General Virology*, **59**, 295–308.

5.3

Genetically Engineered Vaccines against Rabies and Parasites

J.P. LECOCQ
TRANSGENE S.A., Strasbourg, France

ABSTRACT

Contrary to popular belief, rabies remains an important problem in the world today. Despite extensive prophylactic measures such as poisoning and gassing, wild animals (foxes in Europe, raccoons in the U.S.A.) remain the reservoir of the virus. The control of the disease is thus extremely difficult. In collaboration with the Wistar Institute, Philadelphia, U.S.A. we recently developed a recombinant vaccinia virus expressing the rabies glycoprotein (Kieny *et al*, 1984). After a single inoculation of the live recombinant virus, laboratory animals are protected against intracerebral challenge with virulent rabies virus (Lecocq *et al*, 1985) . The vaccine is also totally efficient when used for oral administration and is thus suitable for vaccination of wild animals. A preliminary field trial was organized in Belgium in October 1987 (Pastoret *et al*, 1988) and the outstanding success of the experiment led the Belgian authorities to extend such trials in 1989 and convinced the French to initiate independent trials in November 1988.

Along with malaria, schistosomiasis remains the most important disease in humans. Recent WHO estimations indicate 200 million affected people with 800,000 deaths per year. Immunization of the human population would represent major advance for public health in many developing countries.

In collaboration with Professor Capron's laboratory, we have cloned (Balloul *et al*, 1987) a cDNA encoding a 28k antigen of *Schistosoma mansoni*. This antigen is in fact a glutathion transferase excreted by the parasite (Taylor *et al*, 1988). Recombinant protein expressed in *E. coli* and yeast induced significant protection not only in mice and hamsters, but also in baboons. The 28 k antigen thus appears a very promising candidate for vaccine against schistosomiasis.

REFERENCES

Balloul *et al* (1987). ?, **326**, 149–153.
Kieny, M.P. *et al* (1984). *Nature,* **312**, 163–166.
Lecocq, J.P. *et al* (1985). *Annales de Médecine Vétérinaire,* **129**, 249–261.
Pastoret, P.P. *et al* (1988). *Veterinary Record,* **123**, 481–483.
Taylor *et al* (1988). *EMBO Journal,* **7**, 465–472.

5.4

Vaccines against Enteric Pathogens

D. R. SNODGRASS

Moredun Research Institute, Edinburgh, Scotland

INTRODUCTION

One of the major challenges facing veterinary science is the control of the complex disease syndromes that have developed largely as a result of intensification of livestock husbandry. These diseases principally of the respiratory, enteric and reproductive systems have replaced the great plagues as the most important causes of morbidity and mortality in most countries where intensive livestock farming is practised. The study of neonatal diarrhoea in young animals and children is a good example of the way in which conventional approaches to infectious disease research can be combined with modern biotechnology to make significant progress in understanding such a complex syndrome, and to lead towards control through vaccination. This is illustrated by reference to rotavirus vaccine development in man and animals.

ROTAVIRUS

Rotaviruses remained undescribed in the first waves of viral identification in the 1950s and 1960s, largely because they were not amenable to isolation in cell culture by routine techniques. However since they were first described by Mebus, Underdahl, Rhodes and Twiehans (1969) in young calves, they have been identified as significant causes of diarrhoea in virtually all mammalian and avian species studied, perhaps particularly in children (Kapikian, Flores, Hoshino, Midthun, Gorziglia, Green, Chanock, Potash, Sears, Clements, Halsey, Black and Perez-Schael, 1989).

Rotaviruses are endemic in calves and most other species. Infection is a

TABLE 1 *Rotavirus serotypes (defined by VP7).*

Serotype	Host species
1	man
2	man
3	man, primates, horses, pigs, rabbits, mice, dogs, cats
4	man, pigs
5	pigs, horses
6	**cattle**
7	chicken, turkeys
8	man, **cattle**
9	man
10	**cattle**
11	pigs

normal calfhood event, and indeed it is likely that repeated infection throughout life is the norm. The outcome of infection is determined by a complex interaction between the host, the virus, and external influences i.e. the environment. Infection is usually subclinical, and a variety of factors can trigger the switch to clinical disease, probably most importantly the size of the infecting dose. This is exemplified by the significance of poor hygiene, overcrowding, and occurrence later in the calving season.

Immunity in the young animal is largely effected locally in the intestine, either by antibody passively acquired from colostrum (Snodgrass and Wells, 1978) or by both cellular and humoral mechanisms as a result of previous infection.

The genome of rotavirus contains 11 segments of double-stranded RNA. The outer capsid structure of rotavirus consists of two proteins – VP4 of 88 kd is coded for by gene segment 4, and VP7 is a glycosylated protein of 38 kd that is coded for by gene segment 8 or 9 (reviewed by Matsui, Mackow and Greenberg, 1989). Rotavirus serotype is determined by the VP7 reaction, on the basis of both serological reactions by cross-neutralization tests, and by sequencing the variable regions of the VP7 gene (Table 1). There is less information available on the relationships of the VP4s of different rotavirus strains.

Serotype classification is not merely a virologist's convenience, but relates directly to protection. There is good evidence that infection with one serotype protects against reinfection with viruses bearing the same VP4 or VP7, but not if both are distinct (Bohl, Theil and Saif, 1984; Hoshino, Saif, Sereno, Chanock and Kapikian, 1988). Similarly, passive antibody to one serotype will also confer only homotypic protection (Snodgrass, Ojeh, Campbell and

Herring, 1984). This has been demonstrated elegantly by passive immunization of young mice with VP7-specific and VP4-specific monoclonal antibodies (Offit, Shaw and Greenberg, 1986).

It is apparent, therefore, that rotavirus vaccine design must be concerned with stimulating immunity to both VP4 and VP7 of the different rotaviruses that the young animal may be exposed to. The approaches to this have evolved round the quite different concepts of active and passive immunization.

Active immunization

Live oral vaccination of the young calf with an attenuated serotype 6 rotavirus vaccine was developed in the U.S.A. in the early 1970s (Mebus, White, Bass and Twiehaus, 1973). However, its use has been largely discontinued, largely due to the observation that oral live vaccine was promptly neutralized by antibody present in all normal colostrum samples (Van Zaane, Ijzerman and De Leeuw, 1986).

The greatest stimulus to development of oral rotavirus vaccines has come from the high priority given to development of a human rotavirus vaccine. Initially a 'Jennerian' approach was adopted, utilizing the fact that human and animal rotaviruses shared common group antigens (reviewed by Kapikian *et al*, 1989). The same calf serotype 6 strain used initially for calf vaccination was used in children. Early results in Finnish children were quite promising, even although the field challenge virus was of serotype 1. However, results from trials in developing countries suggested a lack of efficacy in this high-challenge epidemiological situation.

Candidate human rotavirus vaccines currently being trialled are based on a simian serotype 3 virus, RRV. Genetic reassortants have been made with only the VP7 genes of serotypes 1, 2 and 4 and the other 10 genes including the VP4 gene from RRV. Thus these four viruses all share the VP4 specificity of RRV, but have VP7 specificities of serotypes 1–4. This quadrivalent vaccine is currently undergoing trials in various countries.

Passive immunization

The concept of passive immunization rests on the immunization of a pregnant dam, and the transfer through colostrum and milk of protective antibodies. It has achieved widespread use as an effective method of protecting young calves against rotavirus diarrhoea.

As rotavirus is endemic, all normal cows have antibody titres to a wide range of rotavirus serotypes. Vaccination of such mature animals produces a response very different from the serotype-specific response of rotavirus-naive young animals and children described above. Vaccination with a serotype 6 vaccine produces heterotypic responses to most or all other rotavirus serotypes (Snodgrass *et al*, 1984). These antibodies are then passed on through colostrum and milk to protect the intestine of the young calf against infection with all the serotypes likely to be encountered. The mechanism of this heterotypic response is not fully understood, but may involve T-helper cells recognizing common rotavirus epitopes.

Thus passive immunization using conventional whole virus vaccines in adjuvant can provide very effective protection against diarrhoea caused by many rotavirus serotypes, although this has so far been widely applied only in cattle. Unfortunately, there are several reports of ineffective commercial vaccines, presumably due to insufficient viral titres and inadequate adjuvants (Waltner-Toews, Martin, Meek, McMillan and Crouch, 1985).

Possible future developments

Biotechnology has already been used in the preparation of the reassortant rotavirus strains being trialled in children. The important epitopes on both VP4 and VP7 have been identified and sequenced (Matsui *et al*, 1989). One possible development is that the appropriate genes will be inserted into genetically disabled *Salmonella* or other vector to deliver these defined antigens into the intestine.

The application of further biotechnological developments to passive immunization is a more formidable task. Any peptide, whether used as a direct vaccine or delivered through a vector, would require to possess the correct T- and B-cell epitopes to stimulate the desired heterotypic response currently achieved by conventional vaccination – a formidable hurdle.

CONCLUSIONS

The progress outlined in rotavirus vaccination has been made by a combination of conventional virology and biotechnology. Existing commercial cattle rotavirus vaccines often contain other antigens, notably fimbriae from enterotoxigenic *Escherichia coli*, and bovine coronavirus. Such vaccines against multiple pathogens that contribute to the aetiology of the same clinical syndrome will become more frequent.

REFERENCES

Bohl, E.H., Theil, K.W. and Saif, L.J. (1984). Isolation and serotyping of porcine rotaviruses and genetic comparison with other rotaviruses. *Journal of Clinical Microbiology*, **19**, 105–111.

Hoshino, Y., Saif, L.J., Sereno, M.M., Chanock, R.M. and Kapikian, A.Z. (1988). Infection and immunity of piglets to either VP3 or VP7 outer capsid protein confers resistance to challenge with a virulent rotavirus bearing the corresponding antigen. *Journal of Virology*, **62**, 744–748.

Kapikian, A.Z., Flores, J., Hoshino, Y., Midthun, K., Gorziglia, M., Green, K.Y., Chanock, R.M., Potash, L., Sears, S.D., Clements, M.L., Halsey, N.A., Black, R.D. and Perez-Schael, I. (1989). Prospects for development of a rotavirus vaccine against rotavirus diarrhea in infants and young children. *Reviews of Infectious Diseases*, **11**, S539–S546.

Matsui, S.M., Mackow, E.R. and Greenberg, H.B. (1989). Molecular determinant of rotavirus neutralization and protection. *Advances in Virus Research*, **36**, 181–214.

Mebus, C.A., Underdahl, N.R. Rhodes, M.B. and Twiehaus, M.J. (1969). Calf diarrhoea (scours): reproduced with a virus from a field outbreak. *University of Nebraska Agricultural Experimental Station Research Bulletin*, **233**, 1-18.

Mebus, C.A., White, R.G., Bass, E.P. and Thiehaus, M.J. (1973). Immunity to neonatal calf diarrhea virus. *Journal of the American Veterinary Medical Association*, **163**, 880-883.

Offit, P.A., Shaw, R.D. and Greenberg, H.B. (1986). Passive protection against rotavirus-induced diarrhea by monoclonal antibodies to surface proteins VP3 and VP7. *Journal of Virology*, **58**, 700-703.

Snodgrass, D.R. and Wells, P.W (1978). Passive immunity in rotaviral infections. *Journal of the American Veterinary Medical Association*, **173**, 565-568.

Snodgrass, D.R., Ojeh, C.K., Campbell, I. and Herring, A.J. (1984). Bovine rotavirus serotypes and their significance for immunization. *Journal of Clinical Microbiology*, **20**, 342-346.

Waltner-Toews, D., Martin, S.W., Meek, A.H., McMillan, I. and Crouch, C.F. (1985). A field trial to evaluate the efficacy of a combined rotavirus-coronavirus/*Escherichia coli* vaccine in dairy cattle. *Canadian Journal of Comparative Medicine*, **49**, 1-9.

Van Zaane, D., Ijzerman, J. and De Leeuw, P.W. (1986). Intestinal antibody response after vaccination and infection with rotavirus of calves fed colostrum with or without rotavirus antibody. *Veterinary Immunology and Immunopathology*, **11**, 45-63.

5.5

Vaccination against Rinderpest – Success and Failure

G. R. SCOTT
Centre for Tropical Veterinary Medicine,
University of Edinburgh, Scotland

INTRODUCTION

The pestilence of 'horned cattel' now called rinderpest is an ancient plague that has probably ravaged cattle every since Neolithic man first domesticated animals more than 5000 years ago. Its original name in English 'steppe murrain' dates from 1490 and reflects the widespread belief in western Europe that the source of the disease was the steppes of eastern Europe and western Asia. The current usage of the German word 'Rinderpest' crept into the language in the latter half of the 19th century. It is an unfortunate euphemism because it hides the threat of devastation, death, despair and destitution implied by the words 'cattle plague' first used in 1551.

Rinderpest belongs to a small notorious group of diseases known to have changed the course of history and it has done so on many occasions because for centuries rinderpest was the inevitable sequel to every major military campaign in the Old World. Military commanders from as early as the 4th and as late as the 19th century favoured Grey Steppe cattle as baggage animals because of their hardiness and resistance to rinderpest and, in doing, so seeded rinderpest into Europe and the Far East at irregular intervals. Work oxen died in their thousands, fields lay fallow, peasants starved and governments collapsed. Examples include the Fall of Rome in the 5th century, the conquest of Christian Europe by Charlemange in the 9th century, the Mongol invasions of Europe by Genghis Khan and Kublai Khan in the 12th and 13th centuries, the preservation of the Habsburg dynasty in central Europe in the 15th and 16th centuries and the Napoleonic wars of the 18th and 19th centuries. The great African pandemic of rinderpest at the end of the

19th century began when cattle in India were purchased as live provisions for the Italian army when it invaded Eritrea in 1889. The disease swept north to the Mediterrean, west to the Atlantic, and south to the Cape of Good Hope changing the fauna of Africa.

And yet the greatest pandemic known was initiated with trade cattle shipped from Dalmatia across the Adriatic Sea to Padova in Italy in the first years of the 18th century. A succession of crippling wars disseminated the disease throughout Europe and more than 200 million cattle were estimated to have died between 1711 and 1769.

The 18th century was the century of the Enlightenment, a philosophical movement that stressed the importance of reason in the critical reappraisal of existing ideas. The havoc brought by rinderpest attracted the intelligensia. Dr. Bernardino Ramazini Professor of Medicine at Padova University studied the disease at first-hand and wrote the first accurate description of the clinical signs and post mortem lesions of rinderpest. Dr. Giovanni Lancisi, personal physician of Pope Clement the XIth, investigated the nature of the disease, recognized its contagiousness and formulated measures to contain the plague, measures as applicable today as in 1714. Thomas Bates, surgeon to King George I, independently recommended similar measures that successfully eradicated the disease from England. Memories however were short and Bates's advice went unheeded when rinderpest again broke out in England 30 years later and persisted for a further 11 years. Henri Bertin, Controller-General of Finances in France recognized the need for a cadre of trained manpower to combat rinderpest and other animal diseases and he provided funds to found the first modern veterinary school at Lyons in 1762 with this objective. Other states were quick to follow; by the end of the century there were 17 new veterinary schools in mainland Europe. The spur to found the first veterinary schools in Africa and Asia was also the need to combat rinderpest.

Rinderpest is caused by a virus that is the archetype of the Morbillivirus genus of the Paramyxoviridae family of single-stranded RNA viruses. The other well-known members of the genus are measles virus of man, canine distemper virus and peste-des-petits-ruminants virus. Probable but still unofficial members of the genus are PMV 107 virus isolated from German cattle with encephalitis, *Paramyxovirus callithrix* isolated from marmosets with stomatitis and gastroenteritis, Hh1 isolated from hedgehogs with encephalitis in England and, more recently phocine distemper virus isolated from North Sea seals. The morbilliviruses not only look alike they have similar physical chemical properties, share antigens and exist as single serotypes. They are all highly immunogenic. Rinderpest virus, moreover, fulfils Thomas Francis Jr's Group 2 criterion of viruses that induce diseases in which infection does not persist but immunity does (Table 1). In other words, rinderpest virus is an ideal candidate for the production of a vaccine. The twin markers of horrific pathogenicity and high immunogenicity have singled out rinderpest virus for close research attention and it is not surprising that work

TABLE 1 *Francis's classification of virus diseases.*

Group	Infectious virus persists	Protective immunity persists	Example
1	+	–	African swine fever
2	–	+	Rinderpest
3	–	–	Newcastle disease
4	+	+	Bovine rhinotracheitis

on rinderpest virus has been at the forefront of and has often led biotechnological advances in vaccine development and production.

FIRST GENERATION VACCINE: VARIOLATION

Mr. Dobson, a 'Gentleman of Yorkshire' is credited with being the first to immunize cattle against rinderpest. He adapted the Asiatic technique of in-grafting known as variolation introduced into England in 1721 by Lady Mary Wortley Montagu wife of his Majesty's ambassador to Turkey to protect children from smallpox. Mr. Dobson by dipping coarse wool fibres or tow in the morbid discharges from the nostrils and eyes of an infected beast and inserting them into an incision in the dewlap protected nine out of ten of his cattle. In China and India in-grafting had been practised for centuries and it is likely that the practitioners there had applied the technique to cattle to protect them from rinderpest then thought by many to be a virulent cattle pox.

Mr. Dobson's 90% success in protecting his cattle in 1754 spurred others to emulate his methods. Professor P. Camper, in particular, in the Netherlands popularized the cult of inoculation in the 1770s thereby, according to Fleming the 19th century veterinary historian, ensuring the longevity of rinderpest in Europe!

SECOND GENERATION VACCINES: ATTENUATED VIRUSES

Jessen's dried infected seton

Russia was greatly troubled by rinderpest in the first half of the 19th century. The role of variolation, therefore, was re-examined and found wanting until 1853 when Professor P. Jessen carried out preliminary trials in cattle at Odessa using physically attenuated 'virus'. Setons of cotton threads soaked in the 'plague matter' were dried and stored in a cool place before being threaded through the skin of the dewlap of susceptible cattle. If the setons provoked a nonfatal reaction lifelong protection against rinderpest ensued. If the setons failed to provoke a reaction the 'virus' was considered to be over-attenuated and the inoculated animals were deemed still susceptible. These Russian attentuation studies were carried out 25 years before Pasteur turned his attention to the study of the causes and prevention of infectious diseases in man and animals.

In the latter half of the 19th century most European states banned the import of cattle from the Russian Empire following the disastrous European pandemic of 1857–1866. The loss of this important source of income stimulated the Tsar's government to take constructive steps towards elucidating the cause of rinderpest and to develop methods for its control. Rinderpest Vaccine Experiment Stations were established in various parts of the Empire to exploit Jessen's technique and several thousand cattle were immunized. The results were equivocal; the group of experimenters led by Professor Semmer known as the Dorpat faction claimed their preventive inoculation was the way to control rinderpest whereas the St Petersburg faction lead by Professor Ravich denounced the method as being far too risky. The latter view prevailed and the technique was abandoned.

TABLE 2 *Second generation vaccines.*

1853	Jessen's dried infected setons.
1893	Semmer's immune serum.
1896	Theiler's immune serum followed by virulent blood.
1897	Koch's bile method.
1898	Simultaneous immune serum and virulent blood.
1899	Edington's glycerinated bile followed by virulent blood
1931	Jacotot's dried infected spleen powder.

Semmer's immune serum

Although Raynaud had demonstrated in animals passive protection against vaccinia by injecting convalescent serum as early as 1877 no attention was paid to the phenomenon until Emil von Behring published his seminal paper in 1890 showing that the immunity of rabbits to tetanus was associated with antitoxin properties of their serum. Shortly afterwards Professor Semmer working in Russia found that serum drawn from animal recently recovered from rinderpest had protective properties. The Vaccine Experiment Stations in Russia were retitled Serum Production Centres. However the protection conferred by antiserum, as it was called, was shortlived. Nevertheless, the technique of injecting antiserum alone was in vogue in many countries in Africa, Asia and Europe up until the 1920s.

Immune serum and virulent blood

Theiler and his colleagues in South Africa utilized the protective powers of immune serum to mitigate the pathogenicity of virulent blood which they injected several days after injecting the immune serum. Kolle and Turner shortly afterwards simplified the technique by injecting the immune serum and the virulent blood simultaneously. Ideally the injected animal reacted and developed a mild attack of rinderpest. Animals that failed to react might or might not be immunized. Occasionally a nonreactor contracted rinderpest from one of the reacting animals. Claims that the overall mortality rate was less than 1% seem optimistic; nevertheless the serum-virus simultaneous method was a significant advance over all previous methods and was the key preventive measure adopted in tropical Africa and Asia up until the 1930s. The logistics involved were formidable because of the need to obtain a regular supply of susceptible animals every five days to maintain the virulent virus. A major drawback to the method was the risk of inadvertently transmitting other bovine pathogens along with the blood.

Koch's bile method

In the 1890s Professor Robert Koch was one of several European scientists that accepted an invitation from the Cape Government to investigate the pandemic of rinderpest then ravaging Africa. He confirmed the claims of Boer farmers that bile from animals that had died of rinderpest protected susceptible animals when injected into them and within a year more than two million cattle had been successfully inoculated with bile. The bile was obtained from sick animals killed five or six days after the onset of illness. It had to be collected fresh because it decomposed quickly, and, if not used in two to three days, became inert. When rinderpest bile was mixed with virulent blood and the mixture injected into a susceptible animal no reaction ensued but the animal was immune to challenge. Bile from normal animals had no protective nor immunizing powers. The immunity conferred by Koch's bile method lasted for only three to six months. The method in the hands of others was not so successful; some claimed no protection and others reported that rinderpest resulted. The major drawbacks, however, were, first, the small number of animals (25–50) that could be inoculated with bile from one sick animal and, secondly, the transient duration of the immunity induced. Interestingly the mode of action of bile protecting against rinderpest has yet to be elucidated; Professor Koch believed that the infectivity of the virus in the bile was restrained by the presence of an albuminoid chemical in the bile.

Two years later Dr. A. Edington introduced improvements by adding glycerine to the bile to attenuate its virulence coupled with an injection of virulent blood ten days after the bile injection.

Jacotot's dried spleen powder

Dr. H. Jacotot working in Indo-China in the 1930s demonstrated that a vaccine could be prepared by drying and powdering the spleens of infected cattle. The powdered spleens retained their immunogenicity if kept in the dark at ambient temperatures.

THIRD GENERATION VACCINES: INACTIVATED VIRUSES

In the late 18th century a Frenchman, Dr. Vicq d'Azyr, found that Dobson's method of immunization often killed. He therefore tried to destroy the virulence of the inoculum by steeping the setons of tow soaked with 'matter' in oils, aromatic fluids, acids and ammonia; unhappily cattle threaded with the treated setons all developed rinderpest.

Kakizaki's glycerinized vaccine

While studying the properties of the causative agent of rinderpest Robert Koch noted in South Africa that glycerine inactivated the infectivity of the agent. This phenomenon was exploited by Dr. C. Kakizaki in Japan who showed that when rinderpest virus present in the blood and spleen of an infected animal was treated with glycerine it became noninfective and remained noninfective when kept at 6° C for three months without losing its immunogenic properties. Dr. Kakizaki's original papers were published in Japanese and his work remained unheralded until he published a review in English in 1918. Meantime independently in the Philippines Dr. W.C. Boynton also developed an inactivated vaccine using tissue extracts particularly spleen, lymph gland and liver which were minced with phenol-glycerine.

TABLE 3 *Third generation vaccines.*

1906	Kakizaki's glycerinized organ pulp.
1917	Boynton's phenol-glycerine organ pulp.
1926	Curasson and Delpy's formalized spleen.
1931	Prunier's lipo-vaccine.
1950	Delpy's saponin-adjuvanted formalized pulp.
1958	Adjuvanted inactivated cell-cultured virus.

The treated mixture was heated for three hours at 42° C and then stored in the refrigerator for one to six months before use. Cattle were inoculated subcutaneously and boosted with a second inoculation seven days later.

The inactivated vaccines were safer and more reliable than the serum-virus simultaneous method of immunization. Cattle inoculated with the inactivated vaccines did not develop a clinical reaction, did not propagate the virus, and did not transmit infection to in-contact susceptible animals. Moreover the vaccines did not transmit protozoal diseases and they could be used in rinderpest-free areas without risk. Most inactivated vaccines were issued as fluid preparations and the problems arising from the sheer bulk of the vaccines led to the development of techniques for powdering the vaccines and issuing them in the dried state. The first powdered vaccines were dried in desiccators over sulphuric acid *in vacuo*, a technique superseded in the late 1930s by lyophilization. The major drawback however was the short duration of immunity induced that required at least annual revaccination.

Kakizaki's and Boynton's findings stimulated laboratories throughout the rinderpest-endemic areas to attempt to produce this new safe vaccine. Many inactivating agents were used, the favourites being formalin and chloroform.

Ramon's discovery of adjuvants markedly increased the efficacy of the inactivated vaccines. Even Freund's complete adjuvant has been tried and induced high antibody titres in cattle. Unfortunately vaccine with Freund's complete adjuvant provoked persistent and objectionable lesions at or near the site of inoculation and the vaccine had to be withdrawn. Today emergency stocks of inactivated vaccines are available in disease-free countries, the source of virus being cell culture-adapted rinderpest virus.

FOURTH GENERATION VACCINES: LIVE VIRUS MODIFIED BY PASSAGE IN ANIMALS

Caprinized rinderpest virus vaccine

Dr. J.T. Edwards was appointed Director of the Imperial Veterinary Research Institute at Mukteswar in the early 1920s. He initiated a major research programme to alleviate the risks associated with the serum-virus simultaneous method of immunization and to ease some of the logistic difficulties associated with the method. To this end, he began experiments in passaging virulent bovine rinderpest virus in goats, sheep and rabbits. Goats proved to be the most useful and he considered that the virus was 'fixed' after serial passages in goats over a period of one year. Thereafter goats were used in the field in India as virus donors in the serum-virus simultaneous method. An unexpected and unplanned bonus was the discovery that after prolonged serial passage in goats the so-called virulent virus had lost its virulence for cattle and lost its epithelial trophism with the result that inoculated goats did not shed the virus and transmit infection to in-contact susceptible animals. Cattle could now be immunized against rinderpest with goat virus alone. Edwards's protocols were never published in detail and scant attention was paid to his discovery outside India. Fortunately Drs. P.T. Saunders and K.K. Ayyar repeated Edwards's study and passaged bovine rinderpest virus serially in 150 goats keeping meticulous records at every stage. Their paper convinced workers elsewhere that something new and valuable had taken place. A major improvement in the production of goat virus was to replace the use of goat blood with pulped spleen tissue dried in desiccators over sulphuric acid. The technique enabled Dr. G. Pfaff to mount a prolonged immunization scheme in the heart of Burma without returning to base.

In Africa Drs. Daubney and Hudson working at the Kabete Veterinary Laboratory in Kenya obtained the Mukteswar strain of caprinized rinderpest virus and found that it was too pathogenic for East African cattle. They therefore started passaging four local strains in goats. One of these strains was the stock virulent bovine strain known as the Kabete 'O' strain and it was from this strain that the Kabete attentuated goat (KAG) vaccine was derived. For the first 84 passages the strain killed all inoculated cattle although the number of days to death steadily increased. At the 83rd passage the first recovery occurred but it was not until the 250th goat passage that it was judged sufficiently free from risk for use in the field for the immunization of East African Shorthorn Zebu cattle. It was still regarded as being too lethal for European cattle or animals with more than 50% European blood. Meantime the Kabete Laboratory had acquired one of the newfangled Stoke lyophilization machines with which Daubney and Hudson produced the first veterinary freeze-dried vaccine using spleen pulp from caprinized rinderpest virus-infected goats. The combination of Edwards's type of attenuated caprinized vaccines and lyophilization in vacuum-sealed ampoules revolutionized the control of rinderpest; for the first time it was possible to produce and store millions of doses of rinderpest vaccine so enabling the planning of mass countrywide vaccination campaigns. The success of such campaigns in controlling rinderpest in East Africa in 1940 moved Daubney to suggest that rinderpest was now eradicable. Although caprinized rinderpest virus vaccine has been supplanted in Africa by cell culture-adapted viruses it is still the most widely used vaccine elsewhere.

Caprinized rinderpest vaccine is far from being the ideal vaccine. Nevertheless its success in controlling rinderpest in endemic areas lessened the fear of the disease amongst stockowners who increasingly demanded a safer vaccine. Less responsible stockowners avoided bringing their susceptible animals forward for vaccination because even cattle with a high innate resistance to rinderpest developed post-vaccinal fevers and serous nasal and lacrimal discharges. These mild clinical signs were normally acceptable because they assured the stockowners that their animals had been properly vaccinated. However caprinized rinderpest virus also depressed lymphocytes with the result that other infections lying latent in the animal were exacerbated occasionally with disastrous results and deaths. In addition vaccinated animals were more prone to superinfections.

In recent years the production costs of caprinized rinderpest vaccine have increased enormously; goats worldwide are expensive and the procurement of steady supplies is logistically more and more difficult. In West Africa, the Sudan, the Middle East, and, more recently, southern India the increasing prevalence of goat plague (peste des petits ruminants) has further complicated the supply of susceptible goats for the production of caprinized rinderpest vaccine.

TABLE 4 *Fourth generation vaccines.*

1928	Edwards's caprinized virus.
1938	Lyophilized KAG virus.
1938	Nakamura III lapinized virus.
1946	Grosse Isle avianized virus.
1950	Hudson and Wongsongsarn's pig-passaged lapinized virus.
1951	Avianized-bovine virus.
1953	Avianized-lapinized virus.
1957	AKO avianized-lapinized virus.

The Botswana Vaccine Institute now uses KAG virus grown in cell cultures as a safe and noninfectious rinderpest challenge virus to test the immune potency of their substrain of Plowright's cell-cultured rinderpest virus vaccine.

Lapinized rinderpest vaccine

A young Japanese veterinarian stationed in Korea, Dr. Junji Nakamura, visited the Indian Veterinary Research Institute at Mukteswar in the early 1920s where he was impressed by Edwards's ideas of passaging the virus in a foreign 'host'. Nakamura returned to Korea and there adapted the Fusan strain of rinderpest virus to rabbits. Even after 600 serial passages in rabbits this strain, then known as the Nakamura III strain, was still too virulent for use as a live virus vaccine in Korean Yellow cattle and Japanese Black cattle. Nevertheless it was used successfully to control rinderpest in the more resistant Mongolian cattle in the early 1940s and it was a major factor in the eradication of rinderpest from China after the Second World War.

An international meeting organized by FAO and held in Nairobi in 1948 focused attention on the possibilites of lapinized rinderpest vaccine. The Nanking National Research Bureau of Animal Industry distributed samples of this new vaccine in that year to countries in Africa and Asia. Several comparative studies quickly showed that the lapinized virus vaccine was much less virulent than caprinized rinderpest vaccine. Thereafter the Nakamura III strain of lapinized vaccine enjoyed a decade of popularity in Asia and in Africa where it was used to protect cattle that reacted too severely to caprinized rinderpest vaccine. The demand for this more attentuated vaccine however always exceeded the supply. The problem was the difficulty of breeding and rearing enough European rabbits in the tropics. Drs. Hudson and Wongsongsarn solved the problem in Thailand by adapting their lapinized virus to pigs as young as two years and the pig-adapted lapinized rinderpest virus vaccine was largely responsible for the eradication of the disease from Thailand.

Grosse Isle avianized rinderpest virus vaccine

The potential role of rinderpest virus as a microbiological weapon was mooted during the Second World War and research to counteract the threat was conducted by a joint US-Canadian commission on Grosse Isle, a former Canadian immigrants' quarantine station in the mouth of the St. Lawrence River. The most promising finding was the development of an avianized vaccine by passaging a virulent bovine strain of rinderpest virus serially in the chorioallantoic membrane of 10-day incubated embryonated hen eggs. After adaptation to the embryonated eggs the passages were continued by the yolk sac route. The field trials of the Grosse Isle avianized vaccine were carried out in East Africa and in China. It proved to be more attenuated than caprinized rinderpest vaccine but unfortunately its keeping qualities were poor and the strain was lost.

Japanese avianized rinderpest virus vaccines

Publication of the findings at Grosse Isle stimulated several groups to attempt to passage rinderpest virus in embryonated hen eggs. Only the Japanese persevered; they developed two lines, one direct from the virulent bovine Fusan strain of the virus and the other from the Nakamura III lapinized strain. Although the bovine strain passaged in the yolk sacs of embryonated eggs lost its virulence it never became attenuated enough to protect the local cattle. However, when it was sent to East Africa for testing it was considered to be more attenuated than the caprinized strain but less attenuated than the Nakamura III lapinized strain. Further trials led to the conclusion that the avianized yolk sac strain was not as satisfactory in practice as the lapinized vaccine.

Further passages of the avianized bovine yolk sac strain were made in eggs by the intravenous route and further attenuation resulted. Meantime passage of the Nakamura III lapinized strain intravenously in embryonated eggs resulted in further attenuation of the virus, such that it could be used safely to immunize the hyper-susceptible Japanese Black cattle. Because of the difficulty of detecting rinderpest virus in embryonated eggs the avianized-lapanized strain was back-passaged in rabbits. After a series of alternative passages the lapinized-avianized-lapinized virus was passaged continuously by the yolk sac route in embryonated eggs to give a new line, the AKO line of rinderpest virus vaccine which was widely used in south-east Asia. The other avianized rinderpest virus strains never proceeded beyond field trials.

FIFTH GENERATION VACCINES: LIVE VIRUSES MODIFIED BY PASSAGE IN CELL CULTURES

Plowright's cell-cultured rinderpest virus vaccine

Production problems with both the lapinized and avianized rinderpest virus vaccines severely limited the number of doses that could be produced. Dr. Walter Plowright solved the problem by passaging the Kabete 'O' virulent bovine strain of virus serially in cultures of calf kidney cells. At first there was an exaltation of its virulence but after the 10th serial passage a steady lowering of the virulence was observed. Only a few rinderpest-susceptible cattle injected with the 45th passage virus exhibited mild transient fevers. Further passages increased the attenuation and the vaccine was supplied to Nigeria at its 65th passage level and was used there as a vaccine. In East Africa the virus was used as a vaccine between the 90th and 96th passage. Plowright's vaccine is arguably the best veterinary virus vaccine so far developed; it is so well-attenuated that post-vaccinal reactions in all species of domestic and wild animals so far tested have not been observed and are not expected. The immunity induced in fully susceptible cattle free of maternal antibodies is lifelong. Like its parent strain it grows only in lymphoid cells of inoculated animals and so is noninfectious. Nevertheless it has only a minor effect on lymphocytes and therefore does not potentiate latent pathogens or exacerbate super-infections. Protection through interference develops within 3–5 days of vaccination. The attenuation is stable and serial back-passages in cattle do not alter the level of attenuation.

Plowright's rinderpest cell-cultured virus vaccine is cheap to produce and easy to assay for both potency and safety. A major drawback is its innocuity in vaccinated animals. Unlike caprinized rinderpest virus vaccine neither the vaccinator nor the stockowner can assess if viable vaccine has been administered or not. In the emergency conditions that occurred in 1983 in Nigeria when the country was ravished with rinderpest numerous entrepreneurs exploited the known innocuity of rinderpest cell-cultured vaccine and offered to vaccinate cattle for a high fee using poultry vaccines of which there were ample supplies in Nigeria. The disease continued unchecked and the Fulani stockowners clamoured for the authorities to bring back the 'vaccine that made the animals cry'. It is essential therefore that the efficiency of a rinderpest vaccination campaigned be assessed by returning later to bleed identified animals for serum so that antibody levels can be determined.

An unexpected drawback of rinderpest cell-cultured vaccine that has arisen in recent years stems from the requirements laid down by the World Health Organisation for the production of a rinderpest cell-cultured vaccine (live) which stressed that only primary calf kidney cells were to be used in the production of the vaccine. The requirements also laid down procedures for ensuring that the calf kidney cell cultures were free of infection with bovine virus diarrhoea virus but sadly few production laboratories in fact carry out these procedures; too many cattle in Africa and Asia have been inoculated simultaneously with rinderpest cell culture virus and bovine virus diarrhoea virus.

TABLE 5 *Fifth generation vaccines.*

1959	Plowright's BK cell-cultured attenuated Kabete 'O' rinderpest virus.
1961	Isogai's BK cell-cultured derivative of the Nakamura III lapinized virus.
1963	Russian BK cell-cultured derivative of the Nakamura III lapinized virus.
1970	Mirchamsy's Vero cell-cultured derivative of Plowright's cell-cultured attenuated Kabete 'O' virus.
1971	Japanese Vero cell-cultured derivative of the Nakamura III lapinized virus.
1972	Provost and Borredon's heat-stable derivative of Plowright's cell-cultured attenuated Kabete 'O' virus combined with KH_3J pleuropneumonia vaccine.
1976	Sonoda's Vero cell-cultured AKO lapinized-avianized-lapinized virus.
1976	Bansal and Joshi's lamb kidney cell-cultured derivative of Plowright's cell-cultured attenuated Kabete 'O' virus.
1990	Mariner's heat-stable, Vero cell-cultured derivative of Plowright's cell-cultured attenuated Kabete 'O' virus.

Plowright's rinderpest cell culture virus vaccine also has a logistic snag. The shelf-life of the freeze-dried vaccine above 50° C is very short and after reconstitution the virus loses its potency within 40–60 minutes at ambient tropical temperatures. An expensive cold-chain infrastructure is therefore essential and it has to be closely monitored and supervised.

Derivatives of Plowright's cell-cultured rinderpest virus

In an attempt to alleviate the shelf-life problem of Plowright's virus vaccine, Drs. Provost and Borredon selected a heat-resistant clone of the cell-cultured rinderpest virus which retained its potency after freeze-drying for 15 days at 45° C. More recently Dr. Mariner and his colleagues working in Niger have achieved the classical stability bench-mark of immunogenic potency after exposure to 30° C for 30 days that was used as the standard for vaccinia vaccines. Dr. Mariner exploited the fact first demonstrated by Dr. Mirchamsy and his colleagues in Iran that Plowright's cell culture rinderpest virus strain grew to high titres in Vero-cell cultures. The higher yield ensured that after 30 days at 30° C there was still sufficient virus to induce a solid immunity. Mariner demonstrated the practicability of his technique by carrying out a rinderpest vaccination campaign in Niger without refrigeration using instead boxes wrapped in soaked hessian exposed to air currents while in the shade. Evaporation from the damp hessian maintained a temperature within the box between 26 and 30° C.

An added advantage of the Vero-cell derivative vaccine is that its production obviates the risk of contamination with bovine virus diarrhoea virus or other bovine pathogens in harvested bovine kidneys and serum supplements if the latter are gamma-irradiated. A potential hazard, however, was identified in Japan where the growth of rinderpest virus in Vero-cells selected an undesirable mutant that persistently infected the cells; hitherto rinderpest virus unlike distemper and measles viruses has not been known to induce persistent infections.

In India socio-cultural considerations limit the availability of calf kidneys and the use of cattle for testing the potency and safety of attenuated cell culture-adapted rinderpest vaccine. Plowright's cell culture-adapted rinderpest virus, therefore, was adapted to grow in lamb kidney cells and the resultant vaccine has characteristics similar to the original cell culture-adapted virus. The potency and safety testing of the lamb kidney cell vaccine was carried out in buffalo calves instead of cattle.

In Francophone Africa Plowright's cell-cultured rinderpest virus vaccine was combined with the KH$_3$J strain of live contagious bovine pleuropneumonia vaccine and used in mass vaccination campaigns against both diseases. Although there was no significant effect on the immunity induced to each agent the incidence of post-vaccinal lesions at the inoculation sites has limited the popularity of the dual vaccine to Francophone Africa.

In Kenya Dr. P.B. Rossiter and his colleagues grew Plowright's cell-cultured rinderpest virus in cloned lymphoblastoid cell lines that had been immortalized by the persistent presence of *Theileria parva*. The titres attained by the rinderpest virus were so high that the authors predicted that the technique offered advantages for biochemical studies and even vaccine production.

Cell-cultured derivatives of Nakamura III lapinized rinderpest virus

Plowright's success in adapting bovine rinderpest virus to cell culture was quickly followed by reports from Japan of the adaptation of Nakamura's III lapinized rinderpest virus. The first derivative was the adaptation of the lapinized virus to bovine kidney cells in 1961 and to Vero-cells in 1971. Russian workers also propagated the Nakamura III virus in cultures of bovine kidney cells and this vaccine is, today, used in the U.S.S.R. to protect its borders.

In 1976 a new type of cell-cultured virus vaccine was developed by the Japanese using the AKO line of lapinized-avianized-lapinized virus grown in Vero-cells. This vaccine is now stockpiled in Japan for emergency use. Meantime in Korea the avianized-lapinized rinderpest virus was adapted to fowl embryo fibroblasts for the production of rinderpest vaccine.

SIXTH GENERATION VACCINES: RECOMBINANT VIRUSES

Not surprisingly, the attention of the biological engineers developing new vaccines using recombinant DNA technology quickly turned to rinderpest virus because of its high immunogenicity. Consequently a sixth generation of recombinant rinderpest vaccines has been created in America, Europe and Asia. All the research groups favoured vaccinia virus as the vector because of its long history as an easily administered vaccine, its exceptional heat-stability, its wide host range, and its large DNA capacity that permits easy introduction of foreign genes. A further claimed advantage of vaccinia virus recombinant vaccines was their suitability for production in countries with poor technical infrastructures.

Yilma's vaccinia-recombinant-rinderpest virus

Dr. T.D. Yilma and his colleagues in the U.S.A. were the first in the field when they constructed on to the Wyeth strain of vaccinia virus recombinants expressing H- or F-genes cloned from the original highly virulent Kabete 'O' strain of rinderpest virus at the Plum Island Animal Disease Center. The recombinant vaccines were applied through a simple skin scratch, an unskilled technique using the simplest of equipment that induced a visible tissue reaction or 'take' at the scarified site that indicated that viable virus had been administered.

The vaccinia-recombinant-rinderpest-virus vaccines were administered to cattle intradermally in two doses, four weeks apart. All the vaccinated cattle developed neutralizing antibodies, but the antibody responses in the cattle receiving the recombinant expressing the rinderpest F-gene were significantly lower than the responses in cattle given the recombinant expressing the rinderpest H-gene and to the responses of cattle injected once with Plowright's cell-cultured rinderpest virus vaccine. The latter two vaccines had similar antibody titres 28 days after a single dose namely 1/208. After two doses the titre induced by the recombinant expressing the rinderpest H-gene was higher than that induced by a single dose of Plowright's vaccine; the difference however was not statistically significant. All the vaccinated cattle including the two animals vaccinated with the recombinant expressing the F-gene withstood challenge with virulent rinderpest virus at 42 days after primary vaccination.

When single doses of the recombinant vaccines only were used in a second trial the recombinants expressing the F-gene induced antibody levels 35-fold lower than the other recombinant vaccines which induced titres slightly lower than Plowright's cell-cultured vaccine. All the vaccinated animals survived challenge with virulent rinderpest virus but 8 of the 15 cattle given recombinant vaccines had four-fold or higher increases in neutralizing antibodies induced by challenge indicating that replication of the challenge virus had probably occurred. In short, solid immunity with recombinant vaccine required two doses.

TABLE 6 *Sixth generation vaccines.*

1988	Yilma's vaccinia-recombinant rinderpest virus.
1989	Barrett's vaccinia-recombinant rinderpest virus.
1989	Yamanouchi's vaccinia-recombinant rinderpest virus.

Barrett's vaccinia-recombinant-rinderpest virus

Meantime at Pirbright Dr. T. Barrett and his group had more success when they inserted the F-protein gene, from Plowright's cell-cultured rinderpest vaccine virus into the thymidine kinase gene of the WR1 strain of vaccinia virus. Rabbits vaccinated intradermally with this recombinant F-gene virus developed antibodies detectable by ELISA but the titres varied widely and only five out of eight rabbits had neutralizing antibodies. The vaccinated rabbits survived challenge although all but two developed post-challenge fevers and diarrhoeas. In a subsequent trial in which F-gene recombinant vaccine was injected intradermally into cattle and pigs, half the 12 cattle and all the three pigs developed neutralizing antibodies within four weeks of a single dose of the vaccine being administered. Six cattle were given a second dose of vaccine and exhibited anamnestic antibody responses although the resulting antibody titres remained low. The antibody responses in the three pigs given a second dose of vaccine were significantly higher. Neither the vaccinated cattle nor the vaccinated pigs developed fevers or other clinical signs when challenged but the increases in neutralizing antibodies were very significant indicating that 'a low level of rinderpest virus lachrymation had occurred'.

Yamanouchi's vaccinia-recombinant-rinderpest virus

In Japan Dr. Yamanouchi's group inserted the H-protein gene into the Lister vaccine strain of vaccinia virus using two different promoters. When they tested each vaccine in seven rabbits using the intradermal route, the vaccinated rabbits developed low titres of neutralizing antibodies as well as anti-H precipitating antibodies. When challenged intravenously with the virulent L strain of lapinized rinderpest virus 13 of the 14 rabbits did not show clinical signs. However, one rabbit that had had a very low neutralizing titre before challenge had a mild transient fever, lost weight, and was immunosuppressed. The eight control rabbits developed typical clinical signs of rinderpest 2–7 days after challenge and four died.

As yet none of these vaccinia-recombinant-rinderpest virus vaccines possesses the immunogenicity of Plowright's cell culture vaccine and their heat stability is no better than Mariner's Vero-cell derivative of Plowright's vaccine. In their present stage of development none warrants or is likely to proceed to field trials.

Major problems with vaccinia-recombinant-virus vaccines that have been glossed over by the bioengineers, are the virulence of vaccinia virus itself and the risk of hybridization with other indigenous pox viruses present in the immunized host species. The known risks from vaccinia are not inconsiderable; Behbehani estimated in a paper in the 1983 issue of Microbiological Reviews that 1,000 serious complications occurred per one million vaccinations in man, that 18 required hospitalization and one per million died. The current pandemic of HIV, however, has so enhanced the risks that Dr. B.R. Bloom predicted in an authoritative paper on vaccines in the Third World that plans to immunize millions of cattle in Africa against rinderpest using recombinant-vaccinia-virus expressing rinderpest antigens are bound to result in adventitious infection of the vaccinators unless they are pre-immunized against vaccinia virus.

Recent experiments in the U.S.A. on the response of dairy calves to vaccinia virus expressing foreign genes was manifested by localized pocks at the sites of inoculation from which virus could be isolated indicating replication of the vaccinia virus. Attempts to recover vaccinia virus from the blood of three infected calves failed. Nevertheless it is pertinent to remember that 50 years ago it was shown that vaccinia virus applied to the scarified skin of cattle can generalize and, if the animals are pregnant, will colonize the amnion to produce considerable amounts of virus in the amniotic fluid.

The virulence of vaccinia virus can be decreased by insertion or deletion of genes not essential for its multiplication. For example, inactivation of the thymidine kinase gene, the growth gene factor, the haemagglutinin gene and the block of genes near the left end of the vaccinia virus genome greatly attenuate the virulence of vaccinia virus for mice. Similarly, the insertion of lymphokine genes will also decrease the virulence. Nevertheless the risk is not eliminated.

Hopefully given luck and good fortune the global eradication of rinderpest will be achieved before vaccinia-recombinant-rinderpest-virus vaccines are fit to be licensed for use!

RECOMMENDED FURTHER READING

Behbehani, A.M. (1983). The smallpox story: life and death of an old disease. *Microbiological Reviews*, **47**, 455–509.

Belsham, G.J., Anderson, E.C., Murray, P.K., Anderson, J. and Barrett, T. (1989). Immune response and protection of cattle and pigs generated by a vaccinia virus recombinant expressing the F protein of rinderpest virus. *Veterinary Record*, **124**, 655–658.

Blaker, G.H. (1936). Intra-uterine vaccinia in pregnant animals. *Indian Medical Gazette*, **71**, 446–449.

Bloom, B.R. (1989). Vaccines for the Third World. *Nature*, London, **342**, 115–120.

Curasson, G. (1932). *La Peste Bovine*. Paris: Vigot.

Daubney, R. (1948). Immunization against rinderpest by means of the goat-adapted virus. *Proceedings of the Fourth International Congress of Tropical Medicine and Malaria, Washington, 1948*, **2**, 1358–1365.

Edwards, J.T. (1928). Rinderpest; active immunization by means of the serum simultaneous method; goat virus. *Agricultural Journal of India*, **23**, 185–189.

Fleming, G. (1871). *Animal Plagues: their History, Nature and Prevention.* London: Chapman and Hall.

Hudson, J.R. and Wongsongsarn, C. (1950). The utilisation of pigs for the production of lapinised rinderpest virus. *British Veterinary Journal*, **106**, 453–472.

Kakizaki, C. (1918). Study on the glycerinated rinderpest vaccine. *Kitasato Archives of Experimental Medicine*, **2**, 59–66.

Kesteven, K.V.L. (ed.) (1949). *Rinderpest Vaccines. Their Production and Use in the Field, Washington*: Food and Agriculture Organization.

Kolle, W. and Turner, G. (1897). Ueber den Fortgang der Rinderpest-forschungen in Koch's Versuchestation in Kimberley. Mit spezieller Berücksichtigung einer Immunisirungsmethode durch gleichzeitige Einspritzung der Thiere mit virulentem Infektionsstoff (Blut kranker Thiere) und Serum hochimmunisirter Thiere. *Deutsche Medizinische Wochenschrift*, **23**, 793–795.

Mariner, J.C., van den Ende, M.C., House, J.A., Mebus, C.A., Salifou, S. and Stem, C. (1990). The serological response to a thermostable Vero cell-adapted rinderpest vaccine under field conditions in Niger. *Veterinary Microbiology*, **22**, 119–127.

Mirchamsy, H., Shafyi, A. and Bahrami, S. (1970). Use of Vero cells for titration of rinderpest virus and its neutralizing antibody. *Applied Microbiology*, **19**, 545–546.

Nakamura, J., Wagatuma, S. and Fukusho, K. (1938). [On the experimental infection with rinderpest virus in the rabbit. I. Some fundamental experiments.] *Journal of the Japanese Society of Veterinary Science*, **17**, 185–204. (In Japanese). Abstracted in the *Veterinary Bulletin*, **8**, 639 (1938).

Pfaff, G. (1938). Immunization against rinderpest with special reference to the use of dried goat spleen. *Onderstepoort Journal of Veterinary Science*, **11**, 261–330.

Plowright, W. (1962). The application of monolayer tissue culture techniques in rinderpest research. II. The use of attenuated culture virus as a vaccine for cattle. *Bulletin de l'Office International des Epizooties*, **57**, 253–277.

Saunders, L.Z. (1980). *Veterinary Pathology in Russia, 1860–1930*. Ithaca: Cornell University Press.

Saunders, P.T. and Ayyar, K.K. (1936). An experimental study of rinderpest virus in goats in a series of 150 direct passages. *Indian Journal of Veterinary Science*, **6**, 1–86.

Sonoda, A. (1983). Production of rinderpest tissue culture live vaccine. *Journal of Agricultural Research Quarterly*, **17**, 191–198.

Tsukiyama, K., Yoshikawa, Y., Kamata, H., Imoaka, K., Asano, K., Funahashi, S., Maruyama, T., Shida, H., Sugimoto, M. and Yamanouchi, K. (1989). Development of heat-stable recombinant rinderpest vaccine. *Archives of Virology*, **107**, 225–235.

Yilma, T., Hsu, D., Jones, L., Owens, S., Grubman, M., Mebus, C., Yamanaka, M. and Dale, B. (1988). Protection of cattle against rinderpest with vaccinia virus recombinants expressing the HA or F gene. *Science*, **242**, 1058–1061.

5.6

Conventional Vaccines against Tick-borne Diseases

C.G.D. BROWN
Centre for Tropical Veterinary Medicine,
University of Edinburgh, Scotland

ABSTRACT

Tick-borne diseases of domestic animals are widespread throughout tropical and subtropical regions of the world. Their main impact is in impeding the development of the livestock industry in countries within these regions since imported or improved livestock, particularly cattle, are highly susceptible to these diseases. One approach to the control of tick-borne diseases has been to develop vaccines against them in order to protect the most valuable and productive animals in the population. The most important and widely prevalent tick-borne diseases, and hence those to which most attention has been paid, are the protozoan diseases of cattle: babesiosis, caused by *Babesia bovis* and *B. bigemina* and theileriosis, caused by *Theileria parva* (East Coast fever) and *T. annulata* (tropical theileriosis), and the rickettsial diseases: anaplasmosis caused by *Anaplasma marginale* and heartwater, *Cowdria ruminantium* infection of cattle, sheep and goats. The history of the development of vaccines against these diseases to the present day will be reviewed in this paper.

Simple and pragmatic, yet effective 'vaccines' against these diseases were developed and used almost as soon as the causative organisms themselves were recognized in the late 19th and early 20th century. In an approach more akin to dealing with virus diseases rather than those caused by bacteria, animals were immunized by 'salting' or deliberate infection with the organism. This infection could be achieved by exposing cattle to infected ticks in the field or by inoculating blood from known infected animals. This latter approach gave rise to the classical 'blood vaccines' which, in one form or another are still recognized and widely used against tick-borne diseases today.

Such vaccines generally comprised the inoculation of a small volume of blood from a clinically-infected or carrier animal demonstrating a patent parasitaemia. This blood might contain:

- virulent parasites, requiring a partially resistant recipient, e.g. a young calf, or the use of chemotherapy to 'block' the infection

or

- selected mild or attenuated strains of the pathogen.

The essential component of these vaccines, as with similar vaccines used today, was that the immunity they induced was dependent on the establishment of the parasite in the host. This in turn produced a full portfolio of cellular and humoral responses to the disease agent and consequently, effective protective immunity. However, the use of such vaccines almost invariably resulted in the development of a carrier state in the recipient – 'premunition' or 'co-infectious immunity'.

With few exceptions, and these are almost entirely at an experimental level as yet, the vaccines used today to control tick-borne diseases in the field are living, infective vaccines which may be fully virulent or attenuated. They are, in the main, derived from infected animals though increasingly now cell culture is used to modify or attenuate the disease agents. These living vaccines have become safer and more effective as inoculum doses are quantified more accurately, methods of storage – notably cryopreservation – are improved and novel chemotherapeutic agents are developed to block infection with virulent organisms.

Current vaccine protocols require for:

- *Babesia bovis* and *B. bigemina*-defined numbers of erythrocytes infected with attenuated parasites harvested from splenectomized calves.

- *Theileria annulata* – macroschizont-infected bovine mononuclear cells attenuated by prolonged passage in cell culture.

- *Theileria parva* – a cryopreserved suspension of sporozoites harvested from infected ticks, with blocking of the infection with theileristatic chemotherapeutic agents – 'infection and treatment'

- *Anaplasma marginale* – blood from splenectomized donor calves infected with either an 'avirulent' species, *Anaplasma centrale,* or with virulent *A. marginale* blocked chemotherapeutically, or 'attenuated' *Anaplasma* isolated from deer and passaged through sheep.

- *Cowdria ruminantium* – either blood infected with the virulent Ball 3 strain of *Cowdria* or a suspension of the organism isolated from infected ticks and cryopreserved as an infective stabilate. Inoculation with either requires the potentially lethal infection induced to be blocked with tetracyclines some two weeks later.

Each of these vaccines is constantly being improved and, in the search for improvements, techniques are being developed which are helping to bridge the biotechnological gap. Cryopreservation has helped to preserve stocks of parasite and, with the development of cold chains, ensures effective delivery of viable vaccines; cell culture offers methods for attenuation and, particularly, cloning of parasite strains; monoclonal antibodies, complemented by isoenzyme electrophoresis and other biochemical techniques have further improved our ability to define parasite strains, immunochemical studies of parasite antigens and investigations into disease pathogenesis and protective mechanisms of immunity have indicated the epitopes necessary to stimulate the cellular and humoral responses required for protection. These are all stepping stones in the development of genetically engineered vaccines.

5.7

Development and Testing of *In Vitro* Derived Vaccines against Bovine Theileriosis in India

D.K. SINGH

Animal Disease Research Laboratory,
National Dairy Development Board, Anand, India

INTRODUCTION

Theileria annulata infection has been endemic in India as an inapparent infection of indigenous cattle and buffaloes. However, since the early seventies, it has emerged as one of the serious diseases of the improved dairy breeds of cattle. Presently, this infection known as tropical theileriosis is the major cause of illness for the eight million taurine and crossbred cattle in India. During 1978–79, in Kaira District, out of 550 purebred Holstein Friesian heifers imported from Canada, 85 died of tropical theileriosis and the remaining suffered from this disease resulting in debility and impaired fertility. Further, during the year 1988–89, in an approximate population of 40,000 exotic and crossbred cattle in Kaira District, 3,800 acute cases of the disease were recorded. Results of serological surveys undertaken under the Indian Council of Agricultural Research (ICAR) sponsored schemes indicate that the infection is extensively prevalent in the entire country, and that 30–60% animal are reported to be serologically positive (Fig. 1).

General aspects of research in India

Realizing its importance, several institutes have been engaged in research on tropical theileriosis viz. Punjab Agricultural University (PAU), Ludhiana; Haryana Agricultural University (HAU), Hisar; Indian Veterinary Research Institute (IVRI), Izatnagar. Several *ad hoc* research schemes funded by the ICAR were also operating. During the seventh five year plan in collaboration with USAID, ICAR has initiated an 'All India Coordinated Research Project on Blood Protista' with major emphasis on tropical theileriosis. Many

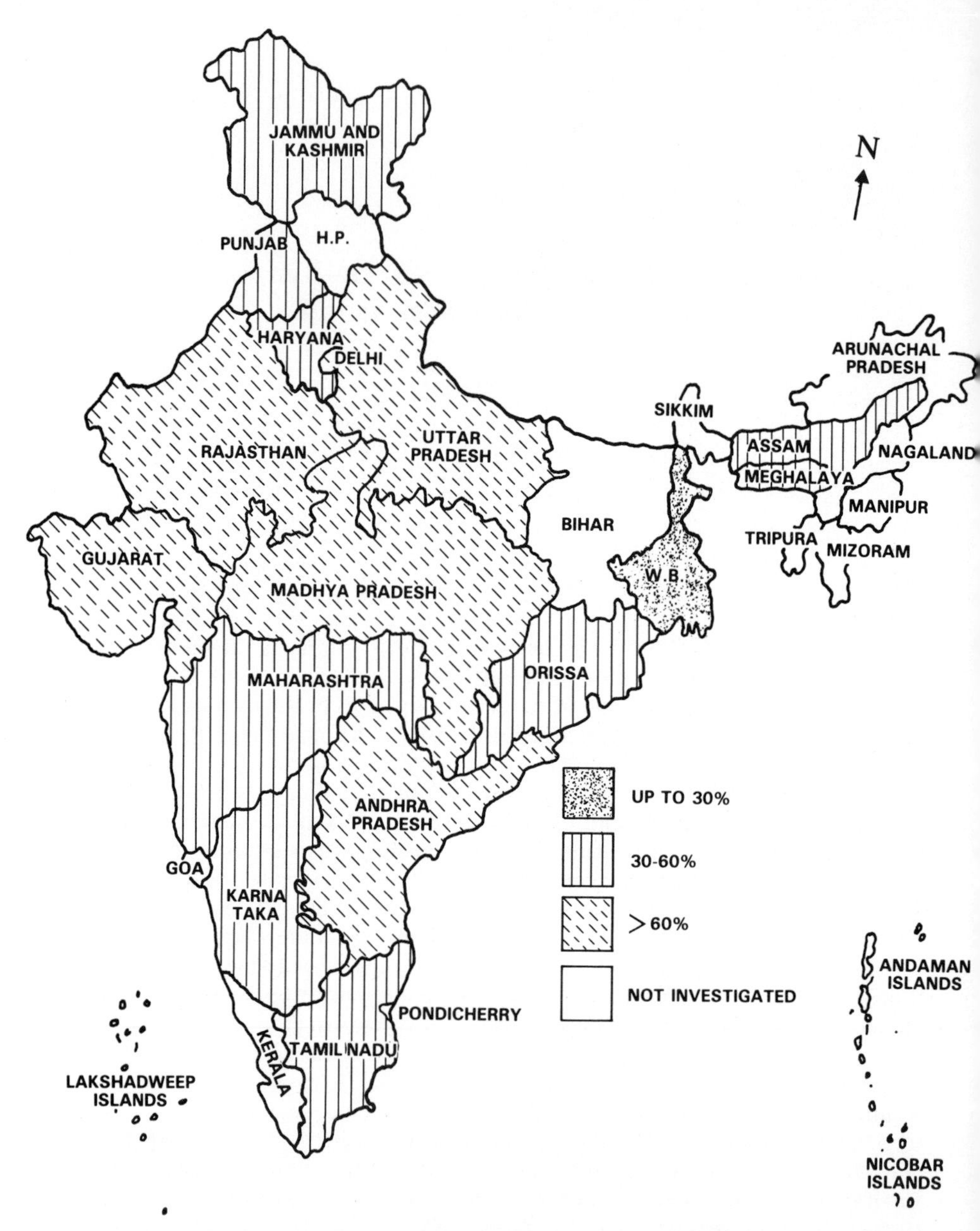

Fig. 1 *Seroprevalence of bovine tropical theileriosis in cattle of different states of India.*

institutes in India are participating in the programme. As a result of these studies, various aspects of the disease such as transmission, symptoms, clinical pathology, nature of immunity, serology and chemotherapy have been investigated (Sharma and Gautam, 1971, 1973; Bhattacharyulu, Choudri and Gill, 1975a, 1975b; Singh, Jagdish and Gautam, 1977; Dhar, 1973; Singh, Jagdish, Gautam and Dhar, 1979; Singh, Jagdish and Gautam, 1980).

Sporozoite-derived vaccines Following the infection and treatment method, immunization trials were conducted, using tetracyclines as prophylactic agents against controlled infections with sporozoites (Gill, Bhattacharyulu and Kaur, 1976; Jagdish, Singh, Gautam and Dhar, 1979; Khanna, Dhar and Gautam, 1980). Some immunization studies were also conducted with gamma-ray irradiated sporozoites (Singh, Jagdish and Gutam, 1978). However, because of their inherent problems none of these have been accepted under field conditions.

Culture-derived vaccines First reported attempts for developing *in vitro* derived culture vaccines were made at PAU, where a small number of crossbred male calves were successfully immunized under laboratory conditions (Gill *et al*, 1976). Subsequently, immunization under laboratory conditions, using culture attenuated schizonts were also reported from IVRI, Izatnagar (Anon, 1979).

STUDIES AT THE NATIONAL DAIRY DEVELOPMENT BOARD (NDDB), ANAND

Since 1982, extensive studies have been conducted at the Animal Disease Research Laboratory (ADRL), NDDB, Anand, as a result of which, a commercial vaccine has been developed for the immunization of susceptible cattle under field conditions. So far, this is the only vaccine available for large-scale protection of susceptible cattle in India.

Initial research at ADRL, NDDB, Anand included collection of several isolates of *T. annulata* from clinical cases recorded in taurine cattle from different parts of the country. These were adapted and maintained in susceptible animals, *Hyalomma anatolicum anatolicum* ticks, stabilates of ground up tick supernate (GUTS) and *Theileria* schizont infected bovine lymphoblastoid suspension cultures. Seven cell lines developed from four isolates viz. ODA-Anand (Gujarat), Bhopal (Madhya Pradesh), Hisar (Haryana) and Dapchari (Maharashtra) were maintained and cultivated *in vitro*. They were continuously grown *in vitro* for 5–6 years and cryopreserved in liquid nitrogen (LN_2) at regular passage intervals.

Extensive immunization studies using homologous as well as heterologous challenge were conducted using *T. annulata* ODE-Anand as the principal isolate. This isolate was collected from Holstein Friesian heifers on a farm near Anand, where serious cases of tropical theileriosis were occurring during 1982–83.

Many immunization trials were conducted under laboratory conditions to find out the optimum levels of attenuation of *Theileria* schizonts in cultures, their optimum dose, appropriate age for immunization, level of cross protection against other isolates and the ideal method of storing the vaccine. Finally the vaccine developed was tested under field conditions and its commercial production including marketing has been underway since February, 1989.

Laboratory immunization trials

Laboratory immunization trials were conducted with *T. annulata* ODE-Anand isolate in lymphocytes at different passage levels.

Animals and the inoculum Crossbred (CB) calves (*Bos taurus* x *Bos indicus*) of 5–6 months age were used for the study. Before starting the trials, animals were kept under observation usually for a period of two months. Deworming was undertaken with broad spectrum anthelmintics. Repeated screening of blood smears for piroplasms of *Theileria* in particular and other blood protozoa in general was carried out. Serum samples were collected for estimating antibody titres by the indirect fluorescent antibody (IFA) test. Packed cell volumes were estimated weekly and morning rectal temperatures were recorded daily. After establishing their freedom from any intercurrent infection, the calves were randomly divided into groups of five. In all the experiments, a group was kept as susceptible controls, whereas each calf in other groups was injected subcutaneously at right mid-neck region with the cultures to be tested.

Challenge after vaccination Subsequently, on day 45 post-vaccination, all the animals were challenged with GUTS prepared from 25 *T. annulata* positive *Hyalomma anatolicum anatolicum* adult ticks.

Observations Each animal following immunization was observed for a period of 45 days. Morning rectal temperatures and prescapular lymph node enlargements were recorded daily. The enlargement compared to the normal size of lymph nodes were graded from 1 to 4 for individual animals and total enlargements for the groups were estimated. Peripheral blood smears were prepared at regular intervals for the estimation of piroplasm parasitosis. Packed cell volume percentages were estimated. Serum IFA titres were measured on days 0 and 45, post-immunization.

Following infective GUTS challenge, each animal, in immunized as well as in susceptible groups, was monitored for 21 days for the parameters described earlier. In case of death, if any, a detailed post-mortem examination was conducted to establish the cause of death.

Various immunization trials

Cultures at low passage Initial immunization trials conducted with cultures at 12 passage (p) (54 days *in vitro*), 27 p (121 days *in vitro*), 48 p (216 days *in vitro*) and 100 p (450 days *in vitro*) indicated that subcutaneous inoculation of $5x10^6$ schizont infected bovine lymphocytes initiated variable degrees of tropical theileriosis in susceptible calves. Following recovery from the immunizing reactions, all the surviving animals withstood infective GUTS challenge at doses causing acute theileriosis in susceptible controls.

Cultures at 150 p Analysis of various reaction parameters observed in CB calves immunized with $5x10^6$ *T. annulata* schizont infected lymphoid cells, at 150 p (675 days *in vitro*) and subsequently challenged with infective GUTS, indicated that ODE-Anand isolate of *T. annulata* at 150 p either as fresh cultures or stored in liquid nitrogen could be used for immunization of susceptible calves against homologous challenge (Fig. 2).

In all subsequent experiments, unless stated to the contrary, vaccination was inoculation of $5x10^6$ infected *T. annulata* ODE-Anand schizont infected lymphoid cells at 150 p.

Laboratory trial on milking cows For evaluating the safety and potency of 150 p cultures for milking cows, an experiment was conducted on eight

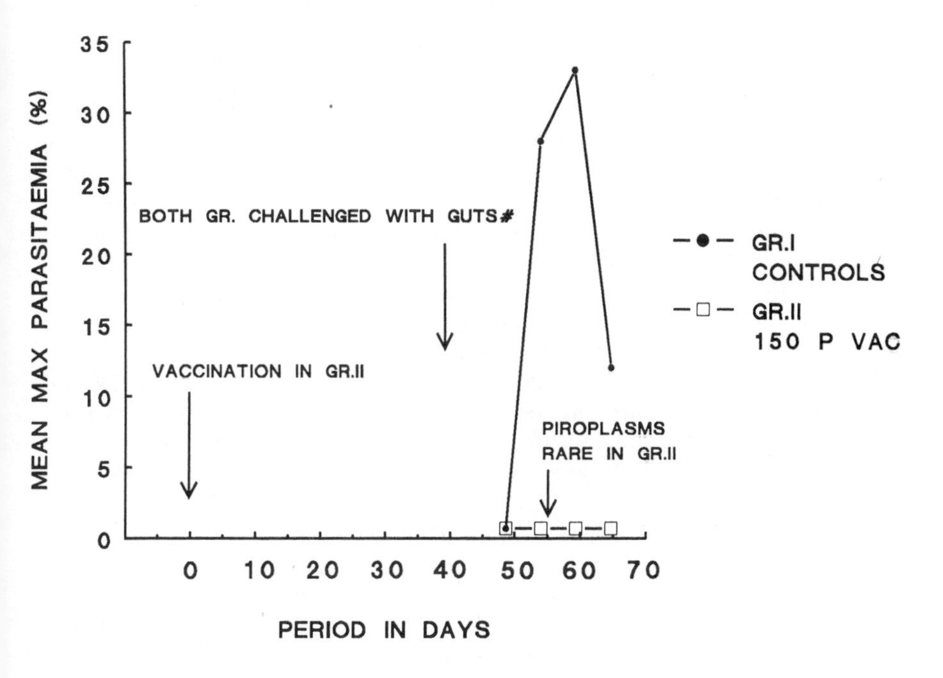

Fig. 2 *Parasitaemia in CB calves immunized with 150p* T. annulata* *vaccine.*

TABLE 1 *Reaction of Jersey cows to vaccination* and challenge** with ODE isolate of* T. annulata.

Groups	Inoculum	Mean max. piroplasmosis %	Total lymph node enlargement	Mean max temperature °F
Vaccination reactions				
Controls	Nil	Nil	Nil	Nil
Vaccinates	Vaccine	Rare	2	101.1
Challenge reactions				
Controls	GUTS	22.0	17	103.9
Vaccinates	GUTS	1.8	8	101.7

* Vaccinated with 5x10⁶ cryopreserved schizont infected lymphoid cells PBLS at 150 p.

** Challenged with GUTS equivalent to 25 infected *H. a. anatolicum* adults.

susceptible purebred Jersey cows. Results summarized in Table 1 indicated that ODE-Anand isolate at 150 p, stored in liquid nitrogen, was reasonably immunogenic and safe.

Cross protection trials An experiment was conducted on 20 CB calves randomly divided into four groups of five each. Each animal in groups III and IV was first immunized with ODE-Anand 150 p culture vaccine. Subsequently, on day 45 post-vaccination, each calf in groups I (susceptible controls) and III was challenged with *T. annulata* Dapchari strain positive GUTS, whereas each calf in groups II (susceptible controls) and IV was challenged with *T. annulata* Bhopal strain positive GUTS. Results summarized in Table 2 indicate that the vaccine prepared from ODE isolate provides cross protection against Bhopal as well as Dapchari isolates of *T. annulata.*

Vaccine storage In order to explore the possibilities of storing the culture vaccine at different temperatures, two experiments were conducted. In the first, calves divided into four groups of five each were used. Each calf in groups II, III and IV was immunized with fresh vaccine, vaccine stored at 4° C for four days and vaccine at −196° C respectively. Calves in group I were kept as susceptible controls. Animals in all the four groups were challenged with ODE-Anand isolate positive GUTS. Post-vaccination and post-challenge reactions indicated that all the three vaccines provided comparable protection (Fig. 3).

Observations of another experiment, indicated that schizont vaccine cannot be stored for long at 4° C or at −20° C because after 30 days of storage at these temperatures, it failed to provide protection against the challenge.

TABLE 2 *Reactions of susceptible and immune calves to heterologous challenge*.*

Group	No. of calves	Status	Challenged with GUTS	Mean max. temperature °F	% Piros.	MR**	Status
I	5	Susc.	Dapchari	104.6	57.8	3/5	Susc.
II	5	"	Bhopal	103.8	32.4	1/5	Susc.
III	5	ODE	Dapchari	102.0	Rare	0/5	Immune
IV	5	"	Bhopal	102.2	Rare	0/5	Immune

* Dapchari and Bhopal GUTS equivalent to 25 *H. a. anatolicum* infected adults.
** Mortality Rate

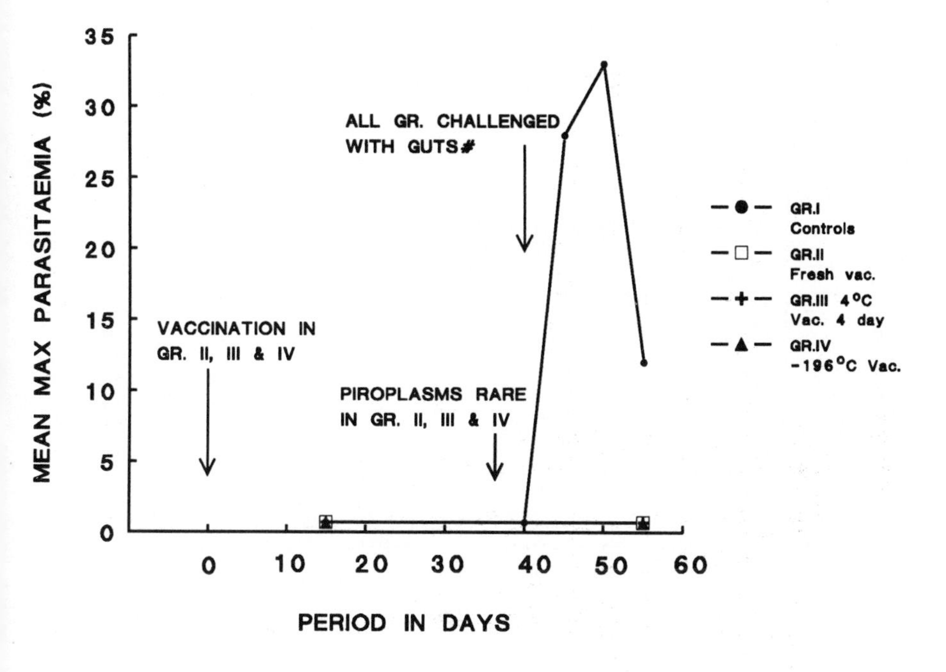

Fig. 3 *Parasitaemia in CB calves immunized with differently stored 150p* T. annulata* *vaccine.*

Variations in dosage An experiment involving 30 calves, divided into six groups of five each, was conducted. Calves in group I were kept as controls, whereas each calf in groups II, III, IV, V and VI was immunized with cryopreserved 0.02, 0.2, 2.0, 10.0 and 100.0 million *T. annulata* ODE-Anand infected lymphoid cells in culture at 150 p. Analysis of various post-immunization and post-challenge reactions indicated that this vaccine is safe as well as immunogenic, at the doses ranging from 0.2 to 100.0 million cells (Figs. 4 and 5). Maximum antibody response was recorded in another group immunized with $5x10^6$ schizont infected cells (Fig. 5).

Immunization with culture extracts Two separate immunization trials, each involving 15 calves were organized. In the first experiment, five calves were kept as controls (group I) whereas, each of the five calves in group II was injected subcutaneously with 5 mls of 0.2 micron millipore membrane filtered supernatant fluid taken from 150 p cultures grown for 48 hours. Each calf in group III was immunized with cryopreserved vaccine.

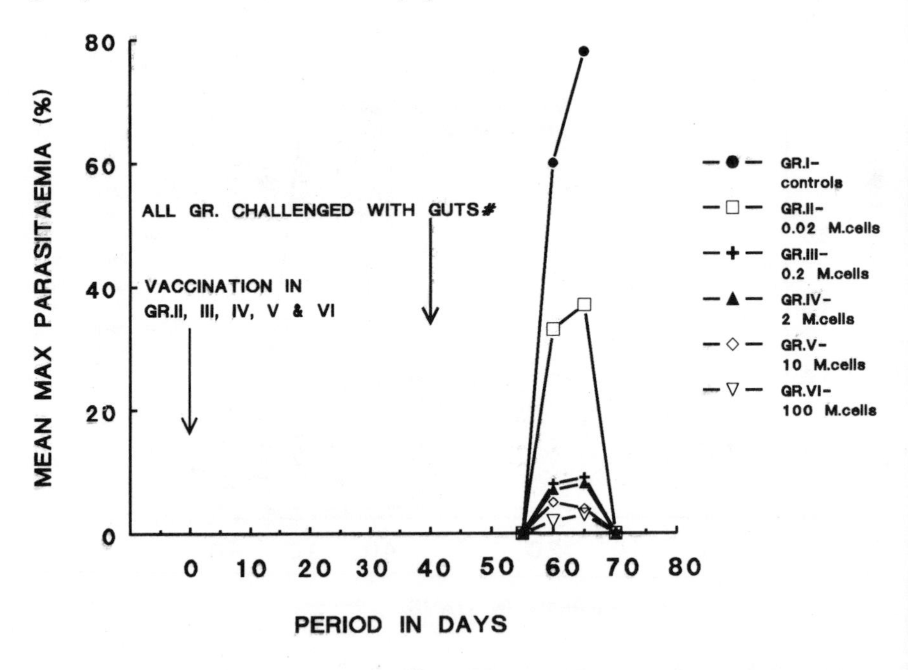

Fig. 4 *Parasitaemia in CB calves immunized with different doses of 150p* T. annulata* *vaccine.*

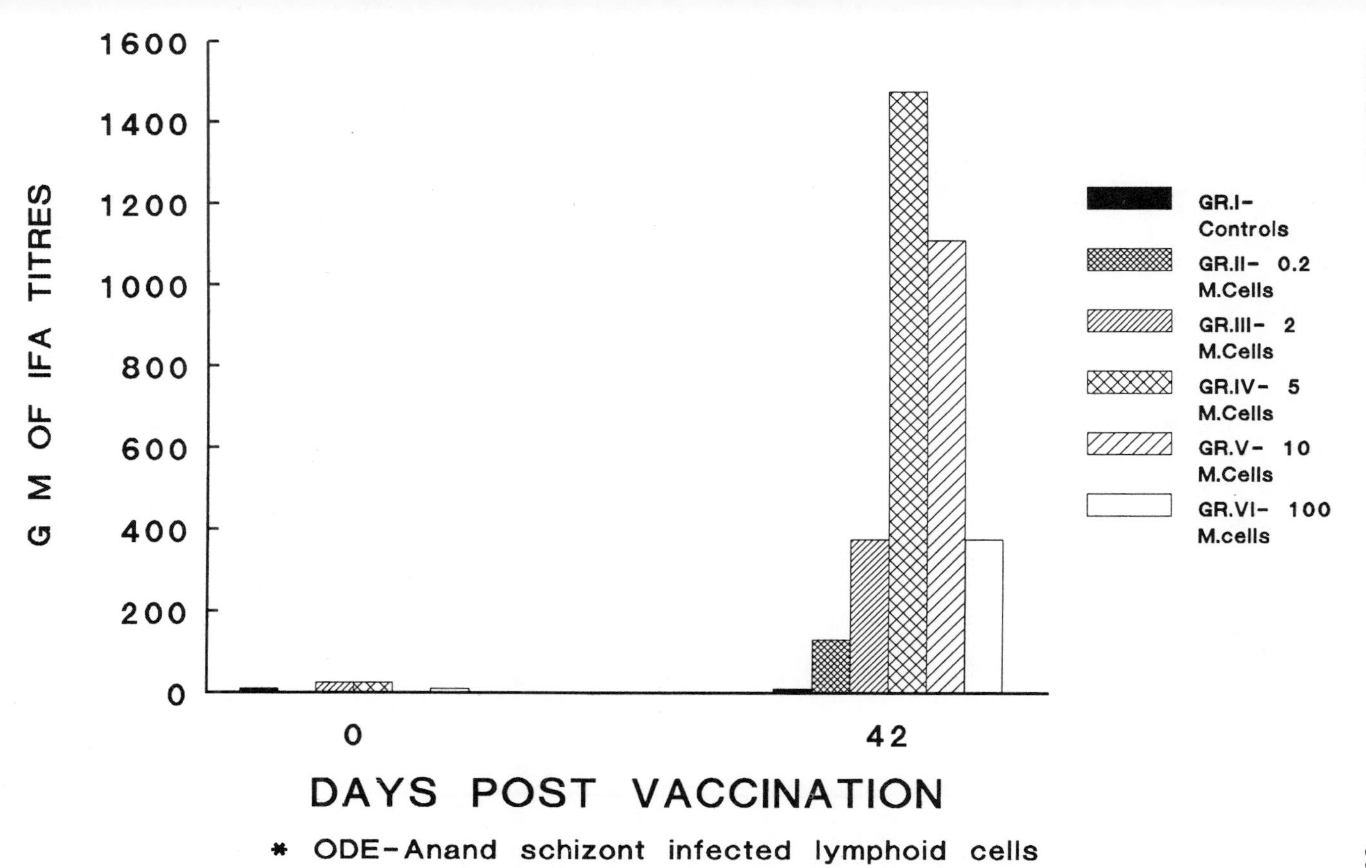

Fig. 5 *IFA titres in calves immunized with different doses of 150p* T. annulata* *vaccine.*

In the second experiment, five calves in group I were controls, whereas each calf in group II received 5 mls of 0.2 micron millipore membrane filtered extract of culture cells at 150 p, lysed in a glass grinder kept on ice. Calves in group III were immunized with cryopreserved vaccine.

Each calf in both these experiments was challenged on the 45th day of the post-immunization period. Post-challenge reactions indicated that neither the supernatant nor the lysate obtained from *T. annulata* cultures have immunogenic properties. Mean maximum piroplasm parasitaemias recorded in these animals are summarized in Fig. 6, whereas Fig. 7 depicts the geometric mean (GM) of IFA titres recorded in these groups.

Field immunization trials

Considering the encouraging results obtained in the laboratory immunization trials, the cryopreserved *T. annulata* ODE-Anand isolate vaccine at 150 p

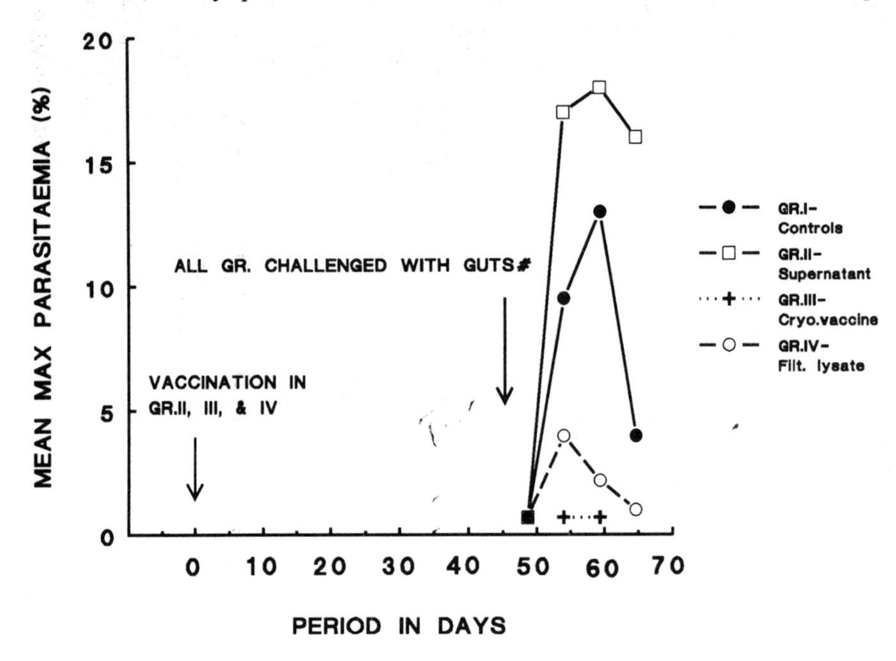

2 DEATHS IN GR.I & GR.IV AND 3 IN GR.II AFTER CHALLENGE

* ODE Anand schizont injected lymphoid cells at 150p

From 25 H.a. anatolicum ticks infected with T.annulata

Fig. 6 *Parasitaemia of CB calves immunized with extracts of* T. annulata* *cultures and cryopreserved* T. annulata* *vaccine (5 × 10⁶ infected cells).*

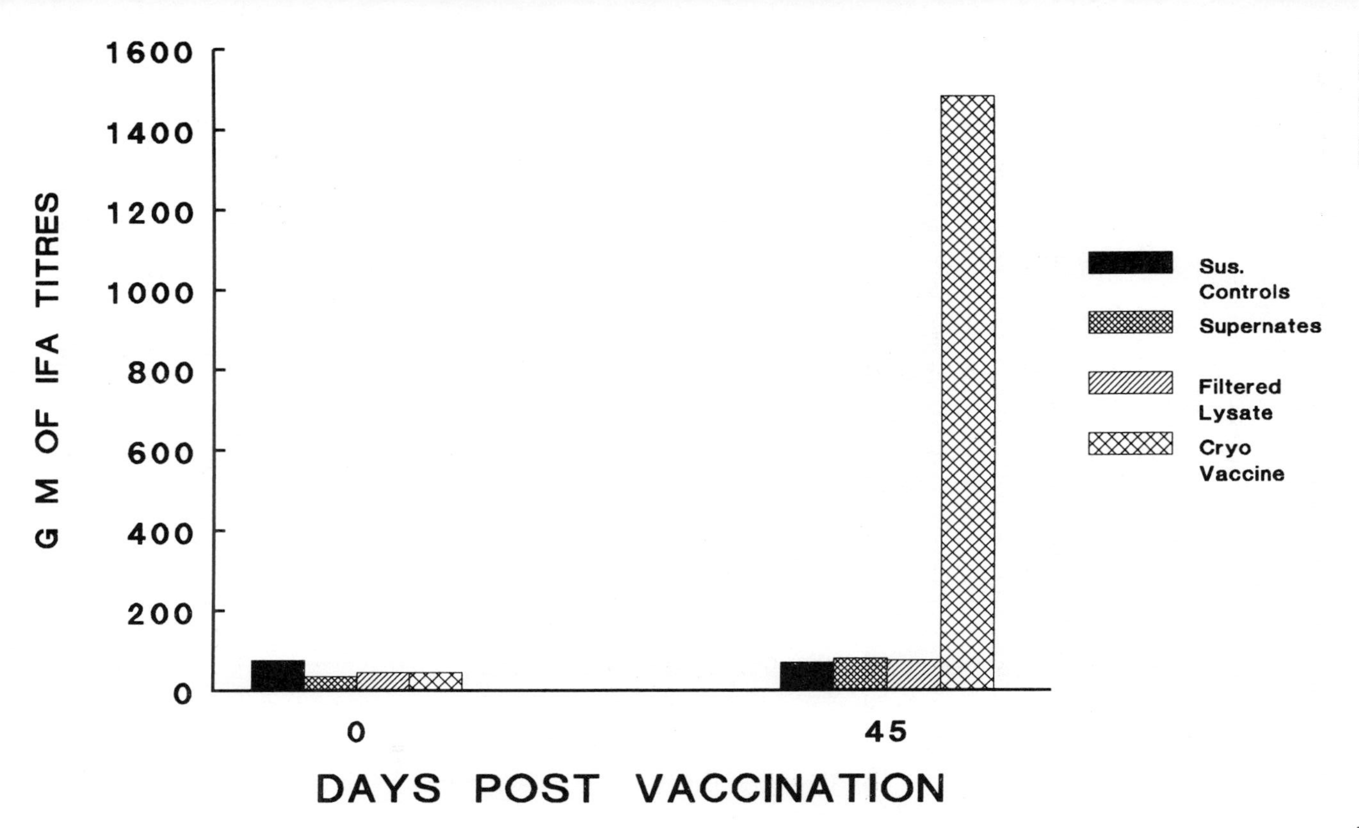

Fig. 7 *IFA titres in calves immunized with various theilerial antigens.*

was tested under field conditions. Initial vaccinations were taken up on a small number of Jersey bulls at an organized farm near Anand. Later, Jersey, Holstein Friesian and crossbred cows were also included in the study. Observations were made with regard to the enlargement of prescapular lymph nodes, morning rectal temperatures, piroplasms in peripheral blood smears, effect on milk yield etc. Serum samples were collected at the beginning and on the 45th day of vaccination and IFA titres were estimated at three-months interval up to 12 months. Approximately 15,000 animals were test vaccinated till December, 1988 (Table 3). This included 2,000 imported purebred German Holstein Friesian heifers in the last stages of pregnancy. Results available, so far, indicate that the vaccine is safe and effective for the immunization of susceptible animals of 4 months of age and above.

TABLE 3 *Experimental immunization against theileriosis in various states of India.*

	Number of animals vaccinated	
States	**Organized farms**	**Field**
Gujarat	1,531	6,227
Madhya Pradesh	840	Nil
Maharashtra	599	Nil
Andrha Pradesh	505	Nil
Karnataka	1,446	1,100
Haryana	100	Nil
Uttar Pradesh	539	Nil
West Bengal	282	Nil
Tamil Nadu	1,220	424
TOTAL	**7,062**	**7,751**

Commercial vaccine

The Government of India has approved the large-scale production, marketing and use of this vaccine in the country. Indian Immunologicals (IIL), Hyderabad, a company managed by the National Dairy Development Board, has taken up its commercial production and marketing since February, 1989, under the trade name RAKSHAVAC-T. Within three months of marketing, more than 20,000 doses of this vaccine have been used by the farmers for protecting their animals.

The returns to the investment for a mass vaccination programme in a country like India are quite encouraging. Based on the limited figures available from the Kaira District Cooperative Milk Producers' Union, the estimated cost-benefit ratio of the vaccination programme is 1:4 (Tables 4 and 5).

TABLE 4 *Theileriosis vaccination costs in Kaira District, Gujarat.*

	Rs. Million	U.S. $
Vaccine costs		
@ $ 1.52/dose for 40,000 animals	1.000	60,975.60
Remuneration to vaccinators	0.054	3,292.68
Conveyance	0.036	2,195.12
Coldchain, LN_2 etc.	0.015	914.63
Overheads		
syringes, needles, equipment etc.	0.036	2,195.12
TOTAL	**1.141**	**69,573.15**

TABLE 5 *Estimated avoidable losses by theileriosis vaccination in Kaira District, Gujarat.*

	Rs. Millions	U.S. $
Losses by theileriosis		
Cost of treatment		
3,800 clinical cases/40,000 population		
Average 4 visits @ $4.7656/visit	1.185	72,256.00
Loss in milk		
@ $91.46 for 1,900 clinical cases		
in cows	2.850	173,780.50
Mortality 5%		
190 animals @ $304.8/animal	0.095	57,926.80
Sub total	**4.985**	**303,963.30**
Unavoidable losses		
Animal import, breakdown	0.327	19,939.00
NET BENEFITS	**4.658**	**284,024.30**

Recently, three more institutes viz., HAU, Hissar; PAU, Ludhiana and IVRI, Izatnagar have reported on the development of *in vitro* derived culture vaccines, awaiting test under field conditions.

There is an encouraging response to the commercial vaccine released by the IIL and it is expected that in the near future tropical theileriosis would cease to be a threat to the large-scale crossbreeding programmes taken up for milk production enhancement in India.

REFERENCES

Anon, (1979). Final report of Research Scheme submitted to ICAR by I.V.A.R., Izatnagar, India.

Bhattacharyulu, Y., Choudri, R.P. and Gill, B.S. (1975a). Studies on the development of *Theileria annulata* (Dschunkowsky and Luhs, 1904) in the tick, *Hyalomma anatolicum anatolicum* (Koch, 1844). *Annales de Parasitologie (Paris),* **50 (4)**, 397–408.

Bhattacharyulu, Y., Choudri, R.P. and Gill, B.S. (1975b). Trans-stadial transmission of *Theileria annulata* through common Ixodid ticks infesting Indian cattle. *Parasitology,* **71**, 1.

Dhar, S. (1973). Studies on some aspects of theileriosis in cattle with special reference to its serological diagnosis. PhD Thesis, Haryana Agricultural University, Hisar, India.

Gill, B.S., Bhattacharyulu, Y. and Kaur, D. (1976). Immunization against bovine tropical theileriosis (*Theileria annulata* infection). *Research in Veterinary Science,* **21**, 146–149.

Jagdish, S., Singh, D.K., Gautam, O.P. and Dhar, S. (1979). Chemoprophylactic immunization against bovine tropical theileriosis. *Veterinary Record,* **104**, 140.

Khanna, B.M., Dhar, S. and Gautam, O.P. (1980). Chemotherapy of experimental *Theileria annulata* infection in bovine calves. *Proceedings of Seminar on Haemoprotozoan Diseases, Haryana Agricultural University, India*, October 27–November 1, 1980, pp. 74–78.

Sharma, R.D. and Gautam, O.P. (1971). Theileriosis. II. Clinical cases in indigenous calves. *Indian Veterinary Journal,* **48**, 83.

Sharma, R.D. and Gautam, O.P. (1973). Cerebral theileriosis in a Haryana calf. *Indian Veterinary Journal,* **50**, 83.

Singh, D.K., Jagdish, S. and Gautam, O.P. (1977). Cell mediated immunity in tropical theileriosis (*Theileria annulata* infection). *Research in Veterinary Science,* **23**, 391–392.

Singh, D.K., Jagdish, S. and Gautam, O.P. (1978). Immunization against bovine tropical theileriosis using CO-60 irradiated infective particles of *Theileria annulata* derived from ticks. *American Journal of Veterinary Research,* **46**, 767–769.

Singh, D.K., Jagdish, S., Gautam, O.P. and Dhar, S. (1979). Infectivity of ground up tick supernates prepared from *Theileria annulata* infected *Hyalomma anatolicum anatolicum. Tropical Animal Health and Production,* **11**, 87–90.

Singh, D.K., Jagdish, S and Gautum, O.P. (1980). Demonstration of *Theileria annulata* in the salivary glands of *Hyalomma anatolicum anatolicum* ticks. *Proceedings of Seminar on Haemoprotozoan Diseases, Haryana Agricultural University, Hisar, India,* October 27–November 1, 1980.

5.8

Potential for New Vaccines against Parasitic Diseases of Livestock

A. TAIT
Wellcome Unit of Molecular Parasitology, University of Glasgow, Scotland

ABSTRACT
The application of molecular techniques to the study of parasite antigens represents a major advance in the task of producing vaccines against parasites of domestic livestock, however there are still many unknowns and problems to be investigated before recombinant subunit vaccines become available. The aim of this paper is to discuss what progress has been made towards achieving the goal of subunit vaccines against parasites of domestic livestock and to discuss, by reference to other disease systems, the future research needs and prospects in this area.

At the present time there are 'live' vaccines available for three parasitic diseases (*Babesia, Theileria* and *Dictyocaulus*). These vaccines are effective and relatively easy to produce. The control of all other parasitic diseases relies on the application of chemotherapeutics either directly to animals or, in the case of protozoan diseases, to their vectors coupled with appropriate pasture management. It is clear that the application of these measures is costly and labour intensive, coupled, in the case of chemotherapy, with the selection of drug resistant parasites. Vaccines, in contrast, do not suffer from these disadvantages and are therefore highly desirable.

The ability of modern recombinant DNA techniques to produce specific antigens cheaply and in quantity makes available the necessary components of a vaccine without the need for large quantities of parasite material. Thus, at a biotechnical level there is little, in principle, to hinder the production of subunit vaccines.

The main problems are associated with identifying the antigen or antigens that can evoke a protective immune response, defining the portions of such molecules which are recognized by the immune system, investigating the variation between strains of the parasite in these regions and investigating host variation in the portions of the molecule that it is able to 'recognize'. If all the information on these parameters were known, then it should be possible to 'engineer' a polypeptide which would contain all the appropriate elements allowing protection against all strains of the parasite in all or most host individuals. However, with many parasites of veterinary importance, our knowledge of the protective immune response is limited and, in the case of helminth parasites, is complicated further by their location within the host.

Thus, a recombinant vaccine is not going to be available in the near future, but the prospect in the more distant future is promising. It is clear that a thorough knowledge of the immune response is required in order to devise an effective vaccine whether this is based on 'hidden' antigens or those normally exposed to the immune system.

5.9

The Development of Vaccines against Malaria: Lessons for Animal Equivalents

J.G. SCAIFE and R.G. RIDLEY
Department of Molecular Biology, University of Edinburgh, Scotland

INTRODUCTION

The beginning of this decade signalled an exciting time for the molecular parasitologist. The World Health Organization (WHO), through its Tropical Disease Research Programme, had focused attention on a few major diseases – malaria, filariasis, schistosomiasis, African trypanosomiasis, Chagas' disease, leprosy and leishmaniasis, whilst, in the laboratory, the potential of monoclonal antibodies and genetic manipulation was being realized and it became clear that these techniques could be applied to basic medical problems. Certain figures long-established in tropical disease research, such as Barry Bloom and Ruth Nussenzweig, should take credit for attracting a rising generation of molecular biologists into the field during this period. Amongst the parasites on the WHO list, the malaria parasite was particularly attractive to molecular biologists. As a relatively simple, unicellular eukaryote comparable in complexity to yeast, it promised to respond to the available techniques, and perhaps conform to current ideas of gene organization and expression. In addition, the most virulent species, *Plasmodium falciparum*, could be cultured in human erythrocytes and purified virtually free of host DNA and protein. The main goal was to develop a vaccine for widespread use in the Third World.

Ten years on seems a good time to take stock. Although some of the more optimistic predictions have not been fulfilled, great progress has been made. We have learnt much about the parasite itself and have had to develop a new and realistic vision of the anti-malarial vaccines of the future. I hope to give an overview of these conclusions in this paper. Some of our insights and mistakes will surely be of interest to those wishing to develop animal vaccines using similar methods.

PLASMODIUM FALCIPARUM

The malaria parasite infects man in the saliva of the feeding female anopheline mosquito. The injected sporozoites quickly find their way to parenchyma cells of the liver, which they invade by a process which may involve an intermediary cell type. After two weeks' growth and division, several thousand progeny merozoites are released into the bloodstream where they invade erythrocytes. Here rapid growth yields up to 20 progeny merozoites in 48 hours and the cycle is repeated. During the blood stage a developmental switch leads to distinct sexual forms, gametocytes, which mature into gametes if ingested by another mosquito. In the insect gut the gametes form a zygote which gives rise to an ookinete. This migrates to the gut wall and becomes an oocyst in which new sporozoites develop. On release into the body cavity, the sporozoites migrate to the salivary glands.

Thus, the parasite is exposed to the immune system at two stages of development in the vertebrate host – the invading sporozoite and the blood stage merozoite. Classical studies on *P. falciparum* and related simian and rodent malaria parasites led to the view that an immune response to either or both of these stages could be protective (Cohen, McGregor and Carrington, 1961; Cohen, 1979; Nussenzweig and Nussenzweig, 1984). They suggested that one or more proteins isolated from the sporozoite and merozoite stages might be used in a subunit vaccine eliciting a protective immune response in man.

Most research has since focused on identifying candidate proteins from sporozoite and merozoite stages, providing evidence that they are protective, cloning their genes and using them either to produce large quantities of the protein by expression in a heterologous system (*Esherichia coli*, yeast, vaccinia virus) or to elucidate peptide sequences for chemical synthesis. Parallel studies on antibodies blocking parasite transmission by the mosquito vector through their effects on the gametocytes, gametes and zygotes could also be important for future management of the disease.

DEFINING THE ANTIGENS

Before we look in detail at the 'chosen few' malaria antigens, it is worth making some general observations about the current status of malarial immunology. Firstly, we are not certain whether the best protection against *falciparum* malaria is afforded by the humoral or cellular arms of the immune system. Early studies suggested that the antibodies of immune adults protected against the disease (Cohen *et al*, 1961). Since then, extensive work on rodent parasites, more recently supported by human data, suggests that cellular mechanisms (perhaps antibody-mediated) may be involved in protection (Playfair, 1982). Probably, in many individuals, protection against malaria depends on a combination of several immune mechanisms. It is thus fair to say that classical immunological studies have not given a clear lead in defining a few individual antigen molecules to be pursued by the molecular biologists. As a result, it has been necessary to base the search on, perhaps naive, first principles.

Secondly, the search is constrained by a technical problem. In practice, it is difficult to identify individual antigens which promote killing by cellular mechanisms. The methods used to detect killing of this kind are complex and cannot be easily adapted to screen many individual antigens for their capacity to operate in this way. Thus, more success has been achieved in identifying those proteins which elicit antibody responses. Of course, the proteins which have been chosen for this reason may also stimulate cellular responses operating to our advantage in a vaccine. Thirdly, it is the proteins of the parasite which have been investigated in most detail. This is because gene cloning and sequencing methods facilitate analysis of primary protein structure and open a route to production on a large-scale. Other macromolecules may be less easily analyzed and produced.

What, then, have been the criteria and techniques used to define the potential protective value of malaria antigens?

Monoclonal antibodies

Monoclonal antibodies (McAbs) have played an important role in this process. Their high specificity means that they usually bind to a single protein species in the cell. This allows a protein to be located in the parasite by optical and electron microscopy. The location of an antigen in a pathogen tells us whether it is likely to be a good target for immune attack. For example, surface proteins become important vaccine candidates in the belief that they are most accessible to attack by the immune system. Another group of proteins has been located to the rhoptries in the merozoites. These flask-shaped organelles open to the anterior end of the merozoite which makes contact with the red cell during invasion. Electron microscope studies suggest that their contents, which are released during invasion, may be important for this process. Thus, rhoptry proteins are increasingly attracting attention as vaccine candidates.

Since judiciously chosen McAbs can bind to their target proteins both specifically and tightly, they can be used in affinity purification to great effect. Once purified antigen is available, the way is open to rigorous evaluation of its protective potential. For example, the major surface antigen (MSA) of merozoites, MSA-1, purified by affinity chromatography from cultured blood stage parasites, could be used to assay antibodies in immune individuals (Hall, Osland, Hyde, Simmons, Hope and Scaife, 1984a). Such tests revealed antibodies against MSA-1. The purified protein could also be evaluated in animal models. Both Saimiri (Hall, Hyde, Gomen, Simmons, Hope, Mackay, Scaife, Merkli, Richle and Stocker, 1984b) and Aotus (Siddiqui, Tam, Kramer, Hui, Case, Yamaga, Chang, Chan and Kan, 1987) monkeys immunized with affinity-purified MSA-1 are protected against a parasite challenge, encouraging the view that they will protect man.

Monoclonal antibodies can also suggest a mechanism for protection by antibody against a given protein. For example, a McAb against MSA-1 blocks parasite growth in culture (Pirson and Perkins, 1985), suggesting that, following vaccination, antibodies against this protein could interfere with the process of erythrocyte invasion by the merozoite and thus prevent development of malaria after infection.

Immune sera

Immune sera from individuals repeatedly exposed to malaria in endemic areas have been of value in antigen evaluation. A related approach has used sera from immune monkeys previously immunized by *P. falciparum* infection or by parasite extracts. Analysis of human sera led to identification of a protein (150 Kdaltons (Kd)) released by the merozoite during invasion and dispersed beneath the membrane of the infected erythrocyte (Coppel, Cowman, Anders, Bianco, Saint, Lingelbach, Kemp and Brown, 1984; Udomsangpetch, Lundgren, Berzins, Wåhlin, Perlmann, Troye-Blomberg, Carlsson, Wahlgren, Perlmann and Björkman, 1986). Human antibodies recognizing this protein, termed p155 or RESA, were widespread in endemic sera and found to block parasite growth *in vitro*. Comparisons between sera of protected and unprotected Saimiri monkeys drew attention to a protein migrating on sodium dodecyl sulphate-polyacrylamide gel electrophoresis (SDS-PAGE) at 70–80 Kd (Dubois, Dedet, Fandeur, Roussillion, Jendoubi, Pouillac, Mercereau-Puijalon and Pereira da Silva, 1984). An affinity-purified protein in this size range was later successfully used to immunize Saimiri monkeys against parasite challenge (Perrin, Merkli, Loche, Chizzolini, Smart and Richle, 1984).

CLONING THEIR GENES

Gene isolation and sequencing has contributed greatly to our knowledge of the vaccine candidates. In addition, gene cloning has allowed the malarial proteins to be synthesized in heterologous systems and opened the doors to large-scale production. It was realized at an early stage that cultured parasites could not be used for this purpose, so a high priority was placed on the generation of genomic and cDNA libraries for *P. falciparum*.

Cloning of parasite DNA

Cloning of parasite DNA into bacteriophage λ has proved to be very productive. Libraries of both genomic (Goman, Langsley, Hyde, Yankofsky, Zolg and Scaife, 1982) and cDNA (Hyde, Goman, Hall, Osland, Hope,

Langsley, Zolg and Scaife, 1984) inserted into the expression vector, λgt11 (Young and Davis, 1983), have been successfully used to select clones for antigen genes of interest. This system provides the signals for transcription and translation of foreign DNA sequences, thus allowing them to be expressed in the prokaryotic cell. The whole or part of an antigen gene cloned in the correct frame and orientation into this vector can be expressed as a fusion protein with the antigen sequence joined to β-galactosidase from *E. coli.* A rare phage plaque containing a cloned antigen sequence can thus be detected by using a specific antibody as a probe.

The ease of manipulation of the bacteriophage and its plaques strongly recommend this vector as the primary step in antigen gene isolation. Once the clone has been isolated, it is usually better to tranfer its insert to a high copy number plasmid, which is more efficient in producing DNA for analysis.

Genes expressed at a stage in the life cycle which cannot be grown in the laboratory present a special problem, because the mRNA from such genes cannot be isolated and converted into cDNA for cloning. However, several groups have found that such genes can be expressed from genomic DNA in libraries of λ gt11 (Young and Davis, 1983) or equivalent expression vectors (Koenen, Scherf, Mercereau-Puijalon, Langsley, Sibilli, Dubois, Pereira da Silva and Müller-Hill, 1984; Dame, Williams, McCutchan, Weber, Wirtz, Hockmeyer, Maloy, Haynes, Schneider, Roberts, Sanders, Reddy, Diggs and Miller, 1984). The genomic DNA can, of course, be isolated from any stage of the parasite life cycle.

In our experience, the vector λNM1149 (Murray, 1983) is very valuable as an adjunct to λgt11 in gene cloning. It is designed to give high yields of recombinant phage from small amounts of input DNA. This is often an important factor in cloning DNA from some parasites. The main purpose of λNM1149 libraries is to provide a source of genomic DNA fragments from which a complete picture of an antigen gene can be built up after the first cloned fragment has been isolated in λgt11.

Very often the only way to detect a gene initially is to screen an expression library with an antibody probe. The quality and specificity of the antibody is of paramount importance at this stage. Polyclonal sera against a partially purified parasite protein can lead to isolation of the wrong gene whose product has been recognized by contaminating antibody in the probe. It is therefore important to verify a candidate expression clone by additional tests. For example, it may be possible to show that the product of the gene contains the epitope for a monoclonal antibody known to be specific to the antigen of interest. Alternatively, limited sequencing of peptides from the parasite protein can be equated with the nucleotide sequence in the candidate clone.

A fully cloned gene is open to manipulation for expression and other purposes such as sequencing and epitope characterization. The techniques of large-scale production of parasite proteins in heterologous systems is a topic too large to be considered here, but they have been reviewed elsewhere. We shall return to epitope characterization in the course of the discussion which follows.

SURFACE ANTIGENS OF *P. FALCIPARUM*

Returning to the parasite surface, we shall discuss the two proteins which have been studied in detail. The first of these is an abundant molecule on the surface of the sporozoite, called the circumsporozoite (CS) protein. Monoclonal antibodies against CS proteins in different *Plasmodium* species allowed the Nussenzweigs and others to determine its location, synthesis and basic organization and to estimate the protective value of anti-CS protein antibodies in endemic sera (Nussenzweig and Nussenzweig, 1984). Monoclonal antibodies were successfully used to detect cDNA and genomic DNA clones encoding this antigen (Enea, Ellis, Zavala, Arnot, Asavanich, Masuda, Quakyi and Nussenzweig, 1984; Dame *et al*, 1984).

Sequencing of the DNA in these clones reveals a protein of remarkable structure. It was first seen in the simian parasite, *P. knowlesi*, whose gene was the first to be cloned and sequenced (Ozaki, Svec, Nussenzweig, Nussenzweig and Godson, 1983). As could be expected, it has an N-terminal signal peptide targeting it to the surface and a hydrophobic sequence at its C-terminus, presumably acting as an anchor. However, its most striking feature is its central region which, in *P. knowlesi,* contains 12 tandemly repeated peptides each 12 amino acids long. The repeats, which comprise 40% of the total protein are flanked by highly charged regions. The CS protein of *P. falciparum* has the same basic organization (Enea *et al*, 1984; Dame *et al*, 1984). Different amino acids appear in the repeat region. Here they are only four amino acids long and comprise a majority repeat, Asn-Ala-Asn-Pro, which is present in 35–40 copies interspersed with a minority repeat (about four copies), Asn-Val-Asp-Pro. The biological function of the CS protein is not understood. The suggestion that it may be important in host cell recognition has not been confirmed. On the other hand, we do know that the protein is immunogenic. Some surveys have suggested that most, if not all, of the anti-CS protein antibodies active in human endemic sera are directed against the repeat region (Nussenzweig and Nussenzweig, 1984). These observations have led to the speculation that the function of the central region in this protein is to provide the organism with an immunological smoke-screen, eliciting a strong antibody response against a part of the protein which is not functionally important. Thus, the host immune system would be actively occupied in a futile response. This interesting idea must be viewed with some scepticism in the light of more recent surveys suggesting that not all individuals in endemic areas have antibodies against the repeat.

Despite these uncertainties the CS protein was chosen as a candidate for human trials, and curiously, although two independent trials were mounted, both used peptide sequences based on the repeats discussed above (Zavala, Tam, Hollingdale, Cochrane, Quakyi, Nussenzweig and Nussenzweig, 1985; Ballou, Rothbard, Wirtz, Gordon, Williams, Gore, Schneider, Hollingdale,

Beaudoin, Maloy, Miller and Hockmeyer, 1985). This decision was justified in part by comparisons at the protein level which suggested that the repeats did not vary in the parasite population. It is clearly reassuring to find evidence that there is no genetic diversity in a protein to be used in a vaccine. If it changed readily by mutation, vaccinees may not be protected against the new parasites. Moreover, a wide-scale vaccination programme could serve to select these resistant mutants. Subsequent studies at the DNA level have shown that moderate variability does occur in the repeats of the gene for the CS protein of *P. falciparum*. In addition, mutations have also been found in the flanking regions in the gene (del Portillo, Nussenzweig and Enea, 1987; de la Cruz, Lal and McCutchan, 1987). These mutations, which may be more central to the vaccination issue, will be discussed below.

The major surface antigen of merozoites (MSA-1) has also been extensively studied at the molecular level (Tanabe, Mackay, Goman and Scaife, 1987; Weber, Leininger and Lyon, 1986; Schwartz, Riveros-Moreno, Lockyer, Nicholls, Davey, Hillman, Sandhu, Freeman and Holder, 1986; Weber, Sim, Lyon and Wolff,1988). It was also first recognized by specific blood stage McAbs. This protein is larger and more complex than the CS protein. It appears on both exoerythrocytic and erythrocytic merozoites and is synthesized during schizogony as a large precursor (200 Kd) which is transported to the parasite surface and processed to a number of smaller products. It has a signal peptide of 18 amino acids which is cleaved from the precursor during maturation. Its C-terminus, which is hydrophobic, was first thought to act as an anchor sequence, but we now believe that MSA-1 uses a glycophosphatidyl inositol (GPI) linkage for membrane attachment (Halder, Ferguson and Cross, 1985). The hydrophobic domain has analogues in other proteins tied by GPI linkers to the C-terminus of the protein.

The MSA-1 protein contains a block of tripeptide repeats about 60 amino acid residues from the N-terminus. The repeats are variable but take the basic form; Ser-X-X, and comprise a total of approximately 30 amino acids. Again the function of this repeat zone is not understood. However, a variant parasite has been described, which, at least in culture, can grow normally although its MSA-1 protein lacks tripeptide repeats completely, suggesting that this peptide is not essential for protein function.

The wider question of genetic diversity in the MSA-1 gene has also been addressed. Early studies employing a panel of monoclonal antibodies suggested that this protein was polymorphic. However, extensive studies at the DNA level have revealed that, apart from the tripeptide repeat region, variation in MSA-1 is under an unusual constraint. The gene can be divided into blocks, some of which are highly conserved. Others are variable, but all the data collected so far shows that here, given minor base substitutions, variation is strictly dimorphic. Recombination between these variants has been described, but the crossovers appear to be limited to the 5′ end of the gene. The consequence is that the greater part of the MSA-1 gene in all the parasites isolated from nature to date has one or other of two basic alleles.

These are radically different from one another and do not recombine. Thus, if peptide sequences from the conserved or even the dimorphic regions of this protein are protective, the problem of genetic evasion may not be important in this case.

RHOPTRY-ASSOCIATED PROTEINS

Two rhoptry-associated proteins (RAP) deserve mention here. The first, RESA (ring-infected erythrocyte surface antigen), has been extensively studied by two groups (Coppel *et al*, 1984; Ruangjirachuporn, Wåhlin, Perlmann, Carlsson, Berzins, Wahlgren, Udomsangpetch, Wigzell and Perlmann, 1988; Perlmann, Berzins, Wahlgren, Carlsson, Björkman, Patarroyo and Perlmann, 1984). It first attracted attention because anti-RESA antibodies are found in most immune sera. Moreover, when these are affinity purified, they block parasite growth in culture. The protein (155 Kd), which contains two blocks of tandem repeats, appears to be associated with the rhoptries before invasion, but shortly afterwards it is found in the surface membrane of the infected erythrocyte. The gene for RESA has been cloned, sequenced and expressed in *E. coli* and its product has been used in Aotus monkey protection experiments (see below).

The second rhoptry-associated protein, RAP-1, is a 90 Kd molecule which is processed to smaller products. Its amino acid sequence contains potential amphiphilic α-helices, which might penetrate and disorganize the red cell membrane during invasion, thus facilitating merozoite entry. A monoclonal antibody against RAP-1 blocks parasite growth in culture (Ridley *et al*, in preparation). This protein, purified by affinity chromatography from the parasite, protects Saimiri monkeys (see below).

MOLECULAR EVALUATION OF MALARIA ANTIGENS IN VACCINE TRIALS

Animals were never tested beforehand for protection by derivatives of the circumsporozoite protein, since it was argued that the primate models available could not be reliably challenged with live sporozoites. Consequently, clinical trials were immediately set up using human volunteers. Two independent trials have been reported (Zavala *et al*,1985; Ballou *et al*, 1985). They both used short peptide sequences based on the major repeat NANP. In one study, a synthetic peptide was used with the structure: acetyl-cysteine $(NANP)_3$-OH. This was conjugated to tetanus toxoid prior to injection. Forty five volunteers participated in the trial. In the other, a fusion protein made in *E. coli* from a recombinant clone had a more complex structure comprising a CS protein sequence, $MDP(NANP)_{15}NVDP\ (NANP)_{15}$ NVDP, fusing to 35 'irrelevant' amino acids derived from the *tet* gene of *E. coli* read out of frame. Here, a total of 15 volunteers participated in the trial. Note that the latter peptide contains two representatives of the minority repeat, NVDP, and 30 copies of the majority repeat and is thus nearer in structure to the whole central region of the CS protein. However, neither of the polypeptides tested contained the flanking sequences of the protein.

The results of these trials have been disappointing. All the vaccinees responded to the injected agent by making antibodies in proportion to the dose of antigen, but only a few made high levels. Protection was at best partial. For example, in one trial the three vaccinees with the highest rises in antisporozoite antibody were challenged with infected mosquitoes. Only one was protected.

It is clear that the trials were very limited in scope. Much more could be done to try to improve the efficacy of the vaccine. However, parallel tests in mice on the second of these polypeptides has raised questions about the wisdom of choosing the repeats as the antigen.

Congenic mice, homozygous for different alleles of the class II major histocompatibility locus were tested for their ability to respond to the fusion protein described above and to smaller derivatives of it (Good, Berzofsky, Maloy, Hayashi, Fujii, Hockmeyer and Miller, 1986). The mice provide an assay for T-helper cell epitopes in an antigen. T-helper cells can only respond to parts of an antigen presented by an accessory cell in combination with a major histocompatibility complex (MHC) class II molecule. Thus, if an antigen cannot interact with any MHC class II molecule in an individual, it will not be able to interact with T-helper cells and the immune response will be blocked. Normally, a heterozygous mammal has a significant repertoire of MHC class II molecules amongst which there is a good chance that one or more will be able to interact with a particular antigen, allowing epitopes to be presented to T-cells. However, in the congenic mice used here inbreeding has generated a panel of stocks which allow individual alleles of the MHC class II genes to be tested for their ability to mediate in presenting a given antigen to T-cells. The results were quite striking. Only one of six class II alleles tested allowed presentation of the NANP repeat. Two others were able to use epitopes in the 32 amino acid segment of the fusion peptide (see above)

These results raise the possibility that an antigen comprising simple peptide repeats may be ineffective in certain individuals even in the outbred human population. This may in part explain the poor antibody response in some volunteers. It could also be the reason why $(NANP)_n$ conjugates only stimulate proliferative T-cell responses in a minority of individuals living in The Gambia (Good, Pombo, Quakiyi, Riley, Houghton, Menon, Alling, Berzofsky and Miller, 1988). This is a complicated issue since the immune response in individuals in endemic areas is boosted repeatedly by mosquito bites. Presumably the high rates of anti-NANP antibody found by some workers in such sera are due to T-cell epitopes in other parts of the protein. Such epitopes have now been found in both of the regions flanking the repeats. Unfortunately, it is in these regions that significant polymorphism has been found.

Thus for those who would pursue the CS protein as a candidate antigen, the major lesson to be learnt has been that *the whole protein* should be tested in pilot trials. Smaller fragments, which may be easier to handle in the vaccine, could be tested after the protective value of the protein is confirmed.

These studies have considerable intrinsic interest for the molecular immunologist. They have defined an experimental system which allows the interactions between an antigen and components of the immune system to be studied in detail at the molecular level. Short peptides spanning the whole CS protein are available and human T-helper cells of known human leucocyte antigen (HLA) class II genotype have been cloned. They were selected for their response to the CS protein and could thus be used to study how individual parts of the antigen molecule interact with the class II MHC β chain and, in the longer term, how they interact with T-cell receptors.

Although some evidence suggests that antibodies against CS protein can protect, it is uncertain to what extent the humoral response to the CS protein could be relied upon. Why, then, does immunization with whole, irradiated sporozoites protect against infection? Part of the answer to this question may come from recent studies on rodent malaria species. Mice immunized with irradiated *P. berghei* and *P. yoelii* have been used to study this question. Cell depletion and other studies in these animals suggest that the class of cells carrying the CD8 surface marker are important in defending the mice against infection. These results suggest that cytotoxic T-cells (which carry the marker) may mediate the protection induced by irradiated sporozoites (Kumar, Miller, Quakyi, Keister, Houghton, Maloy, Moss, Berzofsky and Good, 1988; Romero, Maryanski, Corradin, Nussenzweig, Nussenzweig and Zavala, 1989).

Parallel studies on the T-cell epitopes of RESA also lead to the conclusion that MHC restriction may limit the value of the repeats of this protein in a vaccine (Kabilan, Troye-Blomberg, Patarroyo, Björkman and Perlmann, 1987). Perhaps more seriously, monkey trials using the whole RESA protein and parts of it have given conflicting results (Collins, Anders, Pappaiuanou, Campbell, Brown, Kemp, Coppel, Skinner, Andrysiak, Favaloro, Corocoran, Broderson, Mitchell and Campbell, 1986; Collins, Campbell, Campbell, unpublished).

To date, the most promising evidence for protection in monkeys comes from the MSA-1 protein and peptides of it (Hall *et al.*, 1984a; Siddiqui *et al*, 1987; Patarroyo, Romero, Torres, Clavijo, Moreno, Martinex, Rodriguez, Guzman and Cabezas, 1987). This conclusion comes from tests on protein isolated from the parasite. Several groups have expressed parts of this large protein in bacteria and studied their ability to protect monkeys - without success so far.

CONCLUSION

In conclusion, the studies to date point to a complex interaction between the malaria parasite and its host. It seems quite possible that in different patients and different parasite strains there will be variation in the mechanisms of defence and pathogenesis. For this reason, we must keep an open mind about the possible efficacy in widespread vaccination programmes of individual parasite proteins.

REFERENCES

Ballou, W.R., Rothbard, J., Wirtz, R.A., Gordon, D.M., Williams, J.S., Gore, R.W., Schneider, I., Hollingdale, M.R., Beaudoin, R.L., Maloy, W.L., Miller, L.H. and Hockmeyer, W.T. (1985). Immunogenicity of synthetic peptides from circumsporozoite protein of *Plasmodium falciparum*. *Science,* **228**, 996–999.

Cohen, S. (1979). Immunity to malaria. *Proceedings of the Royal Society of London* (B), **203**, 323–345.

Cohen, S., McGregor, J.A. and Carrington, S.P. (1961). Gammaglobulin and acquired immunity to malaria. *Nature,* **192**, 733–737.

Collins, W.E., Anders, R.F., Pappaiuanou, H., Campbell, G.H., Brown, G.V., Kemp, D.J., Coppel, R.L., Skinner, J.C., Andrysiak, P.M., Favaloro, J.M., Corocoran, L.M., Broderson, J.R., Mitchell, G.F. and Campbell, C.C. (1986). Immunisation of Aotus monkeys with recombinant proteins of an erythrocyte surface antigen of *P. falciparum. Nature,* **323**, 259–262.

Coppel, R.L., Cowman, A.F., Anders, R.F., Bianco, A.E., Saint, R.B., Lingelbach, K.R., Kemp, D.J. and Brown, G.V. (1984). Immune sera recognize on erythrocytes a *Plasmodium falciparum* antigen composed of repeated amino acid sequences. *Nature,* **31**, 789–791.

de la Cruz, V.F., Lal, A.A. and McCutchan, T.F. (1987). Sequence variation in putative functional domains of the circumsporozoite protein of *Plasmodium falciparum. Journal of Biological Chemistry,* **262**, 11935–11939.

Dame, J.B., Williams, J.L., McCutchan, J.F., Weber, J.L., Wirtz, R.A., Hockmeyer, W.T., Maloy, W.L., Haynes, J.D., Schneider, I., Roberts, D., Sanders, G.S., Reddy, E.P., Diggs, C.L. and Miller, L.H. (1984). Structure of the gene encoding the immunodominant surface antigen on the sporozoite of the human malaria parasite, *Plasmodium falciparum. Science,* **225**, 593–599.

Dubois, P., Dedet, J.P., Fandeur, T., Roussillion, C., Jendoubi, M., Pouillac, S., Mercereau-Puijalon, O. and Pereira da Silva. L. (1984). Protective immunisation of the squirrel monkey against asexual blood stages of *Plasmodium falciparum* by use of parasite protein fractions. *Proceedings of the National Academy of Sciences, USA,* **81**, 229–232.

Enea, V., Ellis, J., Zavala, F., Arnot, D.E., Asavanich, A., Masuda, A. Quakyi, I. and Nussenzweig, R.S. (1984). DNA cloning of *Plasmodium falciparum* circumsporozoite gene: Amino acid sequence of repetitive epitope. *Science,* **225**, 628–630.

Goman, M., Langsley, G. Hyde, J.E., Yankofsky, N.K., Zolg, J.W. and Scaife, J.G. (1982). The establishment of genomic DNA libraries for the human malaria parasite *P. falciparum* and identification of individual clones by hybridization. *Molecular and Biochemical Parasitology,* **5**, 391–400.

Good, M.F., Berzofsky, J.A., Maloy, W.L., Hayashi, Y., Fujii, N., Hockmeyer, W.T. and Miller, L.H. (1986). Genetic control of the immune response in mice to *Plasmodium falciparum. Journal of Experimental Medicine,* **164**, **2**, 655–660.

Good, M.F., Pombo, D., Quakiyi, I., Riley, E.M., Houghton, R., Menon, A., Alling, D.W., Berzofsky, J.A. and Miller, L.H. (1988). Human T-cell recognition of the circumsporozoite protein of *Plasmodium falciparum:* Immunodominant T-cell domains map to the polymorphic regions of the molecule. *Proceedings of the National Academy of Sciences, USA,* **85**, 1199–1203.

Haldar, K., Ferguson, M.A.J. and Cross, G.A.M. (1985). Acylation of a *Plasmodium falciparum* merozoite surface antigen via sn-1 2-diacyl glycerol. *Journal of Biological Chemistry,* **260**, 4969–4974.

Hall, F.R., Hyde, J.E., Goman, M., Simmons, D.Ll., Hope, I.A., Mackay, M., Scaife, J., Merkli, B., Richle, R. and Stocker, J. (1984b). Major surface antigen of a human malaria parasite cloned and expressed in bacteria. *Nature,* **311**, 379–382.

Hall, R., Osland, A., Hyde, J.E., Simmons, D.Ll., Hope, I.A. and Scaife, J.G. (1984a). Processing polymorphism and biological significance of p190, a major surface antigen of the erythrocytic forms of *Plasmodium falciparum. Molecular and Biochemical Parasitology,* **11**, 61–80.

Hyde, J.E., Goman, M., Hall, R., Osland, A., Hope, I.A., Langsley, G.W., Zolg, J.W. and Scaife, J. (1984). Characterisation and translation studies of messenger RNA from the human malarial parasite *P. falciparum* and construction of a DNA library. *Molecular and Biochemical Parasitology,* **10**, 269–285.

Kabilan, L., Troye-Blomberg, M., Patarroyo, M.E., Bjorkman, A. and Perlmann, P. (1987). Regulation of the immune response in *Plasmodium falciparum* malaria, IV T-cell dependent production of immunoglobulin and anti-*P. falciparum* antibodies *in vitro. Clinical and Experimental Immunology,* **68**, 288–297.

Koenen, M., Scherf, A., Mercereau-Puijalon, O., Langsley, G., Sibilli, L., Dubois, P., Pereira da Silva, L. and Müller-Hill, B. (1984). Human antisera detect a *Plasmodium falciparum* genomic clone encoding a nonapeptide repeat. *Nature,* **311**, 382–385.

Kumar, S., Miller, L.H., Quakyi, I.A., Keister, D.B., Houghton, R., Maloy, W.L., Moss, B., Berzofsky, J.A. and Good, M. (1988). Cytotoxic T-cells specific for the circumsporozoite protein of *Plasmodium falciparum. Nature,* **334**, 258, 260.

Murray, N. (1983). Phage lambda and molecular cloning. In *Bacteriophage Lambda* (eds. R. Hendrix, R.A. Weisberg, and F.W. Stahl). Vol. II, pp. 395–432. Cold Spring Habor, New York.

Nussenzweig, R.S. and Nussenzweig, V. (1984). Development of sporozoite vaccines. *Philosophical Transactions of the Royal Society of London, B,* **307**, 117–128.

Ozaki, L.S., Svec, P., Nussenzweig, V. and Godson, G.N. (1983). Structure of the *Plasmodium knowlesi* gene coding for the circumsporozoite protein. *Cell,* **34**, 815–822.

Patarroyo, M.E., Romero, P., Torres, M.L., Clavijo, P., Moreno, A.

Martínex, A., Rodríguez, R., Guzman, F. and Cabezas, E. (1987). Induction of protective immunity against experimental infection with malaria using synthetic peptides. *Nature,* **328**, 629–632.

Perlmann, H., Berzins, K., Wahlgren, M., Carlsson, J., Björkman, A., Patarroyo, M.E. and Perlmann, P. (1984). Antibodies in malarial sera to parasite antigens in the membrane of erythrocytes infected with early sexual stages of *Plasmodium falciparum. Journal of Experimental Medicine,* **159**, 1686–1704.

Perrin, L.H., Merkli, B., Loche, M., Chizzolini, C., Smart, J. and Richle, R. (1984). Antimalarial immunity in Saimiri monkeys. Immunisation with surface components of asexual blood stages. *Journal of Experimental Medicine,* **160**, 441–451.

Pirson, P. and Perkins, M. (1985). Characterization with monoclonal antibodies of a surface antigen of *Plasmodium falciparum* merozoites. *Journal of Immunology,* **134**, 1946–1951.

Playfair, J.H.L. (1982). Immunity to malaria. *British Medical Bulletin,* **38**, 153–159.

del Portillo, H.A., Nussenzweig, R.S. and Enea, V. (1987). Circumsporozoite gene of a *Plasmodium falciparum* strain from Thailand. *Molecular and Biochemical Parasitology,* **24**, 289–294.

Romero, P., Maryanski, J.L., Corradin, G., Nussenzweig, R.S., Nussenzweig, V. and Zavala, F. (1989). Cloned cytotoxic T-cells recognise an epitope in the circumsporozoite protein and protect against malaria. *Nature,* **341**, 323–326.

Ruangjirachuporn, W., Wåhlin, B., Perlmann, H., Carlsson, J., Berzins, K., Wahlgren, M., Udomsangpetch, R., Wigzell, H. and Perlmann, P. (1988). Monoclonal antibodies to a peptide corresponding to a repeated sequence in *Plasmodium falciparum* antigen Pf155. *Molecular and Biochemical Parasitology,* **29**, 19–28.

Schwartz, R.T., Riveros-Moreno, V., Lockyer, M., Nicholls, S.C., Davey, L.S., Hillman, Y., Sandhu, Y.S., Freeman, R.R. and Holder, A.A. (1986). Structural diversity of the major surface antigen of *Plasmodium falciparum* merozoites. *Molecular and Cellular Biology,* **6**, 964–968.

Siddiqui, W.A., Tam, L.Q., Kramer, K.J., Hui, G.S.N., Case, S.E., Yamaga, K.M., Chang, S.P., Chan, E.B.T. and Kan, S.C. (1987). Merozoite surface coat precursor protein completely protects Aotus monkeys. *Proceedings of the National Academy of Sciences, USA,* **84**, 3014–3018.

Tanabe, K., Mackay, M., Goman, M. and Scaife, J.G. (1987). Allelic dimorphism in a surface antigen gene of the malaria parasite, *Plasmodium falciparum. Journal of Molecular Biology,* **195**, 273–287.

Udomsangpetch, R., Lundgren, K., Berzins, K., Wåhlin, B., Perlmann, H., Troye-Blomberg, M., Carlsson, J., Wahlgren, M., Perlmann, P. and Björkman, A. (1986). Human monoclonal antibodies to Pf155, a major antigen of the malaria parasite, *Plasmodium falciparum. Science,* **231**, 57–59.

Weber, J.L., Leininger, W.M. and Lyon, J.A. (1986). Variation in the gene encoding a major surface antigen of the human malaria parasite *Plasmodium falciparum. Nucleic Acids Research,* **14**, 3311–3322.

Weber, J., Sim, B.K.L., Lyon, J.A. and Wolff, R. (1988). Merozoite surface protein sequence from the Camp strain of the human malaria parasite, *Plasmodium falciparum. Nucleic Acids Research,* **16**, 1206.

Young, R.A. and Davis, R.W. (1983). Efficient isolation of genes using antibody probes. *Proceedings of the National Academy of Sciences, USA,* **80**, 1194–1198.

Zavala, F., Tam, J.P., Hollingdale, M.R., Cochrane, A.H., Quakyi, I., Nussenzweig, R.S. and Nussenzweig, V. (1985). Rationale for development of a synthetic vaccine against *Plasmodium falciparum* malaria. *Science,* **228**, 1436–1440.

DISCUSSION - SESSION FIVE

MORENO-LOPEZ, SWEDEN *The conformation and presentation of antigens to the immune system is very important for an immune response. Now that we know the 3-dimensional crystalographic structure of FMD virus, do you think that the problems of peptide vaccines will be solved?*

DOEL Unfortunately, the structure of the 141–160 sequence has not been resolved due, apparently, to the high mobility of this region of the VPI. While this information will prove valuable to the development of synthetic FMD vaccines, I believe it is more likely that we will solve the problems by manipulation of the immune response with adjuvants, cytokines and by appropriate presentation of the peptide to the target species.

TEALE, KENYA *Does the 200–213 peptide have a predicted or overt T-cell epitope?*

DOEL Little or no immune response can be generated against the 200–213 sequence, nor does it contain a T-cell epitope based on the commonly accepted algorithms. However, work by Norman Flynn in Ian McConnell's laboratory has shown that a peptide, in which an alanine is replaced with a glycine to create a Rothbard motif, does induce an immune response in sheep.

SNOWDEN, U.K. *Concerning the FMD peptide 40, have various carriers or adjuvants been used to attempt to influence the isotype of antibody produced by the host to the vaccine and therefore influence the degree of protection?*

DOEL Firstly, attaching peptide 40 to a carrier drastically reduces its immunogenicity. We have carried out a number of studies with adjuvants and while there is nothing to report at the moment, we are continuing these studies with particular reference to the isotypes induced.

SINGH, INDIA *The immunity of most FMD vaccines made by different methods breaks down within six months. What is the cause and what can be done?*

DOEL There are too many variables in the system to give a simple answer. You should certainly consider the quantity of virus in the antigen harvests and, possibly, the quality of virus with respect to integrity of VPI.

Of course the problem you have identified is yet another justification for novel FMD vaccines.

WAFULA, KENYA *Has any attempt been made to compare the duration of immunity conferred by the conventional FMD virus vaccines and the synthetic peptide vaccines?*

DOEL The titre of peptide induced anti-viral antibody in cattle appears to follow a similar pattern to that seen with conventional vaccines. Unfortunately, we have not had an opportunity to compare peptide with virus vaccines using the same adjuvant, and breed and age of cattle. Results in guinea pigs indicate that the duration of immunity to FMD challenge following peptide vaccination is as good as seen with conventional FMD vaccines - approximately six months.

TEALE, KENYA *Could Dr. Snodgrass explain the seasonal incidence of rotavirus diarrhoea in children in temperate climates?*

SNODGRASS The factors are not clearly understood, as the rotavirus season occurs in winter whether the climate is very cold e.g. Northern Europe or Northern U.S.A., or relatively mild e.g. Australia.

JEGGO, AUSTRIA *Does exposure sequentially of two rotavirus types give rise to an antibody response to other types?*

SNODGRASS Although studies on this have not been done, the existence of a broad response to many serotypes in cattle would suggest this is true as it is unlikely that these animals would have been exposed to all these different serotypes.

RANGNEKAR, INDIA *Is there any progress in developing a thermostable rinderpest vaccine to overcome cold chain problems in vaccination campaigns.*

SCOTT The major justification for vaccinia-recombinant-rinderpest virus vaccines was the well-known thermo-stability of vaccinia virus. This justification, however, has been usurped by Dr. Mariner's experiments and field demonstrations showing that his Vero-cell derivative of Plowright's vaccine retained potency without refrigeration for 30 days at 26–30° C

RANGNEKAR, INDIA *Is there any difference in the duration of immunity from tissue culture rinderpest vaccine and goat tissue freeze dried vaccine.*

SCOTT No difference.

SUDI, TANZANIA *The assumption that control of rinderpest in cattle also controls rinderpest in wildlife is too simple since we do not know whether the 1982 outbreak in Tanzania was of wildlife or domestic livestock origin.*

SCOTT The assumption is correct everywhere except in Eastern Africa with its rich fauna of plains wildlife. More work is required to unravel the interplay between infection in cattle and wildlife in Eastern Africa. Happily, a start has been made.

MAJOK, U.S.A. *Taking into consideration the experience of JP-15, the present civil wars in Africa, and the capabilities of the governments to deliver adequate veterinary services and surveillance, how confident are you that rinderpest might be eradicated from Africa before the recombinant-vaccinia vaccines are licensed?*

SCOTT I sincerely hope that vaccinia-recombinant rinderpest virus vaccines are NEVER licensed for use in countries where many human beings are immunosuppressed by other persistent infections. Vaccinia virus is NOT a safe vaccine and its host range is dangerously wide.

SINGH, INDIA Is there one simple method to differentiate rinderpest and mucosal disease?

SCOTTThe detection of antigen in tears by agar gel immuno-diffusion, or better counter immuno-electrophoresis, using as test sera a hyperimmune rinderpest antiserum prepared in rabbits and an anti-hog cholera serum prepared in rabbits. BUT any case of fever, stomatitis and enteritis in buffaloes or cattle in equatorial Africa, the Middle East or the Indian subcontinent is RINDERPEST until proven otherwise.

NANA-NUKECHAP, CAMEROON *Will the vaccines against* Babesia bovis *and* Babesia bigemina *in cattle in the temperate region be equally efficacious against similar strains in the tropics?*

BROWN Yes. All the evidence shows that the live *Babesia* vaccines protect against all challenges. It is not clear yet whether killed antigens such as in the *B. bovis* culture supernate vaccine do.

MASAKE, KENYA *When you vaccinate cattle against three organisms simultaneously is there any interference in the immune response directed to each of them?*

BROWN Yes, but presently it appears possible in calves at least, to administer both *Babesia* and *Anaplasma* at the same time.

MASAKE, KENYA *Do you know the reason why* T. annulata *schizonts are able to immunize heterologous animals while* T. parva *schizonts are unable to do so?*

BROWN No, though the fact that *T. annulata* selectively infects B-cells or macrophages, while *T. parva* produces cell lines manifesting T-cell epitopes may have something to do with it.

ASSOKU, GHANA *Would Dr. Brown clarify the shelf-life and stability of the conventional vaccines against tick-borne diseases described, especially babesiosis and theileriosis? Also what are his views on the best material for vaccines against theileriosis – schizonts or sporozoites?*

BROWN

- Live vaccines of the type described have a 'shelf-life' at room temperature (constant 20° C) of approximately one week. If cryopreserved at −70° C, they are infective for at least 10 years.
- It is evident that any vaccine against theileriosis should induce cytotoxic T-cells against schizont-infected lymphoblasts. This genetically-restricted mechanism is the only mechanism which is known to protect on its own. Other mechanisms may play a role in immunity to theileriosis, however, e.g. humoral mechanisms blocking sporozoite invasion, although they have not yet been shown to operate on their own. Immunization at present is effected by infecting cattle and allowing or persuading them to recover. Currently sporozoites are used for *T. parva* and schizont-infected cells for *T. annulata.*

PANDEY, ZAMBIA *In Zambia, Lechwe antelope recently translocated for game ranching have died of heartwater. Does Dr. Brown think that heartwater vaccine presently used in South Africa in domestic animals could be administered safely to this species?*

(This question was redirected to Dr. Bruce Fivaz who has experience in using the Ball 3 heartwater vaccine in game animals)

FIVAZ, SOUTH AFRICA The heartwater vaccine can be used in antelope species but, as in Angora goats which are very sensitive, this must be done with care and losses must be expected.

BENAVIDES, COLOMBIA *Could you please state your opinion on the use of 'high tech' vaccines in relation to enzootic stability of haemoparasites in tropical areas.*

SINGH Under the present circumstances where effective culture vaccines are available, it is desirable that we use them to attain enzootic stability without the risk of severe reactions. 'High tech' vaccines are welcome but they are likely to take a long time before they are ready for use.

MASAKE, KENYA *Are all your* Theileria *isolates of the same species and can they all be protected against by using any one isolate?*

SINGH All the isolates in our laboratory are of *Theileria annulata.* Results of cross protection trials indicate that one isolate, ODE-ANAND, incorporated in our vaccine provides protection against the isolates collected from different geographical areas of the country. Another *Theileria* species is *T. mutans* which is of little clinical significance and does not need any vaccination. We do not have *T. parva* in India.

IRVIN, U.K. *What is the cost of vaccination for each animal which is charged to the farmer?*

SINGH A farmer is required to pay Rs 25/- (approximately U.S. $1.5) for vaccination of one animal. This includes the cost of the vaccine and its administration by the veterinarian of the dairy cooperatives.

BROWN *As a supplementary to Dr. Irvin's question, may I confirm that your costs for Kaira District were U.S. $69,000 to cover costs and delivery of vaccine to 40,000 cattle?*

SINGH Yes.

SHAMBWANA, TANZANIA *To what extent has vaccination against theileriosis replaced conventional methods of tick control in India?*

SINGH The vaccine has been available commercially for six months. Its use for test vaccination, however, has been undertaken on about 40,000 animals. So far none of these animals has required conventional treatment, but further studies are required to assess the usefulness of the vaccine accurately.

TAIT, U.K. *In malaria is the sporozoite surface antigen expressed on the liver cell and how does the immune response recognize the infected cell?*

RIDLEY The CSP, or parts of it, have not been detected on the surface of liver cells. However, for cytotoxic T-cell response only a small region of the antigen would be presented with Class I molecules. These 'epitopes' are only now being defined and antibodies raised against these cytotoxic T-cell epitopes would be required to detect this part of the protein on the surface.

SPOONER, U.K. *Can you generate a CTL response against piroplasm stages or against liver stage cultures?*

RIDLEY As red blood cells do not express Class I molecules, a classic cytotoxic T-cell response cannot be mounted against the erythrocytic stages of the parasite life cycle. Liver cells do express Class I molecules and strong experimental evidence exists to show that there is a cytoxic T-cell response against parasitized liver cells.

RASTOGI, TRINIDAD *I believe that an anti-malaria vaccine was developed at the State University of New York about four to five years ago, but attempts to commercialize it fell through due to excessive profit demands from the private company involved. Can you comment on this, please?*

RIDLEY There is as yet no effective vaccine against malaria. I think the work you refer to concerns the work using peptides derived from the circumsporozoite protein which I outlined in the talk. Vaccines based on CSP or any other malarial protein have not yet proved successful enough to merit full-scale commercialization. Whether or not companies involved in malarial vaccine development will find it sufficiently profitable to widely market their vaccine is another question, which I am not qualified to answer.

6.

BIOTECHNOLOGY IN DEVELOPING COUNTRIES

Chairman: S. Anderson,
University of Yucutan,
Mexico

6.1

Biotechnology in Latin America – Reproductive Techniques in Cattle

C.S. GALINA, I. RUBIO, A. PORRAS and R. NAVARRO-FIERRO
Departamento de Reproduccion, Facultad de Medicina Veterinaria y Zootecnia, Universidad Nacional Autonoma de Mexico, Mexico

INTRODUCTION

It has been customary to transfer technology developed in industrialized countries to the developing world with the aim of improving traditional husbandry procedures for livestock management. This approach has been reasonably successful with respect to cattle raised in environments similar to those for which the technology was created. In Latin America (L.A.) this is particularly true of Holstein cattle living in temperate zones such as those found in the highlands of Colombia, Mexico and Chile. However three-quarters of the cattle raised in L.A. populate the lowland areas where the native breeds of cattle (generically known as Zebus) predominate, and where environmental temperatures usually exceed 30° C. This situation has created the need to adapt imported technology to the unique local conditions prevailing in the L.A. lowland tropics. Cattle of European origin introduced into these areas have shown poor adaptation resulting in reduced reproductive performance (Vaccaro, Cardozo and Vaccaro, 1983; Morales, Hinojosa and Aguilar, 1981).

The most popular types of cattle in the lowland tropics therefore continue to be indigenous *Bos indicus* breeds whose physiological reproductive traits are different from those of European cattle (Randel, 1984). Consequently, appropiate technology will have to be created to maximize the reproductive potential of these animals. The objective of the present paper is to analyze the application of three established techniques, namely semen collection and preservation, oestrus synchronization and embryo transfer to cattle reproduction in the lowland tropics as examples of the need to generate technology in accordance with local conditions.

SEMEN COLLECTION AND PRESERVATION

Artificial Insemination (AI) procedures have been applied in L.A. almost since the technique became first available in the late fifties. However, in many of these countries the lack of adequate AI centres has created the need for veterinary practitioners to custom-freeze semen from sires in the farm situation. The semen is usually evaluated on the premises and, after adding the first diluent (equilibration period), is transported to a laboratory where the second diluent is added and samples are packed and frozen. This procedure has several pitfalls that need to be explored. Electroejaculation techniques are usually employed as bulls have not been trained to have their semen collected in an artificial vagina, and the quality of the resulting ejaculate from the former method has been questioned (Austin, Hupp and Murphree, 1961). In fact unpublished data have shown that the percentages of ejaculates discarded one week after freezing of semen collected by electroejaculation and by an artificial vagina are significantly different (Leon, 1990). This important technological variation, coupled with the frequent need to transport the ejaculate considerable distances before freezing, needs to be examined as it has been shown that the number of ejaculates discarded after freezing increases with distance from the farm to the laboratory (Hernandez, 1989).

There is increasing evidence for a seasonal production of quality ejaculates from bulls raised in L.A. tropics, although this is a very controversial issue. Several workers have found that the concentration of sperm in the ejaculate has been affected by the time of year when collection occurred (Alba, Martinez and Rodriguez, 1982; Menendez, Morales, Perez and Guerra, 1984) while others have found that the quality of the ejaculated semen is similar except for sperm abnormalities which increase in the summer months (Gauthier, 1984). Several studies carried out independently in Mexico have failed to find significant differences in the volume, concentration and morphology of semen from different Zebu breeds (Cuevas, 1976; Herrera, 1978; Hernandez, 1989). However, in the latter of these studies a comparison was made of ejaculates discarded one week after freezing in relation to the time of the year when collection occurred. The highest number of ejaculates discarded were those obtained in winter and spring irrespective of breed or distance transported prior to freezing.

Another feature of semen in tropical bulls concerns sperm quality following thawing. In a survey carried out by Rhodes, Galina, Duchateau and Soto (1985), semen from *Bos indicus* bulls averaged 30% motility in contrast to the 45% obtained in semen collected from *Bos taurus* bulls. This significant difference in motility needs to be taken into consideration when evaluating semen after thawing, especially as an adequate supply of liquid nitrogen is not always available on the farm and the containers with frozen semen are sometimes left with the minimal permissible level recommended by the manufacturers.

Proper biotechnology in this field is therefore in demand in order to improve semen preparation for use in AI programmes.

OESTRUS SYNCHRONIZATION

This is probably one of the most popular techniques used in cattle reproduction raised under lowland L.A. conditions. Galina and Russell (1987) in a survey of trends in research on tropical cattle found that the four most active L.A. countries in this field, namely Brazil, Cuba, Venezuela and Mexico had the control of oestrus as a common research objective. Interestingly in the same study only Cuba was found to conduct research on the other two topics chosen for discussion in the present paper.

One of the main difficulties associated with oestrus synchronization programmes concerns the selection of adequate biological material. Landivar, Galina, Duchateau and Navarro-Fierro (1985) while attempting to test the efficacy of prostaglandin $F_{2\alpha}$ in Gyr cattle encountered as much as 30% of the cattle chosen for the programme, to be pregnant. This situation, also found in a later experiment by Wild (1989), creates several problems. Firstly, the animals to be administered a luteolytic drug like $PGF_{2\alpha}$ have to be subjected to a previous rectal examination that in many instances is time consuming and inaccurate (Vaca, Galina, Fernandez-Baca and Ramirez, 1983). Secondly, the assortment procedure requires quite frequently that the selected nonpregnant herd will frequently have to be formed from different lots of animals thus upsetting the hierarchy order naturally present in the herd, which in turn will probably affect oestrous expression (Orihuela, Galina, Duchateau, 1988). Thirdly, the cows pregnant before the start of the oestrus synchronization programme are predictably the most fertile animals in the herd, thus the technician in charge is usually left with the cows difficult to get in calf by AI.

Other aspects to be considered are the age of the cow, date of last calving and time of the year when calving previously occurred in relation to the beginning of the synchronization programme. In a large sample of cows to be synchronized with $PGF_{2\alpha}$, Wild (1989) found that the average age of the experimental herds was six years but the interval from synchronization to calving was as long as 360 days. Similar problems had been faced earlier in Brazil by Mucciolo, Barnabe and Barnabe (1977). These findings indicate the farmer does not necessarily select the most fertile cows for a synchronization programme or that he picks only those cows that he cannot readily identify in oestrus during an AI programme. Galina, Murcia, Beatty, Navarro-Fierro and Porras (1990), found that only 30% of a nonsynchronized herd is detected in oestrus.

Porras (1990) in a large trial on the use of progestagens as synchronizing agents in tropical cattle, found that the efficacy of the drug tested, in this case Synchromate B (Ceva Laboratories, U.S.A.), was significantly affected when noncycling cows (as indicated by the palpation of a mature corpus luteum per rectum) had a calf present at the time of treatment. Even when the same group of technicians carried out the same synchronization programme, there was large variation with respect to oestrus response and fertility following AI in all the commercial farms that participated in the trial. This indicates that results will be affected by the degree of expertise in husbandry procedures within farms. Similar findings in relation to body condition, and presence of the calf have been reported earlier by several groups in L.A., in Mexico (Rodriguez and Rodriguez, 1978; Santos, Taboada, Montano, Gonzalez-Padilla and Ruiz, 1979), in Venezuela, (Gonzalez, Goicochea and Soto, 1981), in Brazil (Torres, Fonseca, Torres and Ruas, 1984), and in Guadeloupe (Gauthier, Couland and Valee, 1985). Generally it can be said that no differences in fertility are obtained when a prostaglandin or a progestagen are used (average 40% to first insemination), the presence of the calf and poor body condition accounting for approximately 10% loss in fertility.

Lastly, for unknown reasons data had to be forfeited from long-term fertility trials using AI following synchronization on private farms as Wild (1989) found that as many as 35% of the cows that were initially selected could not be located for rectal examinations to evaluate pregnancy rates. This situation leaves the researcher with the dilemma whether or not to include in the final calculations, the total number of animals present when the experiment started. Unfortunately whatever decision is taken, there is bound to be a bias in the conclusions of the study.

EMBRYO TRANSFER

In spite of increasing interest to make this procedure available on a large-scale in L.A., recently published surveys indicate that this is not happening. For example Del Campo and Del Campo (1988) sent a questionnaire to various L.A. countries to collect information on the use of this technique and dissapointingly received only 14 replies. More important, it was obvious from the data given that many of them were just starting on the basic procedures currently widely used in developed countries. Galina and Russell (1987) in their survey on trends in cattle reproduction in the tropics found that less than 3% of the studies published over a period of 17 years were on the subject of embryo transfer. Anta, Rivera, Galina, Porras, Zarco and Russell (1989) in a recent survey of information published in Mexico in this same field found a similar situation. Nonetheless, this important and fashionable activity seems to be growing in L.A. However, as is the case of semen biotechnology, the fact that the service is provided by private practitioners makes it difficult to evaluate the development of this technique under L.A. conditions.

Recently, the annual meeting of the International Embryo Transfer Society dedicated a considerable amount of time to the analysis of the present situation of embryo transfer (ET) in developing countries. Seidel and Seidel (1989) proposed that technicians in this field should carefully evaluate the conditions under which an ET programme is going to be conducted thus discouraging those with inadequate facilities. In this report they also pointed out the importance of research using the locally available biological material unique to lowland tropics, citing the example of N'Dama cattle which have proved to be trypanotolerant but little is known of their physiological qualities particularly under a regime of superovulation. Cunningham (1989), stated that, in spite of the fact that ET could benefit the genetic quality of L.A. livestock, it is evident from experiences related to AI services in many developing countries, that difficulties associated with the widespread application of ET in these areas may well be insurmountable. In the same meeting McGuirk (1989) opined that if ET is going to have a positive impact in developing countries it is necessary to pay special attention to management and nutrition as the local breeds do not present any inherent problems to limit their reproductive potential.

In spite of obvious technical limitations, the majority of L.A. governments have channelled considerable resources in developing nationwide ET programmes. Published results of experiences in this field are rapidly becoming available. Armas and Holy (1988), have published a booklet on ET procedures carried out under Cuban conditions with very encouraging results. Also Peeples and Oden (1989), and Elsden (1989), have recently published their experiences in Paraguay and Mexico, respectively.

ET is probably one of the best examples of a biotechnological procedure that needs to be redefined through research to meet the demands of a particular set of geographical, political and economical circumstances such as those found in L.A. As pointed out by Seidel and Seidel (1989) it serves little purpose to finance the construction of flamboyant buildings which will have to operate on meagre budgets insufficient for the purchase of drugs and reagents. In many developing countries ET has been developed as an end in itself rather than as a useful tool and this has been one of the major obstacles in the development of ET in L.A. It is important to emphasize that embryo transfer will not have genetic merit until adequate testing of both male and female is established under L.A. conditions. Under the present circumstances genetic improvement is better obtained by using AI with tested bulls (Navarro-Fierro and Posse, 1985). So therefore it is not surprising that after the initial excitement associated with the arrival of a new revolutionary technique that would solve the problems of poor animal production in their countries, users soon become discouraged by the poor results achieved, in many instances probably as a consequence of financial and technological restraints, thus spreading disenchantment among their peers.

In conclusion regional experiences obtained with the application of these three techniques of vital importance for improving animal production in L.A. indicate that what is required is an adequate adaptation of imported technology taking into consideration the special circumstances and requirements present at local level. Only in this way will these techniques prove to be as successful in the Latin American situation as they have been in other parts of the world.

REFERENCES

Alba Gomez, L.O., Martinez Morales, C. and Rodriguez Fleites, J. (1982) Caracteristicas del semen de toros Brahman americano (*Bos indicus*) en condiciones de inseminacion artificial en Cuba. Semen characteristics of Brahman bulls (*Bos indicus*) raised under AI conditions of Cuba. *Revista de Salud Animal*, **4**, 153–163.

Anta, E., Rivera, J.A., Galina, C.S., Porras, A., Zarco, L. and Russell, J.M.(1989). Analisis de la informacion publicada en Mexico eficiencia reproductiva de los bovinos. I. Estudio bibliometrico. *Veterinaria, Mexico* **20**, 3–10.

Armas, R. and Holy, L. (1988). Transferencia de Embriones. Embryo Transfer. *Ministerio de Agricultura, Centro de Informacion y Documentacion Agropecuario, La Habana, Cuba.*

Austin, W.J., Hupp, W.E. and Murphree, L.R. (1961). Comparison of the quality of bull semen collected in artificial vagina or electroejaculation. *Journal of Dairy Science*, **44**, 2292–2297.

Cuevas, de la H. J.M. (1976). Contribucion del estudio de las caracteristicas del semen Cebu (*Bos indicus*). *Tesis Licenciatura*, Instituto Tecnologico de Monterrey, Mexico.

Cunningham, E.P. (1989). The genetic improvement of cattle in developing countries. *Theriogenology*, **31**, 17–27.

Del Campo, M.R. and Del Campo, C.H. (1988). Current status, advantages and potential applications of embryo transfer in relation to animal production and/or species preservation in Central and South America; the West Indies. *Proceedings of the International Embryo Movement Symposium, Montreal, Canada* **1**, 55–62.

Elsden, R.P. (1989). Mexican government uses embryo transfer to increase production of national dairy herd. *Theriogenology*, **31**, 47–48.

Galina, C.S., Murcia, C., Beatty, A., Navarro-Fierro, R. and Porras, A. (1990). Reproductive performance of Zebu cattle in Mexico using artificial insemination. *Proceedings of the Regional Network for Improving the Reproductive Management of Meat and Milk-Producing Livestock in Latin America with the Aid of Radioimmunoassay Techniques, Bogota Colombia,* pp.213–220.

Galina, C.S. and Russell, J.M. (1987). Research and publishing trends in cattle reproduction in the tropics: A global analysis. *Animal Breeding Abstracts*, **55**, 820–828.

Gauthier, D. (1984). Variations saisonnieres de la production spermatique et du comportement sexuel des taureux creoles en Guadeloupe. (Seasonal variations in sperm production and behaviour in Criollo bulls raised in Guadeloupe) Reproduction des ruminants en zone tropicale. *Reunion Internationale, Point-a-Pitre, Guadeloupe*, **501**.

Gauthier, D., Couland, G. and Vallee, F. (1985). Induction d'une ovulation postpartum chez la vache Creole a l'aide d'une separation temporaire du veau et de l'utilisation prealable d' un implant de Norgestomet. (Induction of post partum ovulation in Criollo cows using Norgestomet implants and temporary calf removal.) *Reproduction, Nutrition, Developpement*, **25**, 1029–1035.

Gonzalez-Stagnaro, C., Goicochea, J. and Soto, E. (1981). Tratamiento hormonal del anestro posparto en vacas mestizas. (Hormonal treatment of post partum anoestrous in crosbred cows.) *Memoria, Asociacion Latinoamericana de Produccion Animal*, **16**, 127–128.

Hernandez, E. (1989). Estudio sobre las caracteristicas del semen y evaluacion de la libido en toros *Bos indicus*. (Study on semen characteristics and libido evaluation in *Bos indicus* bulls.) *Tesis, Maestria, Universidad Nacional Autonoma de Mexico*.

Herrera, D.J. (1978). Variaciones de las caracteristicas del semen de las razas Indobrasil, Gyr, Guzerat y Brahman en los distintos meses y epoca del ano. *Tesis, Licenciatura, Universidad Nacional Autonoma de Mexico*.

Landivar, C., Galina, C.S., Duchateau, A. and Navarro-Fierro, R. (1985). Fertility trial in Zebu cattle after a natural or controlled estrus with prostaglandin $F_{2\alpha}$, comparing natural mating with artificial insemination, synchronization, AI, mating. *Theriogenology*, **23**, 421–427.

Leon, V.H. (1990), Efecto del metodo de coleccion sobre las caracteristicas del semen en ganado Cebu y Europeo bajo condiciones tropicales. *Tesis, Maestria , Universidad Nacional Autonoma de Mexico*.

McGuirk, B. (1989). The revelance of MOET programmes to developing countries. *Theriogenology*, **31**, 29–42.

Menendez, A., Morales, J.R., Perez, A.P. and Guerra, Y.D. (1984). Seasonal variation in semen production of Holstein, zebu and criollo bulls under artificial insemination conditions in Cuba. Reproduction des ruminants en zone tropicale. *Reunion internationale, Point-a-Pitre, Guadeloupe Les Colloques de L'INRA 20, Paris, France*, 239–249.

Morales, H., Hinojosa, J.A. and Aguilar, J.A. (1981). Comportamiento reproductivo de un hato Holstein en la Chontalpa Tabasco. I. Intervalo parto-primer servicio e intervalo parto-concepcion. (Reproductive performance of a Holstein herd in the area of Chontalpa Tabasco. I. Intervals from calving to first service and conception.) *Veterinaria, Mexico*, **12**, 217–221.

Mucciolo, R.G., Barnabe, R.C. and Barnabe, V.H. (1977). Utilizacao da prostaglandina $F_{2\alpha}$ ($PGF_{2\alpha}$) na sincronizacao do ciclo estral em bovinos. III. Inseminacaes artificiais praticadas em horarios predeterminados, sem observacao de sintomas de cio. *Revista da Facultade de Medicina Veterinaria e Zootecnia da Universidade de Sao Paulo*, **14**, 4551.

Navarro-Fierro, R. and Posse, C. (1985). Utilidad del trasplante de embriones para la seleccion de vacas lecheras. *Veterinaria, Mexico*, **16**, 167–178.

Orihuela, A., Galina, C.S. and Duchateau, A. (1988). Behavioural patterns of Zebu bulls towards cows previuosly synchronized with prostaglandin $F_{2\alpha}$. *Applied Animal Behaviour Science*, **21**, 267–276.

Peeples, J.G. and Oden, A.J. (1989). Establishment of a permanent embryo transfer and semen production enterprise and facility in Latin America. *Theriogenology*, **31**, 45.

Porras, A. (1990). Control del estro en ganado *Bos indicus* en condiciones tropicales: Efecto de la utilizacion del Norgestomet combinado con estrogenos. *Tesis, Maestria, Universidad Nacional Autonoma de Mexico*.

Randel, R.D. (1984). Seasonal effects on female reproductive functions in the bovine (Indian breeds). *Theriogenology*, **21**, 170–185.

Rhodes, F., Galina, C.S., Duchateau, A. and Soto, C. (1985). An investigation into the properties of bovine semen in the Mexican tropics, semen, AI, thawing. *World Review Animal Production*, **21**, 15–19.

Rodriguez, O.L. and Rodriguez, A. (1978). Tratamientos para resolucion del anestro en vaquillas criollas encastadas de Cebu. Treatment of anoestrous in Criollo heifers cross with zebus. *Tecnica Pecuaria, Mexico, No. 34*, 105–107.

Santos, S.G. de los, Taboada, J.J., Montano, M., Gonzalez-Padilla, E. and Ruiz, R. (1979). Efecto de la lactacion controlada, y tratamientos con hormonas esteroides en la induccion y sincronizacion del estro en vacas encastadas de cebu. (Effect of controlled lactation and treatment with steroid hormones on the induction and synchronisation of oestrus in cows mated with Zebu bulls.) *Tecnica Pecuaria, Mexico No 36*, 9–14.

Seidel, G.E. and Seidel, S.M. (1989). Analysis of applications of embryo transfer in developing countries. *Theriogenology*, **31**, 3–15.

Torres, C.L.A., Fonseca, F.A., Torres, C.A.A. and Ruas, J.R.M. (1984). Efeito do GnRh, PRID, amamentacao limitada e suas combinacoes na inducao do estro e na eficiencia reproductiva de vacas de corte. Effects of GnRh, PRID, restricted suckling and a combination of these on the induction of oestrus and reproductive efficiency in beef cows. *Revista de Sociedade Brasileira de Zootecnia*, **13**, 418–425.

Vaca, L.A., Galina, C.S., Fernandez-Baca S., Escobar, F.J., and Ramirez, B. (1983). Progesterone levels and its relationship with the diagnosis of a corpus luteum by rectal palpation during the estrous cycle in zebu cows. *Theriogenology*, **20**, 67–75.

Vaccaro, R., Cardozo, R. and Vaccaro, L. (1983). Milk production, reproduction and death rates of Holstein heifers imported into the tropics. *Tropical Animal Production*, **8**, 77–86.

Wild, C. (1989). Distribucion de la fertilidad en los 90 dias siguientes al estro natural o inducido con prostaglandinas bajo monta natural o inseminacion artificial. *Tesis, Maestria, Universidad Nacional Autonoma de Mexico.*

6.2

Biotechnology in Africa

P. CHIGARU, T.J. RUREDZO, S.A. OKANTAH and K.J. PETERS
International Livestock Centre for Africa, Ethiopia

INTRODUCTION

Africa has an estimated population of 572 million (FAO, 1986) which is increasing at a high rate in comparison with the developed world. The continent's population is one of the most undernourished in terms of *per capita* protein and calorie consumption. Agriculture, the major industry of the continent is in a very undeveloped state with traditional subsistence farming dominating. There is a need for radical development and application of improved technology packages in crop and livestock production. It is the application of such technologies that has led to self-sufficiency and surpluses for exports in the agriculturally developed continents of the world.

Africa is yet to witness her own green revolution. Strategically, modern technologies particularly the new scientific breakthroughs of information technology and biotechnology could be employed to generate the necessary increases in sustainable crop and animal production in Africa. Only modest gains have been achieved so far through appropriate and/or low grade technologies. Therefore technologies of high promise such as biotechnology need to be adapted and used in Africa if the continent's nutrient and food deficiencies are to be brought under control in the next century.

This paper deals with the status of biotechnology in Africa, the implications of biotechnological advances elsewhere in Africa, the potential benefits and the major constraints to the adoption of biotechnology in Africa with respect to sustainable agricultural production. Livestock and crop production systems are closely linked in Africa; the paper reflects this system of approach.

CURRENT STATUS OF BIOTECHNOLOGY IN AFRICA

The application of biotechnology in agricultural production systems in Africa is generally low particularly in sub-Saharan Africa (SSA). In certain North African countries though, biotechnology has gained inroads into agriculture. There are on the ground some ongoing schemes in some National Agricultural Research Systems (NARS) and International Agricultural Research Centres (IARCs) involving both animal and crop agriculture. A summary of the current state of application of biotechnology in the agricultural systems of some African countries is shown in Table 1.

Vaccine production

The use of vaccines for immunization of livestock is an old biotechnology which is well-subscribed in Africa. A number of countries have well-equipped laboratories for local manufacture of vaccines. Nigeria produces most of her vaccine and sera requirement from the National Veterinary Research Institute (NVRI) at Vom. Egypt has excellent laboratory facilities for vaccine and sera production as well as tissue culture at the Animal Health Research Institute (AHRI), at Dokki, whilst Ethiopia exports various vaccines to other African countries. Similarly, the Central Vaccine Laboratory (CVL) in Bamako, Mali produces most of the country's vaccine needs and exports some to a number of Francophone West African countries.

Modern biotechnological developments in vaccine production however are not yet in practice in the NARS. With the exception of Egypt, most NARS do not have laboratories capable of exploiting modern techniques in immunology at the molecular level. The production of novel vaccines therefore, is not within the capabilities of most African countries at the present time.

Among the IARCs only the International Laboratory for Research in Animal Diseases (ILRAD) in Kenya has the facilities for molecular research in immunology involving recombinant DNA technology.

Artificial insemination

Artificial insemination (AI) in livestock, particularly cattle, is one of the most widely utilized biotechnology in the African agricultural systems. AI technology is being employed in cattle production schemes in several countries of East and Southern Africa.

In Kenya there is a Central Artificial Insemination Station (CAIS) at Kabete. CAIS provides semen of high quality pedigreed dairy and beef bulls to cattle farmers, through a network of substations in Kenya. Farmers are trained to recognize heat in cows and present them for insemination at specific points. Mobile inseminators make their rounds daily and provide AI to cows at the insemination points.

In Tanzania there is a Small Scale Dairy Development Project (SSDDP); a bilateral, Swiss-aided Tanzanian project with the objective of promoting smallholder dairy production in the Iringa and Imbeya regions (Mehau,

TABLE 1 *Biotechnology in some African countries.*

Institute	Type of biotechnology	Experi-mental/ applied	Years in operation	Types of breeds/species or products	Imported or local	Distribution localized or countrywide
Tanzania (including Zanzibar)						
Central Veterinary Laboratory	Vaccine	A	5+	Anthrax	L	C
	AI production	A	6	Friesian	L	C
National AI Centres	AI	A	8	Friesian, Ayrshire, Jersey, Brahman, *S. gertrudis*	I	C
University of Sokoine/Uyole Agricultural Research Institute	RIT	E	Many	Legumes		
Ukirigurua Research Institute	RST, green house	E	10	Legumes	L	L
Senegal						
Institut Sénégalais de Recherches Agricoles	Vaccine	A	Many	Livestock	L	C
	AI	E	5+	Cattle	L	L
Ecole Inter-Etats des Sciences et Médecine Vétérinaires	ET	E	1+	Zebu	L	L
Zaire	RIT	E		Legume	L	L
Ethiopia						
National AI Centre	AI	A	8	Friesian, Jersey, Brahman	L	C
International Livestock Centre for Africa	Tissue culture	E	2	Cynodon	L	L
	in vitro gene bank			Digitaria	L	L
The Gambia						
International Trypanotolerance Centre		E	2	N'Dama	L	L
Ghana	AI					
Central Veterinary Laboratory		A	20+	Anthrax	L and I	C
Ministry of Agriculture	Vaccine	A, E	2	Yams	L	C
University of Ghana	Minisett	E	10	Jersey, Friesian	Imported semen	L
	AI					
Egypt						
Animal Health Research Inst.		A,E	20+	Cattle, sheep	L	C
	Vaccine, serum production, tissue culture					
Nigeria/.....						

TABLE 1 *Biotechnology in some African countries.* (Contd.)

Institute	Type of biotechnology	Experi-mental/ applied	Years in operation	Types of breeds/species or products	Imported or local	Distribution localized or countrywide
Nigeria						
National Veterinary Research Institute		A, E	30+	Ruminants, poultry	L	C
National Animal Production Research	Vaccine	E		Friesians	I	L
Institute	AI					
IITA		A, E		Crops	L	L
IITA/Umudike	Tissue culture	A, E	6	Yams	L	C
Zimbabwe	Minisett					
Private dairies		A, E	20+	Cattle	I	L, C
	AI	A		Cattle	I	L
University of Zimbabwe	ET	A		Legumes	L	C
	RIT	E	5	Cassava	L	L
	Tissue culture	A		Tobacco	L	L
		E		*Salmonella*	L	L
Kenya	DNA					
Veterinary Services Division		A		Friesians	L	C
Kenya Gene Bank	AI	E				
	Tissue culture	A		Legumes	L	C
International Livestock Research on Animal	RIT	E		Cattle	L	L
Diseases	DNA	E		Cattle	L	L
	Monoclonal					
	antibodies	A	5	Boran, N'Dama	L	L
	ET					

Key:

RIT = *Rhizobium* Inoculant Technology; RST = *Rhizobium* Strain Testing; L = Local, localized; C = Countrywide; A = Applied; E = Experimental; I = Imported personal communication). Challenging features of this project are the small herd sizes of about two cows per herd, and the wide distribution of herds over a large area. Tanzania possesses over 100,000 crossbred (Zebu x exotic dairy) cattle standing in small-scale herds.

In Ethiopia AI started over fifty years ago in Eritrea. It was reorganized in 1981 into a National Artificial Insemination Centre (NAIC) with headquarters at Kaliti. The Kaliti centre has two bull studs and processes and freezes semen from Friesian, Jersey and Brahman bulls. AI is offered through a network covering the Ethiopian highlands for upgrading of cattle in commercial dairy and small-scale cattle herds. The scheme has Finnish technical aid. The centre has been selected by the FAO for the establishment of a subregional gene bank for Anglophone Africa.

Similar improvement programmes in cattle are being carried out in Zimbabwe, Botswana and Malawi involving AI of indigenous cows with exotic dairy cattle, usually Friesian semen.

The picture is different in West and Central Africa. AI practice in this subregion is only exploratory. Trials have been made with AI aimed at upgrading cattle in Ghana. Major problems encountered were disease and logistics. In Cameroon and in Nigeria there are some crossbreeding programmes employing AI.

In Senegal and to some extent in Mali, there is an increasing use of AI for the establishment of crossbred Zebu Maure x exotic dairy cattle for peri-urban milk production.

The IARCs also have programmes in AI. ILRAD has programmes in Kenya. The International Trypanotolerance Centre (ITC) jointly with the International Livestock Centre for Africa (ILCA) runs an AI project in The Gambia on the N'Dama cattle breed. This breed is noted for its outstanding trypanotolerance and biotechnology is being used to multiply and propagate the breed.

Embryo transfer in livestock production in Africa

Embryo transfer (ET) has not achieved the extent of adoption AI has in the livestock production systems on the continent of Africa. ET as a more sophisticated technique, is not yet in practice within NARS with the exception of Zimbabwe. In Zimbabwe, some private dairies have limited application of ET. There are some experiments in ET in Senegal, and plans are afoot to establish an ET unit with the collaboration of Canada (A. Diop, personal communication). The IARCs such as ILCA, ILRAD and ITC have started exploratory research in ET.

At ILRAD the technique is well-developed with regular production of N'Dama and Boran calves by embryo transfer. Methods have been developed for synchronizing the ovulation of donor and recipient cows, stimulating superovulation in donors, as well as assessing suitability of recipients, handling and splitting of embryos prior to implantation. About three embryos are harvested per superovulated cow. ET is used in producing

N'Dama and Boran calves of genomes required for supporting research in trypanosomiasis and theileriosis (ILRAD, 1987).

PLANT BIOTECHNOLOGY IN AFRICA

Developments in plant biotechnology is relevant to livestock production. Several crops are fed directly to livestock as forages, concentrates and by-products.

Biological nitrogen fixation and related technologies

The role of *Rhizobium* inoculant technology in soil fertility and crop production through biological nitrogen fixation (BNF) and the decomposition of legume plant litter has been known for a long time. In the developed countries *Rhizobium* inoculant production is a major industry closely associated to seed production and has made major contributions to plant production.

In sub-Saharan Africa, most countries recognize the role of BNA in agriculture as shown by the application of inoculants to most imported legumes and the formation of the African Association for Biological Nitrogen Fixation (AABNF) in 1980 which first met in Nairobi, Kenya in 1984. At the experimental level, most countries are involved in BNF investigations from nodule collection through strain/plant testing to *Rhizobium* inoculant production covering a wide range of leguminous crop, pasture and tree species. Even so, relatively few countries Kenya, Nigeria, Senegal, Zaire and Zimbabwe are producing inoculants for country wide distribution. Only Zimbabwe is known to export inoculants to other African and Asian countries although Kenya and Senegal might be exporting to neighbouring countries.

BNF in nonlegume trees is under investigation and utilized in Senegal whilst *Mycorrhizae* are under investigation in several countries and known to be utilized in Senegal, Zaire and Zimbabwe. The blue-green algae, *Azolla (Cyanophyceae)*, are under investigation and utilized in Senegal, Sierra Leone and Rwanda. *Frankia* which fixes nitrogen in nonleguminous trees is being utilized in Senegal for the stabilization of sand dunes using *Casuarina* species. The role of *Azotobacter* and *Azospirillum* in nitrogen fixation is under investigation by interested scientists in a few laboratories.

The current role of the IARCS in BNF in Africa is minor. The International Institute of Tropical Agriculture (IITA) has a *Rhizobium* bank and has been producing inoculants at its headquarters (HQ) in Ibadan, Nigeria, for its pulses programme and legumes in alley cropping. In the last two years, ILCA has implemented *Rhizobium* inoculant technology and is now producing inoculants for its forage agronomy programme and for dissemination to the NARS through its genebank at its HQ in Ethiopia. ILCA is also putting considerable efforts into a *Rhizobium* bank in which freeze-dried cultures will be kept for subsequent evaluation and utilization in different African environments. Further, ILCA has held and is planning training courses in *Rhizobium* inoculant technology for NARS scientists. The Centro International de Agricultura Tropical (CIAT) imports its inoculants for use in its African bean programme activities from its headquarters in Cali, Colombia. The West African Rice Development Association (WARDA) is seriously involved in the use of *Azolla* as an alternative supply of nitrogen in Northern Senegal where it can supply up to 50% of the nitrogen and in the mangrove swamps of Siera Leone where *Azolla* nitrogen can completely replace mineral nitrogen (Diara, Van Brandt, Dip and Van Hove, 1987).

Plant in vitro *culture*

Plant *in vitro* culture is a relatively new technology which started producing applicable results in developed countries in the late 1960s. Even so, its impact on plant production has been revolutionary especially in vegetatively propagated plants and ornamentals. Major multinational companies in developed countries are now reaping the benefits of their foresight in adopting the technology two decades ago. In North Africa, most countries have adopted the technology for crop plant improvement and are investing considerable efforts in applying it. In sub-Saharan Africa, the situation is disappointing.

It seems most sub-Saharan countries are feebly aware of the potential benefits of plant *in vitro* culture. The technology does not exist in most NARS or even at the experimental level in institutes of higher education. Most of the projects which are currently going on are the efforts by interested individual scientists with very few resources. The most developed efforts are in Zimbabwe where *in vitro* culture research is in progress at the Tobacco Research Board and the university. Nigeria and Zimbabwe are planning to build Biotechnology Centres to bring together scientists from different disciplines for biotechnology research and teaching. In Kenya, the Deutsche Gesellschaft für Technische Zusammenarbeit (GTZ) funded gene bank which was completed in 1988 has *in vitro* culture facilities for genetic resources purposes but these are not yet in use. Plant *in vitro* projects are known to be taking place at the experimental level in Senegal, Zaire and Zambia.

The IARCs have implemented *in vitro* culture to the applied level in Africa. IITA leads with an *in vitro* gene bank for cassava methods for *in vitro* dissemination of cassava and research on adventitious regeneration in cassava and cowpea. IITA (1984) in conjunction with the National Root Crop Research Institute in Nigeria, came up with the minisett technology for the propagation of yams. In the last three years the ILCA Genetic Resources Unit (GRU) has been using *in vitro* techniques for the dissemination of *Brachiaria* species and in the last two years, in collaboration with the International Board for Plant Genetic Resources (IBPGR), the ILCA GRU built an adequate facility for plant *in vitro* collection, conservation, multiplication, adventitious regeneration and re-establishment of cultures of forage grasses and legumes to soil (Ruredzo and Hanson, 1988). ILCA is emphasizing the development of minimum facility *in vitro* methods that can be adopted by NARS scientists for forage genetic resources activities and production in Africa.

DEVELOPMENTS IN BIOTECHNOLOGY IN DEVELOPED COUNTRIES AND ITS IMPACT ON AFRICA

The mainstream of development in biotechnology will come from the developed countries particularly of the West. These developments may have beneficial or adverse effects on African countries.

Certain developments and application of biotechnology in developed countries could have serious adverse economic effects on African countries: Africa being basically a primary producer of various agricultural products. The West African subregion is the source of a large proportion of the world's cocoa supply. Application of biotechnology in the manufacture of food flavouring is fairly advanced. When chocolate flavour so derived finds its way, as it is increasingly, into the manufacture of chocolate products, a whole subregional economy could be put in disarray. The economy of Botswana and to some extent Zimbabwe, depends on export of beef. Improvements in meat substitutes e.g. soya 'steak' would have adverse effects on such exports.

Biotechnology as a science is repeatable anywhere once the required conditions are fulfilled. In this regard African countries could benefit from advances in biotechnology evolved in the developed countries. These third world countries are rich in solar energy and organic or biologically derived resources. These are potential substrates for bioengineering. Developments in recombinant DNA technology and enzymology could lead to mass production of novel enzymes. Such biocatalysts then could be used in the bioconversion of various substrates *in vitro* for all sorts of imaginable products. It is the prerogative of African countries and for that matter other third world countries to take steps to turn these advances into advantage.

POTENTIAL CONTRIBUTION OF BIOTECHNOLOGY TO AGRICULTURE IN AFRICA.

Applications in animal production

Livestock production in Africa is bedevilled with endemic diseases, poor feed resources and animal stock of poor genetic potential. Biotechnological techniques hold promise for improvement of several aspects of livestock production on the continent.

Genetic improvement Many African nations have no clearly defined breeding programmes. At the same time several countries are initiating or carrying out some form of crossbreeding or the other. Programmes in East Africa e.g. Ethiopia, Kenya and Tanzania aim at grading up local indigenous cattle stock with exotic dairy cattle. To this end AI programmes with limited coverage have been initiated in these countries. Most nations have large well-adapted indigenous cow herds. AI technology offers a simple well-established method of reaching several cows of the national herd at moderate costs. Superimposition of breeding and selection schemes on the AI projects will lead to rapid genetic gains. Since environmental conditions in sub-Saharan Africa will not readily permit complete grading up or breed substitution for temperate dairy breeds, there must be a blood level at which the current crossbreeding schemes will have to stop. Further genetic progress could then be sought from selection under performance testing programmes designed to combine adaptation and productivity, multiple ovulation and embryo transfer (MOET) technology offers a good opportunity to increase selection intensities (Smith, 1988; Ruane, 1988) and multiply outstanding dams and sires. Under the extensive grazing conditions of Africa, application of AI, ET and MOET in nucleus situations would offer opportunity for higher genetic improvements, without resorting to blood levels that have adaptation problems under African environmental conditions.

Cryopreservation of gametes and embryos The dangers of breed substitution include the possible loss of genetic diversity. Current emphasis on improved production could lead to neglect and possible loss of less favoured indigenous cattle. Cryoconservation offers the opportunity for avoiding complete loss of such genotypes. In most domesticated species the technology exists for deep freezing of gametes or at least the male gamete and in some species such as cattle, the embryo. Cryoconservation could therefore be used to preserve *in vitro* gametes and / or embryos of currently less favoured species for future regeneration of such species. The FAO has declared the Mpwapwa cattle in Tanzania an endangered breed. In West Africa, along the west coast of Ghana, there is the Dwarf Shorthorn cattle. This is a miniature breed which is currently receiving little or no research attention. A list of endangered cattle species in Africa has been provided by the Inter-African Bureau for Animal Resources (Adeniji, 1983).

Embryos and gametes of such breeds are candidates for cryopreservation as they are probably facing extinction. Cryoconservation also offers the opportunity for preserving offspring of outstanding individuals *in vitro* for future use. In this regard the proposed FAO regional Animal Gene and Data Bank for Ethiopia must be established without delay and possibly another one in the West Africa subregion

Disease control Several diseases plague livestock in sub-Saharan Africa, a major one being trypanosomiasis. Together with dermatophilosis (streptothricosis), trypanosomiasis hampers the production of cattle particularly crossbred (grade) cattle in large areas of East, Central and Western Africa. In addition to these diseases, helminthiasis also take a major toll. Other important diseases are East Coast fever (ECF) and foot-and-mouth disease (FMD).

Most of the above mentioned diseases are of peculiar importance to Africa. To illustrate with a more international disease, let us consider FMD which plagues large areas of Europe, America, Asia and Africa. The presence of the disease in a nation means a great economic loss (Howell, 1984; Kay, 1989). It severely curtails a nation's international trade in livestock and livestock products. The Frenkel inactivated vaccine for FMD is prepared from lesion material. Developments in the past few years employing tissue culture have led to very high production of a trivalent vaccine covering several serological types. Research for novel FMD vaccine employs DNA technology. The FMD causal organism is an RNA virus. This has been copied into DNA and the nucleotide sequence of the immunogenic viral protein expressed in *Escherichia coli*. The resulting protein has been shown to be immunogenic in animals (Kleid, Yansura, Small Dowbenko, Morie, Grubman, McKercher, Morgan, Robertson and Bachrack, 1981). A U.S. company and the U.S. Department of Agriculture have collaborated in making advances in this direction (Howell, 1984). Monoclonal antibody techniques may be used for FMD control.

Developments in monoclonal antibody technology could also lead to the mass production of effective immunogenic agents against the pathogens of the major diseases mentioned above.

Some basic research in monoclonal antibody technology is in progress appropriately at the IARCs. ILRAD is using molecular biology in investigations of immunogenesis for trypanosomiasis and theileriosis (ECF) in cattle.

There is no vaccine for dermatophilosis whilst there is a need to improve the vaccine system available for ECF. The current regime for ECF developed in Kenya involves immunization by infection and treatment with antibiotics. This requires live *Theileria* parasites. ILRAD is helping with isolation of parasites from infected cattle and ticks for cloning and characterization *in vitro*. ILRAD is in collaboration with the NARS of Kenya, Rwanda, Zimbabwe and Tanzania in the immunization by infection and treatment technique. The long-term objective is to develop a safe vaccine which stimulates immunity without risk of the disease.

An antigen on sporozoite surface which stimulates neutralizing antibodies in cattle has been identified. The gene responsible for the antigenic protein has also been identified and partially sequenced through recombinant DNA techniques. It is hoped that a vaccine will be produced for theileriosis through these developments (ILRAD, 1987).

ILCA is in collaboration with ILRAD, using monoclonal antibody techniques for investigation of polymorphism in cattle lymphocyte antigens (ILRAD, 1987). The polymorphic systems of the major histocompatibility complex (MHC) and the common leucocyte antigens (CLA) are of major interest in trypanotolerance. So far ovine lymphocyte antigens of the MHC loci have been used to identify breed differences in resistance to *Haemonchus contortus* in sheep (Peters, Hanson and Ruredzo, 1989).

MHC research at ILRAD concentrates on development of improved techniques for typing cattle according to class I and class II MHC genes and their products, studies of the structure of MHC and the relationship of individual genes to the MHC antigens expressed on the surface of bovine cells. A major thrust is the role of bovine MHC in immune responses to *Theileria* and in collaboration with ILCA and ITC, resistance to trypanosomiasis, recombinant DNA technology is proving useful in the search for control of the major diseases of cattle in Africa. ILRAD has started mapping the MHC region of the bovine genotype. DNA has been digested into fragments with restriction enzymes and subsequently separated by electrophoresis (ILRAD, 1987). Embryo transfer and splitting techniques are being used to produce Boran cattle of specified MHC types for the research in bovine MHC.

The N'Dama cattle breed is found in West Africa with large concentrations in The Gambia, Guinea and Senegal. The breed is remarkable in its trypanotolerance properties and its tolerance to dermatophilosis. The loci responsible for these properties are candidates for DNA probes. When elucidated, genetic engineering or specific breeding programmes could be used in transferring the genes to other cattle, particularly the higher potential crossbred cattle. The genes could also be cloned using recombinant DNA techniques and DNA transferred into bacteria for mass production of antigens for the control of trypanosomiasis.

In the area of disease diagnosis, a significant contribution from Africa is the current work of Dr. Gopo at the University of Zimbabwe. Gopo and coworkers are developing a rapid method for the diagnosis of *Salmonella* using DNA hybridization. The technique can detect the presence of *Salmonella* within 12 hours of infection. This could be a breakthrough for the early detection and control of salmonellosis, a disease that has serious effects on both man and his animals (BBC, 1989).

Growth and reproduction The low productivity and reproductive performance of African livestock provides opportunity for improvement through the use of growth hormones (Ward, Murray and Nancarrow, 1986). Administration of hormonal preparations could also improve milk production of cattle in SSA.

However experiments on growth promotion involving transgenic livestock have yielded variable results. Work in this area from Australian laboratories (Nancarrow *et al*, 1988; Ward *et al*, 1989) is of interest to tropical Africa. Long exposure of sheep to very high levels of growth hormone produced toxic effects, degeneration of kidney and liver, endocrine disturbances, skeletal abnormalities and elevated metabolic rate (Nancarrow, Ward and Murray, 1988). Gene constructs that improve efficiency of production will be of greater interest to Africa than enhanced growth *per se*.

Advances in hormonal manipulation for reproduction especially fertility is of great interest to Africa. The use of inhibin for increasing fertility (Ward, Murray and Nancarow, 1989) will have specific application for improvement of reproduction rates in the Zebu cattle which is known to have poor fertility and reproductive performance (ILCA, 1987). The long and protracted post-partum anoestrous and poor expression of oestrus in Zebu cattle is a vexing problem that should ameliorate through increased use of hormone preparations and techniques such as radioimmunoassay (RIA) and enzyme linked immunosorbent assay (ELISA). The ELISA progesterone test technique used at ILCA is being introduced to NARS for improvement of reproduction in farm livestock.

Nutrition Biotechnology also has potential application in the nutrition of livestock in Africa. The vast natural grazing fields of Africa are characterized by unpalatable species. The grass species have adapted to the short growing seasons and long dry seasons characteristic of these lands by developing short life cycles. They are quickly lignified, setting inflorescence and seeds by the end of the rainy season. Biotechnology research could lead to the discovery, isolation and/or production of novel enzymes and technologies that can help break down the lignins and hemicelluloses in this feedstuff for livestock. Interestingly enough, termites that abound in Africa are able to digest all woody species including the hardest woods. The possibility exists for identifying and isolating the enzymes by which this is accomplished in termites and could be the key to digestion or pre-digestion of the material for African livestock.

Applications in plant production

In vitro culture offer significant possibilities for solving some of Africa's problems in plant production such as disease, drought and nutritional content. Unfortunately, these problems are not the major problems of the developed countries and Africa needs to adopt these techniques to solve her own problems.

Biological nitrogen fixation and related technologies Most African farmers cannot afford to buy inorganic fertilizers, neither can most governments afford to import them. *Rhizobia* and other soil microorganisms play a very important role in the supply and/or uptake of certain inorganic nutrients. The technology which is associated with the exploitation of these soil microorganisms is widely applied in the developing countries and has great potential application in Africa. The yield of legumes which are treated with appropriate inoculants approaches that of plants that are supplied with nitrogen fertilizers; furthermore, the residual nitrogen that remains in the soil can supply a cereal crop the next season. It is also believed that the use of these technologies for soil fertilization is sustainable since they do not have the deleterious residual effects of inorganic fertilizers.

Rhizobium *Rhizobium* inoculant technology has great potential applications in soil amelioration and hence increased production of crops, crop residues, forages and multipurpose trees through the use of legumes in the agricultural systems. Grain and forage legumes can be used in crop rotation, intercropping, alley farming and fodder banks to enrich the soil on which cereals are subsequently or simultaneously grown. Tree legumes can be grown in marginal and eroding soils to enrich the soil, check erosion and to supply fodder and wood for construction and fuel. Fodder from leguminous plants is rich in nitrogen and therefore increases milk and meat production. The legume/*Rhizobium* symbiosis offers an inexpensive alternative to nitrogen fertilizer.

Mycorrhizae Vesicular-arbuscular mycorrhizal (VAM) symbiosis has been shown to influence uptake of nutrients especially nonlabile elements such as phosphate. Their role is especially significant in marginal lands which suffer from frequent drought periods and low available phosphorus in the soils such as those of the Sudano-Sahelian region of Africa where phosphorus shortage is probably more serious than lack of nitrogen for plant production (ICRISAT, 1986). Most of the work on VAM in marginal soils has been carried out in developed countries; U.S.A., Israel, and Australia (Miller, 1987; Krikun, Hass and Bar-Yosef, 1987; McGee, 1986 respectively) where farmers are in a better position to afford phosphorus fertilizers than their African counterparts. In Somalia, Michelson and Rosendahl (1988) found great potential for the use of VAM in the revegetation of degraded semi-arid areas which would directly benefit livestock production. The adoption of VAM technology in Africa would therefore reduce the financial burden of importing or producing phosphate fertilizers which most of the farmers cannot afford.

Other nitrogen fixing organisms Recently, the potential role of the *Azolla-Anabaena* symbiosis in BNF has been recognized outside China and Vietnam where it is used by farmers as green manure for their crops. This fern/blue algae symbiosis can be exploited for other purposes including animal and fish nutrition and water purification (IRRI, 1987). African countries would benefit greatly from the use of this multipurpose biofertilizer and more effort should be invested in its exploitation by farmers.

In addition free nitrogen fixing bacteria e.g. *Azotobacter* and those that fix nitrogen in association e.g. *Azospirillum* need more investigation in Africa to meet the needs of the rising population with relatively cheaper inputs for sustainable crop and animal production.

In vitro *culture of plants* Plant *in vitro* culture encompasses the artificial manipulation of plant tissues, organs, cells, protoplasts, embryos, and gametes. *In vitro* culture offers solutions to several problems in plant improvement.

Multiplication Some plant species cannot be conveniently multiplied using conventional methods. These include species which are vegetatively propagated but produce very few propagules such as the tropical forage grasses *Cynodon*, *Digitaria* and *Brachiaria* and some tropical starch crops such as sweet potato (*Ipomoea batatas*), yam (*Dioscorea* sp), banana (*Musa*) and taro (*Colocasia esculenta*) species which are outcrossing, where multiplication of elite plants using seeds would produce variable offspring e.g. potato

(*Solanum tuberosum*) and cassava (*Manihot esculenta*); and most tree species e.g. coconut and oil palms where conventional methods of multiplication would require a lot of space, time and labour and those which do not produce many seeds or take a long time to reach maturity and produce seeds. Most of these species are used for both human and animal consumption in Africa and can benefit from *in vitro* multiplication. Furthermore, breeders' lines sometimes take a long time to multiply due to seasonal limitations. Such species and lines may be rapidly multiplied *in vitro* under artificial conditions which are independent of the seasons.

Production of disease free germplasm Most plants and their seeds carry bacterial, fungal and viral diseases which reduce yield and present quarantine problems in the movement of plant germplasm across international boundaries. *In vitro* culture is carried out under aseptic conditions in which bacteria and fungi are excluded. Furthermore viruses can be eliminated from *in vitro* cultures using meristem culture techniques and disease free materials can be produced and multiplied (Kartha, 1981).

Germplasm collection and conservation Africa is rich in plant genetic resources of world importance e.g. coffee (*Coffea*) cacao (*Theobroma*), sorghum (*Sorghum*), millet (*Pennisetum* and *Panicum*) cassava, sweet potato, and the forage species of the genera *Sesbania*, *Erythrina*, *Cynodon*, *Digitaria* and *Brachiaria*. The conservation of plant genetic resources plays a key role in plant improvement. Most plants can be conveniently collected and stored for a long time at low temperatures as seeds but some plants do not produce seeds, produce very few seeds or recalcitrant seeds which are very short lived and cannot be conveniently collected or stored in this form. *In vitro* collection (Withers, 1987) and storage (Withers, 1980) offers alternative ways of collecting and conserving such plant genetic resources.

Breeding The major task of plant improvement is to produce plants that have desirable characteristics such as disease resistance, drought tolerance, high nutritional quality and high productivity. The genetic materials that carry these characteristics are usually found in related wild species and land races. Plant breeders then have the task of crossing these plants with these different but related species and selecting from the offspring for the characteristics they require. It takes a long time to transfer the necessary genetic material, let alone produce a new variety using these crosses; further, such breeding is often not possible due to incompatibility. Adventitious regeneration in tissue culture produces considerable variation in the resulting plants. These may have enhanced desirable characteristics or reduced undesirable characteristics (Larkin and Scowcroft, 1981). Plants which have desirable characteristics can therefore be collected from regenerated plants of the same species, avoiding the problems presented by crossing with land races or wild species.

Plant breeders sometimes want to see the expression of the characters for which they are selecting. This can be done by producing haploid and dihaploid plants. These plants are very difficult to produce using conventional methods but can be produced relatively easily using the *in vitro* techniques of anther and pollen culture (Sunderland and Cooking, 1978).

In vitro *pollination embryo culture somatic hybridization* New genotypes of plants enrich our plant resources. Sometimes breeders cannot cross the species in question due to incompatibility at the pollination stage or due to the abortion of resulting embryos. Pollination can be carried out *in vitro*; the resulting embryos can be grown under controlled conditions in culture and plants successfully recovered from these crosses. In addition to *in vitro* pollination and embryo culture, somatic hybridization is currently under active investigation for the creation of new genotypes through wide crosses between different species and even genera e.g. potato and tomato (Melchers, Sacristan and Holder, 1978).

Genetic transformation Advances in the last decade allow the purification of genetic material for the expression of certain characters. Techniques have been developed and, in the developed countries, are being employed to transform plants so that they can express certain characters which they do not have in nature. Genetic material can be transferred to the plant material indirectly using bacterial vectors such as *Agrobacterium* or directly into plant protoplasts using electroporation or other physical methods (Wullems, Krens, Peerbolte and Schilpcroot, 1987). Plants recovered from the transformed cells will express the desired characters.

CONSTRAINTS TO ADOPTION AND APPLICATION OF BIOTECHNOLOGY IN AFRICA

Trained manpower

The application of biotechnology for solutions to practical problems involve a multiple of disciplines interacting together. A critical mass of scientific personnel is required to work in a multidisciplinary approach. In most African countries there exist a limited amount of scientific personnel with training in the basic biological and chemical sciences as well as engineering. What is probably limiting is training at the high level research category where scientists are able to vary the elementary principles for solutions to technical problems in biotechnology. This constraint could be overcome by strengthening of local university faculties through collaboration within Africa and bilateral relations with universities and advanced institutes abroad. Countries capable of supporting education in biotechnology could set up such programmes in at least one of their universities. Two or more countries could also jointly equip one university for higher training in biotechnology.

Infrastructure and equipment

A major constraint to adoption and utilization of biotechnology in Africa is the limitation of basic infrastructure and equipment. Well-equipped laboratories are required for research and application of biotechnology. Good and reliable transport and communication facilities are necessary for rapid exchange of information and materials. Biotechnology requires ready access to enzymes, reagents and media. There must be industrial or commercial establishments that take care of such requirements. A reliable supply of electricity is indispensable. There must also be in place organizational and institutional arrangements for implementation, direction and monitoring of the adoption and applications of biotechnology in any African country. Governments must have a commitment to support biotechnology research and development for the improvement of agriculture.

Financial resources

For successful adoption and application of biotechnology, a country needs a combination of well-equipped laboratories, a critical mass of well-trained scientists and rapid access to pertinent scientific databases. These preconditions require substantial financial outlay. For research and teaching purposes the financial requirement may not be too high. However for industrial application of biotechnology a small industry may require about 10 million U.S. dollars (Erdman and King, 1984). This could be a steep figure for many African countries. Most of these countries have problems with foreign exchange and balance of payment. Besides there are many competing equally important projects that require finance. The effectiveness of biotechnology in attracting funding will depend on the level of priority that African governments are willing to put on it.

Bilateral arrangements could be made for funding. In particular entrepreneurs from developed countries could be attracted with competitive investment packages to establish agro-biotechnical industries in Africa. The Holstein Association of U.S. for instance is interested in carrying out AI and ET in Africa. This could be on strictly business terms and should be beneficial both ways.

There are other constraints in addition to the above. Effects of biotechnology on the environment will affect sustainability of agricultural production. There may also be legal, regulatory and ethical requirements for successful and peaceful implementation of biotechnology in Africa.

CONCLUSIONS AND RECOMMENDATIONS

Biotechnology offers an opportunity for the improvement of agricultural production in Africa. Application of biotechnology will be of benefit in the areas of animal production and health and plant production. It would also provide techniques for preserving and conserving genotypes of various plants and animals for future use. Cryoconservation of genotypes must be an important role for IARCs in Africa. Biotechnology at the moment has only a limited adoption and application in many African countries. In order to take advantage of advances being made in biotechnology in the developed world, African countries must adopt and apply biotechnology in their agricultural production systems. To facilitate its application, African scientists in collaboration with IARCs, must create the public awareness of the importance of biotechnology, and keep governments and policy makers well-informed. A Pan-African workshop on biotechnology is recommended.

Adoption of biotechnology though, must be carried out cautiously particularly those aspects that may adversely influence composition of food and the environment. Nevertheless those biotechnologies that facilitate rapid improvement, multiplication and propagation of food crops and animals have great potential and favourable implications for sustainable agricultural production in Africa.

GLOSSARY OF OFFICIAL NAMES.

SSA	Sub-Saharan Africa.
NARS	National Agricultural Research Systems.
IARC	International Agricultural Research Centre.
ILRAD	International Laboratory for Research in Animal Diseases.
CAIS	Central Artificial Insemination Station (Kabete, Kenya).
SSDDP	Small Scale Dairy Development Project (Tanzania).
ITC	International Trypanotolerance Centre, The Gambia.
ILCA	International Livestock Centre for Africa, Ethiopia.
AABNF	African Association for Biological Nitrogen Fixation.
IITA	International Institute of Tropical Agriculture.
CIAT	Centro International de Agricultura Tropical (Cali, Colombia).
WARDA	West African Rice Development Association.
IBPGR	International Board for Plant Genetics Resources.
OAU	Organization of African Unity.

REFERENCES

Adeniji, K.O. (1983). Review of endangered cattle breeds of Africa. In *Animal Genetic Resources of Africa High Potential and Endangered Livestock. Proceedings of the 2nd OAU Expert Committee Meeting on Animal Genetic Resources in Africa. Bulawayo, Zimbabwe*, pp. 20–32. OAU/STRC/IBAR, Nairobi, Kenya.

BBC (1989). Interview with Dr. Gopo of University of Zimbabwe on DNA hypridization method for rapid diagnosis of Salmonella. 28th July 1989. BBC London.

Diara, H.F., Van Brandt, H., Diop, A.M. and Van Hove, C. (1987). *Azolla* and its use in rice culture in West Africa. In *Azolla Utilisation. Proceedings of the Workshop on Azolla Use.* Fuzhou, Fujian, China. International Rice Research Institute, Manila, Philippines.

Erdman, J.C. and King, A.C. (1984). Biotechnology: an opportunity for the Americas. In *Biotechnology in the Americas: Prospects for Developing Countries* (ed. W.D. Sawyer), pp. 23–27. *Proceedings of the Symposium, San Jose, Costa Rica.*

FAO (1986). *FAO Production Yearbook*. Vol. 40, 19. FAO, Rome.

Howell, D.G. (1984). Biotechnology and animal health. In *Biotechnology in the Americas: Prospects for Developing Countries* (ed. W.D. Sawyer), pp. 35–38. *Proceedings of the Symposium, San Jose, Costa Rica.*

ICRISAT (1986). International Crops Research Insitute for the semi-arid tropics. Andhra Pradesh, India.

ILCA (1987). *ILCA Annual Report*. Addis Ababa, Ethiopia. 105 pp.

ILRAD (1987). *Annual Report of the International Laboratory for Research on Animal Diseases*. ILRAD, Nairobi, Kenya.

International Institute for Tropical Agriculture (1984). IITA Research Highlights for 1983, pp. 103–107. Ibadan, Nigeria.

IRRI (1987). *Azolla* Utilisation. *Proceedings of the Workshop on Azolla Use. Fuzhou, Fujian, China.* International Rice Research Institute, Manila, Philippines.

Kartha, K.K. (1981). Tissue culture techniques for virus elimination and germplasm preservation. In *Genetic Engineering for Improvement* (eds. K.O. Rachie and J.M. Lyman), pp. 123–138. Rockefeller Foundation.

Kay, J.M. (1989). Opening Address: Workshop on Cattle Milk and Meat Research in East and Southern Africa. In *Cattle Research Network Summary of Proceedings of ILCA Workshop on Collaborative Cattle Milk and Meat Research in East and Southern Africa. Kadoma, Zimbabe*. pp. 29–32. ILCA, Addis Ababa.

Kleid, D.G. Yansura, D., Small, B., Dowbenko, D., More, D.M., Grubman, M.J., McKercher, P.D., Morgan, D.O., Robertson, B.H. and Bachrach, H.L. (1981). Cloned viral protein vaccine for foot-and-mouth disease: responses in cattle and swine. *Science*, **214**, 1125–1128.

Krikun, J., Haas, J.H., Bar-Yosef, B. (1987). Use of VA mycorrhizal-fungus inoculum in soils in arid and semi-arid climates: a field study with bell pepper and transplants. *Angew. Botanik*, **61**, 97–105.

Larkin, P.J. and Scowcroft, W.R. (1981). Somaclonal variation – a novel source of variability from cell culture for plant improvement. *Theoretical and Applied Genetics*, **60**, 197–214.

McGee, P. (1986). Mycorrhizal associations of plant species in a semi-arid community. *Australian Journal of Botany*, **34**, 585–593.

Melchers, G., Sacristan, M.D. and Holder, A.A. (1978). Somatic hybrid plants of potato and tomato regenerated from fused protoplasts. *Carlsberg Research Communications,* **43**, 203–218.

Michelsen, A. and Rosendahl, S. (1988). Mycorrhizal symbiosis in *Acacia-Commiphora* bushland in Somalia and the significance of VA-mycorrhizal fungi for revegetation of degraded semi-arid areas.

Miller, R.M. (1987). Mycorrhizae and succession. In *Restoration Ecology* (eds. W.R. Gilpin, M.E. Aber and J.D. Jordan III), pp. 205–219. Cambridge University Press.

Mukassa-Mugerwa, E. (1989). A review of reproductive performance of female *Bos indicus* (zebu) cattle. *ILCA Monograph No. 6*. International Livestock Centre for Africa, Addis Ababa, Ethiopia.

Nancarrow, C.D., Ward, K.A. and Murray, J.D. (1988). The future for transgenic livestock in Australian agriculture. *Australian Journal of Biotechnology*, **2**, 39–44.

Peters, K.J., Hanson, J. and Ruredzo, T.J. (1989). Biotechnology at ILCA. A position paper for discussion by the ILCA Board of Trustees. ILCA, Addis Ababa. pp. 25.

Ruane, J. (1988). Review of embryo transfer in the genetic improvement of dairy cattle. *Animal Breeding Abstracts*, **56(6)**, 437–446.

Ruredzo, T.JM. and Hanson, Jean (1988). Practical applications of *in vitro* techniques to forage germplasm. In *Proceedings of the Annual Workshop jointly organised by the Pastures Network for Eastern and Southern Africa (PANESA) and the African Research Network on Agricultural By-products (ARNAB). Lilongwe, Malawi (5–9 December 1988).* ILCA, Addis Ababa, Ethiopia. In press.

Smith, C. (1988). Application of embryo transfer in animal breeding. *Theriogenology*, **29(1)**, 203–212.

Sunderland, N. and Coking, E.C. (1978). Plant tissue culture in China – Major change ahead? *Nature*, **274**, 643–644.

Walgate, R. (1989). Zimbabwe scientist perfects *Salmonella* test. In *New Africa, 1989*. No. 266, 26.

Ward, K.A., Murray, J.D. and Nancarrow, C.D. (1986). The insertion of foreign DNA into animal cells. In *FAO Expert Consultation on Biotechnology for Livestock Production and Health.* FAO, Rome. AGA:Biot/86/6.

Ward, K.A., Murray, J.D. and Nancarrow, C.D. (1989). Current research programmes in animal biotechnology in Australia. *Agricultural Biotechnology News and Information*, **1(1)**, 19–22.

Withers, L.A. (1980). Tissue culture storage for genetic conservation. *IBPGR Technical Report*. IBPGR, Rome, Italy.

Withers, L.A. (1987). *In vitro* methods for collecting germplasm in the field. Plant Genetic Resources. *Newsletter* 69, 2–6.

Wullems, G., Krens, F., Peerbolte, R. and Schilpcroot, R. (1982). In *Plant Tissue Culture 1982* (ed. A. Fujiwara), pp. 505–506. Japanese Association for Plant Tissue Culture, Tokyo.

6.3

Biotechnology in India

D.K. SINGH and K.R. TRIVEDI
National Dairy Development Board, Anand, India

INTRODUCTION

To ensure that the powerful tools of biotechnology are available in the country, the Government of India (GOI) has initiated several steps to evolve an infrastructure for education, training, research and product development through biotechnology, covering broad sectors of medical care, agriculture, aquaculture, livestock production, animal health care, energy, environment, industry, etc.

India has emerged as a leader amongst the Third World countries in harnessing the fruits of biotechnology. The GOI, in 1986, created a fully fledged Department of Biotechnology (DBT) under the Ministry of Science and Technology.

This paper mainly reviews the status of biotechnology in livestock production and health care in India. However, at places, references have been made to vaccines and diagnostics being developed for use in human medicine. The infrastructure facilities relevant to the work of biotechnology and created in the country are described first, followed by the programmes and the achievements.

INFRASTRUCTURAL FACILITIES

At the apex level, the DBT in the Ministry of Science and Technology, plans, promotes and coordinates the biotechnological programmes in plant, animal and human medicine. The major tasks undertaken by the department include:-

- Creation of infrastructural facilities.

- Evolvement of manpower development programmes.
- Identification and support of R&D programmes and biotechnology-related manufacturing.
- Import of new recombinant DNA based processed products and technologies.
- Organizing measures to commercialize research for public welfare.

The major infrastructural facilities created by the DBT include:–

- Collection of microbial cultures and a gene bank facility at the Institute of Microbial Technology (IMT), Chandigarh.
- National level animal house facilities to maintain genetically disease free and microbiologically defined laboratory animals at the Central Drug Research Institute (CDRI), Lucknow; the National Institute of Nutrition (NIN), Hyderabad; and the Indian Institute of Science (IISc), Bangalore.
- Facilities for animal tissue and cell culture for the entire country at the University of Poona, Pune.
- Production and importation of biochemicals and enzymes and their distribution through the Council of Scientific and Industrial Research (CSIR), Delhi.
- Facilities for oligonucleotide synthesis at IISc, Bangalore and the Centre for Cellular and Molecular Biology (CCMB), Hyderabad.
- Biochemical engineering research and process development centre at IMT, Chandigarh.
- Genetic engineering units at IISc, Bangalore; Madurai Kamaraj University (MKU), Madurai; Jawaharlal Nehru University (JNU), Delhi; and Banaras Hindu University (BHU), Varanasi (DBT 1990).

The DBT has also established two research institutes for undertaking research in biotechnology, one at the National Institute of Immunology (NII), New Delhi for conducting research in immunology and the second at the International Centre for Genetic Engineering and Biotechnology (ICGEB), New Delhi established under the auspices of the United Nations Industrial Development Organisation (UNIDO) to develop and strengthen technological competence of developing countries in the field of biotechnology and genetic engineering. The ICGEB is linked with a similar institute at Trieste in Italy and a network of research centres in the developing countries. The ICGEB at New Delhi will also undertake research in agriculture and tropical medicine. In addition, ICGEB will provide training to the scientists from Third World countries. Biotechnology programmes with specific reference to animal sciences are being operated at the Indian Veterinary Research Institute (IVRI), Izatnagar; the National Dairy Research Institute (NDRI), Karnal; the National Dairy Development Board (NDDB), Anand;

and several veterinary colleges in the state agricultural universities. A number of private firms such as Hindustan Lever Limited, Vulcan Laval, Ranbaxy, Hoechst and Ciba-Geigy have also entered the field of biotechnology. The Genetic Engineering Advisory Committee has been created at the national level for evaluating various research programmes using genetically manipulated organisms.

Many institutions in the country offer courses in biotechnology, important among them are JNU, Delhi; MKU, Madurai; Maharaja Sayajirao (MS) University, Baroda; University of Poona, Pune; the Indian Institute of Technology (IIT), Delhi, Khargpur and Bombay; the IISc, Bangalore; IVRI, Izatnagar; Indian Agricultural Research Institute (IARI), New Delhi; CCMB, Hyderabad, etc.

In spite of such a large-scale infrastructure, the country depends to a large extent on imported chemicals. Further importation restrictions affect the research work. The GOI has been reasonably liberal in funding the research institutes engaged in the field of biotechnology. However, many a time, the funds are not effectively utilized due to the time targeted programmes. In spite of the above said constraints, considerable progress has been made in the areas of embryo transfer, food processing, preparation of diagnostics, immunizing agents etc.

R&D PROGRAMMES

R&D programmes in biotechnology for enhancing production and productivity of animals are summarized under the following headings:

- Multiple Ovulation and Embryo Transfer (MOET) and related technologies
- Open Nucleus Breeding Systems (ONBS)
- Production related hormones
- *In vitro* treatment of feed and use of manipulated microorganisms
- Manipulation and control of rumen fermentation
- Immunodiagnostics
- Vaccines

Multiple Ovulation and Embryo Transfer (MOET) and related technologies

The DBT in January 1987 launched a multiagency project entitled 'Cattle Herd Improvement for Increased Productivity Using Embryo Transfer Technology' with the NDDB as the lead implementing agency and IVRI, NDRI, NII and Central Frozen Semen Production and Training Institute (CFSP&TI) as collaborating agencies. The major objectives of the project are:

- To develop an infrastructure for MOET and associated techniques like cryopreservation, micromanipulation, sexing, cloning, *in vitro* maturation and fertilization of oocytes and purification and production of selected hormones required for MOET work in cattle, buffaloes etc.

- To transfer these technologies to the field through the establishment of a main ET centre, four regional centres and 25 state centres with the primary aim to increase production and productivity of cattle and buffaloes in the country.

The NDDB has been given the task of large-scale production of embryos and their transfer in the field through its cooperative infrastructure created under the 'Operation Flood' programme, while the collaborating agencies have been entrusted to provide a research and training input to the project.

A main ET laboratory has been established at Sabarmati Ashram Gaushala (SAG) Bidaj, near Ahmedabad in Gujarat, plus six state centres and four regional ET centres namely the Buffalo Breeding Centre (BBC), Nekarikallu in Andhra Pradesh, the Animal Breeding Centre (ABC), Salon in Uttar Pradesh, Shri Nasik Panchawati Panjrapole (SNPP), Nasik in Maharashtra, and CFSP&TI at Hessarghatta in Karnataka. Research and development is carried out in laboratories at NDRI, IVRI, and NII.

A large number of progenies of cattle, buffaloes and sheep have come up through ET. Progress made by the NDDB through its main laboratory including regional centres and the collaborating agencies in production and transfer of embryos till March 1990 is summarized in Table 1.

The NII has standardized the technique of micromanipulation. Five calves have been born through transfer of split embryos. Limited success has been achieved in the area of *in vitro* maturation and fertilization. Work is in progress in the area of microinjection, sexing of embryos, and production of gonadotropins. The NDRI has standardized techniques of *in vitro* maturation and fertilization. Work is in progress in the area of micromanipulation and sexing of embryos. The IVRI has achieved success in the production and

TABLE 1 *Progress of NDDB and the associated laboratories in the production and transfer of embryos to cattle and buffaloes till March, 1990.*

Items	NDDB		NDRI		IVRI		NII		CFSP&TI	
	C	B	C	B	C	B	C	B	C	B
Animals flushed	495	394	118	101	375	7	54	7	60	11
Embryos recovered	1,694	569	532	114	573	29	293	16	146	11
Embryos transferred	426	208	197	59	187	10	128	8	57	6
Embryos frozen	704	128	18	8	40	2	54	4	13	2
Recipient pregnant	108	30	499	9	26	1	40	3	12	–
Calves born	68	13	30	4	6	–	21	–	5	–

C = Cattle
B = Buffaloes

purification of gonadotropins. Work on sexing, cloning and micromanipulation of embryos is in progress.

NDDB at its laboratories in Bombay and Indian Immunologicals, Hyderabad has produced follicular stimulating hormone and pregnant mare serum for their ET programmes

Open Nucleus Breeding System (ONBS)

Theories of 'Open Nucleus Breding Systems' (ONBS) are now well-established. It has been shown that the genetic progress expected through ONBS can be as high as, if not higher than what is achieved through conventional progeny testing programmes. As the merit of males under ONBS is judged on the performance of their full sisters and half sisters (the 'sibling test'), and not on the performance of their daughters, the accuracy of selection is generally lower than that achieved in progeny testing; however, the benefits of reducing generation interval outweighs the loss of accuracy. In developing countries where establishment of infrastructure for field recording is generally very difficult, the implementation of ONBS acquires greater significance.

All preliminary requirements to initiate ONBS in crossbred animals at the SAG, Bidaj and an ONBS in buffaloes at the BBC, Nekarikallu have been completed. These two programmes will be in operation very soon.

Production related hormones

Three different approaches are being standardized for the utilization of growth hormone (GH) for increased meat and milk production. They are exogenous injection of GH, creation of transgenic animals with increased GH production, and exogenous methods of GH level manipulation.

Exogenous injection of GH is reported to increase milk production by 10 to 30% in bovines. Results of recent experiments conducted at NDRI in collaboration with NDDB indicated that the use of GH offers great promise. However, before its use for commercial milk production is recommended, further studies for its evaluation are necessary. Negotiations are also taking place for importing the technology for the indigenous production of genetically engineered bovine somatotropin hormones.

In vitro *treatment of feeds and fodder including use of manipulated organisms*

Many methods have been developed to convert structural carbohydrates into more soluble compounds, thereby improving digestibility of crop residues. The methods being practised include physical such as steam treatment, chemical such as ammonia or urea treatment and biological such as use of certain fungi.

Some of the biological processes developed for lignin degradation have proved to be highly useful. Experiments conducted at the Biochemical Enginering Research Centre, IIT Delhi for the improvement of digestibility of wheat and rice straw using white rot fungus and application of solid substrate fermentation have shown that the technique increases lignin degradation considerably and improves digestibility of crop residues in the rumen; the two-stage treatment procedure developed by NDRI, Karnal for cereal straws has been shown to increase their digestibility.

Manipulation and control of rumen fermentation

Rumen fungi are known to digest cellulose, hemicellulose, pectin and xylan and break lignin-hemicellulose complexes. Experiments are being conducted for improving the fibre digestion in the rumen by increasing the population of anaerobic fungi. Supplementation of feeds with live cultures of the *Saccharomyces cervisiae* yeast has been shown to increase feed conversion rate in rumen and consequently increase milk production.

Attempts are being made to produce strains of *E. coli* and yeast with genes coding for cellulolytic enzymes. Use of such organisms as feed additives have been shown to increase the digestibility of crop residues.

Immunodiagnostics

Several institutes are engaged in research for developing immunodiagnostics for human and animal diseases. Half a dozen diagnostic agents, primarily for the diagnosis of infectious diseases are ready for commercialization. Kits for diagnosing amoebiasis, leprosy and hepatitis have been developed at NII, Delhi. Kits for detecting early pregnancy have been in field use. NDDB's research laboratory at Bombay is in the process of developing an ELISA test for progesterone to detect early pregnancy in dairy animals. Some of the diagnostics have been licensed for commercial production. ELISA tests have been developed against brucellosis, theileriosis and some of the viral diseases of animals.

Animal tissue cultures are produced in several institutes (Table 2).

Several research institutes are also involved in the production of monoclonal antibodies for the diagnosis of various viral diseases of man and animals.

Vaccines

At NDDB, Anand, an effective and safe vaccine against tropical theileriosis has been developed with indigenous technology. The vaccine has been commercialized and is being marketed by Indian Immunologicals, Hyderabad, under the brand name of 'Rakshavac-T'. Presently the vaccine is being used for large-scale protection of taurine cattle and their crosses against *Theileria annulata* infection (Singh, this volume).

NII has been doing research on development of immunological approaches for control and promotion of male and female fertility and on development of diagnostic kits and vaccines for communicable diseases. One of the important contributions of the NII has been the development of a single injection

TABLE 2 *Various animal cell lines cultured in India.*

Origin		
Species	**Tissue**	**Designation of strain**
Syrian hamster	Kidney	BHK-21
Cattle	Kidney	NBL-1 (MDBK)
Dog	Kidney	NBL-2 (MDCK)
Pig	Kidney	PK (15)
Pig	Kidney	IBRS-2
African Green monkey	Kidney	BS-C-1
African Green monkey	Kidney	VERO
Rhesus monkey	Kidney	LLC-MK_2
Human	Amnion	FL Amnion
Human	Larynx (carcinoma)	HEp-2
Human	Cervix (carcinoma)	HeLa
Human	Liver	Chang Liver
Human	Sternal bone marrow from carcinomatosis	Detroit-6
Human	Oral epidermoid (carcinoma)	KB
Human	Synovial fluid	McCoy

vaccine for sterilizing male animals. This vaccine is available under the name of 'Talsur'.

Three vaccine candidates are also identified by the NII for birth control in humans and they are completing phase-I clinical trials. The vaccine candidates identified are:

- vaccine against the human chorionic gonadotropin hormones (anti-hCG vaccine)
- vaccine against gonadotropin-releasing hormone (GnRH)
- vaccine against sperm antigen.

NII has also made a genetically engineered vaccine against rabies known as vaccinia-rabies glycoprotein (VRGP) vaccine. This vaccine has been successfully tested in mice and the laboratory trials are being extended to dogs.

Presently, tissue culture produced vaccines are being used against rabies, foot-and-mouth disease (FMD), rinderpest (RP) of animals and several other diseases of poultry. Efforts are being made to bring in the technology for commercial production of genetically engineered vaccines against RP and FMD.

GLOSSARY OF OFFICIAL NAMES

ABC	Animal Breeding Centre.
BBC	Buffalo Breeding Centre.
BHU	Banaras Hindu University.
CCMB	Centre for Cellular and Molecular Biology.
CDRI	Central Drug Research Institute.
CFSP&TI	Central Frozen Semen Production and Training Institute.
CSIR	Council of Scientific and Industrial Research.
DBT	Department of Biotechnology.
GOI	Government of India.
IARI	Indian Agricultural Research Institute.
ICGEB	International Centre for Genetic Engineering and Biotechnology.
IISc	Indian Institute of Science.
IIT	Indian Institute of Technology.
IMT	Institute of Microbial Technology.
IVRI	Indian Veterinary Research Institute.
JNU	Jawaharlal Nehru University.
MKU	Madurai Kamaraj University.
NDDB	National Dairy Development Board.
NDRI	National Dairy Research Institute.
NII	National Institute of Immunology.
NIN	National Institute of Nutrition.
SAG	Sabarmati Ashram Gaushala.
SNPP	Shri Nasik Panchawati Panjrapole.

REFERENCES

Department of Biotechnology (1990). Annual Report 1989–90.

Singh, D.K. (1991). Development and testing of *in vitro* derived vaccines against bovine theileriosis in India. In *The Application of Biotechnology in Developing Countries* (ed. A.G. Hunter), pp. 361–374. Centre for Tropical Veterinary Medicine, University of Edinburgh.

6.4

Biotechnology in South East Asia

K.T. LIM
Veterinary Research Institute, Ipoh, Malaysia

INTRODUCTION

Biotechnology is a series of enabling technologies involving the use of biological organisms (or their subcellular components) or systems or processes for product manufacturing, service rendering or management of the environment. In the broad sense, biotechnological processes have been practised in South East Asia (SEA) for centuries and these include the production of alcohol, vinegar, citric acid, vaccines, biogas, fermented food and biofertilizers by traditional or improved methods. However, with the recent advances in molecular biology and recombinant DNA technology, embryo transfer and hybridoma technologies, biotechnology has undergone a 'rebirth', giving rise to 'new' biotechnology. The implications of this new biotechnology in improving and solving problems in livestock production, health and nutrition are enormous and irresistible and in the international market, some of its products may even have a leading edge over similar products produced by traditional methods in SEA countries in the near future.

Faced with the new biotechnology, SEA countries have the choice of either to ignore it or to harness it to the best of their ability and derive the benefits. On the evidence of current research activities in SEA region, it is apparent that most of these countries are seriously preparing to acquire the new biotechnology but only in selective areas relevant to their needs.

In a region dominated by smallholder farming systems with a strong socioeconomic background, the challenges faced by the countries to acquire and develop the technologies and adapt them under the Asian environment to solve problems in livestock production, health and nutrition must be numerous. With recession still lingering in the region the efforts of the countries in the pursuit of the new biotechnology in priority areas relative to the environment and livestock situation are highlighted together with some of the possible implications.

MALAYSIA

Malaysia has a livestock population of 60.487 million (Table 1). The livestock industry of Malaysia is currently estimated at Malaysian $2.6 billion (U.S. $0.97 billion) of which poultry and pigs account for approximately 90% of the industry while ruminants constitute the balance of 10%. Although the country is self-sufficient in the former with a small percentage for export, the same status however has not been achieved for the ruminant sector. Efforts had been made in the past to increase ruminant production through expansion of the commercial feedlot system for beef cattle and integrated farming under tree crops for sheep and goats. These efforts increased beef and mutton production by 6.5% and 11.5% respectively in 1987, corresponding to only 50% and 20% of the national requirements (Asian Livestock, 1988a). Greater efforts are currently made through improvement of management, upgrading of local breeds and improved health services. Problems relating to insufficient green fodder and pasture land and increasing cost of nutritive feeds and imported feed ingredients have been recognized for many years (Yussof, Mustaffa and Chin, 1985). Concentrated efforts are being directed towards commercial cultivation of maize and sorghum and the search for alternative feed sources in locally abundant agro-industrial by-products and unconventional feeds. However, the high fibre contents in these residues often present problems in digestibility and nutrition and more research is required to enhance their breakdown.

The major constraints to livestock development in Malaysia are therefore poor reproductive performances and problems relating to animal nutrition

TABLE 1 *1987 Livestock population (in millions).*

Livestock	Indonesia	Malaysia	Philippines	Thailand
Cattle	6.47	0.62	1.659	4.931
Buffalo	2.994	0.245	2.857	6.350
Pig	6.216	2.2	7.0	4.2
Sheep	5.3	0.075	0.03	0.73
Goat	12.9	0.347	2.027	0.80
Chicken	400.0	57.0	50.0	80.0
Duck	28.0	–	5.0	19.0
Total	461.88	60.487	68.573	116.011

Source: Asian Livestock (1988)

for which the solutions would rely partly on research into the specific areas where the problems lie. With the recent advances in biotechnology in animal health and production in developed countries, the government recognizes the relevance and supports the application of these new technologies in solving some of the country's problems in livestock production and development.

A recent survey showed that the research activities in biotechnology in the country are not well-coordinated. Following the report made by the National Science Development and Research Council (MPKSN) in 1985 on biotechnological activities in the country, the National Biotechnology Committee was set up and chaired by the science advisor to the Prime Minister to coordinate research and development (R&D) activities at the national level with the following six functions (Gibbons, 1989).

- To advise the government on policies pertaining to research, funding and incentives to industries in biotechnology.
- To monitor development of biotechnology in relation to national needs.
- To report on status and advancement of biotechnology in the country.
- To coordinate R&D between research institutions and the industry.
- To obtain funding for R&D activities.
- To establish guidelines on ethics and safety in all aspects of biotechnological development.

Five priority areas for R&D in biotechnology are identified, namely medical, animal, industrial and environmental, molecular biology/genetic engineering and plant biotechnology. The goals of R&D activities are visualized as acquisition of knowledge to formulate policies and provide services on the one hand and the development of technologies and skills and innovative capabilities on the other for commercialization and creation of wealth. With the recognition for the need of an integrated approach for biotechnology development, the first Seminar on National Biotechnology Programmes was organized by the Ministry of Science, Technology and Environment in June 1989 where the priorities for R&D in biotechnology under the sixth Malaysian Development Plan for 1991 to 1995 could be collectively identified in relation to market demands against Asian and developed countries, taking into account the existing national facilities and institutional research infrastructure and the enabling technologies that would be required.

Current biotechnological activities in the country are mostly undertaken at the basic or preliminary stages as shown in Table 2.

Under animal biotechnology, the four priority areas for R&D to improve livestock health, production and nutrition are identified as embryo transfer (ET) technology, animal nutrition using agricultural products, animal health involving monoclonal antibodies, vaccine production and nuclear probes and finally, genetics involving chromosome mapping for breeding purposes.

TABLE 2 *Biotechnology activities in Malaysia.*

Subject	Activities	Institutes
Alcohol production	Microbial fermentation Cellulose digestion/fermentation Microbial degration Enzymic hydrolysis	UM, UPM, UKM, RRIM, SIRIM
Biogas production	Biogas from agricultural and animal waste, anaerobic waste digestion, electricity from palm oil effluent	UPM, USM, MARDI, SIRIM, PORIM, FELDA
Biomass conversion/ production	Single cell protein production Mushroom culture, submerged and solid substrate fermentation. Microbial proteins and enzymes Hydroponics	UM, UPM, USM, MARDI, SIRIM, FELDA
Biofertilizer production	Biofertilizers from agricultural waste. Biofertilizers from composting cellulosic materials	UPM, MARDI, SIRIM
Plant tissue culture	Plant tissue culture and protoplast fusion of hevea (rubber)	RRIM
	Plant tissue culture of legumes, oil palm, beans, vegetables, fruits, cocoa, orchids	UPM, UKM, MARDI, PORIM, FELDA
Food processing	Traditional food fermentation Pectin from cocoa Symbiotic fermentation for food adjuncts	UPM, UM, MARDI
Animal feed production	Feed from agricultural waste Feed from palm oil sludge and from coffee husk	UPM, MARDI
Animal nutrition health	Rumen fermentation and vaccine production Antibody production	UPM, UM

Source: Gibbons (1989)

ET technology

Research in ET technologies are undertaken by the University of Agriculture, Malaysia (UPM), Malaysian Agricultural Research and Development Institute (MARDI) and the Department of Veterinary Services (DVS) using various hormones including pregnant mare serum gonadotrophin (PMSG) and follicular stimulating hormone (FSH) for superovulation in buffalo, cattle and goats (Mukherjee, 1989a; Rosnina, Jainudeen, Sharifuddin and Nihayah, 1989; Sharifuddin, Rosnina and Jainudeen, 1989). The following techniques are currently established:-

- Surgical and nonsurgical collection of embryos.
- Freezing of cattle and goat embryos.
- Transfer of frozen embryos to local recipients.
- Embryo bank for indigenous animals.

Research in nonsurgical embryo transfer, refinement of embryo thawing and embryo splitting are in progress. Future development of ET would be focused on techniques for *in vitro* fertilization, embryo sexing and micromanipulation.

Animal nutrition

In animal nutrition based on fibrous crop residues and agro-industrial by-products, research in manipulation of rumen microorganisms to improve fibre digestion has been carried out (Ho, Abdullah and Jalaludin, 1989) using anaerobic fungi that colonized and digested plant fragments. Similar studies of rumen fungi in cattle and swamp buffaloes are in progress (Abdullah, Ho and Jalaludin, 1989). At the University of Malaya (UM), characterization of rumen bacteria is carried out with the aim of genetic manipulation for effective fibre digestion. Future R&D includes selection and manipulation of superior fibre degrading strains of fungi and bacteria and increasing their population density in the rumen.

Animal health and genetics

Most research institutions are actively developing enzyme linked immunoassay (ELISA) kits for their own diagnostic and research purposes, including the measurement of autoantibodies (Ng, Goh, Rajna and Khalid, 1989). Under the DVS, the Veterinary Research Institute Ipoh is developing various ELISA kits for the diagnosis of mammalian and poultry diseases. In hybridoma technology, R&D activities are in progress at various universities. The UM is setting up a unit for the production of monoclonal antibodies (MAb) for the diagnosis of infectious diseases caused by bacteria, chlamydia and viruses and the determination of important epitopes of pathogenic microorganisms (Lam, Devi, Pang and Iskandar, 1989). Good progress has been made in cell fusion techniques as numerous hybridomas secreting detectable monoclonal antibodies have been obtained. Characterization of these antibodies to determine their usefulness for large-scale production of the useful clones is in progress. Molecular analyses of virulent Malaysian Denge-2 viral genomes are also carried out at the UM (Pang, 1989). Research is undertaken at the National University Malaysia (UKM) for the production of MAb against *Pseudomonas pseudomallei* lethal exotoxin (Rahmah, Noor and Ghazally, 1989). At the UPM, R&D activities in genomic location and identification of viral epitopes (Khatijah Yusoff, 1989), extraction and purification of DNA (Cheow and Abdul Latiff, 1989) and analysis of mitochondrial DNA (Gan, 1989) are in progress. Studies on DNA analysis have been completed by Nyonya, Aini and Abdul Latiff (1989) and ligation of restricted DNA fragments into a cloning vector for transfer into *E. coli* is in progress at the UPM. In the field of livestock breeding, some preliminary research on mitochondrial and nuclear restriction fragment length polymorphism (RFLP) as markers for useful traits in buffaloes and chickens are carried out at UPM and UM respectively. Well-equipped laboratories for recombinant DNA research work are now existing at UPM and UM. These universities are offering degree and postgraduate courses in biotechnology. Training courses on gene cloning are being scheduled at UKM in August, 1989. Facilities for DNA extraction, size fractionation, DNA sequencing and mapping are also available.

The educational and institutional facilities and infrastructure for supporting and sustaining R&D in biotechnology are gradually being developed and strengthened. The number of trained researchers in biotechnology will increase in the future as more degree and postgraduate courses in biotechnology are offered at the universities. There is however a need for further training for researchers in some of the 'finer points' in the more advanced fields of biotechnology that involve recombinant DNA gene cloning and hybridoma technologies. Such training may be organized through attachment training at institutions active in the specialized fields concerned or through collaborative research with knowledgeable scientists locally or abroad.

Malaysia is in the initial stages of acquiring knowledge and skills in biotechnology, a stage which requires much funds with few benefits in return. At the recent budget, only about $5 million (Malaysian) has been allocated for R&D in all the five areas of biotechnology, of which only $2 million (Malaysian) or U.S. $0.77 million trickled through to animal biotechnology to be shared among 22 R&D projects for the years 1988 to 1989. Such funding is insufficient.

INDONESIA

Indonesia has a livestock population of 461.88 million which is dominated by the poultry sector at 92.6% while ruminants and pigs constitute the remaining 6.0 and 1.4% respectively (Table 1). The poultry population is made up mostly of village chickens that attain body weights of 0.75 kg to 1.0 kg at maturity. The farming system is smallholder with an average area of 5 ha. per farm. About 58% of the cattle and buffalo are kept as draught animals and as a source of meat, milk and manure. The animals are fed mainly with crop residues and unwanted forage (Djojosoebagio, 1986). Goats and sheep account for approximately 10% of total meat consumed in the country while pork is less. Recently, pig farms were established in Northern Sumatra for exportation purposes.

Since 1980, there has been importation of cattle to meet local demand for animal protein. However, the average consumption of poultry, beef (from cattle and buffalo), lamb and mutton is currently estimated at only 2.0 g to 2.6g/capita/day, which is below the targeted minimum requirement of about 4g/capita/day (Gunawan, 1989). With a predicted human population of 200 million by the year 2000 the necessity to increase livestock production in the country especially in the ruminant sector is urgent.

The problems of livestock production in Indonesia are identified as poor animal productivity, nutrition and economic losses from diseases (Djojosoebagio, 1986). Poor productivity and nutrition are attributed to lack of grazing land and lack of digestible protein from alternative feed sources as well as inferior breeds and the harsh tropical environment. Viral, bacterial and parasitic diseases accounted for significant annual losses which were estimated at U.S. $138.56 million for the year 1984. Other constraints to the industry are identified as management and marketing. Under the five year development plan for agriculture and livestock production, the following strategies were proposed:-

- Intensification of the dairy industry to minimize importation of dairy products.
- Importation of exotic breeds of animals to improve local stock.
- Raising indigenous breeds which perform better under local environment.
- Domestication of indigenous wild species.

Biotechnology has been given a high priority for development at the national level by the Agency for Development and Application of Technology (O. Koswara, personal communication). Early plans for biotechnology began in 1982 when the Indonesian Institute of Science (LIPI) submitted programmes to develop natural resources, including a centre for biotechnology at Cibinong which will act as a multidisciplinary R&D centre with collaborative basic research linkages to universities and government institutions for transfer of new technologies to the industries (Gibbons, 1989). To coordinate R&D activities in biotechnology, various InterUniversity Centres (IUC) for biotechnology were set up as follows:-

- Agricultural biotechnology at the Institute of Agriculture in Bogor.
- Industrial biotechnology at the Institute of Technology, Bandung.
- Medical biotechnology at the Gajah Mada University.

The SEA Regional Centre for Tropical Biology at Bogor is involved in plant tissue culture.

With the recognition of trained manpower and facility requirements for biotechnology research and bioindustrial development, a four-stage policy for biotechnology acquisition was put forward:-

- Development of bioindustries through direct importation and transfer of technical skills and processes to instantly produce valuable products or provide valuable services while offering opportunities for local staff to learn and understand the technologies involved at first hand.
- Integration of biotechnology necessary in the formulation of new designs and development.
- Development of new local biotechnology to suit local environment.
- Local basic research to support ongoing bioindustrial development.

Under livestock production, R&D activities are carried out in four areas, namely animal health, animal nutrition, recombinant DNA technology and embryo transfer technology (Gunawan, 1989; Mukherjee, 1989b).

Animal health

Research in the development of ELISA for the following diseases is in progress:-

- Infectious bronchitis and Newcastle disease in chickens.
- Brucellosis, anthrax, babesiosis and anaplasmosis in cattle.
- Anaplasmosis in buffalo.
- Research into hybridoma technology is also planned.

Animal nutrition

Research into the use of mushroom and yeast strains to increase digestibility and protein content respectively of agricultural by-products for animal feed has been carried out to maximize utilization of these by-products. At the Research Institute for Animal Production, research into the fermentative bioconversion of cassava tuber starch by yeasts (*Candida* spp.) into protein rich products is undertaken (Gunawan, 1989). Highest protein content obtained in the final product was 35%. Studies into the degradation of lignin in rice straws by oyster mushrooms (*Pleurotus* spp.) have been carried out to improve their digestibility from 39% to 45 or 54%. Similar studies on protein enrichment of rice straws with *Coprinus* sp. are carried out at the National Centre for Biotechnology Research. Manipulation of microorganisms in the control of rumen fermentation is another area of research in the country.

Recombinant DNA technology

R&D activities in this technology are planned for future application to produce transgenic sheep and ducks with superior reproductive traits.

Embryo transfer (ET) technology

Research in estrous synchronization, superovulation, embryo collection and nonsurgical transfer to recipients has been carried out in Bali cattle (Pane and Suprapto, 1986). Out of a total of 98 transfers, 52 calvings were obtained, giving a calving rate of 53%. Embryo transfer was also carried out as a project between the Granada International Corporation, Texas, U.S.A. and a local company, P.T. Berdikari United Livestock, at Cicurug, West Java (Embryo Transfer Report, 1984). Frozen embryos were imported by the foreign company and transferred to 74 local dairy cattle that were selected from a total of 150 animals. A pregnancy rate of 35% (26 pregnant animals) was obtained. This project is an attempt to introduce exotic breeds into the country through the use of frozen embryos. ET is also being attempted in local buffaloes.

ET technology is currently developed to assist genetic improvement programmes for livestock. At the Central Research Institute (CRI) for animal science and the Central Animal Production Research Institute in Bogor, plans are proposed for the identification of genetic traits in breeding programmes for disease resistance (e.g. Marek's disease B-complex blood types in chickens) and for the application of ET in genetic improvement of breeds.

THAILAND

Thailand is an agricultural country in which more than half the population is employed in agricultural related work, including livestock production. The country has a livestock population of 116.011 million (Table 1) of which poultry accounts for 99 million, corresponding to 85.4%, while the remaining 11.0% and 3.6% are made up of ruminants and pigs respectively. In terms of agricultural produce, livestock and livestock products contributed 20% to the total estimated value in 1984 which was equivalent to 3% to 5% of the gross domestic product of the country (Charan and Pakapun, 1986). The farming system is by majority (>90%) small-scale integrated farming for buffalo and cattle. Small-scale integrated farming is also common for backyard swine, poultry and dairy cattle in which wastes and by-products from farm crops are fed to the animals which in return provide the smallholder farmer with a regular source of animal proteins and in the case of cattle and buffaloes, draught animal power as well. Large-scale commercial farming is practised for poultry and to some extent for pigs also. Both livestock farming systems are expected to continue to coexist in the future.

Due to its intensive agricultural activities, the country has ample supplies of animal feeds and feed ingredients and these include corn, cassava, soya bean, rice bran, molasses, copra cake, cotton seed meal and rice straw. Thailand is one of the few countries in Asia that is self-sufficient in agricultural products (Asian Livestock, 1988c). Surplus products like corn and cassava are exported through international markets.

With an estimated human population approaching 60 million in the next decade, there is much pressure to increase livestock production to cope with future demands. Poultry and pig production will have to be increased even though the country is currently self-sufficient. Production of beef and dairy products will require even greater efforts. At present, only 5% of the national requirements for milk is produced locally. To assist in the expansion of the livestock industry, especially in regard to ruminants, research is being undertaken into embryo transfer and utilization of agricultural wastes and agro-industrial by-products for animal feeds.

The importance of biotechnology to the country was realized when it was identified for special support in the Sixth Social and Economic Plan of 1987 to 1991 (Gibbons, 1989). A National Centre for Genetic Engineering and Biotechnology (NCGEB) under the Ministry of Science Technology and Energy was also set up in 1983 to support R&D in agriculture and agro-industries and promote centres of excellence at local universities and institutes. Among its other functions are the following:-

- To strengthen capabilities in genetic engineering and biotechnology for application in economic and social development.
- To provide information, training and links to local and international industries.
- To provide funds for activities related to biotechnology and encourage cooperation among researchers in biotechnology. Towards this purpose the Centre has supported numerous conferences, seminars and workshops in biotechnology.

To further support the biotechnology industry, the Board of Investment was formed to provide various incentives to investors in the form of tax incentives, reduced import duties and special permits for foreign experts. In addition, special incentives for technology transfer or development could also be considered.

With the importation of foreign biotechnology which is increasing about 8% per year, the Technology Transfer Centre was set up by the Government to facilitate transfer of foreign technology to develop local business industries and technical capabilities. In the area of livestock production, embryo transfer in cattle has been successful to the extent of reducing cattle importation by approximately U.S. $2 million per year. The technology has been developed locally through the years from as early as 1981 when the first successful superovulation in swamp buffalo using PMSG was recorded. Studies in surgical and nonsurgical transfers followed, resulting in the first successful calving in dairy cows in 1984 using frozen embryos from the Carnation American Company (S. Muangcharoen, personal communication). To date, several successful transfers of embryos to dairy cattle leading to the birth of 20 calves have been recorded. In 1989 Dr. Peerasak reported the successful embryo transfer in swamp buffalo in which twin calves were delivered (S. Muangcharoen, personal communication). The Department of

Livestock Development (DLD) has projects in embryo transfer for beef and dairy cattle, swamp buffalo, sheep and goats to improve livestock breeding rapidly and economically. In dairy cattle, a national project supported by NCGEB was established through the collaboration between institutions and private sectors to improve breeding stock for maximum milk and meat production (Samphan, Vanda and Chamnean, 1989). Research in embryo sexing, *in vitro* fertilization and genetic engineering and creation of an embryo bank are in progress. Embryo transfer in pigs is also studied in regard to genetic traits for disease control (Peerasak, 1989). In animal health, development of ELISA for detection of swine fever and monoclonal antibodies for pig pneumonia is in progress at the National Institute of Animal Health and Production in Bangkok. Research into monoclonal antibody production for assay of progesterone and Newcastle disease viral strains is also in progress at Chulalongkorn University and the DLD in Bangkok respectively. Research on genetic manipulation and genetic improvement of microorganisms is undertaken at the local universities.

PHILIPPINES

Livestock production in the Philippines was estimated at 24.9 million pesos in 1985, contributing to 15.4% of the total agricultural produce and 4.1% of the gross domestic product (Caspe, 1987). In terms of population, poultry is the majority species, comprising 80.2% of the total number of 68.57 million (Table 1) while ruminants and pigs each account for 9.6 and 10.2% of the population respectively. Backyard farmers own 80% of the livestock industry. The country has a surplus of pigs and poultry but is deficient in ruminants. Only about 2% and 40% of the country's requirements of dairy products and beef respectively were produced in the country in 1987 resulting in their large-scale importation. A major area of constraint to livestock production has been the insufficiency of animal feeds and the high cost of feed importation that resulted in a heavy drain on the country's foreign exchange reserves. Since pasture land for cattle continues to diminish, some farms have been raising sheep and goats in addition to cattle because the former are cheaper and easier to raise and do not compete for cereal feeds (Baconawa, 1986). In the face of these problems, the challenges of the livestock industry to meet the present and future demands for livestock products are great. Some of the priorities suggested by the government through the Bureau of Animal Industry to assist the industry are:-

- To conserve and increase the carabao (buffalo) population.
- To pursue local production of corn and soya bean and develop nonconventional feed sources.
- To rehabilitate and restock dairy farms and improve and speed up livestock breeding.
- To develop and upgrade technical skills and knowledge of institutional personnel.

The National Institute of Biotechnology at Los Banos was set up in 1979 to develop technologies for microbiological industries (Gibbons, 1989). Studies involving broad aspects of biotechnology are undertaken at this institute including protoplast fusion and recombinant DNA in the research of antibiotics production by microorganisms. Research into production of tylosin, feed antibiotics, monoclonal antibodies against *Pasteurella haemolytica* and genetically improved lignolytic microorganisms is also carried out. Research into treatment of fibrous crop residues with enzyme producing microorganisms to improve digestibility is in progress (Dalmacio, 1989).

Other biotechnological activities in botany, ecology, biology and biochemistry are undertaken at the National Science Research Institute at the Diliman campus. The Industrial Technology Development Institute (ITDI) under the Ministry of Science and Technology has among its 10 technical divisions, the Microbiology and Genetics Division dealing with genetic engineering and process development.

In the livestock sector, the Bureau of Animal Industry is involved in R&D in embryo transfer technology and its Laboratory Services Division is currently planning guidelines and research proposals on genetically engineered pseudorabies vaccines (R.N. Alcasid, personal communication). Research in feed resource development via manipulation of microorganisms is carried out at the ITDI while production of monoclonal antibodies and vaccines and research into recombinant DNA technology and interferon are actively pursued at the Research Institute for Tropical Medicine.

Research and development of embryo transfer technology in the Philippines has been reviewed by Capitan (1989). Besides the College of Veterinary Medicine, University of the Philippines, private farms have also shown much interest in embryo transfer since the early 1980s as evidenced by the presence of foreign consultants in many farms to assist in breeding programmes, the holding of seminars on embryo transfer involving private companies and foreign experts and the embryo transfer attempts in private companies. The Asian Society for Embryo Transfer was founded with 23 countries as members to encourage development of the technology in the region. The first successful farrowing was reported in 1983 following ova transfer in pigs in a private farm in Rizal. Following this, other transfers were attempted, often in collaboration with foreign companies. The ANSA Cattle Crop Farms Incorporation carried out transfers in beef cattle to improve its genetic breeds. Out of 83 recipients, 28 animals were pregnant, resulting in 25 calvings over the period of 1984 to 1985. At the Lopez Sugar Corporation, 12 calvings were obtained between 1985 to 1986. Embryo transfers have also been attempted at the Magnolia Dairy Farm and Philippine Genetic Institute (Philgene) in cattle. Transfers of Indo-Brazil embryos in cattle resulted in 21 pregnancies recently in 1988 at a farm in Laguna. The author (Capitan, 1989) concluded that progress in embryo transfer has been slow in the country on account of lack of funds and facilities and inadequate support from research institutes.

SINGAPORE

The livestock population of Singapore is estimated at 8.25 million in 1987, consisting of 6.88 million chickens, 0.92 million ducks and 0.45 million pigs which is reflected by the country's capability of meeting the total domestic requirements for chickens at 25%, ducks at 74%, pork at 58% and chicken eggs at 55% with a turnover value of U.S. $129 million (Asian Livestock, 1989). In terms of size, the Republic covers an area of 620 km^2 of which only about 33 km^2 is allocated for agriculture and this will be reduced to 20 km^2 in 1995 in favour of housing and industrial developments. However, before this date, pig farming will be phased out by the end of 1989. Livestock development in Singapore would therefore involve intensive high technology farming to meet domestic requirements for poultry meat and eggs.

Biotechnology on the other hand has been identified for intensive development by the Science Council of Singapore (SCS) after the diversification of the country's economy in 1986 (Gibbons, 1989). Government support for biotechnology is provided in the form of funding and financial backing for R&D through the Product Development Assistance Scheme, R&D Assistance Scheme, and tax incentives for new biotechnological industries. There are currently four biotechnology-related companies operating at the Singapore Science Park which is an area designated for industrial R&D, including biotechnology. Two more biotechnology-related companies are planned for the future. Further efforts to strengthen the basic infrastructure for biotechnology comes from the inauguration of the Institute of Molecular and Cell Biology in 1987 to undertake research in areas of importance and relevance to the country and the region and training of personnel for manpower requirements in biotechnology. There are three major research groups, namely Cell Regulation, Infectious and Genetic Diseases and Plant Genetic Engineering and a staff of 100 or more researchers divided into 11 teams.

In the biotechnology industry, a Biotechnology Office has been set up under the Economic Development Board to promote the industry internationally with Singapore as its centre. The Office liaises between the Government and the investors, manufacturers and the scientific community. At present there is a need to improve cooperation and coordination among these groups.

With a livestock population consisting mainly of poultry, interests in embryo transfer technology, ruminant nutrition, breeding and related technologies are expected to be low. The main interest would shift to R&D activities for the manufacture of biotechnology products with immediate commercial markets, including enzymes, animal hormones and disease diagnostic kits.

FOOD AND AGRICULTURE ORGANISATION (FAO)

To assist developing countries in Asia in the rapid acquisition of biotechnology, an FAO network of Biotechnology Collaborating Centres was proposed at the recent Regional Workshop on Biotechnology in Animal Production and Health in Asia held in Bangkok in October 1988. The proposed network would incorporate a three year plan for technical cooperation among Asian developing countries and would include information exchange, training requirements and other related activities with funding from FAO and other donor agencies like UNDP. Among the general recommendations made to FAO were:-

- The immediate initiation of technical cooperation through the regular programme funds of FAO.
- The acceptance of requests for short-term assistance from member countries under the Technical Cooperation Programme (TCP).
- The possibility of obtaining long-term funding for the network from UNDP or other donor agencies.
- The organization of training courses and meetings of scientists from the region.
- The provision of consultants for attending to specific issues encountered in the region.

Priority areas in biotechnology identified at the workshop and recommended for immediate application, research and training in the region included:-

- ET and related technologies
- Ruminant nutrition studies to increase digestibility of agro-industrial by-products
- Gene mapping
- Monoclonal antibody production
- Development of ELISA
- Gene cloning and molecular characterization and application of expression system for cloned genes.

Following the 13th FAO-Animal Production and Health Commission for Asia, Far East and the South Pacific (APHCA) session in October 1988 at Bangkok, the recommendations of the Regional Workshop for the establishment of a biotechnology network was supported by the Commission (Asian Livestock, 1988b). Project documents for establishment of a UNDP network on biotechnology in animal production and health are currently being prepared for presentation at another workshop scheduled in Beijing from 9th to 14th October 1989. The interests in biotechnology in SEA are perhaps best reflected from the R&D activities in the individual countries and their collective efforts to establish a collaborative network for technical cooperation.

DEVELOPMENT AND IMPLICATIONS OF BIOTECHNOLOGY IN SEA

Availability of local livestock and livestock products in SEA countries to meet national requirements is generally most deficient in the ruminant sector and less in the poultry and pig sectors. Problems in livestock production and development pertaining to health include economic losses due to diseases. In the ruminant production sector, the problems are mainly poor nutrition, breeding, performance and reproductivity. The importance of these problems is expected to increase as the human population and hence, the demands for local livestock and livestock products in the region increase in the future. The urgency of these issues is evident from the recent increased efforts to improve livestock production in SEA, including the possible application of biotechnology which is now actively pursued through R&D in areas of priority relevant to the issues encountered. The development of biotechnology is *dependent* on long-term adequate funding, availability of fully functioning educational and institutional infrastructures that are easily accessible and responsive to the industry, and sufficient number of trained personnel in biotechnology; thus the challenges faced by the SEA countries are numerous at the current initial stages when funds, facilities and trained personnel are insufficient or minimal and progress is slow. The acquisition of biotechnology is mainly a process of learning and experimentation for which funds are limited and monetary returns are minimal or none. The setting up of a collaborative biotechnology network in the region with possibilities of supportive funding, facilities and expert technical assistance is therefore timely as it would supplement national efforts of individual countries to facilitate and speed up the progress in biotechnology development. The regional network is also appropriate because the sharing and transfer of high technology is easier and more acceptable to the farming communities in SEA where the socio-economic livestock and agricultural farming systems and problems are similar under the Asian environment. Although R&D priorities in biotechnology in the region are directed towards utilization of local-based resources of the individual countries to minimize dependence on costly importation for sustaining the bioindustry, it is nevertheless unavoidable that much foreign based technology would be introduced initially. The task of recipients is to absorb the information and understand the principles involved, master their application and develop expertise to generate new local skills and innovative capabilities to suit local operating conditions based on local resources. Towards this purpose, simultaneous development of good engineering capabilities and skills would be required to support innovative manoeuvres with the ultimate goal of achieving self-reliance in the biotechnology industry. Towards this goal, the role of governments in developing functioning institutional infrastructures and providing adequate technical training and educational facilities for self-development of innovative capabilities and creativity is important to the progress of harnessing biotechnology.

Since the priorities of the region are targeted mainly at the ruminant sector, both ruminant nutritional and ET and related technologies will have important applications in SEA. The latter offer possibilities of rapidly increasing and upgrading superior stocks with desirable performance traits while the former helps to overcome the shortage and high cost of conventional feeds through the improved utilization of unconventional feeds and agro-industrial by-products which are abundant in the region.

Through the years there has been an increasing interest in ET and its application in the region. It is perhaps the most actively researched technology in most of the countries, partly because ET is perceived as a natural extension or improvement of the existing artificial insemination infrastructure that requires comparatively little input to initiate and partly because it has direct and rapid access to the target group, namely the smallholder livestock farmers. APHCA has organized various seminars on ET in Thailand, Malaysia, Indonesia and Philippines. In 1983 the APHCA in collaboration with the American Development Foundation organized a regional training course covering all aspects of ET in Manila, Philippines. The following techniques have suitable applications in the region:-

- Nonsurgical recovery and transfer of embryos.
- Embryo freezing and thawing techniques for introduction of improved germ-plasm into the herd.
- ET for buffaloes.

The progress of ET technologies should be accompanied by an equal development in the necessary infrastructures to support the service. The cost of service should also be calculated in terms of:-

- Total cost of hormone injections for donors and recipients.
- Cost of embryo recovery and transfer.
- Cost of delivery (if any).
- Cost of veterinary examination and services.

The successful application and acceptance of ET in the region would depend on the total cost of services, the reliability of the technique (% of successful farrowing) and the availability of the service at the crucial period. These factors would subsequently be weighed against the efficiency, convenience and cost of normal breeding practices. To date, only a few companies are offering ET services in the region. In ruminant nutrition, although useful results have been obtained through research, they are only preliminary and more R&D would be required before useful applications could be derived.

Similarly the application of biotechnology in the manufacturing industries is still premature at present. However, it may be feasible to set up businesses or projects with suitable foreign biotechnology companies with proven technologies for the manufacture of biotechnological products with the condition that local staff have access to specialized training available in the

R&D activities of the parent company. On the other hand, since foreign companies are generally cautious in overseas duplication of investments and are reluctant to divulge or transfer their secrets at the same time, there is a need for favourable investment policies in the recipient countries like tax incentives, reduced import duties and perhaps some degree of market control to attract foreign investments. The lower cost of labour, raw materials and other resources in the SEA region are additional business attractions. The business contract would require careful and tactful negotiation to ensure among other things, the proper technology transfer at favourable terms to the recipient, failing which the latter would have to develop the technology through its own R&D capabilities.

To the entrepreneurs, biotechnology is a tough business in which the product has to compete for price and quality in the domestic and international markets to secure a demand that exceeds the minimum economic production scale. From its profits, a budget would have to be allocated for product quality testing and promotion and for further R&D activities to maintain a leading edge in the business. Issues pertaining to patent laws and standards for minimum quality requirements for the products would have to be worked out efficiently by the government.

Despite all the R&D achievements and success attained, it would be the market demand that eventually determines the fate of biotechnology either as a successful bioindustry on the one hand or a less efficient and limited production scale model that remains at the research institutional level at the other end. As a business enterprise, monetary returns from biotechnology may be rewarding or modest or poor even though the amount spent on R&D and industrial investments may be enormous. Nevertheless, SEA countries in adopting a positive attitude perceive biotechnology as an opportunity to solve some of their livestock production problems and, at the same time, provide beneficial services and quality products to improve the quality of life and for the creation of wealth.

GLOSSARY OF OFFICIAL NAMES

APHCA	Animal Production and Health Commission for Asia, Far East and the South Pacific, FAO.
CRI	Central Research Institute, Indonesia.
DLD	Department of Livestock Development, Thailand.
DVS	Department of Veterinary Services, Malaysia.
FELDA	Federal Land Development Authority.
ITDI	Industrial Technology Development Institute, Philippines.
IUC	InterUniversity Centres, Indonesia.
LIPI	Indonesian Institute of Science.
MARDI	Malaysian Agricultural Research and Development Institute.
NCGEB	National Centre for Genetic Engineering and Biotechnology, Thailand.

PORIM	Palm Oil Research Institute of Malaysia.
RRIM	Rubber Research Institute of Malaysia.
SCS	Science Council of Singapore.
SEA	South East Asia.
SIRIM	Standard & Industrial Research Institute of Malaysia.
TCP	Technical Cooperation Programme, FAO.
UKM	National University of Malaysia.
UM	University of Malaya.
UPM	University of Agriculture, Malaysia.
USM	University of Science, Malaysia.

REFERENCES

Abdullah, N., Ho, Y.W. and Jalaludin, S. (1989). A study of rumen fungi in cattle and swamp buffalo. *Report of the First Seminar on National Biotechnology Programmes, Ministry of Science, Technology and Environment, Malaysia.*

Asian Livestock (1988a). FAO regional conference highlighting livestock development. *Report of the 19th FAO Regional Conference No.* 8, 85-87.

Asian Livestock (1988b). Thirteenth FAO/APHCA Session in Bangkok No. 11, 141-142.

Asian Livestock (1988c). Livestock production and marketing in Thailand – Part I, No. 7, 81-82.

Asian Livestock (1989). Animal disease – current situation in Singapore, No. 3, 34-36.

Baconawa, E.T. (1986). Status and prospects of sheep raising in the Philippines. *Asian Livestock No. 9*, 98-100.

Capitan, S.S. (1989). Country report: Status of embryo transfer technology in the Philippines. *Report of the Regional Workshop on Biotechnology in Animal Production and Health in Asia*, F.A.O.

Caspe, C.E. (1987). Livestock development in the Philippines in the nineties. *Asian Livestock No. 1*, 7–11.

Charan, C. and Pakapun, B. (1986). Livestock development in Thailand during the nineties. *Asian Livestock No. 10*, 135–139.

Cheow, L. and Abdul Latiff, I. (1989). Isolation and purification of DNA from Malaysian isolates of infecitous bovine rhinotracheitis virus. *Report of the First Seminar on National Biotechnology Programmes, Ministry of Science, Technology and Environment, Malaysia.*

Dalmacio, I.F. (1989). Application of biotechnology in improvement of fibrous crop residues. *Report of the Regional Workshop on Biotechnology in Animal Production and Health in Asia*, F.A.O.

Djojosoebagio, S. (1986). Livestock development in Indonesia during the nineties. *Asian Livestock No. 11*, 114-118, 127.

Embryo Transfer Report (1984). First embryo transfer in dairy cattle in Indonesia. *General Report of the Research and Extension Dairy Cattle Pioneer Project, Indonesia.*

Gan, Y.Y. (1989). A new mitochondrial DNA mutation found in Malaysians. *Report of the First Seminar on National Biotechnology Pro-*

grammes, Ministry of Science, Technology and Environment, Malaysia.

Gibbons, G.C. (1989). Biotechnology and its implications on resource-based industries, with special reference to Malaysia. *Report of the Symposium on Managing Technological Change: Policies and Strategies, Ministry of Science, Technology and Environment, Malaysia.*

Gunawan, B. (1989). Country report - Indonesia. *Report of the Regional Workshop on Biotechnology in Animal Production and Health in Asia,* F.A.O.

Ho, Y.W., Abdullah, N. and Jalaludin, S. (1989). Application of biotechnology in improvement of fibrous crop residues: anaerobic rumen fungi in the utilisation of fibrous crop residues as feed resource for ruminant. *Report of the Regional Workshop on Biotechnology in Animal Production and Health in Asia,* F.A.O.

Khatijah Yusoff (1989). Use of monoclonal antibodies in the identification of neutralising epitopes in Newcastle disease virus. *Report of the First Seminar on National Biotechnology Programmes, Ministry of Science, Technology and Environment, Malaysia.*

Lam, S.K., Devi, S., Pang, T. and Iskandar, N.M. (1989). Development and application of monoclonal antibodies. *Report of the First Seminar on National Biotechnology Programmes, Ministry of Science, Technology and Environment, Malaysia.*

Mukherjee, T.K. (1989a). Country report - Malaysia. *Report of the Regional Workshop on Biotechnology in Animal Production and Health in Asia,* F.A.O.

Mukherjee, T.K. (1989b). Review of development of biotechnology in animal production and health in Asia. *Report of the Regional Workshop on Biotechnology in Animal Production and Health in Asia, F.A.O.*

Ng, M.L., Goh, K.H., Rajna, A. and Khalid, B.A.K. (1989). Development of ELISA kits for the measurement of autoantibodies. *Report of the First Seminar on National Biotechnology Programmes, Ministry of Science, Technology and Environment, Malaysia.*

Nyonya, R., Aini, I. and Abdul Latiff, I. (1989). *Haemophilus paragallinarum*: DNA extraction and gene cloning. *Report of the First Seminar on National Biotechnology Programmes, Ministry of Science, Technology and Environment, Malaysia.*

Pane, I. and Suprapto, E. (1986). Embryo transfer trial on Bali cattle. *Report of the Bali Cattle Improvement Project, Bali, Indonesia.*

Pang, T. (1989). Molecular characterisation of Malaysian Denge-2 viral genomes. *Report of the First Seminar on National Biotechnology Programmes, Ministry of Science, Technology and Environment, Malaysia.*

Peerasak, C. (1989). Embryo transfer technology in pigs: experiences in Thailand. *Report of the Regional Workshop on Biotechnology in Animal Production and Health in Asia,* F.A.O.

Rahmah, M., Noor, E. and Ghazally, I. (1989). Monoclonal antibody to the lethal exotoxin of *Pseudomonas pseudomallei. Report of the First Seminar on National Biotechnology Programmes, Ministry of Science, Technology and Environment, Malaysia.*

Rosnina, Y., Jainudeen, M.R., Sharifuddin, W. and Nihayah, M. (1989). Superovulation and egg recovery in goats. *Report of the First Seminar on National Biotechnology Programmes, Ministry of Science, Technology and Environment, Malaysia.*

Samphan, S. Vanda, S. and Chamnean, S. (1989). Embryo transfer technology in cattle: Experience in Thailand. *Report of the Regional Workshop on Biotechnology in Animal Production and Health in Asia*, F.A.O.

Sharifuddin, W., Rosnina, Y. and Jainudeen, M.R. (1989). Superovulation and embryo transfer in goats: The Malaysian experience. *Report of the Regional Workshop on Biotechnology in Animal Production and Health in Asia*, F.A.O.

Yusoff, M.S., Mustaffa, A.B. and Chin, F.Y. (1985). Utilisation of nonconventional feeds and agricultural by-products for ruminants in Malaysia. *Asian Livestock No. 10*, 176–181, 184.

6.5

Biotechnology for Developing Countries

C.J. BOSTOCK
AFRC Institute for Animal Health, Pirbright, England

INTRODUCTION

In the foregoing chapters 'biotechnology' has been defined several times and numerous specific applications of biotechniques to various aspects of livestock production have been described. Such a collection represents a narrow window in the total spectrum of potential applications of biotechnology, but a disproportionately significant one to developing countries. Table 1 compares the relative value of world livestock production in 1980 in developing and developed countries and, when considered in relation to world population in these two categories, it is clear that there is considerable scope to improve productivity in developing countries. As has been discussed in previous chapters, a significant factor affecting the efficiency of livestock production in developing countries is disease, which accounts for worldwide losses in excess of U.S. $ 100,000 million annually (Table 2). Much of this loss occurs in developing countries and thus represents an immediate target for attack by today's biotechnology.

Using a rather broad definition of biotechnology I have grouped the various methods into two categories; those that are based on the selection of pre-existing genetic diversity from populations of cells or organisms, and those that create new genes or combinations of genes by 'directed' genetic manipulation *in vitro*. The first of these includes 'conventional' breeding methods long practised in the selection of high yielding lines of plants or animals, but also includes novel techniques such as hybridoma production, where individual pre-existing antibody gene rearrangements can be selected on the basis of their antibody specificity following fusion with a myeloma.

TABLE 1 *World animal production.*

	Developing Countries			Developed Countries		
Commodity	**Gross value (U.S. $ m)**	**% of regional value**	**% of world production**	**Gross value (U.S. $ m)**	**% of regional value**	**% of world production**
Dairy products and meat	92,000	65	32	196,000	92	68
Other animal products, e.g. skins, wool	4,000	3	40	6,000	3	60
Manure and fuel	6,000	4	60	4,000	2	40
Draught power	40,000	28	87	6,000	3	13
Total	142,000	100	40	212,000	100	60
cf. % world population			74			26

Sources: FAO Situation Report (1982)
FAO Production Yearbook (1985)

TABLE 2 *Costs worldwide of principal animal diseases (in U.S. $ m).*

	U.S. $ m
Foot-and-mouth disease	50,000
Mastitis	35,000
Rift Valley fever	7,500
Leptospirosis	4,500
Brucellosis	3,500
Bluetongue	3,000
Shipping fever	3,000
Trichinellosis	2,500
Gastroenteritis	1,800
Calf diarrhoea	1,750
Retrovirus infections	1,000
Aujesky's disease	650
Pasteurellosis	500
Fowl cholera	200
Total	**114,900**

Source: The Impact of Biotechnology on Animal Care (1986). Technology Management Group Inc.

TABLE 3 *Biotechnology which could improve livestock production in developing countries.*

Methods which select and use existing genetic diversity, e.g.

- Traditional animal or plant breeding for increased productivity or disease resistance, enhanced through MOET, embryo cloning etc.
- Isolation of biologically active molecules from microorganisms, e.g. enzymes, antibiotics.
- Attenuation of infectious agents for vaccines.
- Production of antibodies for diagnostic purposes, enhanced through selection of monoclonal specificities.

Methods which create and select new genetic combinations

- Engineering of novel viruses for vaccines.
- Cloning of gene sequences for diagnostic purposes.
- Creation of novel bacteria which produce biologically active molecules (e.g. growth hormones, antibiotics, enzymes). These could be used in fermentation processes or used to manipulate the gut flora of domestic livestock.
- Production of novel plants for livestock food.
- Creation of novel animals (transgenic) with enhanced growth properties, disease resistance etc.

With all of these techniques it is important to remember that successful application relies on a wide spread of background knowledge and expertise in more 'conventional' techniques. Secondly, while some successful attempts have been made to introduce simplified diagnostic biotechnology to developing countries (Jeggo, Richards and Dargie, this volume) it has to be recognized that much biotechnology uses sophisticated equipment and sensitive reagents. Thus, for any effective and substantial transfer of biotechnology it is essential that it is preceded by the establishment of a 'knowledge base' through which training is retained within the national system and is accompanied by the provision of an infrastructure necessary to support such technology. Even the simplest of biotechnologies can fail because of inadequate supplies of water or electric power. In this respect it is important to distinguish between biotechnology which is relevant to the problems of developing countries, but which can realistically only be carried out in developing countries, and that biotechnology which is relevant and capable of being successfully carried out in developing countries in the foreseeable future. In this article only the latter is discussed.

Most of the biotechnologies listed in Table 3 have been described in detail in other chapters, so only certain aspects of those relating to animal health will be discussed here. While there is no doubt that the current techniques for manipulating and cloning embryos could bring improvements in the genetic stock of indigenous breeds, there will be little benefit to be gained in overall increased productivity until losses resulting from disease are drastically reduced.

SEROLOGICAL SURVEILLANCE IN PARC – A SUCCESSFUL INTRODUCTION OF INDIRECT ELISA

An essential part of any vaccination campaign to eliminate a disease is knowledge of the serological status of herds after vaccination has been carried out. This enables the level of protection to be measured, and alerts coordinators to failures in the system so that problems (e.g. inefficient vaccination team, breakdown in cold chain etc.) can be identified and corrected early in the campaign.

Traditional methods of detecting serum antibodies relied on virus neutralization tests which have several problems associated with them (e.g. requirement for good tissue culture facilities, contamination of sera, low throughput), especially for the large numbers of samples necessary in a national vaccination campaign. The ease and accuracy of serological tests was increased dramatically by the introduction in the 1970s of the enzyme-linked immunosorbent assay (ELISA, Engvall and Perlmann, 1971a,b; Voller, Bidwell and Bartlett, 1977), and, in combination with the specificity of monoclonal antibodies, ELISA becomes a powerful technique for diagnosis. Various methods currently being used for animal disease diagnosis in developing countries are reviewed in Mahy, Knowles and Pedley (1989).

The Pan African Rinderpest Campaign (PARC) uses a simple indirect ELISA to identify the presence of antibodies to rinderpest virus (RPV) in bovine sera (Anderson, Rowe, Taylor and Crowther, 1982; Anderson and Rowe, 1983). The original rinderpest ELISA was developed into a simple kit; the antigen (sonicated and clarified rinderpest virus-infected Madin Derby bovine kidney (MDBK) cells and positive and negative control sera are supplied by AFRC Institute for Animal Health (IAH), Pirbright Laboratory, and the other reagents (including anti-bovine antibody conjugate and substrates for the colour reaction) and ELISA readers are supplied by the International Atomic Energy Agency (IAEA), Vienna. This kit is now being used successfully in several laboratories around Africa (Dargie *et al*, this volume; Fig. 1). This success lies in the fact that:–

- Careful thought was given to the local conditions in which the technology was used.
- The test was designed to be workable within the limitations of resources available.
- Individual contract holders in each of the participating countries were identified and given training.
- Back-up visits from experts were arranged to consolidate training on site and to help 'trouble-shooting' where problems arose.

Fig. 1 *Map of Africa showing the countries participating in PARC in which the indirect ELISA for detecting serum antibodies against rinderpest is being successfully used.*

- The on-going involvement of IAEA and IAH ensures continuity of supply of materials necessary to carry out the tests.

Using this kit a team of three trained people could carry out some 20,000 tests in two months, although in practice the throughput is much less than this.

An example of two serological surveys carried out in the same region before and after vaccination is shown in Fig. 2. From this it can easily be seen that, following this single vaccination, approximately 80% of the herd are showing positivity in the RP ELISA and vaccination is being carried out successfully by that team. However, the real power of the overall technology is its ability to rapidly point to problem areas. Table 4 summarizes the overall

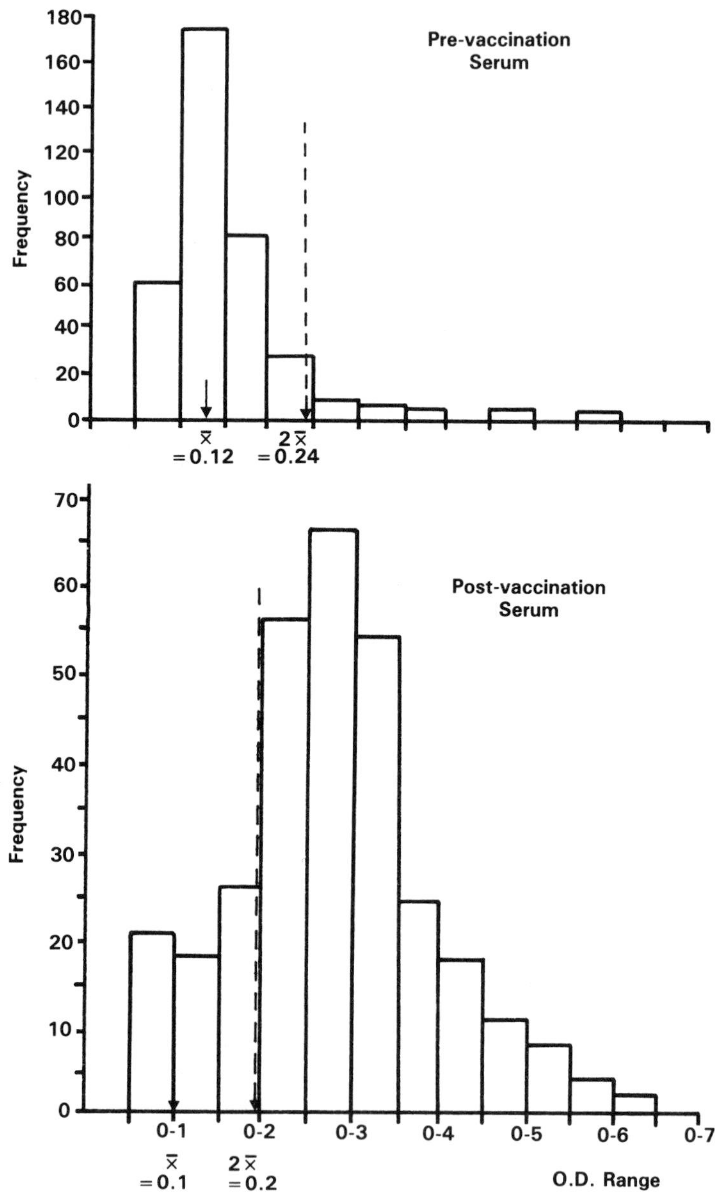

Fig. 2 *Serological survey in the Iringa district of cattle before and after a single vaccination with rinderpest vaccine. From the pre-vaccination serum the negative O.D. value is set at twice the mean value. Following vaccination approximately 80% of sera show antibodies against RPV above this level, indicating that vaccination was successful. (Kindly supplied by Dr J. Anderson).*

TABLE 4 *Percentage immunity levels in different Regions in Tanzania following 2–3 rounds of vaccination during PARC.*

Regional (districts)	Age group				
	<1–1 yr	1–2 yrs	2–3 yrs	3 yrs	Overall %
Arusha (4)	45 (23–63)	61 (53–69)	68 (55–79)	70 (38–92)	59 (47–72)
Coast (3)	35 (12–64)	50 (36–65)	75 (42–100)	75 (60–86)	60 (49–75)
Dodoma(3)	31 (24–37)	53 (34–67)	67 (44–85)	75 (62–86)	54 (49–58)
Iringa (2)	74 (68–79)	66 (57–74)	55 (42–67)	55 (47–50)	60 (52–67)
Kagera (5)	30 (2–81)	52 (12–82)	61 (30–90)	70 (36–95)	55 (23–90)
Kigoma (3)	46 (40–58)	NS	82 (71–88)	80 (62–96)	76 (64–82)
Kilimanjaro (4)	48 (43–51)	87 (77–93)	87 (68–97)	73 (55–94)	73 (66–85)
Lindi (4)	25 (13–87)	48 (24–65)	76 (42–100)	90 (89–92)	63 (50–75)
Mara (3)	19 (10–29)	45 (13–77)	54 (27–72)	51 (30–71)	43 (36–52)
Mbeya (5)	51 (43–62)	65 (55–73)	68 (50–86)	68 (18–98)	66 (45–79)
Morogoro (4)	55 (13–80)	72 (17–99)	92 (83–100)	86 (57–100)	80 (51–99)
Mtwara (3)	35 (20–53)	63 (44–94)	74 (51–91)	78 (62–86)	62 (44–75)
Mwanza (4)	85 (74–93)	84 (75–100)	88 (63–98)	91 (75–98)	88 (79–96)
Rukwa (3)	86 (80–93)	97 (95–100)	95 (86–100)	95 (87–100)	94 (88–99)
Ruvuma (3)	51 (19–79)	32 (15–60)	64 (52–75)	91 (86–96)	63 (56–75)
Shinyanga (1)	37	60	63	47	46
Singida (3)	54 (24–77)	74 (66–80)	83 (79–94)	82 (67–98)	72 (64–87)
Tabora (3)	46 (34–100)	66 (36–81)	84 (69–96)	89 (75–97)	78 (53–93)
Tanga 94)	68 (39–92)	70 (60–87)	55	77 (59–95)	73 (56–86)
Mean (x)	**48%**	**64%**	**73%**	**76%**	**67%**

The results are expressed as a mean value for each Region (with the range of values indicated in brackets). Each Region consisted of a number of Districts (indicated in brackets) and two crush sites were sampled in each District. Notice that the percentage immunity increases to 68% after 3 years, although in some Regions wide variations still exist.

From: Anderson *et al* (1989)

level of protection recorded in various regions during different stages of the campaign, where it can be seen that not all vaccination teams are as successful as the one above. Getting the results quickly and accurately permits the necessary remedial action to be taken which greatly enhances the potential success of the campaign.

The RP indirect ELISA is a good example of appropriate technology for developing countries – it is directly related to the potential eradication of a disease of major economic significance and it has been taken up successfully. In as much as it was originally conceived and designed in European laboratories, and the reagents are supplied from Europe, transfer of the technology cannot be said to be complete. However, it is encouraging to see the way in which some contractors have developed their own ELISA tests, using the experience and training gained from using the RP kit, for serological surveys of disease of local significance (e.g. *Mycoplasma* in goats; Wamwayi, Wafula, Litamoi and Nandokha, 1989). Once this stage has been achieved one can say that the technology has been transferred, and, given continuity of financial and technical support, it is hoped that it will continue to develop in a way which is appropriate to the needs of the host country.

THE BLOCKING ELISA

The indirect ELISA for RP is one of the simpler tests for detecting serum antibodies. The next level of 'technical complexity' is the competition or blocking ELISA, which relies upon the interaction between an antigen and a specific antibody preparation being blocked or competed out by the presence of cross-reacting antibodies in the test serum (Fig. 3). The extra component in this test is the antigen-specific antibody which is raised in a species for which the disease does not require to be diagnosed (e.g. rabbit, mouse or guinea pig), and it may be polyclonal or monoclonal. One advantage of this ELISA is that the same test can be used on sera from different species of animals. An example, which is currently being used successfully in Indonesia is the blocking ELISA for bluetongue virus (BTV) (Anderson, 1984). Using the group-specific monoclonal antibody, serum antibodies to all 22 serotypes of BTV can be detected and distinguished from antibodies to orbiviruses in different serogroups (Fig. 4). For this type of test to be developed locally not only does antigen need to be prepared (as in the indirect ELISA) but also the detecting antibody. This requires additional technologies, either for affinity purification of polyclonal antibodies raised in laboratory animals or the production and screening of monoclonal antibodies. Both of these represent

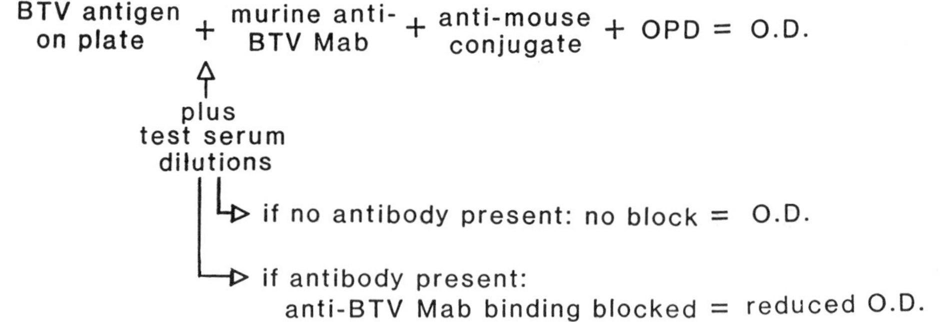

Fig. 3 *Blocking or competition ELISA for bluetongue. The anti-BTV monoclonal antibody is able to bind specifically to all serotypes of BTV and is thus group-specific. The presence of BTV-group-specific antibodies in the test serum will compete with the BTV-specific monoclonal antibody for binding sites on the antigen preparation and will thus reduce the amount of colour developed* (O.D.) *during the test. OPD = ortho-phenylenediamine, which is the chromogen.*

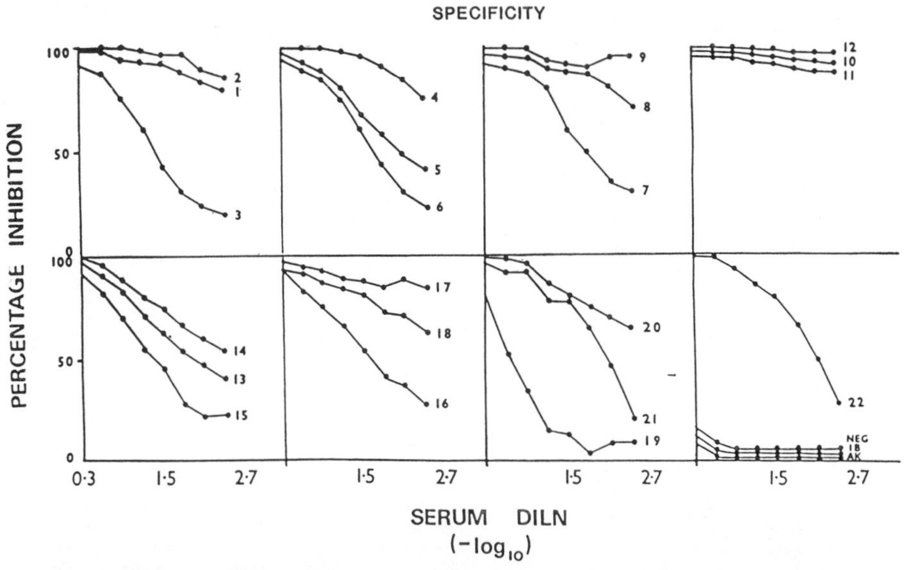

Fig. 4 *Experimental demonstration of the blocking ELISA for the detection of serum antibodies against BTV. Percentage inhibition values from a blocking ELISA using guinea-pig antisera against all 22 serotypes of BTV (numbered 1-22). These are compared to negative guinea-pig serum and sera raised in guinea-pigs against Ibaraki (IB) and Akabane (AK) viruses, which are members of unrelated serogroups. (Kindly supplied by Dr J. Anderson).*

logical and achievable steps in the process of building up technical expertise in this area.

THE SANDWICH ELISA

A further step in ELISA technology, currently being introduced into developing countries, is the sandwich ELISA (Fig. 5; Crowther and Abu Elzein, 1979) which differs from the previous methods described in that the microtitre plate is coated with an antigen-specific antibody. The antibody is used to trap the antigen, rather than coating the plate directly with antigen. This improves the sensitivity and specificity of the test as well as allowing the test to be used for the detection of both serum antibody (in a liquid phase competition sandwich ELISA; Hamblin, Barnett and Hedger, 1986) and antigen. Using high titre rabbit antisera to each of the seven serotypes of foot-and-mouth disease virus (FMDV), and similarly high titre type-specific guinea pig antisera as the 'detecting' antibody, the test is used to type isolates of FMDV. A similar approach is the typing and subtyping of FMDV using panels of monoclonal antibodies of known specificity as the detecting antibody (Crowther and Samuel, 1987). Facilities for the production of monoclonal antibodies would be required if national disease control agencies are to establish independence from outside sources for the supply of necessary

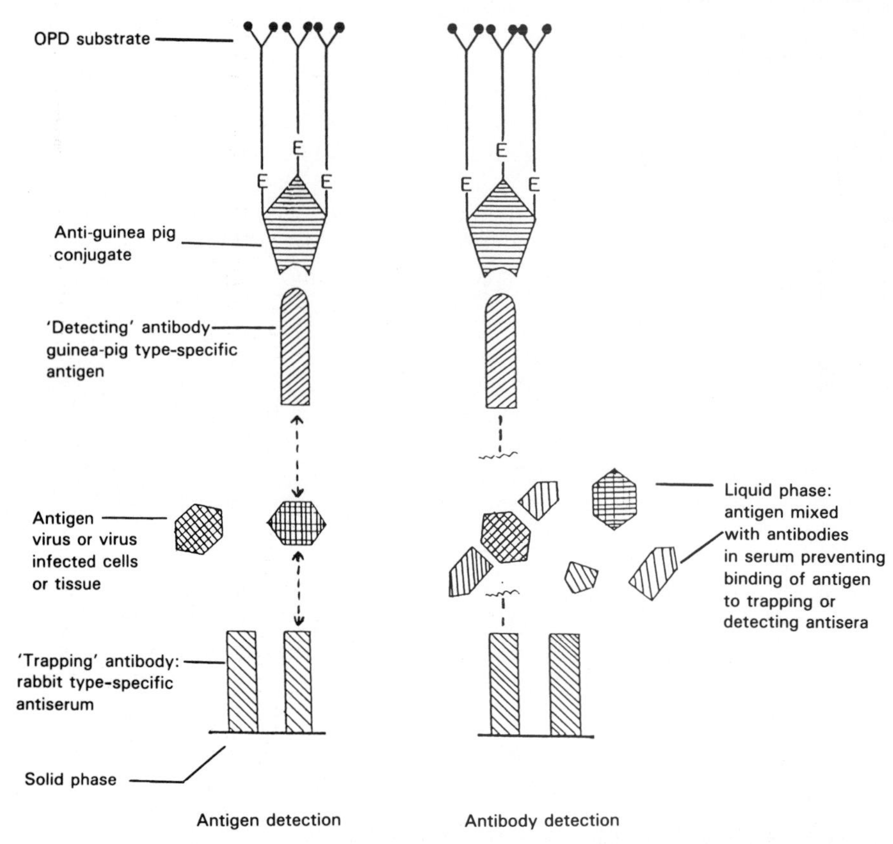

Fig. 5 *Diagrammatic representation of the sandwich ELISA for the detection of either antigen or serum antibodies. The plate is coated with an antiserum which is specific for the antigen of interest. If antigen is present in the test sample it will be trapped by the antibody, and subsequently detected by another antigen-specific antibody which is raised in a different animal species. Finally the presence of bound 'detecting' antibody (and therefore antigen) is identified by a conjugate. The method can also be used to detect serum antibodies by liquid phase incubation of the antigen with the test serum, which could block the binding sites on the antigen in a similar way to the blocking ELISA.*

reagents for these assays. An alternative test for antigen detection which is appropriate for developing countries is the latex agglutination test (e.g. for rinderpest virus; Bansall, Joshi, Chandra and Sharma, 1988).

In summary, diagnostic tests based on ELISA provide an important component of programmes to control and eradicate animal diseases in developing countries. The technology is, and has been shown to be, suitable for effective transfer to home-based laboratories and is forming the nucleus from which to develop their own technology base. One drawback with many of these tests is the requirement to produce virus for the antigen, and this limits the number of laboratories in which such tests could safely be developed. It is probable that the next generation of ELISAs will use noninfectious antigens, such as virus infection-associated antigens, VIA (Villinger, Mueller, Bruckner, Ackermann and Kihm, 1989), antigens 'expressed' from cloned genes (e.g. Villinger *et al*, 1989) or synthetic peptide antigens (Doel, this volume). For developing countries to participate in this they will need to acquire the nucleic acid technology necessary to clone and express the coding sequences of genes.

NUCLEIC ACID TECHNIQUES

While antibody-based techniques have the advantage of speed, specificity, high throughput and ease of use, they presently have limitations for certain diagnostic purposes. For example some virus isolates are immunologically indistinguishable and it is often not possible to identify positively virus in infected tissues, except through the use of nucleic acid probes.

To produce a DNA probe requires a great range of advanced molecular biology. Initially the genetic material of the disease agent needs to be purified, isolated and analyzed, for example, by gel electrophoresis, restriction enzyme mapping or hybridization. If the infecting agent has a DNA genome (e.g. the DNA viruses such as capripoxvirus, or all bacteria or protozoa), it may be cloned directly after treatment with a suitable restriction endonuclease to fragment it. On the other hand, if the infectious agent is an RNA virus (e.g. FMDV, BTV or RPV), or if it is decided to clone an RNA message, the RNA must be first copied into DNA by reverse transcriptase. The fragment of DNA can then be cloned by insertion into one of a number of bacterial plasmids or phages, which would subsequently be used to transform or infect, respectively, a suspension of bacterial cells.

Once a fragment of DNA has been cloned it can be manipulated to optimize its use as a probe or as a template for the expression of a protein antigen for which it might code. Although all of this technology is highly appropriate to various aspects of disease control, it would be a major task to introduce it all at a single stroke. However, just as with ELISA, it is possible to identify parts of the whole, each of which represents a technique in its own right for the identification of disease agents, and is a useful stage in the acquisition of the basic technology.

RESTRICTION ENDONUCLEASE MAPPING

The ability to characterize whole, or parts of, genomes through restriction enzyme mapping is an essential component of many molecular manipulations. It is also a method to identify, for epidemiological studies, individual isolates of infectious agents. For example, an outbreak of capripox in Bangladesh was linked with the disease in India, since the viruses isolated during the Bangladesh outbreak were very similar to Indian isolates on the basis of their restriction enzyme fragment profiles (Kitching, Hammond and Taylor, 1987). Capripoxvirus has a complex DNA genome some 146 kb in

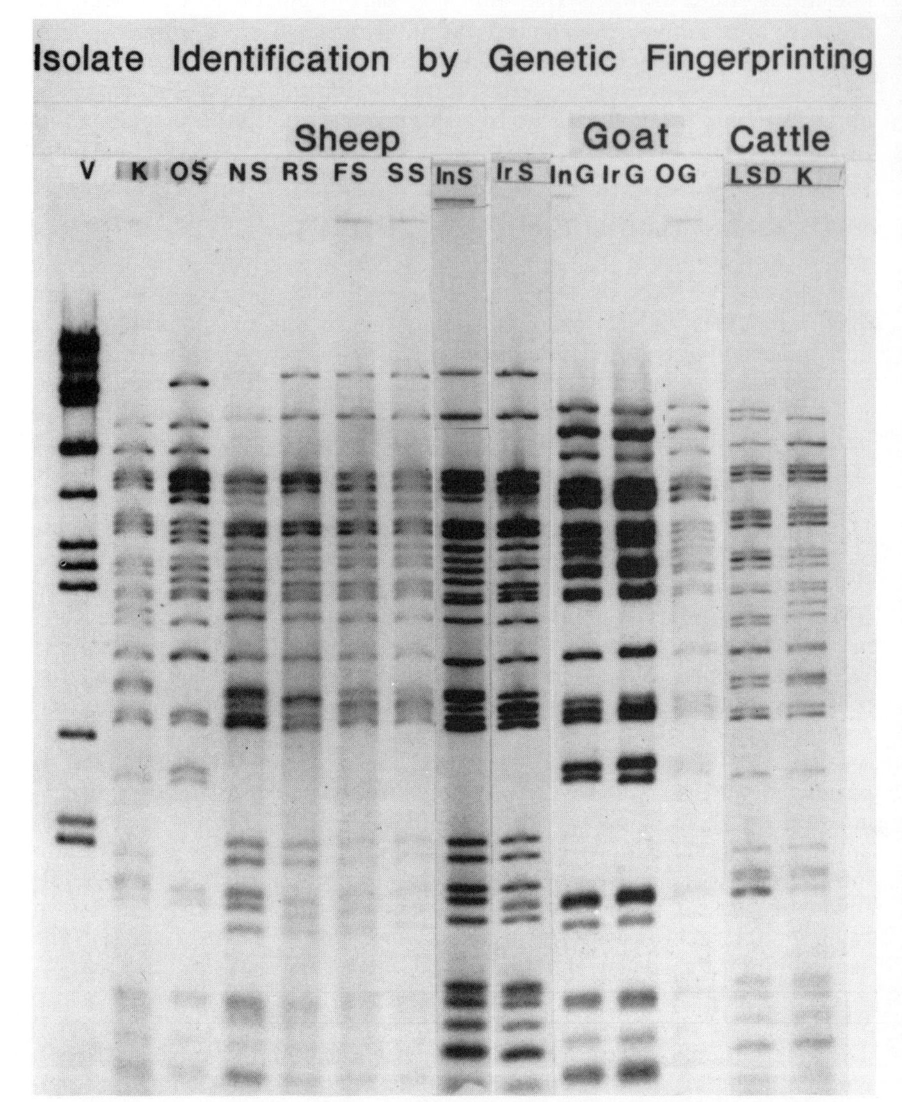

Fig. 6 *Agarose gel electrophoresis of DNA from several isolates of capripoxvirus which had been digested with HindIII restriction endonuclease. Notice the similarity of patterns of fragments of certain isolates, indicating their closer relatedness than to other isolates. (Kindly supplied by Dr D.N. Black).*

size. Digestion with restriction enzymes produces several fragments of different sizes, the distribution of which is characteristic for a particular isolate (Fig. 6). The same basic approach is being used to study the source of outbreaks of African Swine fever, caused by another virus with a large DNA genome, in Malawi and Zambia (Dixon and Wilkinson, 1988) and Cameroon (Wesley and Tuthill, 1984). Although these studies have been carried out in European laboratories, the techniques are relatively simple and do not require sophisticated equipment. In essence, all that is required is to (1) grow and purify virus, (2) purify DNA from the virus, (3) digest the DNA with restriction enzymes and (4) separate the DNA fragments by agarose gel electrophoresis and visualize the pattern of fragments.

NUCLEIC ACID HYBRIDIZATION

Nucleic acid hybridization is the process by which one single strand of nucleic acid can bind specifically to another single strand of nucleic acid through hydrogen bonding between complementary base pairs. If the sequences of bases on the two strands are sufficiently similar, enough bases will pair and stabilize the formation of a hybrid duplex. At this point hybridization can be said to have occurred. By altering the physical conditions (e.g. temperature, salt concentration) under which hybridization is allowed to take place, the requirement for a stable match of sequence can be made more or less stringent, allowing the investigator to determine the level of specificity of hybridization. This can be important for diagnosis if the detection of closely related, but nonidentical, infectious agents is being sought with a single probe, or, conversely, if one is trying to differentiate between two closely related infectious agents. Hybridization is a powerful diagnostic tool since it is possible to probe very low levels of infectious agents in tissues, without having to grow and purify the infectious agent.

As with restriction enzyme mapping, the methods are not complex, and should be able to be used in laboratories in developing countries. In brief outline, nucleic acid is prepared from a tissue, which is suspected of being infected, bound to a membrane support and incubated with a labelled nucleic acid probe. If the offending agent is present, hybridization will take place and label will be retained for detection by an appropriate means.

This basic technology can be used for a wide range of epidemiological and diagnostic purposes important to disease control in developing countries. One recent example of the application of probe hybridization is the ability to distinguish between rinderpest and peste des petits ruminants viruses in infected tissues on the basis of the noncross hybridization under stringent conditions of probes made from their N-genes (Fig. 7; Diallo, Barrett, Barbron, Shaila and Taylor, 1989). This property was used to show that the origin of a recent outbreak of rinderpest in cattle in Sri Lanka may have been caused by goats imported from India, in which the disease may have been subclinical (Hassan, Anderson, Barrett and Anderson, 1989). The use of a probe for detecting persistence of A, O and C serogroups of FMDV in bovine

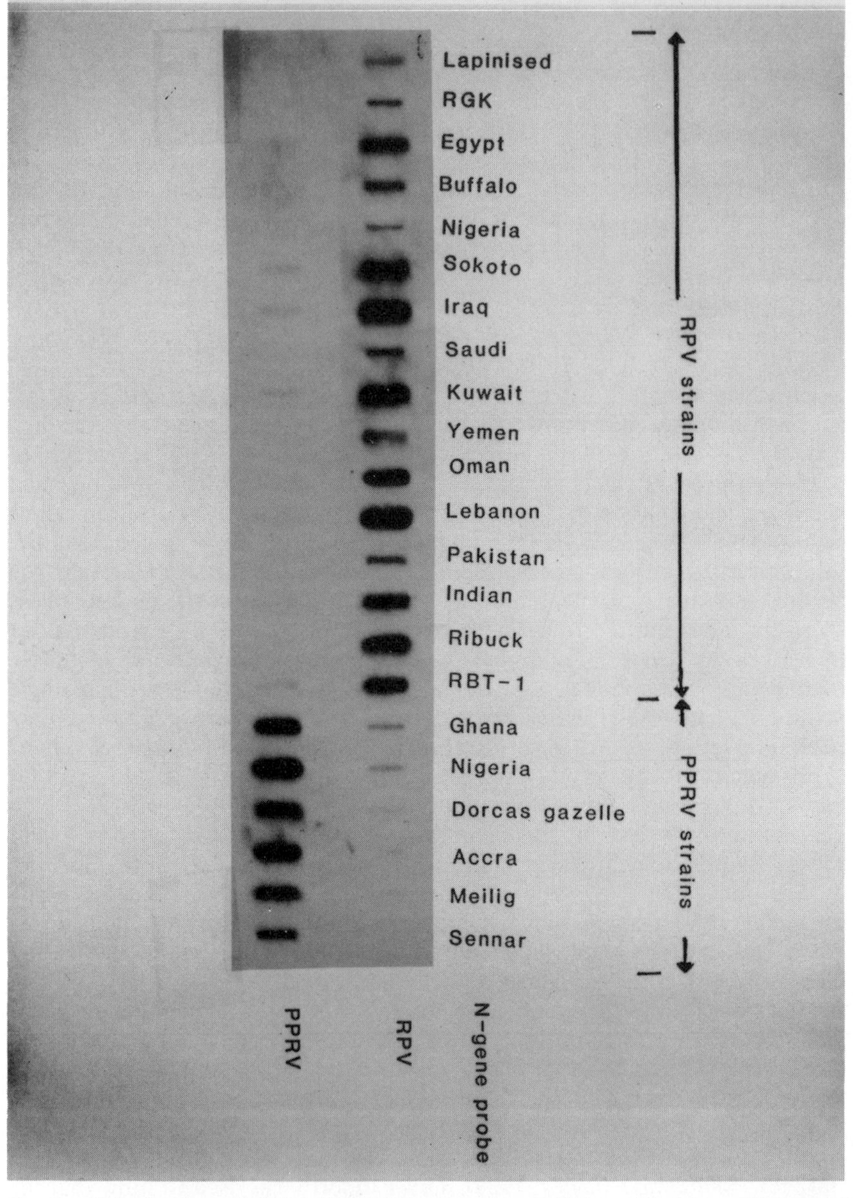

Fig. 7 *Hybridization of RPV and PPRV N-gene probes to RNAs purified from cells infected with a range of RPV or PPRV isolates. Notice that, under the stringent hybridization conditions used, the RPV N-gene probe only hybridizes to RPV strains, whereas the PPRV N-gene probe only hybridizes to the PPRV strains, thus forming the basis for a test to distinguish between the two viruses. (Kindly supplied by Dr T. Barrett).*

oesophageal-pharyngeal fluids after infectious virus could no longer be isolated has also been described (Rossi, Sadir, Schudel and Palma, 1988).

A further development of the hybridization technology, which greatly increases its sensitivity and, potentially, its ease of use, is the so-called 'polymerase chain reaction' or PCR (Ou, Kwok, Mitchell, Mack, Sninski, Krebs, Feorino, Warfield and Schochetman, 1988; Saiki, Scharf, Faloona, Mullis, Horn, Erlich and Arnhein, 1985). This method uses the specificity of hybridization of two short synthetic oligonucleotide primers, each of which defines one end of a segment of nucleic acid sequence which is characteristic of the infectious agent to be identified. By repeated cycles of denaturation,

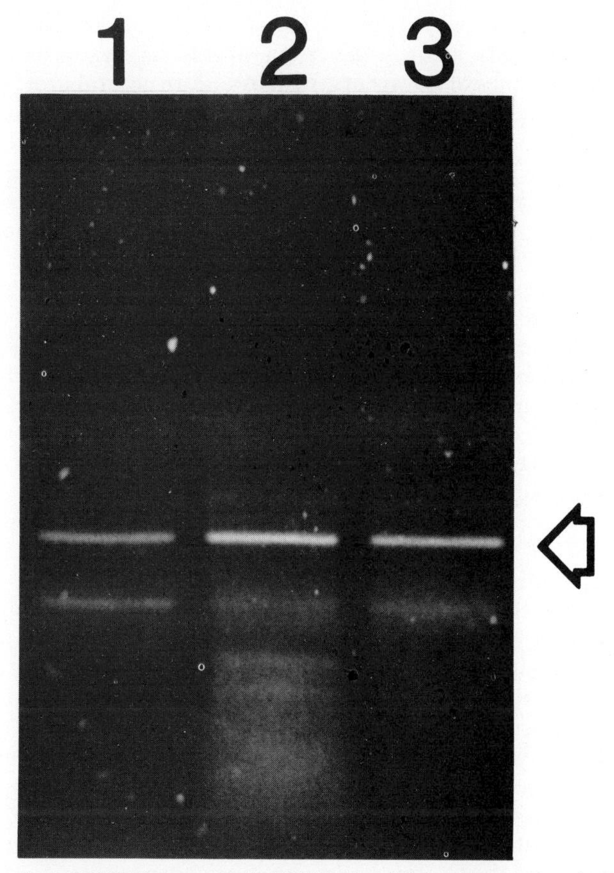

Fig. 8 *Identification of FMDV sequences in RNA isolated from tissues taken from guinea-pigs experimentally infected with FMDV O_1 Kaufbeuren. RNA was isolated from tonsils (track 2) and ventral soft palate (track 3). In track 1 is pMR11, which is a cDNA plasmid control containing the major portion of the coding sequence of O_1K. The oligonucleotide primers defined a segment of 230 bases with the VP1 region and it is a band of this size (arrowed) which is visible in the gel. (Kindly supplied by M. Hofner).*

annealing and chain elongation using a heat-stable DNA polymerase, the chosen segment of DNA (if present in the nucleic acid being probed) is amplified so that it is directly visible on an agrose gel (Fig. 8). This technology requires prior knowledge of the nucleotide sequence of the portion of the genome to be used for diagnostic purposes, in order to synthesize the specific primers, and the facility to make synthetic oligonucleotides. Apart from this it is an inherently simple and quick method, has many potential applications in the field of diagnosis and should be transferrable to laboratories in developing countries.

NUCLEOTIDE SEQUENCE ANALYSIS

In their different ways the ELISAs, restriction enzyme mapping and hybridization tests identify infectious agents on the basis of information carried in the genes of the agents; ELISAs via structural proteins specified by the gene sequences and the latter two through the sequence of bases recognized by restriction enzymes or reacting single strands of nucleic acid. The ultimate test for genetic identity is to compare the sequence of genomes of infectious agents, and this is now becoming a reality for the accurate identification of strains of FMDV. Although the original methods of sequencing used DNA as the starting material (Maxam and Gilbert, 1977; Sanger, Nicklen, Coulson, 1977) and required cloned DNA templates, they were modified for the direct sequencing of RNA by the use of reverse transcriptase (e.g. Zimmern and Kaesberg, 1978). This avoided the necessity to clone an intermediate DNA copy of the RNA molecule and therefore made it possible to apply the technology to RNA isolated from infected cells. As with the PCR, some prior knowledge of the sequence is required in this method of direct RNA sequencing as a specific initiating oligonucleotide primer for the reverse transcriptase must be synthesized.

Apart from numerous studies aimed at establishing the genetic determinants of FMDV serotypes and subtypes and the regions of the capsid proteins involved in antigenicity, nucleotide sequencing of FMDV has been applied to epidemiological studies to establish the origins of outbreaks. For example, Beck and Strohmaier (1987) showed that many recent outbreaks of FMD serotypes A and O in western Europe were probably the result of incompletely inactivated vaccines or escapes from laboratories. A more recent study (Knowles, Marquar and Samuel, 1988) showed that isolates from outbreaks of FMD serotype O in the Federal Republic of Germany during 1987 and 1988 were closely related to the vaccine virus strain. Thus sequencing of informative regions of the genome is a useful tool in the precise identification of infectious agents and is one which could be introduced into suitably equipped and supported laboratories in developing countries.

RECOMBINANT VACCINES

Restriction mapping, sequencing and hybridization are analytical tools and, although they play a necessary part in the molecular characterization of genetic material, they do not in themselves mediate the step into the powerful technologies of gene cloning and manipulation. However, acquisition of skills in these techniques would provide a useful base from which to approach genetic engineering. In the area of animal health, most of the immediate applications of gene cloning will be in the development of tailor-made probes and genetically engineered vaccines. The use of cloned probes for diagnosis has been discussed above, and in this last section there will be a brief consideration of the potential of recombinant vaccines using rinderpest as the example.

The current rinderpest vaccine (Scott, this volume) is based on a tissue culture attenuated isolate and, although it is extremely effective in giving lifelong immunity after a single vaccination, it can be rapidly inactivated by warmth so that effective vaccination requires a good cold chain. Therefore, increased thermostability would result in a significant improvement in the effectiveness of the vaccine in large campaigns. One way of achieving this would be to engineer a recombinant poxvirus (poxviruses are relatively resistant to inactivation by heat) to carry and express the genes coding for rinderpest virus protein which elicits protective immune responses (Lecocq, this volume).

The major surface glycoproteins of rinderpest virus are the haemagglutinin (HA) and fusion (F) proteins, and recombinant vaccinia viruses expressing these proteins have been made and shown in experimental tests to protect cattle against lethal challenge with rinderpest virus (Yilma, Hsu, Jones, Owen, Grubman, Mebus, Yamanaka and Dale, 1988; Barrett, Belsham, Subbarao and Evans, 1989; Belsham, Anderson, Murray, Anderson and Barrett, 1989).

Vaccinia virus has proved to be extremely useful in establishing the principle of recombinant vaccines based on poxviruses, but some people would argue against the widespread use of vaccinia virus recombinants, at least for agricultural use (even though for the WR strain of vaccinia virus the resultant vaccines are similarly attenuated to those strains used for human vaccination). If this view prevails, it will not be necessary to abandon the notion of recombinant poxvirus-based vaccines, for there are alternative vector systems which either cannot replicate in humans (e.g. avipoxvirus) or which are specific to species of farm livestock. One such potential poxvirus vector system of particular relevance to developing countries is capripoxvirus, which causes pox disease in sheep and goats and lumpy skin disease in cattle.

An attentuated Kenyan isolate of capripoxvirus was first used as a live vaccine (Davies and Mbugwa, 1985) and this was further developed to produce a single vaccine currently in use against both sheep and goat pox (Kitching *et al*, 1987). Thus if this accepted vaccine virus could be engineered to express one or more additional 'foreign' genes coding for immunologically protective proteins of other disease agents, a multivalent live virus vaccine could be developed. Such a recombinant vaccine would have several potential advantages over conventional vaccines. It would be genetically and environmentally stable, being unable to revert to virulent forms of the nonpoxvirus components and retaining the thermal stability characteristic of poxviruses. In its simplest form it would be a divalent vaccine, immunizing by a single 'shot' against capripoxvirus disease as well as the disease caused by the agent which was the source of the foreign gene. There is also no reason why two or more foreign genes could not be recombined into the capripoxvirus genome, giving it the potential to be a multivalent vaccine. Finally, marker genes could be incorporated in the vaccine allowing the easy distinction between vaccinated animals and those naturally infected in the wild. The ability to make this distinction is important in any disease control programme, but especially so in the later stages of eradication programmes. Work to realize some of these aims has been carried out at IAH, Pirbright Laboratory, and has been reviewed elsewhere (Bostock, 1990).

The potential benefits to be gained from recombinant poxvirus-based vaccines are such as to make this a highly appropriate, if difficult to achieve, biotechnology for developing countries. The poxvirus vector is only one half of the story, since to make a recombinant vaccine requires DNA clones of genes known to code for antigenically active proteins of disease agents. Achievements of the overall goal will require the assembly of a wide range of biotechnological expertise, but it is something to which all of the methodologies described before would contribute and something worth aiming for.

ACKNOWLEDGEMENTS

I would like to thank Dr. John Anderson for helpful discussions in the course of writing this article and Rosanna Day for typing the manuscript.

REFERENCES

Anderson, J. (1984). Use of a monoclonal antibody in a blocking ELISA to detect group specific antibodies to bluetongue virus. *Journal of Immunology and Methodology,* **74**, 139–149.

Anderson, J. and Rowe, L.W. (1983). The use of an enzyme-linked assay as an aid to reading micro virus-neutralization tests. *Journal of Immunology and Methodology,* **53**, 183–186.

Anderson, J., Rowe, L.W., Taylor, W.P. and Crowther, J.R. (1982). An enzyme-linked immunosorbent assay for the detection of IgG, IgA and IgM antibodies to rinderpest virus in experimentally infected cattle. *Research in Veterinary Science,* **32**, 242–257.

Anderson, J., Anderson, E.C., Chidno, F., Joshua, G.E., Mpelumbe, I.E. and Kavishe, T.E. (1989). Further evaluation of the indirect ELISA for the detection of antibodies to rinderpest virus and its suitability for sero-monitoring and management of rinderpest vaccination campaigns. *Tropical Animal Health and Production.* Submitted.

Bansall, P.P., Joshi, R.C., Chandra, U. and Sharma, B. (1988). Detection of rinderpest antigen by latex agglutination test. *Acta Virologie,* **32**, 275–277.

Barrett, T., Belsham, G.J., Subbarao, S.M. and Evans, S.A. (1989). Immunization with a vaccinia recombinant expressing the F protein protects rabbits from challenge with a lethal dose of rinderpest virus. *Virology,* **170**, 11–18.

Beck, E. and Strohmaier, K. (1987). Subtyping of European foot-and-mouth disease virus strains by nucleotide sequence determination. *Journal of Virology,* **61**, 1621–1629.

Belsham, G.J., Anderson, E.C., Murray, P.K., Anderson, J. and Barrett, T. (1989). The immune response and protection of cattle and pigs generated by a vaccinia virus recombinant expressing the F protein of rinderpest virus. *Veterinary Record,* **124**, 655–658.

Bostock, C.J. (1990). Viruses as Vectors. *Proceedings of the 1st Congress of the European Society of Veterinary Virology, Liege. Veterinary Microbiology*, **23**, 55–71.

Crowther, J.R. and Abu Elzein, E.M.E. (1979). Application of the enzyme-linked immunorsorbent assay to the detection and identification of foot-and-mouth disease viruses. *Journal of Hygiene, Cambridge,* **83**, 513–519.

Crowther, J.R. and Samuel, A.R. (1987). Monoclonal antibodies and foot-and-mouth disease. *Rept. Session Research Group Stand. Technical Comm. Control FMD FAO*, Lyons, 1987, 88–102.

Davies, F.G. and Mbugwa, G. (1985). The alterations in pathogenicity and immunogenicity of a Kenya sheep and goat pox virus on serial passage in bovine foetal muscle cell cultures. *Journal of Comparative Pathology,* **96**, 565–572.

Diallo, A., Barrett, T., Barbron, M., Shaila, M.S. and Taylor, W.P. (1989). Differentiation of rinderpest and peste des petits ruminants viruses using specific cDNA clones. *Journal of Virology Methods,* **23**, 127–136.

Dixon, L.K. and Wilkinson, P.J. (1988). Genetic diversity of African swine fever isolates from soft ticks (*Ornithodorus moubata*) inhabiting warthog burrows in Zambia. *Journal of General Virology,* **69**, 2891–2993.

Doel, T.R. (1991). Prospects for novel vaccines against foot-and-mouth disease. In *The Application of Biotechnology in Developing Countries* (ed. A.G. Hunter), pp. 322–333. Centre for Tropical Veterinary Medicine, University of Edinburgh.

Engvall, E. and Perlmann, P. (1971a). Enzyme-linked immunosorbent assay (ELISA). Quantitative assay of immunoglobulin G. *Immunochemistry,* **8**, 871–874.

Engvall, E. and Perlmann (1971b). Enzyme-linked immunosorbent assay. ELISA III. Quantitation of specific antibodies by enzyme-labelled anti-immunoglobulin in antigen coated tubes. *Journal of Immunology,* **109**, 129–135.

Gershon, P.D. and Black, D.N. (1988). A comparison of the genomes of capripox virus isolates of sheep, goats and cattle. *Virology,* **164**, 341–349.

Hamblin, C., Barnett, I.T.R. and Hedger, R.S. (1986). A new enzyme-linked immunosorbent assay (ELISA) for the detection of antibodies against foot-and-mouth disease virus. I. Development and method of ELISA. *Journal of Immunology Methods,* **93**, 115–121.

Hassan, A., Anderson, E.C., Barrett, T. and Anderson, J. (1990). Observations on the pathogenicity and transmissibility for sheep and goats of virus isolated during the rinderpest outbreak in Sri Lanka in 1987. *Archiv für Zoologie*. Submitted.

Jeggo, M.H., Richards, J.I. and Dargie, J.D. (1991). The use of immunoassay diagnostic kits in developing countries. In *The Application of Biotechnology in Developing Countries* (ed. A.G. Hunter), pp. 286–303. Centre for Tropical Veterinary Medicine, University of Edinburgh.

Kitching, R.P., Hammond, J.M. and Taylor, W.P. (1987). A single vaccination for the control of capripox infection in sheep and goats. *Research in Veterinary Science,* **42**, 53–60.

Kitching, R.P., McGrane, J.J., Hammond, J.M., Miah, A.H., Mustafa, A.H.M. and Majumder, J.R. (1987). Capripox in Bangladesh. *Tropical Animal Health and Production,* **19**, 203–208.

Knowles, N.J., Marquardt, O. and Samuel, A.R. (1988). Antigenic and molecular characterization of virus isolates from recent outbreaks of foot-and-mouth disease in the Federal Republic of Germany. *Session of the Research Group of the Standing Technical Committee of the European Commission for the Control of Foot-and-Mouth Disease,* Prague, Czechoslovakia, 20–23 September, 1988.

Lecocq, J.P. (1991). Genetically engineered vaccines against rabies and parasites. In *The Application of Biotechnology in Developing Countries* (ed. A.G. Hunter), pp. 334–335. Centre for Tropical Veterinary Medicine, University of Edinburgh.

Mahy, B.W.J., Knowles, N.J. and Pedley, S. (1989). Biotechnology in animal disease diagnosis in developing countries: new types of diagnostic methods. *FAO Expert Consultation on the Application of Biotechnology in Livestock Production and Health in Developing Countries,* Havana.

Maxam, A.M. and Gilbert, W. (1977). A new method for sequencing DNA. *Proceedings of the National Academy of Science, U.S.A.,* **74**, 560–564.

Ou, C.Y., Kwok, S., Mitchell, S.W., Mack, D.H., Sninski, J.J., Krebs, J.W., Feorino, P., Warfield, D. and Schochetman, G. (1988). DNA amplification for direct detection of HIV-1 in DNA of peripheral blood mononuclear cells. *Science,* **239**, 295–297.

Rossi, M.S., Sadir, A.M., Schudel, A.A. and Palma, E.L. (1988). Detection of foot-and-mouth disease virus with DNA probes in bovine esophageal-pharyngeal fluids. *Archiv für Virologie,* **99**, 67–74.

Saiki, R.K., Scharf, S., Faloona, F., Mullis, K.B., Horn, G.T., Erlich, H.A. and Arnheim, N. (1985). Enzymatic amplification of B-globin genomic sequences and restriction site analysis for diagnosis of sickle cell anaemia. *Science,* **230**, 1350–1354.

Sanger, F., Nicklen, S. and Coulson, A.R. (1977). DNA sequencing with chain-terminating inhibitors. *Proceedings of the National Academy of Science, U.S.A.,* **74**, 5463–5467.

Scott, G.R. (1991). Vaccination against rinderpest – success and failure. In *The Application of Biotechnology in Developing Countries* (ed. A.G. Hunter), pp. 341–357. Centre for Tropical Veterinary Medicine, University of Edinburgh.

Villinger, F., Mueller, H.K., Brucknts, L., Ackermann, M. and Kihm, U. (1989). Antibodies to foot-and-mouth disease virus infection associated (VIA) antigen: use of a bioengineered VIA protein as antigen in an ELISA. *Veterinary Microbiology,* **20**, 235–246.

Voller, A., Bidwell, A.E. and Bartlett, A. (1977). The enzyme-linked immunosorbent assay (ELISA). A review with a bibliography of microplate applications. *Guernsey, Flowline Publications,* pp. 48.

Wamwayi, H.M., Wafula, J.S., Litamoi, J.K. and Nandokha, E.N. (1989). Detection of antibody to mycomplasma F38 in goat sera by an enzyme-linked immunosorbent assay. *Tropical Animal Health and Production,* **21**, 43–49.

Wesley, R.D. and Tuthill, A.E. (1984). Genome relatedness among African swine fever virus field isolates by restriction endonuclease analysis. *Preventive Veterinary Medicine,* **2**, 53–62.

Yilma, T., Hsu, D., Jones, L., Owen, S., Grubman, M., Mebus, G., Yamanaka, M. and Dale, B. (1988). Protection of cattle against rinderpest with vaccinia virus recombinants expressing the HA or F gene. *Science,* **242**, 1058–1061.

Zimmern, D. and Kaesberg, P. (1978). 3'-terminal nucleotide sequence of encephalomyocarditis virus RNA determined by reverse transcriptase and chain-terminating inhibitors. *Proceedings of the National Academy of Science, U.S.A.,***75**, 4267–4261.

6.6

The Commercial Approach to the Use of Biotechnology in the Developing Countries

J. MEADLEY
Rural Investment Overseas Limited, London, U.K.

INTRODUCTION

This talk is addressed primarily to scientists wanting to understand the realities of commerce rather than to those already involved in the commercial sector.

The current, and sometimes glamorous, interest in biotechnology may obscure the fact that biotechnology has a long and respectable tradition in agriculture – brewing, composting, yoghurt and cheesemaking for example – and with the emphasis on high technology we are in danger of forgetting the use of these simpler natural processes. My talk, which is based on my own experience of applying biotechnologies in the developing countries, will lead us to the conclusion that, as a result of market difficulties and inadequate infrastructure in the developing countries, attention should be focused on the simpler types of biotechnologies.

Defining biotechnology as 'the application of scientific and engineering principles to the processing of materials by biological agents to provide goods and services' then our consideration of the commercial approach must concentrate on the production of, and market for, these goods and services. This being the case, a number of commercial questions arise; who will buy the product or services? what is the scale of the demand? can they pay for it? what products are being replaced? can the development costs be recouped? can the intellectual property be controlled? what product liability might be encountered? who is capable of marketing and servicing the product? Let me enlarge on some of these questions to explain the peculiar nature of the market in the developing countries and I must apologize for the fact that, being an agronomist, most of my examples are from the crop rather than the livestock sector – but the principles are the same.

The agricultural sector is by definition, the rural sector. Around 70% of the world's population live in the poorer countries and 70% of them live in the rural areas. These people are generally highly dispersed in small communities, making difficult the establishment of infrastructure. Although most of these people depend upon agriculture for their livelihood, it is likely that only a minority of them would choose farming for a living, given a choice. The market is therefore generally fragmented and, in addition, in many developing countries, there is political uncertainty; companies may have been nationalized; the ground rules for investment barely exist; there is often inadequate infrastructure on which to build a commercial investment; internal pricing policies and the controls of foreign exchange are often restrictive; the currency may be continually devalued. There are, therefore, many risks.

Medicine is the other main area of activity in biotechnology but the medical 'market' has a number of quite different characteristics – for people will pay almost anything for good health; medical products tend to be of low bulk and high value; the human body is basically constant throughout the world; and there is already in place an extensive network of sales outlets through doctors and hospitals. In contrast, agriculture is a low priority activity; its products tend to be bulky and of low value; the sum of the potential combinations of crop and livestock species, soil and climatic conditions and styles of management run into millions – and the market is proportionately difficult to develop.

From a commercial viewpoint therefore, agriculture is of much lower priority than medicine, and interest in developing products for the developing world is a fraction of the interest in the markets of Europe and U.S.A. This is borne out by a recent study done for the World Resources Institute which demonstrated a continuing declining interest by the U.S. biotechnology companies in the developing world. In my early days of involvement in biotechnology, I was surprised to learn that the big agrochemical companies focus their research activity on the major crops such as wheat, maize, soyabean, cotton and rice. Any spin-off in terms of product application to minor crops such as cowpeas or sweet potatoes is considered fortuitous – it is not planned. I can now understand their logic. The markets of the developing world are too small, fragmented and economically weak to justify individual product research and development.

Questions to be asked

In looking commercially at a market in a developing country the following questions have to be asked:

- Who will buy the product? Identify the key people and/or institutes.
- What is the scale of the demand? This is important, because a minimum

level of sales is needed to justify investment in storage and servicing facilities.

- What is the shelf-life of the product and is any specialist infrastructure (cold storage, refrigerated vans etc.) needed?
- What is the effective demand? i.e. – who can actually pay for the products?
- Is foreign exchange available to pay for the products?
- What products currently in use are being replaced? This is important because local farmers do not have access to an independent press to evaluate these products. For example, the use of *Azolla* to reduce the use of artificial nitrogen for rice production has often been limited by unscrupulous salesmen telling farmers that it is harmful to the crops. People do not like to see competition in their markets.
- Can the costs of both product and market development be recouped from this market? In most cases, sales to the lesser developed countries (LDC) markets are seen as a sideline rather than a main focus.
- What product liability might be incurred?
- What local registration is needed in terms of import licences, customs regulations and phytosanitary certificates and what taxes or duties may be imposed?
- Who will market or service the product and in what language? Will they need training?
- What is the reliability of the local infrastructure – roads, rail, air, electricity supply, telecommunications etc.
- Will your product be copied? – important, particularly with the simpler products and technologies.

This is a fairly onerous list – but a practical one nonetheless and one which will immediately eliminate many LDC markets unless there are some particular and exceptional circumstances.

Issues to be faced

Let me now give some examples of the issues which have to be faced and then suggest some general principles which may allow some development in these markets.

Monoclonal antibodies In one Asian country I looked at the possibility of commercially developing a monoclonal antibody for identifying the presence of a virus in Citrus spp. I arranged for the isolate to be tested by a leading international company but found that, although the disease is a major problem locally, the overall world market is too small to justify the commercial development of the product and the anticipated retail price of the product was too high in relation to the potential value of the crop.

Coconut tissue culture The possibility of a cooperative agreement to perfect tissue culture in coconuts in the Philippines – involving European and local interests – both public and private – has also been considered. However, the fact that it would take at least five years to bring it to a point of commercial exploitation; and that the use of aid funds could prevent such commercial exploitation; combined with the political sensitivity of the crop in the Philippines meant that the potential commercial partners were unwilling to take the risk.

Fuel from agricultural products Most high carbohydrate/energy biological products can be converted into fuel – such as molasses into ethanol. However, engines usually have to be modified to use such a fuel; and the product is generally more expensive than oil. To encourage the use of such fuels government have to provide subsidies.

An object lesson can be learnt from the potential use of sunflower oil as a fuel. The oil can be extracted from the sunflower seeds on the farm and, after filtering and addition of a simple additive, be used to power tractors. One hectare of sunflower produces enough fuel for 20 hectares of cultivation. However, in one African country the development of the product was stopped because the Inland Revenue feared that they would be unable to tax such a fuel developed on the farm. The development of such 'biotechnology/biomass' fuels becomes a political rather than a commercial decision.

Other products such as rice and wheat straw are often proposed as suitable raw materials for fuel. In practice, the costs of collection and transport negate any other potential advantage.

The oil palm weevil This weevil, which increases the level of pollination in oil palm, was introduced from Cameroon into Malaysia where pollination was still encouraged manually. There was an immediate and significant increase in yield – but as this additional product was marketed there was a parallel fall in world market prices. Maybe the weevil is not to blame but the apparent beneficial transfer of an insect from Africa to Asia subsequently appeared to cause a decline in palm oil prices received by African countries. There are some parallels here in the application of bovine somatotrophin (bST).

Commercialization of locally developed biotechnologies In the Philippines also I have looked at the commercialization of biotechnologies developed in local scientific institutes to market into Europe and the U.S. The costs of market development and product liability protection proved to be far larger than the financial resources available.

CONCLUSIONS

In the LDCs there are many situations where technology could be applied given the right circumstances. However the circumstances are rarely right and there is frequently a lack of incentives, infrastructure and foreign exchange compounded by the generally low priority given to agriculture. Remember:

- Introducing biotechnology implies change – is the cost of such change justified by the potential buyer? Few people like fundamental change and apparently sensible biological arguments can be invalidated by commercial realities. Does the new product imply any change to the farming system; does it fit in with existing practices; will it affect the market value of the finished product.
- There are many fundamental questions to be answered – listed above. Can these be answered satisfactorily?
- The local people always know the local situation better than you do. Before taking any steps, have extensive discussions with appropriate local people in the government and commercial sector. In addition to all the issues raised above, you may be unwittingly stepping on someone's toes.
- Biotechnology products are often only of economic benefit if all other components in the production chain, such as health, housing, nutrition etc., are of the right standard. For this reason there is often a great deal that can be done to improve productivity through basic good farm practice and the application of existing research results before introducing any biotechnology products or processes.
- It is essential to focus your activities on a limited number of products or technologies and a limited number of markets.
- In a number of countries the local universities have done some useful research in the field of agricultural biotechnology. Regrettably, experience shows that such research is rarely adequately advanced for commercialization and it is likely that soft funding will be needed to bring them to the point of commercialization.

There is scope for the commercial application of biotechnologies in developing countries. The fragmented nature of the markets, their small size and purchasing power and the lack of infrastructure severely limit such applications and the less sophisticated forms of biotechnology and related products, which do not require sophisticated facilities for their storage and handling, are more likely to be relevant. In tackling these markets you are more likely to be successful if you start from trying to meet a need in the agricultural sector rather than simply trying to sell a product.

DISCUSSION SESSION SIX

FIVAZ, R. SOUTH AFRICA *Have you compared fixed time insemination with insemination at observed heat in Zebu cows?*

GALINA Yes, when we compare fixed time insemination with conventional AI at observed oestrus in cows slaughtered four days after breeding, we noticed that more fertilized eggs were recovered from the oviduct of cows previously detected in oestrus.

TERBLANCHE, R. SOUTH AFRICA *Have you used only prostaglandin for oestrous synchronization?*

GALINA We have also experimented with the use of progestagens and results are rather similar with respect to fertility, although the percentage of animals detected in oestrus is higher following progestagen treatment.

SUDI, TANZANIA *Dr. Chigaru's presentation gave the impression that nothing is happening in Africa as far as biotechnology is concerned but this is not the case, e.g. embryo transfer work is being carried out in Kenya and Zimbabwe; in Tanzania there is a biogas production experiment and a biotechnology unit at the University of Dar-es-Salaam?*

CHIGARU In my oral presentation I deliberately omitted some information as I wanted to emphasize constraints. My paper contains more information on developments in biotechnology in some African countries.

ADEBAMBO *Constraints to the improvement of animal production in Africa could be overcome by biotechnology where animal, human and material resources are available. What is needed is the training and application of biotechnology on a wide scale?*

CHIGARU I agree with your comment that training of African scientists in aspects of biotechnology is one of the major needs. However, this would have to be carried out in developed country institutes because there are few institutes in Africa which can do this.

MASAKE, KENYA *How is the embryo transfer programme operated in India? Are both buffaloes and cattle included?*

SINGH We have centres for superovulating and flushing pedigree cows and buffaloes. Flushed ova are cryopreserved and taken to the field or stations where sufficient animals are available. These animals are synchronized in groups and embryos transferred. Both surgical and nonsurgical transfers are made, the latter being preferred. Presently there are five main centres and three field subcentres for the programme. Many more centres for embryo transfer are in the process of establishment where the exercise will be taken up under field conditions.

RASTOGI, TRINIDAD *Could you comment on the use of urea molasses block (UMB) bypass feed in India?*

SINGH UMB feed supplement is a cheap source of nitrogen, minerals and energy for rumen microbes. It enhances rumen fermentation rate when the ruminants are solely fed on straws. Dietary proteins which bypass the rumen intact are called bypass proteins and are utilized more efficiently in the lower part of the gastrointestinal tract by enzymatic action. A bypass protein should contain 30% crude protein out of which 65% should be rumen undegradable. In India large-scale production of UMB and bypass protein is underway for feeding of dairy animals.

ASSELBERGS, MOZAMBIQUE *I noticed that the FAO network presented a priority list for biotechnology application as being ET, nutrition, ELISAs, and genetics. The priority list for Indonesia, however, started with health and ET was last?*

LIM The priorities presented refer to the technical recommendations collectively identified at the Regional Biotechnology Workshop held in Bangkok in 1988. These are of equal importance irrespective of the order they were listed in the presentation.

When it comes to the implementation of the technical cooperation under the Network, however, only some of the biotechnology priority topics could be managed at any one time and member countries of the Network could then decide on the relevance of the selected topics towards their needs so that suitable scientists could be nominated to participate in or contribute towards the programme for mutual benefits.

HUNTER, U.K. *Would Mr. Lim comment on the apparent priority on ruminant research in terms of biotechnology in South East Asia, when pigs and poultry appear to be more important in that area?*

LIM The priority of biotechnology research is directed more towards the ruminant sector than the dominant poultry and pig sectors because in all the SEA countries, the problems and constraints of livestock production are greatest in this sector. To date, none of these countries is self-sufficient in its national requirement for beef and/or dairy products and this has resulted in costly annual imports of much concern. Production of poultry and to some extent pigs on the other hand has attained self-sufficiency in most countries in the region with surplus for export in some instances. Thus in these aspects, the priority for biotechnology research is directed more towards ruminants but not neglecting poultry and pigs altogether. In animal health, biotechnology research into improved vaccines and diagnostic tests apply to all livestock.

WANAPAT, THAILAND *I feel the change towards more intensive ruminant production, particularly for cattle, in South East Asia, could explain the emphasis on ruminant production in the FAO Biotechnology Network.*

LIM I think the primary concern of most countries in SEA in beef and dairy cattle production is to minimize costly importations and satisfy domestic demands. At present it is not known if the traditional backyard (low budget) type of livestock production system or the intensive high budget type of production or both would be the solution towards self-sufficiency in dairy and beef cattle in the region. The issue however remains in that the R&D priorities in biotechnology are still focused more on the ruminant sector.

TEALE, KENYA *Gene mapping was mentioned as a component of the FAO S.E. Asian biotechnology network. Is it to target genes or traits?*

LIM I am unable to specify target genes/traits except to mention only general topics or headings that were discussed at the FAO Regional Biotechnology Workshop of October 1988. Among the technical recommendations made were the organization of training courses and R&D activities and the running of pilot application projects on various biotechnology topics identified at the workshop. Those relating to gene mapping and related technologies are as follows:–

- *Genetic engineering applied to farm animals*
  Mapping of mammalian genome is to be pursued with the aim of creating a genome library for future application such as selection of economically important traits in breeding programmes.
- *Improvement of diagnostic capabilities*
  Restriction endonuclear mapping, nucleic acid probes and sequence analysis are recommended for development as rapid diagnostic aids. Training courses on genome analysis are recommended for the SEA region.
- *Improved vaccines*
  Among the topics selected are:–

  (a) Molecular characterization and cloning of genes encoding protective immunogens of pathogens.

  (b) Application of expression systems for these genes. Biotechnology activities in these selected topics are to be carried out through various means, including the linkages that are being established between institutes in Asian countries and the FAO network of collaborating centres under the provisions of the technical cooperation programme with funding from FAO and other donor agencies like UNDP.

Perhaps the target genes in question would be specified at the later implementation stage of the programme.

NANA-NUKECHAP, CAMEROON *Will the developing countries not be obliged to take up the sophisticated forms of biotechnology just because the developed countries cease to supply the reagents for simpler forms of technology?*

SMITH This possibility exists in the same way as they have had to adopt sophisticated tractors because less sophisticated ones are no longer made in the west. However if there is a demand and a means of financing this demand the supplies of reagents will continue.

TEALE, KENYA *We have been discussing biotechnology development on the one hand, and transfer and use on the other. I would like to ask the panel's view on the danger of developing countries becoming over-involved in basic research in biotechnology development rather than in use and proper application of existing knowledge and techniques.*

LIM The trend of biotechnology development in SEA countries is towards transfer of foreign technologies rather than re-inventing proven or established ones. Such a trend is evident from some of the existing national strategies and policies in the region that encourage and provide incentives to attract foreign bioindustrial investments and technology transfers. However, depending on the type of technology involved, there may be a need for developing countries to acquire some degree of competence beforehand in order to fully understand and master the principles and techniques of the transferred technologies involved. Transfer of foreign technology to developing countries on the other hand should proceed with much caution. Considerations should be given to the socioeconomic farming systems of developing countries, their cultural and religious background, financial constraints, the indigenous breeds and feed and other resources which could influence acceptance and the success or failure of technology transfer, whether technically or economically.

SMITH I believe there is a danger that biotechnological solutions will be seen as panaceas for intractable problems which would be better tackled in other ways.

GALINA Scientists in the developing world should spend more time designing strategies to apply existing technology under their local conditions. Research on new, expensive biotechnology should be avoided. There is plenty to do in developing countries with local facilities already available, if the researcher could only spend the time, energy and dedication to his task.

CHIGARU What we need in most African countries is applied or adaptive research using some of the technologies already developed elsewhere. Basic research is a luxury most countries cannot afford.

BENAVIDES, COLOMBIA *Would the panel comment on the importance of cultural, economical and political constraints to biotechnology in developing countries. For example yesterday we learned that a malaria vaccine is being produced in Colombia but the scientific community of the developed world has doubts about the validity of the results and I wonder if it would have the same doubts if the work had been done in a developed country. Dr. Pataroyo the head of the malaria vaccine group stated that a peptide synthesizer costs less than the engine of a military helicopter; which of these facilities both acquired from developed countries would generate more wealth for a country?*

SINGH Any product should be first evaluated before its use in developing countries.

SMITH There may be a less enthusiastic response to results obtained in developing than in developed countries. All new developments, however, are rightly treated with scepticism. However if findings can be repeated in other laboratories, acceptance will be achieved no matter where the original findings take place.

GALINA It is a pity that the credibility of original discoveries coming from a developing country is poor. This is partially our fault as in many instances results are truly not reproducible. We should work hard to regain our reputation as serious trusting scientists but it will take time I am afraid.

Spending on military research does little to improve the wealth or well-being of the country that spends it. Most governments seem willing, however, to spend large percentages of their income on military hardware. In contrast there is a shortage in the supply of journals and research papers for scientists in developing countries.

JEGGO With respect to that last point, the joint FAO/IAEA programme supplies the contents page of a number of leading journals in the field of animal production and health to scientists in developing countries from which they can request reprints which will be supplied free of charge. The response over the past two years, however, has not been great.

What Can Biotechnology Offer Developing Countries?

A.D. IRVIN
Overseas Development Administration, U.K.

CLOSING ADDRESS

In putting together some thoughts and comments at the closure of the Conference, I would like to address general considerations which relate to the application of biotechnology in developing countries, rather than consider specific techniques which might be applied, since these have been more than adequately covered over the preceding days.

In the last 150 years, which is an exceedingly short time in the life span of *Homo sapiens*, technology has contributed to a number of major advances which have enormously improved the welfare and quality of life of millions of people. Such technological advances include improvements in health, nutrition, communications, transport and housing, but these advances have been at a cost and there are still millions of people who are unable to enjoy the benefits of technological progress. Some of the costs and disbenefits include overpopulation, depletion of natural resources, environmental degradation, urban slums, ozone depletion, the greenhouse effect and Third World debt.

Technological advances are sometimes rather colourfully referred to as 'revolutions'. Thus, we have already witnessed the industrial revolution and the green revolution, which offers great potential but, as yet, this is largely unrealized.

The green revolution centred around development of improved varieties of cereal grains, particularly maize and rice. As a result of these improvements grain production in developing countries increased dramatically, so much so that, in the space of some 10 years, S. America and India became virtually self-sufficient in grain production. Malnutrition, however, still persists, not so much because of grain shortage, but more now because of the absence of purchasing power amongst poor people.

On the basis of the adage that one does not get something for nothing, what then were some of the costs which the green revolution brought? Rice is principally grown on irrigated land which, if improperly managed, can become waterlogged or salinified. Some 18% of the world's cultivated land is now under irrigation, and every year around 5,000 km^2 become unusable and are lost to cultivation. To compensate for this loss, a further 5,000 km^2 of new land are brought into cultivation, often at the expense of indigenous forests. To maintain the ferility of the land and increase crop yields, agro-chemicals, pesticides and fertilizers are being increasingly used, involving high cost and potential pollution problems. Irrigated land is a high producer of methane gas; this now constitutes some 18% of the greenhouse gases and is four times more effective than carbon dioxide in its thermal effects. Thus, although the green revolution has offered us the technology to feed the world, there are costs to be considered. It would have required great foresight to have predicted these costs some 20 or more years ago at the start of the green revolution. We are now on the brink of another potential revolution which could bring further great benefits in developing countries (including to livestock) in terms of improving health, nutrition, productivity and breeding (as we have been hearing this week), but there are likely to be costs. In order to ameliorate the impact of these costs we need to look at both sides of the biotechnology coin: the potential disbenefits as well as the potential benefits. It is the former which are often overlooked.

Before addressing potential disbenefits in more detail, I would like to consider two key words in the title of the Conference: 'biotechnology' and 'developing'.

Numerous definitions have been given of the word 'biotechnology', and it is not my intention to enter this semantic arena, except to say that to me it implies the artificial manipulation of genetic material to produce modified organisms, whether they be viruses, cows or coconuts. The important consideration is not so much that biotechnology can be defined in different ways but more that it can be applied in different ways, ranging from the simple to the bizarre; from the abstruse to the practical. Because of the range of applications, biotechnology can potentially be utilized in many situations in both developed and developing countries. However, should we, in this context, differentiate between developed and developing countries? Most countries, however advanced they may be, would still wish to consider that they were developing, since the antithesis of development is stagnation or even decline. Cynics in developed countries may feel that this perspective is not misplaced.

One parameter which is often used to differentiate between developing and developed countries is mean *per capita* income derived from the country's

Gross National Product (GNP). On this basis, the mean *per capita* income of people in the 50 poorest countries of the world is currently less than U.S. $450 per annum.

While *per capita* income may be a useful means of differentiating between developing and developed countries to determine aid-worthiness of the former, it is not a particularly helpful parameter for determining scientific competence or the applicability of biotechnology. Because a country, institute or laboratory has limited financial resources it does not mean that it cannot carry out good science. Good science is conducted by good scientists; expensive equipment and facilities may be useful adjuncts but they in themselves do not guarantee good science if the human resource is lacking. It is perhaps worth remembering that the foundations of biotechnology, which were laid by Watson and Crick, involved working largely with curtain wire and coloured balls; the key to their success was not the equipment but the human intellect focusing powers of observation, thought and analysis on the molecular basis of genetic inheritance. Although artificial intelligence, through computers, is now making powerful contributions to scientific data recording and analysis, it is likely that the power of human intellect will, for the foreseeable future, remain the most significant force in the progress of science, including biotechnology.

In developing countries it is not usually the human resource that is lacking as population figures show. However, in order for these countries to progress down the biotechnology road, it is necessary to harness and train this resource to produce the good scientists needed to carry out good science. Acquisition of expensive facilities and equipment should be secondary considerations.

Although I shall continue to use the terms 'developing' and 'developed countries', I do this for convenience, because there is a general understanding (albeit ill-defined) of what the terms imply, rather than because there is a clear distinction between them. One should not, therefore, regard biotechnology as a science which can only be carried out in developed countries. The level of resources available, may determine the level of biotechnology that can be tackled in any one country but, as we have heard, there is a range of applications and methodologies which are as relevant to developing as developed countries.

Clearly there are a number of aspects of biotechnology which require great financial resources and sophistication, which are beyond the scope of most developing countries. In these cases, it is logical for research work to be carried out in developed countries, which have the resources, and then to apply the results or products in developing countries. Thus, we may have to accept that there will be biotechnology that can be applied but not conducted in developing countries, as opposed to that which can be both conducted and applied in such countries, but the distinction comes about essentially on the basis of resources available in a country rather than on its state of development.

Biotechnology has to be recognized as a technology or a tool that is applied for a reason; it is not an end in itself. What then are the reasons for using biotechnology? I suggest there are three, which in order of priority are:

- problem solving
- quest for knowledge
- prestige

I sometimes feel that these priorities are reversed, and that countries/institutes/laboratories invest in biotechnology because it is seen as a high profile, gee-whizz science which has to be conducted in order to maintain scientific status, rather than as a tool (albeit complex and sophisticated) for solving problems or generating knowledge. Developing countries, with their limited resources, need to ensure that their priorities are in perspective when justifying investment in biotechnology, and should perhaps concentrate on using and applying the technology in problem solving, rather than in more abstruse or fundamental ways.

The most important problem currently facing the world is the increase in human population which is most critical in developing countries. Other problems such as malnutrition, poverty, war, depletion of resources, environmental degradation, pollution, depletion of the ozone layer etc., all stem directly or indirectly from the pressure which the human population exerts on the globe, and this pressure is increasing. The present world population is around 5 billion people. If present trends continue, the population will have increased in a decade to 6 billion and, in a century, to 12 billion. Most of this increase will happen to poor countries, which at present accommodate 75% of the world's people. The increase will further exacerbate the problems which over-population already brings.

It is outside my remit to try to address these daunting problems but, when one considers the rationale and justification of investing in and applying biotechnology to livestock in developing countries, it has to be against the backcloth of this whole scenario which confronts the developing world to ensure that correct priorities are identified.

Before considering ways in which biotechnology can be applied to tackling livestock problems in developing countries, we should first identify what those problems are. In general terms, they can be summed up as poor health, poor productivity and poor fertility. These problems arise because of a range of factors including lack of resources (whether it be food, water, vaccines, drugs or money), harsh environment, hostile climate, poor management, overstocking and lack of infrastructure. In most cases, problems relate more to resource or management factors than to technical ones. There is, for example, little point in improving productivity potential of livestock, if the realization of that potential is constrained by lack of feed or by poor management and infrastructure. There is, thus, a need to recognize, that many problems can and should be tackled by conventional and nontechnical means, before a technological approach is considered.

The problems of improving health, productivity and fertility of livestock in developing countries are enormous and, unfortunately, technology can provide only some of the answers. Furthermore when we consider applying technology to solve these problems, we should choose appropriate technology, not necessarily biotechnology. However, in the correct context there are ways in which biotechnology can (not necessarily should) be applied to improve livestock health, production and fertility which could have profound and far-reaching benefits in developing countries. As we have heard this week these include:

- In animal breeding; multiple ovulation and embyro transfer, gamete sexing, embryo splitting and transgenics
- In nutrition and production; genetic manipulation of plant and food resources to increase nutritive value or reduce toxicity, modification of rumen bacteria, improved growth rates through synthetic growth promoters or genetic modification of the host.
- In disease control; production of recombinant and polyvalent vaccines; identification and manipulation of disease resistance genes.
- In disease diagnosis; use of monoclonal antibodies, gene probes and restriction fragment length polymorphisms.

Although these technologies could bring great benefits to developing countries, one must, as mentioned earlier, recognize and accept that there will be disbenefits. These may include:

- High cost; for example, some restriction enzymes for a simple biotechnology experiment can cost more than the mean *per capita* income (less than U.S. $450 per annum) of people in poorer countries.
- Time scales; cloning a gene coding for a protective protein is only the first step in producing a viable recombinant vaccine; turning this into an economic, safe and effective product could take decades.
- Loss of genetic diversity; most of the world's livestock production relies on five species; cattle, sheep, goats, pigs and chickens; with buffaloes, camels, equids and ducks being locally important. Within these few species, modern breeding techniques further reduces diversity by focusing on enhancing a small number of characteristics often at the expense of other (possibly beneficial) traits.
- Safety, welfare and ethics; manipulating genetic material raises a number of nontechnical issues which are often overdramatized, but they are nonetheless valid and have to be addressed.

Taking into account the potential benefits and disbenefits which biotechnology can offer, developing countries need to decide, according to their own special needs, circumstances and resources, how they can apply biotechnology within their own countries. They should not necessarily accept or repeat what is done in developing countries but recognize biotechnology for the tool it is and apply it in the most appropriate ways to meet their own needs. Because of the limited resources available in developing countries, application of biotechnology may require assistance from the developed countries. There are a number of ways in which such assistance can be provided:

- Provision of reagents, vaccines, drugs and biologicals which have already been developed. Once relevant genes have been cloned in a vector system, inexpensive production of target protein may be possible on a large-scale.
- Technology transfer through training, scientist exchange visits, information exchange, inter-institute link programmes and collaboration.
- Establishment of international centres of excellence in developing countries.
- Funds, either through bilateral or multilateral aid programmes. It is however, worth emphasizing that funds and capability in themselves will not guarantee good or successful science. This will only be achieved by good scientists.
- International coordination, assistance and communication through agencies such as Food and Agriculture Organisation, Office International des Epizooties and International Atomic Energy Agency.

In conclusion, can we identify and define what biotechnology can offer developing countries? Clearly it offers great potential in a number of fields but furthermore it perhaps offers hope as a means of improving health and productivity in livestock which, in turn, may contribute to improving the welfare and quality of life for poorer people in the developing world. However, the ability to manipulate the blueprints of life gives us awesome power and, although we may be on the threshold of a biotechnology revolution, we need to make sure that we use the power wisely and responsibly, and that we are as aware of the costs as we are of the benefits.

List of Participants

DR. O.A. ADEBAMBO, Institute of Agriculture Research, and Training, P.M.B. 5029, Moor Plantation, Ibadan, Nigeria.

DR. J.L. AFOLAYAN, P.M.B. 3171, Kano, Kano State, Nigeria.

MR. A.F. AL-IRYANI, Associate Researcher, Agricultural Research Authority, P.O. Box 5788, Taiz, Yemen Arab Republic.

DR. O.A.S. AL-SAGHIER, Ministry of Agriculture, Agriculture Research Authority, Range and Livestock Improvement Project, P.O. Box 87180, Dhamar, Yemen Arab Republic.

DR. S. ANDERSON, Universidad Autonoma de Yucatan, Facultad de Medicina Veterinaria y Zootecnia, Apdo. Postal No. 116–D Itzimna, Merida, Yucatan, Mexico.

MS. C. AROSENIUS, International Foundation for Science (IFS), Grev Turegatan 19, S–114 38 Stockholm, Sweden.

PROF. M. ASSELBERGS, Faculdade de Veterinaria, C.P. 257, Maputo, Mozambique.

PROF. R.K.G. ASSOKU, Department of Animal Science, Faculty of Agriculture, University of Ghana, P.O. Box 226, Legon, Ghana.

DR. T.R. AYLIFFE, Samora Machel School of Veterinary Medicine, University of Zambia, P.O. Box 32379, Lusaka, Zambia.

DR. F. BARWINEK, Erlenstrasse 68, D–8440 Straubing, Germany.

DR. R. BARZILAI, Head, Division of Biology, Israel Institute for Biological Sciences, Ness Ziona, Israel.

DR. P.M. BEARDSWORTH, Unilever Research Laboratory, Colworth House, Sharnbrook, Bedfordshire MK44 1LQ.

DR. D.H. BLACK, 159 High Street, Biggar, Lanarkshire ML12 6D4.

MR. S. BORNSTEIN, The National Veterinary Institute, P.O. Box 7073, 750 07 Uppsala, Sweden.

MR. C.G.D. BROWN, CTVM, University of Edinburgh.

DR. P. BRUMBY, Livestock Adviser, The World Bank, 1818H Street N.W., Washington D.C. 20433, U.S.A.

MR. B.S. CAPPER, 5 Wimbridge Close, New Wimpole, Royston, Hertfordshire SG8 5QQ.

MS. E. CARTER, Royal Veterinary College, Department of Animal Husbandry, Boltons Park, Potters Bar, Herts EN6 1NB.

DR. N. CENTINKAYA, Turkish Atomic Energy Authority, Lalahan Nuclear Research, Institute of Animal Health, Lalahan - Ankara, Turkey.

DR. J. CHESHAM, Cambridge Life Sciences PLC, Science Park, Milton Road, Cambridge CB4 4GN.

DR. P. CHIGARU, International Livestock Centre for Africa, P.O. Box 5689, Addis Ababa, Ethiopia.

MR. A.J.C. COOK, National Veterinary Service, Development Project, Sana'a, Yemen Arab Republic.

MR. J.F. COX, Animal Biotechnology Cambridge, 307 Huntingdon Road, Cambridge.

MR. C.J. DABORN, CTVM, University of Edinburgh.

DR. DE ROOVER, Geertruimoer 8, 3128 Baal, Belgium.

DR. T.R. DOEL, Head of Vaccine Research, Animal Virus Research Institute, Pirbright, Surrey GU24 0NF.

DR. R.H. DWINGER, Olympiaplein 45, 1-77 CM Amsterdam, The Netherlands.

DR. D. FIELDING, CTVM, University of Edinburgh.

PROF. B. FIVAZ, Tick Research Unit, Rhodes University, Grahamstown 6140, Republic of South Africa.

DR. C.S. GALINA, Dept. Reproduccion, Facultad de Medicina Veterinaria y Zootecnia, Ciudad Universitaria, 04510 Mexico DF, Mexico.

MRS. J. GIBBENS, c/o FCO (Sana'a), King Charles Street, London SW1A 2AH.

MR. N. GIBBENS, c/o FCO (Sana'a), King Charles Street, London SW1A 2AH.

DR. R.D. GILL, British Technology Group, 101 Newington Causeway, London SE1 6BU.

DR. E. GONZALEZ-PADILLA, Ejido Mexicaltzingo No. 51, Col. Educacion Coyoacan, 04400 Mexico D.F., Mexico.

DR. B.N. GUPTA, Dairy Cattle Nutrition Division, National Dairy Institute, Karnal 132001, Haryana, India.

DR. A.N. HAMIR, School of Veterinary Medicine, University of Pennsylvania, New Bolton Center, 382 West Street Road, Kennet Square, PA 19348, U.S.A.

DR. L.J.S. HARRISON, CTVM, University of Edinburgh.

DR. H.U. HASNAIN, FAO Livestock Expert, Agricultural Research Authority, P.O. Box 5788, Taiz, Yemen Arab Republic.

PROF. R.B. HEAP, Institute of Animal Physiology and Genetics Research, Cambridge Research Station, Babraham Hall, Cambridge, CB2 4AT.

DR. A. HIGGINS, Director, Animal Health Trust, P.O. Box 5, Newmarket, Suffolk CB8 7DW.

DR. J. HODGES, Animal Production, Food and Agriculture Organisation, Via delle Terme di Caracalla, 00100 Rome, Italy.

MR. A.G. HUNTER, CTVM, University of Edinburgh.

DR. A.D. IRVIN, Senior Animal Health Adviser, Overseas Development Administration, Eland House, Stag Place, London SW1E 5DH.

MR. M.H. JEGGO, Regional Expert for Africa, Animal Production and Health Section, I.A.E.A., P.O. Box 100, 5 Wagramerstrasse, A-1400 Vienna, Austria.

DR. E. JIRAN, Scientific and Technical Development Department, State Veterinary Office of the Ministry of Agriculture, Prague, Czechoslovakia.

DR. B.R. JOSHI, Acting Chief Centre Veterinary Officer, Lumle Agricultural Centre, Pokhara, c/o P.O. Box 106, Kathmandu, Nepal.

DR. E. KABAIJA, University of Eastern Africa, P.O. Box 2500, Eldoret, Kenya.

DR. P.B. KNUDSEN, Box 10.452, Roshidiya, Dubai, United Arab Emirates.

DR. P. KRONTORAD, Scientific and Technical Development Department, State Veterinary Office of the Ministry of Agriculture, Prague, Czechoslovakia.

DR. J.P. LECOCQ, Director of Research Transgene, 11 rue de Molsheim, 67000 Strasbourg, France.

MR. K.T. LIM, Veterinary Research Institute, 59 Tiger Lane, P.O. Box 369, 30740 Ipoh, Perak, Malaysia.

MR. J.S. MACFARLANE, CTVM, University of Edinburgh.

DR. A.G. MAJOK, University of California, Department of Epidemiology and Preventive Medicine, School of Veterinary Medicine, Davis, California 95616, U.S.A.

DR. D. MARTINEZ, IEMVT-INRA, B.P. 1232, 97184 Pointe à Pitre, Cedex, Guadeloupe, French West Indies.

DR. R.A. MASAKE, International Laboratory for Research on Animal Diseases, P.O. Box 30709, Nairobi, Kenya.

DR. H.E.A. MBWILLE, Box 20190, Dar-es-Salaam, Tanzania.

DR. T.B. MEPHAM, Department of Physiology and Environmental Science, Faculty of Agricultural and Food Sciences, University of Nottingham, Sutton Bonington, Loughborough LE12 5RD.

DR. J. MORENO-LOPEZ, Department of Veterinary Microbiology, Section of Virology, Biomedicum Box 585, S-751 23 Uppsala, Sweden.

DR. C.A. MORGAN, Edinburgh School of Agriculture, King's Buildings, West Mains Road, Edinburgh.

DR. M.F. NANA-NUKECHAP, The Director, Veterinary Pharmaceutics Office, BP 1988, Yaounde, Cameroon.

DR. J.H.P. NYEKO, Tsetse Control Department, P.O. Box 7033, Kampala, Uganda.

MR. R.J. OLDS, Animal Production & Health Division, F.A.O., Via delle Terme di Caracalla, 00100 Rome, Italy.

DR. E.R. ØRSKOV, Applied Nutrition Department, The Rowett Research Institute, Bucksburn, Aberdeen AB2 9SB.

DR. Y. OZAWA, Office International des Epizooties (OIE), 12 rue de Prony, Paris, France.

DR. G.S. PANDEY, Samora Machel School of Veterinary Medicine, University of Zambia, P.O. Box 32379, Lusaka, Zambia.

DR. R.A. PEARSON, CTVM, University of Edinburgh.

MR. R. PEREZ, Dpto Med. Veterinaria, Universidad de Concepcion-Chillan, Casilla 537, Chillan, Chile.

DR. A.R. PETERS, Hoechst Animal Health, Walton Manor, Walton, Milton Keynes, Bucks MK7 7AJ.

DR. E.J.C. POLGE, Animal Biotechnology Cambridge Ltd., Animal Research Station, University of Cambridge, 307 Huntingdon Road, Cambridge CB3 0JG.

DR. D.V. RANGNEKAR, Bhartiya Agro Industries Foundation, P.B. No. 2030, Asarwa Road, Ahmedabad 380 01 6, India.

DR. R.K. RASTOGI, Department of Livestock Science, Faculty of Agriculture, The University of West Indies, St. Augustine, Trinidad, West Indies.

MR. D.J.M. RUSSELL, West Kilimanjaro Livestock Breeding Project, P.O. Box 1906, Arusha, Tanzania.

DR. S.R. SAMPATH, National Dairy Research Institute, Southern Regional Station, Hosur Road, Adugodi, Bangalore 560030, India.

PROF. J.G. SCAIFE, Dept. of Molecular Biology, University of Edinburgh, King's Buildings, Mayfield Road, Edinburgh EH9 3JR.

DR. G.R. SCOTT, CTVM, University of Edinburgh.

MR. I.A. SHAMBWANA, Department of Livestock Development, P.O. Box 159, Zanzibar, Tanzania.

DR. D.K. SINGH, National Dairy Development Board, P.O. Box 40, Anand 388 001, India.

DR. KARKI N.P. SINGH, Lumle Agricultural Centre, Post Box No. 1, Pokhara, Nepal.

DR. A.J. SMITH, CTVM, University of Edinburgh.

DR. S.W. SMITH, Cambridge Animal and Public Health Ltd, Chesterford Park, Saffron Walden, Essex CB10 1XL.

DR. D.R. SNODGRASS, Animal Diseases Research Association, Moredun Research Institute, 408 Gilmerton Road, Edinburgh EH17 7JH.

DR. K.F. SNOWDEN, Liverpool School of Tropical Medicine, Pembroke Place, Liverpool L3 5QA

Dr. G.S. SSENYONGA, Makerere University, Faculty of Veterinary Medicine, P.O. Box 7062, Kampala, Uganda.

DR. I.G. SUDANA, Head, Subdirectorate of Animal Disease Surveillance, 16 Jalan Salemba Raya, Jakarta, Indonesia.

DR. G. SUDI, Liti-Tengeru, P.O. Box 3101, Arusha, Tanzania.

DR. A. TAIT, Wellcome Unit for Molecular Parasitology, University of Glasgow, Garscube Estate, Bearsden Road, Bearsden, Glasgow G11 5JS.

DR. A.J. TEALE, International Laboratory for Research on Animal Diseases, P.O. Box 30709, Nairobi, Kenya.

DR. S.J. TERBLANCHE, Department of Therigenology, Universiteit van Pretoria, Private Bag X04, 0100 Onderstepoort, South Africa.

DR. J.H. TOPPS, Head, Division of Agricultural Biochemistry and Chemistry, University of Aberdeen, 581 King Street, Aberdeen AB9 1UD.

MR. J.D. TURTON, Chief Managing Editor, Animal Sciences, CAB International, Wallingford, Oxon OX10 8DE.

DR. C.G. VASQUEZ PELAEZ, Instituto Nacional de Invest. Forestales y Agropecuarias, Genetics Department, Km 15.5 Carretera Mexico-Toluca Del. Cuajimalpa 05110, Mexico DF, Mexico.

DR. M. WANAPAT, Faculty of Agriculture, Khon Kaen University, Khon Kaen 40002, Thailand.

MR. T. WEBB, Commonwealth Development Corporation, 1 Bessborough Gardens, London SW1V 2JQ.

DR. W. WIDODO, Animal Husbandry Faculty, Brawijrya University, Jalan Mayjen Haryono 169, Malang, East Java, Indonesia.

MR. G. WIENER, 7 View Park Road, Lanarkshire ML12 6BG.

DR. I. WILMUT, AFRC Institute of Animal Physiology and Genetics Research Edinburgh Research Station, Roslin, Midlothian EH25 9PS.

DR. J.A. WOOLLIAMS, AFRC Institute of Animal Physiology and Genetics Research, Edinburgh Research Station, Roslin, Midlothian EH25 9PS.

Index

All entries refer to tropics and livestock unless otherwise indicated